THE VALUATION OF MONETARY DAMAGES IN INJURY CASES

A Damages Expert's Perspective

MICHAEL SHAHNASARIAN, PH.D.

AMERICANBARASSOCIATION
Solo, Small Firm and
General Practice Division

Cover design by Mary Anne Kulchawik/ABA Design

Printed in the United States of America.

26 25 24 23 22   5 4 3 2 1

A catalog record for this book is available from the Library of Congress.

Discounts are available for books ordered in bulk. Special consideration is given to state bars, CLE programs, and other bar-related organizations. Inquire at Book Publishing, ABA Publishing, American Bar Association, 321 N. Clark Street, Chicago, Illinois 60654-7598.

www.shopABA.org

To my grandchildren.

Contents

Part III: Construction of Opinions on Life Care Plans

Part IV: Special Considerations

Preface

Truth be told,[1] I undertook writing *The Valuation of Monetary Damages in Injury Cases: A Damages Expert's Perspective* soon after the gravity of the COVID-19 pandemic became known in spring 2020. I needed an avenue to escape the gloomy events of the day, and my instincts guided me to a safe place: writing, something I truly love and, as my doctoral dissertation supervisor, Dr. Gary W. Peterson, imbued in me long ago, a tool for thinking. This primal calling, coupled perhaps with a self-preservation need—namely, documenting for posterity what I learned and believe important to perpetuate in the profession to which I committed my life's work—engendered this undertaking.

The Valuation of Monetary Damages in Injury Cases builds on my four editions of *Assessment of Earning Capacity* (Shahnasarian, 2001, 2004a, 2011, 2015), a textbook that addresses evaluating claims of loss of earning capacity in multiple forums and generally discusses expert witnesses' development of life care plans, and the Earning Capacity Assessment Form (Shahnasarian, 2004b, 2010c), a standardized measure designed to facilitate vocational experts' damages assessments. This book focuses on damages claims emanating from injuries—especially those associated with claims of loss of earning capacity and situation-specific future rehabilitation needs that life care plans encapsulate.

Beyond the monetary damages valued in vocational assessments and life care plans, *The Valuation of Monetary Damages in Injury Cases* peripherally addresses far more elusive and difficult-to-assess nonmonetary damages elements: pain and suffering damages that injuries and associated disabling problems can cause. These nonmonetary damages, artifacts of injury damages, often become more discernible after monetary damages have been assessed.

As an example, consider a young woman who sustained significant pelvic ring fracture injuries rendering her incapable of delivering children vaginally. An assessment of her nonmonetary pain and suffering damages raises several hypothetical questions. Assuming she were to conceive one or more children and her injuries presented limitations in her ability to bear and care for them, what is the value of her inability to naturally deliver a child? Nurture, bond, and interact with her children as she would but for her disabling problems? Engage in her children's activities unimpeded by acquired disabling problems?

Most often, the injury damages that expert witnesses evaluate emanate from cases involving personal injury, medical malpractice, workers' compensation, and product liability. Claimed injury-related damages can also arise in other forums such as employment law and family law.

---

1. This opening phrase of *The Valuation of Monetary Damages in Injury Cases: A Damages Expert's Perspective* references the oath pledged by all bearing witness through testimony in litigation: Do you swear [or affirm] to tell the truth, the whole truth, and nothing but the truth, so help you God? Its final sentence (please refer to p. 357), from Holy Scripture, offers timeless, sacred guidance on providing testimony in sync with the pledged ideal. The contents between these bookend sentences address this treatise's technical subject matter, attempting to bridge an ideal with a means to realize it.

In writing *The Valuation of Monetary Damages in Injury Cases*, I aimed to pen a practical, thorough, process-oriented guide to evaluate injury damages, applying methods grounded in sound principles of vocational rehabilitation and life care planning. The many examples cited and work samples presented derive from actual cases, and accompanying discussions intend to provide on-point, insightful, and instructive analyses to promote the discernment and presentation of injury damages. Additionally, *The Valuation of Monetary Damages in Injury Cases* offers many practical, tested resources—information-gathering forms, sample retention letters and agreements, affidavits, and administrative documents, to name a few—to facilitate and safeguard expert and lawyer efforts to gather, assemble, and preserve information necessary to perform competent analyses during adversarial proceedings.

Injury-related damages assessments concern many audiences. Of course, expert witnesses performing damages analyses and lawyers who are either pursuing or defending damages claims constitute the primary audiences, and this work is most applicable to them.

Experts aspire to render competent analyses, ultimately developing and presenting evidence that withstands lawyer and judicial challenges and eventually contributes to the decision-making of those receptive to considering their opinions. From lawyers' perspectives, proper assessments and pursuit/defense of damages are central to their client responsibilities and personal success.

Beyond vocational experts, life care plan experts, and lawyers, others with an interest in injury damages assessments include:

- Other litigation support professionals—Experts who rely on the opinions of vocational rehabilitation professionals and life care planners, including economists and financial experts, can benefit from learning about the methods and underpinnings of those on whom they rely.
- Judges—Charged with ruling on issues ranging from admissibility of evidence to motions to limit or strike a witness via a Daubert hearing, judges must have quality information on the noted topics to guide their decision-making.
- Insurance adjusters—Knowledge of a claim's true value and damages exposure is vital to this audience when evaluating a claim, negotiating settlements, and attempting to contain legal costs.
- Law school students and graduate students aspiring to specialize in providing forensic services—Those aspiring to practice in areas that involve valuing injury damages, both future lawyers and future expert witnesses, benefit from instructional resources to learn their craft.
- Sophisticated plaintiffs—Most plaintiffs competent to discern and appreciate their damages seek to know their damages' value and take initiative to learn about, quantify, and participate in efforts necessary to adjudicate their lawyers' work on their behalf.

The Valuation of Monetary Damages in Injury Cases evolves through four parts, each intended to logically build on its predecessor.

Part I: Expert Witness Damages Assessments

First, *The Valuation of Monetary Damages in Injury Cases* defines injury damages qualified expert witnesses value—namely, claims of loss of earning capacity; types of rehabilitation interventions likely necessary to remedy acquired disabling problems (including potentially aggravated preexisting conditions and new injuries), along with costs; and, to a degree, the discernment and value of causally related pain and suffering damages. Other important topics discussed include the qualifications of those who perform these assessments and the adversarial environment challenging them. An exhaustive discussion and analysis of non-monetary damages associated with injury claims exceeds the scope of this work, although I am continuing to study and evaluate methods to scientifically quantify this very important damages area.

Part II: Construction of Opinions on Claims of Loss of Earning Capacity

Part II begins with a discussion of methodologies to evaluate claims of loss of earning capacity, including an expanded discussion of Earning Capacity Assessment Theory (Shahnasarian, 2010a) and its adjunct, the Earning Capacity Assessment Form. This foundation provides a basis for detailing the processes and mechanics associated with performing an assessment of earning capacity—subject matter that follows. Finally, applying these underlying concepts, Chapter 4 addresses assessments of loss of earning capacity claims in pediatric cases, and Chapter 5 focuses on conducting these assessments in adult cases.

Part III: Construction of Opinions on Life Care Plans

Expanding on the foundational work Part II details—including records review, examination protocols, and clinical assessments—Part III first focuses on constructing opinions essential to sound life care planning, emphasizing life care planner roles and methodological considerations. Ensuing chapters address the development of noncatastrophic life care plans (Chapter 7), catastrophic life care plans (Chapter 8), international life care plans (Chapter 9), and life care plans when healthcare professionals dispute causation (Chapter 10).

Part IV: Special Considerations

Part IV concludes *The Valuation of Monetary Damages in Injury Cases* with a focus on the denouement of damages experts' work: providing opinions to enlighten triers of fact on technical matters in dispute. To provide opinion testimony, expert witnesses must anticipate and survive Daubert challenges that aim to strike or limit the presentation of their opinions—the subject of Chapter 11. The final chapter, "Presentation of Damages Assessments," describes how expert witnesses navigate the numerous adversarial challenges they encounter throughout their involvement in a case—from counsel's initial disclosure of them as expert witnesses through their trial testimony.

Acknowledgments

I remain grateful to the American Bar Association for providing another opportunity for us to work together. A decade ago, our efforts produced a related title: *A Claimant's Guide to Understanding and Presenting Injury Damages: A Damages Expert's Perspective* (Shahnasarian, 2012). Many thanks also to Todd A. Wilber for his invaluable technical writing input—not just with this work, but also for his contributions during the past 20-plus years refining and assembling in good order the myriad details such publications demand.

Timothy F. Field, PhD; Michael A. Schlanger, Esq.; Roger O. Weed, PhD; and C. Steven Yerrid, Esq.—longstanding colleagues whom I greatly respect and who inspired my work for decades—graciously reviewed and commented on a draft of *The Valuation of Monetary Damages in Injury Cases: A Damages Expert's Perspective*. Their ongoing support and mentorship over the years has profoundly shaped my thinking and practice, and for this, I am most appreciative.

Finally and most importantly, of course, my wife, Jeannie, has yet again extended me her patience and support, without which this work—and, frankly, my career as it evolved—would not have happened. We continue to embrace four values that anchor and guide our lives: faith, family, education, and a work hard/play hard ethic. These values, my partner's intercession in keeping me balanced in managing them, and our faith-based gratitude for the gifts afforded us have inspired our journey, committing to efforts we hold dear, including this publication.

About the Author

After completing undergraduate studies in psychology at Indiana University, Dr. Shahnasarian earned a master's degree in clinical psychology at Texas A&M University and a doctorate in counseling psychology at Florida State University. He also completed postdoctoral residency work at Florida State University and the University of Wisconsin–Milwaukee.

Dr. Shahnasarian holds the following specialty credentials: Certified Rehabilitation Counselor, Certified Vocational Evaluator, Certified Life Care Planner, International Psychometric Evaluation Certification, Nationally Certified Counselor (Emeritus), and Nationally Certified Career Counselor (Emeritus). He is also a licensed psychologist.

In 1986, Dr. Shahnasarian founded Career Consultants of America, Inc. (CCA), a private practice specializing in areas that include forensic analyses, specifically related to vocational and life care plan expert testimony. During the past 35 years, CCA has evaluated evidence across five continents contributing to the resolution of more than 5,000 litigated cases. Dr. Shahnasarian's expertise in vocational and life care plan assessment has led to his retention domestically and internationally as a vocational and life care plan expert witness across five decades.

Additionally, CCA has served as a training and internship site for approximately 50 master's, doctoral, and postdoctoral students Dr. Shahnasarian supervised. Beyond providing students clinical supervision, he has lectured at universities and academic forums throughout the United States and internationally.

Over the years, Dr. Shahnasarian has contributed to advancing the state of practice in vocational rehabilitation and life care planning theory, research, and practice. Additionally, he has served in leadership positions within the profession and has a longstanding record of human service work that has bettered the lot of people who have disabilities.

Dr. Shahnasarian has maintained privileges as a rehabilitation psychologist at hospitals in his locale, where he has provided pro bono rehabilitation counseling bedside to hundreds of injured patients experiencing difficulties adjusting to newly acquired, unwelcome lifestyle changes. Additionally, Dr. Shahnasarian has served his church, St. Hagop Armenian Church, as well as the Eastern Diocese of the Armenian Church, in various leadership positions.

Dr. Shahnasarian's publications—including 13 books and approximately 70 peer-reviewed articles, book chapters, and monographs—are widely cited, and expert witnesses worldwide have been applying methods and techniques he developed. His work has also benefited others with an interest in adjudicating damages claims—including judges and other triers of fact, lawyers, insurance adjusters, and people with disabilities. Beyond his published works, Dr. Shahnasarian has served on nine editorial boards publishing periodicals related to rehabilitation subject matter, and he has also been a guest editor.

Two Florida governors, Lawton Chiles and Jeb Bush, appointed Dr. Shahnasarian to the Florida Rehabilitation Council, a board that advises the governor on matters pertaining to rehabilitation in Florida. He has also held significant leadership positions in professional organizations aligned with matters related to his clinical practice. Dr. Shahnasarian is a past president of the National Career Development Association, and he has served as an officer on numerous professional association boards of directors. He is also a past chairman of the board of the Florida Gulf Coast Chapter of the National Multiple Sclerosis Society.

Dr. Shahnasarian's leadership—both in governance positions and as a research practitioner—has led to invitations to speak at state, national, and international conferences of professional associations. Similarly, the media has sought his insights and commentary on current rehabilitation-related issues. Among the media organizations that have interviewed Dr. Shahnasarian are *Business Week*, the *Wall Street Journal*, *Money Magazine*, *Fortune Magazine*, the *Christian Science Monitor*, *Newsweek*, *US News and World Report*, and *Toyo Keizai*. His media experience has also included serving as a columnist for the *USA Today* career website, addressing workplace issues.

In recognition of his sustained and substantial contributions to his profession, three professional organizations (the American Psychological Association, the International Association of Life Care Planners, and the National Career Development Association) awarded Dr. Shahnasarian Fellow status. His professional recognition at the international and national levels is extensive and includes Outstanding Practitioner of the Year awards from both the American Rehabilitation Counseling Association and the National Career Development Association. Additionally, the National Rehabilitation Counseling Association presented Dr. Shahnasarian its Distinguished Service Award.

Regarding his projects that earned awards, the National Rehabilitation Association (NRA) presented Dr. Shahnasarian its W. F. Faulkes Award for his research undergirding the Earning Capacity Assessment Form-2; this research spanned three decades and culminated in a validated instrument vocational experts worldwide have used in their damages assessments. The NRA also presented him an Excellence in Media Award for his novel, *Justice Indicted*.

All three universities that awarded Dr. Shahnasarian degrees presented him outstanding alumni awards. He also received "Health Care Hero" recognition from a business journal in his Tampa Bay, Florida, community.

The American Psychological Association presented Dr. Shahnasarian its Citizen Psychologist Award for Advancing Disability as a Human Rights and Social Justice Issue. Dr. Shahnasarian's composite and longstanding business, scholastic, and professional and community service achievements, including his Armenian-American heritage, led to the Ellis Island Honors Society awarding him a Medal of Honor.

Since 1986, Dr. Shahnasarian and his loving wife, Jean, have made Tampa their home. Their 40-year marriage has produced three children and, thus far, four grandchildren.

Dr. Shahnasarian providing his expert analysis in March 2021 during a video recording used in a mock trial and mediation settlement conference.

PART I

Expert Witness Damages Assessments

First, *The Valuation of Monetary Damages in Injury Cases* defines damages that qualified injury expert witnesses value—namely, claims of loss of earning capacity; types and costs of rehabilitation interventions likely necessary to remedy acquired disabling problems (including potentially aggravated preexisting conditions and new injuries); and, to a degree, the discernment and value of causally related pain and suffering damages. Other important topics discussed include the qualifications of those who perform these assessments and the adversarial environment challenging them.

CHAPTER 1

The Fundamentals of Injury Damages Assessments

Like the coronavirus pandemic, a previously unforeseen mishap can cause life-changing, unwelcome, and profound upheaval to one's being. Every second of every day, people worldwide experience injuries vis-a-vis events they did not anticipate. Automobile accidents, medical procedures gone awry, psychologically traumatizing experiences, altercations, product malfunctions, and industrial accidents, to name a few, are among the most common mechanisms causing injuries.

In some cases, the implications of an injury may be nil or scant; in other cases, the implications are overwhelming, affecting all spheres of one's life. Injuries and their manifestations can adversely affect a person's livelihood; interpersonal relationships; quality of life; and ability to work, pursue recreational activities, and live as independently as before becoming disabled. By extension, such unwelcome lifestyle changes often spawn psychological adjustment issues.

When the mechanism of injury and damages associated with it become scrutinized in a forensic setting and a claim for injury damages ensues, a new group of individuals, beyond those treating the injured party, become involved. This group most often includes lawyers, expert witnesses, insurance adjusters, judges, and, if disputes persist and a settlement cannot be reached, a jury. Depending on a case's complexity, many others—such as mediators, trial consultants, mock jurors, and an appellate court—may also become involved.

The Valuation of Monetary Damages in Injury Cases: A Damages Expert's Perspective presents an experienced damages expert's perspective on valuing monetary damages in injury cases. This perspective differs from others involved in the claim process in that damages experts' assessments emanate from technical, objective, empirical bases that aspire to integrate the science undergirding professional practice standards. These standards include applying the profession's theory, research, and practice bases to case-specific facts and referral questions.

Codes of ethics and standards of practice bind the scope of damages experts' involvement in their valuation of damages. They are neither advocates for parties in dispute nor negotiators in the dispute resolution process. Further, they have no pecuniary interest in a case's outcome; they are compensated for their services only. Their role is to assist those involved in the dispute resolution process with understanding and monetarily valuing damages.

In most injury cases, damages experts—specifically, vocational rehabilitation experts and life care planners—perform assessments to assign value(s) to a claimed damage. Vocational rehabilitation experts evaluate claimed past and future earnings damages an injury caused or may cause, and life care planners evaluate and ascribe values to treatment interventions an injury has caused a person to require.

Because many of the damages vocational rehabilitation experts and life care planners evaluate can be quantified, these damages are typically referred to as economic or monetary damages, as compared to nonmonetary damages—a category in which pain and suffering damages fall. While these latter damages, of course, have an economic value, they are termed nonmonetary because they do not readily lend themselves to a quantitative assessment. Damages experts' efforts directly address claims of monetary damages and, indirectly, nonmonetary damages.

An overview of the vocational rehabilitation and life care planner specialties follows. More detailed discussions on the construction of opinions on claims of loss of earning capacity appear in Part II of *The Valuation of Monetary Damages in Injury Cases*, and Part III elaborates on the construction of opinions on life care plans.

Vocational Rehabilitation Experts

Roles

Questions pertaining to an individual's ability to work and earn wages—both before and after becoming injured—fall under the purview of a vocational rehabilitation expert. This analysis often involves assessments and comparisons of preinjury and postinjury vocational capacities: expert analyses of any differential between these, if it can be assessed within a reasonable degree of vocational rehabilitation probability, provide the grist for lawyers to prosecute or defend wage claims.

As an example, consider a drywall mechanic who experienced an above-knee amputation as a result of a work-related fall from a ladder. A determination that the injured worker cannot resume his former occupation does not necessarily translate into an opinion that a claim of loss of earning capacity is merited. Several factors—such as the worker's historical earnings record, ability to pursue alternate work offering comparable levels of compensation, and ability to mitigate vocational damages through retraining—would require consideration in an expert's analysis to reach an opinion about a claim of loss of earning capacity.

Assessments of claims of loss of earning capacity are multifaceted and often complex. One's phase of career development, transferable skills, labor market factors, and vocational profile are but a few of the factors vocational experts weigh. Ultimately, these experts' assessments respond to the following questions: (1) Did an acquired injury cause a claimant a loss of earning capacity? (2) If so, what is the degree of this loss, with and without reasonable mitigation interventions?

Selection of Qualified Vocational Rehabilitation Experts

Vocational rehabilitation experts typically hold a master's degree and/or a doctorate in rehabilitation counseling, psychology, or a related specialty. Most experts originate from a private practice, although some are university professors pursuing supplemental work. It is not uncommon for a vocational rehabilitation professional to have worked in a private or public setting, providing clinical services—such as vocational testing, career counseling, and job placement—for several years before becoming a vocational rehabilitation expert witness. Some vocational experts derive from professional backgrounds that have afforded them research, case management, and healthcare administration experience.

In addition to their formal education, vocational rehabilitation experts invariably hold board certifications that denote their subspecialization(s). The most relevant certifications include Certified Rehabilitation Counselor, Certified Vocational Evaluator, and Nationally Certified Career Counselor. Obtaining these credentials typically involves satisfying requirements that include completing requisite graduate-level coursework (e.g., medical aspects of rehabilitation, psychosocial aspects of rehabilitation, and standardized tests and measurements), demonstrating clinical competence via a supervised internship (typically one year of structured, clinical supervision under an accredited supervisor), and passing a written examination. The bodies regulating board certifications typically publish both codes of ethics and standards of practice to which the certified are accountable.

In addition to board certifications, many vocational rehabilitation experts hold licenses in rehabilitation-related practice areas such as psychology, mental health counseling, nursing, or physical therapy. While professional associations regulate board certifications, licenses fall under the auspices of governmental regulation.

Once obtained, continuing to hold professional credentials requires periodic maintenance such as continuing education and, of course, paying a maintenance fee. Some credentialing bodies permit retaking and passing a written examination in lieu of continuing education.

Beyond education, experience, and specialty credentials, other factors to consider in the selection of a vocational rehabilitation expert witness include

- Publication history—books, book chapters, monographs, articles in professional periodicals
- Editorial board experience
- Presentations at professional meetings and conferences
- Peer recognition
- Leadership in professional organizations and/or disability-related organizations
- Higher education teaching and/or clinical supervision experience
- Grants secured and research experience
- Hospital privileges
- Related professional and community service
- Contributions to the profession

When selecting a vocational rehabilitation expert, it is important to remain mindful that his or her opinion will be considered and evaluated by the numerous audiences previously described. Ultimately, perceptions of the expert's expertise and credibility, along with the methodology employed, will affect how receptive these audiences are to opinions rendered. If the expert is perceived as inexperienced, underqualified, analytically superficial, a biased "hired gun," or otherwise not fully competent to address referral questions, his or her opinions are likely to be discounted or dismissed. Needless to say, an expert's ethics and professionalism should be unassailable.

The selection of an expert, of course, should also involve consideration of details specific to the pending case. If the claimant, for example, is a young data analytics professional who contends a head injury causes her trouble with memory and processing speed, an expert with training and experience performing assessments that have involved such factors is desirable.

Additionally, it is preferable that an expert have a balanced caseload of retentions between plaintiff and defendant lawyers. An expert who, for example, provides expert witness services exclusively to lawyers representing defendants may be perceived as biased and/or beholden to this group, raising questions about the objectivity of opinions presented.

In our era of ease of access to troves of information via means that include the Internet, listservs, and the Freedom of Information Act, experts are routinely surveilled and fact-checked. Boecher Interrogatories (detailed in Chapter 12), commonly propounded during expert witness discovery, among other things typically inquire whether an expert's testimony has ever been dismissed, stricken, or limited. Of course, the retaining attorney should have knowledge of this, including any special circumstances if the answer is affirmative, before finalizing a retention. Appendix A includes an example of Boecher Interrogatories.

Shahnasarian (2015) discussed how, in addition to developing evidence and informing counsel about the merits and deficiencies of an attorney's damages theory, vocational experts, as a matter of course, may become the voice of the attorney. This voice—both directly and vicariously—presents evidence to persons involved in the settlement process, opposing counsel, other experts, judges, and triers of fact. As such, this voice is subject to intense scrutiny, challenge, and evaluation.

A well-respected vocational expert who possesses a reputation for making objective, reasonable, and credible presentations can be instrumental in helping to resolve a dispute. Effective experts communicate well—both in writing and speech. A pithy message culled from keen insight of facts, synthesized with examination data, could be lost to a jury if conveyed via boring, verbose, overly technical, or incomprehensible testimony. Van de Bittner, Wallace, Cottle, and Simon (2012) discussed qualifications for vocational experts.

Damages Assessments

Depending on case-specific facts and issues at hand, vocational rehabilitation experts analyze a potential wage loss claim from the following perspectives: past wage loss, future wage loss, and loss of earning capacity. Each perspective is discussed next, and Part II of *The Valuation of Monetary Damages in Injury Cases: A Damages Expert's Perspective* details how experts construct their opinions.

Past Wage Loss

Absences due to treatment for injury-related problems are frequently a past wage loss claim of damages. Periods of symptom exacerbation causing diminished work performance can also be a claimed past wage loss damage. The period of a past wage loss claim spans from the onset of the alleged disabling problem to the time of the vocational analysis.

Future Wage Loss

The presumption in asserting a future wage loss claim is that alleged injuries and their adverse effects on a claimant's ability to earn wages can be mitigated in the future. Consider an individual who acquired injuries that render him incapable of resuming the exertional requirements of his preinjury job but who can be retrained to perform a less physically demanding job within his capacity. In this case, the future wage loss damage claim would involve lost wages from the time of the assessment through the time the claimant has completed retraining and reentered the workplace, having secured a job offering compensation comparable to his preinjury pay. This claim could include an allegation that, in addition to acquiring new injuries, a preexisting condition was aggravated, contributing to the future wage loss claim.

The period of a future wage loss claim spans from the time of the vocational analysis to the future date when an alleged injury's effects on work performance can be mitigated.

Loss of Earning Capacity

Among the assumptions undergirding the bases of an opinion that a claimant sustained a loss of earning capacity are (1) no accommodations, retraining, or other interventions can be implemented to offset the differential between preinjury and postinjury earning capacity; (2) vocational handicaps (e.g., employer bias due to claimant's condition, diminished universe of viable, accessible work opportunities) will erode the claimant's ability to secure and maintain employment; (3) the claimant will have a truncated work life; and/or (4) the claimant is totally disabled, unable to perform any work in accord with customary workplace standards. Again, this claim could assert that new injuries and/or an aggravation of a preexisting condition caused the diminution in postinjury earning capacity. The period of loss-of-earning-capacity claim damages spans from the time of the vocational analysis through the remainder of the claimant's work life expectancy, which is often extended to the claimant's mid-60s. There are, of course, exceptions to this general rule, further discussed in Chapter 5.

Life Care Plan Experts

Roles

In the context of litigation, life care plan experts assess rehabilitation interventions that injured persons, within a reasonable degree of life care planning probability, are likely to require secondary to acquired disabling problems associated with an issue(s) in dispute. While performing this task, life care planners restrict recommendations to those associated with injuries caused by an event such as a motor vehicle accident or product malfunction, along with any aggravation of preexisting injuries. The life care plan exempts interventions for unrelated problems, either those predating or postdating the issue(s) giving rise to its development.

Consider the case of a former athlete who underwent a right-shoulder Tommy John operation several years before acquiring a host of orthopedic injuries resulting from a bicycle versus motor vehicle accident. In consultation with an orthopedic surgeon who performed the preaccident shoulder procedure, the life care planner elicited the surgeon's assessment that the new trauma aggravated the preexisting shoulder injury, causing the need for treatment—including another surgery—that otherwise would not have been indicated. Hence, in developing a life care plan for injury damages associated with the accident, the life care planner included along with injuries from this event rehabilitation interventions associated with aggravation of the preexisting shoulder condition.

Typically, life care planners collaborate with multidisciplinary specialists, sometimes including physicians with different specialties, mental health professionals, therapists, and the likes of prosthetists, nurses, home modification contractors, and case managers. In addition to providing treatment recommendations, these life care plan contributors can facilitate analyses of an injured person's comorbidities related and unrelated to an incident(s) giving rise to a life care plan. When appropriate, the life care planner adds recommendations she or he is qualified to make independently.

Providing estimates of costs, within a reasonable degree of life care plan probability, to fund recommendations of a life care plan is another major responsibility life care planners assume. This involves sourcing the availability of interventions in a given locale and determining reasonable costs for them. Part III of *The Valuation of Monetary Damages in Injury Cases: A Damages Expert's Perspective* details the mechanics associated with constructing a life care plan.

The International Academy of Life Care Planners provided the following definition of a life care plan in its *Standards of Practice for Life Care Planners* (2015):

> The life care plan is a dynamic document based upon published standards of practice, comprehensive assessment, data analysis, and research, which provides an organized, concise plan for current and future needs with associated costs for individuals who have experienced catastrophic injury or have chronic health care needs.

In addition to specifying ten standards with measurement criteria for each standard, the *Standards of Practice*, in an appendix, includes ethics for life care planners. The following is an excerpt of the standards and measurement criteria.

1. STANDARD: The life care planner practices within his or her professional scope of practice.

    MEASUREMENT CRITERIA: a. Remains within the scope of practice for his or her profession as determined by state, provincial, or national credentialing bodies. The functions associated with performing life care planning are within the scope of practice for rehabilitation and health care professionals. b. Independently makes recommendations for care items/services that are within the scope of practice of his or her own professional discipline.

2. STANDARD: The life care planner must have skill and knowledge in understanding the health care needs addressed in a life care plan.

    MEASURMENT CRITERIA: a. Consults with others and obtains education when the life care planner must address health care needs that are new or unfamiliar. b. Able to locate appropriate resources when necessary. c. Provides a consistent, objective, and thorough methodology for constructing the life care plan, relying on appropriate medical and other health related information, resources, and professional expertise for developing the content of the life care plan. d. Relies on state-of-the-art knowledge and resources to develop a life care plan. e. Uses specialized skills including, but not limited to, the ability to research, critically analyze data, manage and interpret large volumes of information, attend to details, demonstrate clear and thorough written and verbal communication skills, develop positive relationships, create and use networks for gathering information, and work autonomously.

3. STANDARD: The life care planner performs comprehensive assessment through the process of data collection and analysis involving multiple elements and sources.

    MEASUREMENT CRITERIA: a. Collects data in a systematic, comprehensive, and accurate manner. b. Collects data about medical, health, biopsychosocial, financial, educational, and vocational status and needs. c. Obtains information from medical records, evaluee/family (when available or appropriate), relevant treating or consulting health care professionals and others. If access to any source of information is not possible (e.g., denied permission to interview the evaluee), this should be so noted in the report.

4. STANDARD: The life care planner uses a consistent, valid and reliable approach to research, data collection, analysis, and planning.

MEASUREMENT CRITERIA: a. Identifies current standards of care, clinical practice guidelines, services and products from reliable sources, such as current literature or other published sources, collaboration with other professionals, education programs, and personal clinical practice. b. Researches appropriate options and charges for recommendations, using sources that are reasonably available to the evaluee. c. Considers appropriate criteria for care options such as admission criteria, treatment indications or contraindications, program goals and outcomes, whether recommended care is consistent with standards of care, duration of care, replacement frequency, ability of the evaluee to appropriately use services and products, and whether care is reasonably available. d. Uses a consistent method to determine available choices and charges. e. Uses classification systems (e.g., International Classification of Diseases, Common Procedural Terminology) to correlate care recommendations and charges when these systems are available or helpful in providing clarity. f. Uses and relies upon relevant research that should be readily available for review and reflected within the life care plan.

5. STANDARD: The life care planner analyzes data.

MEASUREMENT CRITERIA: a. Analyzes data to determine evaluee needs and consistency of care recommendations with standards of care. b. Assesses need for further evaluations or expert opinions.

6. STANDARD: The life care planner uses a planning process.

MEASUREMENT CRITERIA: a. Follows a consistent method for organizing data, creating a narrative life care plan report, and projecting costs. b. Develops and uses written documentation tools for reports and cost projections. c. Develops recommendations for content of the life care plan cost projections for each evaluee and a method for validating inclusion or exclusion of content. d. Makes recommendations that are within the life care planner's own professional scope of practice; seeks recommendations from other qualified professionals and/or relevant sources for inclusion of care items and services outside the life care planner's scope of practice. e. Considers recommendations that are age-appropriate, using knowledge of human growth and development, including the impact of aging on disability and function.

7. STANDARD: The life care planner seeks collaboration when possible.

MEASUREMENT CRITERIA: a. Fosters positive relationships with all parties. b. Seeks expert opinions, as needed. c. Shares relevant information to aid in formulating recommendations and opinions.

8. STANDARD: The life care planner facilitates understanding of the life care planning process.

MEASUREMENT CRITERIA: a. Maintains objectivity and assists others in resolving disagreements about appropriate content for the life care plan. b. Provides information about the life care planning process to involved parties to elicit cooperative participation.

9. STANDARD: The life care planner evaluates.

MEASUREMENT CRITERIA: a. Reviews and revises the life care plan for internal consistency and completeness. b. Reviews the life care plan for consistency with standards of care and seeks resolution of inconsistencies. c. Provides follow-up consultation as appropriate and permitted to ensure that the life care plan is understood and properly interpreted.

10. STANDARD: The life care planner may engage in forensic applications.

MEASUREMENT CRITERIA: If the life care planner engages in practice that includes participation in legal matters, the life care planner: a. Acts as a consultant to legal proceedings related to determining care needs and costs in the role of an impartial advisor to the court. b. May provide expert sworn testimony regarding development and content of the life care plan. c. Maintains records of research and supporting documentation for content of the life care plan for a period of time consistent with requirements of applicable authoritative jurisdictions.

Work on the fourth edition of the *Standards of Practice for Life Care Planners* is underway (Woodward, 2021). Like its predecessors, this reference will incorporate core knowledge, skills, and behaviors that life care planners should employ in the course of their work.

Selection of Qualified Life Care Planners

Due to the overlap and interface between vocational rehabilitation and life care planning—including the need to assess examinee impairments and associated limitations, along with means to mitigate them and optimize residual capacities and resources—many vocational rehabilitation experts also have training and experience in life care planning and are competent to perform both earning capacity and future-care-needs damages assessments. Retaining lawyers, of course, need to conduct due diligence in their screening and selection of a life care planner.

The criteria for selection of life care plan expert witnesses are similar to the earlier discussed considerations for vocational rehabilitation experts: namely, ensuring the retained life care plan expert has appropriate education and training, specialty credentialing, relevant clinical experience, and a record of contributing to advance the profession's practice. Again, it goes without saying that the expert should be a good communicator, one who exudes a sense of professionalism and ethics beyond reproach—even under intense, often unfair interrogation by opposing counsel.

Certification as a life care planner is fundamental to one's representation and role as a life care planner. Surprisingly, as the excerpt from a deposition presented later indicates, it is not uncommon for lawyers to retain practitioners who lack this defining credential.

In addition to the International Academy of Life Care Planners, other organizations that regulate the practice of life care planning include the American Association of Nurse Life Care Planners and the American Academy of Physician Life Care Planners. Of note, nonphysicians who hold the Certified Life Care Planner and Certified Nurse Life Care Planner credentials are eligible for membership in this latter organization.

A trend during recent years has been for medical doctors—mostly physiatrists, neurologists, and chiropractors—to enter the life care planning arena. Additionally, a growing number of nurses and case managers are pursuing this work.

The International Academy of Life Care Planners grants the special recognition of Fellow status to certified life care planners who have applied exemplary skills and knowledge to contribute to the advancement of life care planning. At the time of this publication, 17 active practitioners held this distinction.

Discernment of a life care plan's validity should begin with an assessment of its prospective author's qualifications. Those who lack the credentials a profession endorses as being the minimum to competently practice—irreverent to professional practice standards and exempting themselves from codes of ethics, continuing education, and discipline to which legitimate practitioners are held—invite exposure of their deficiencies and defiance of efforts to comply with doctrines that committed life care planners honor. Analogous to the *Three Little Pigs* fable of the wolf dressed in sheepskin, cajoling through deceit a self-serving motive, these rogue life care plan "experts" do disservice to those faithfully attempting to define life care plan damages and deserve being debunked.

Following is an excerpt from a deposition epitomizing one who inappropriately short-cut the credentialing process that experts committed to their practice submit to and respect. Analytical comments follow, focusing on the self-serving testimony, laden with manipulative deceit.

Q   Can I have your specialty?

A   I am a vocational rehabilitation counselor and a life care planner.

Q   What was the scope of work you were retained to do?

A   Well, they asked for a life care plan. I have with me copies of a life care plan I prepared for this case.

Q   Are you, by chance, a certified life care planner?

A   No, I'm a certified rehabilitation counselor, which enables me to do life care plans. We could call them future needs assessments. And there is no need for a certification for looking at future needs assessments, which I've been doing for 30 years.

Q   And future needs assessments and a life care planner, you're saying, are the same thing?

A   In my view, yes. I was trained at XYZ Company, and one of the founders of life care planning was an XYZ person that just reversed, in a sense, or projected forward what we were—and called it something, what we are already doing with XYZ, the health and rehabilitative division.

Q   Are a future needs plan and a life care plan in the professional field viewed as the same thing?

A   Well, it depends. If you're talking to the certifying body, the certifying body wants you to be certified so they can get your certification dollars. But, you know, if you were to look at it and if I had on my cover page that you have, if I wrote future needs assessment, what would you think?

Q   Well, it's not for me to say, really. And that's my question is it doesn't say "Future Needs Plan." It says "Life Care Plan." I'm asking are those the same thing?

A   Yes, they are.

Q   OK. Is there a reason that you have not been certified as a life care planner?

A   I guess maybe because I started doing this maybe only in the last five or ten years, and I'm nearing the end of my career and I didn't see a reason—I didn't see a need for it. I'm a member of the International Association of Rehabilitation Professionals, and I go to the training for life care planners. And I know that lots of different people with different backgrounds do life care plans. So I didn't see the need for it.

Q   Do you know if there's any continuing education requirement for certified life care planners?

A   I've had a lot of continuing education in the field.

Q   All right. Do you know—as a certified life care planner, do you know if they're bound to a certain code of ethics that they have to follow?

A   Anybody who does life care plans is bound to a code of ethics. It's the same code of ethics—it's our standards of practice. Whether they're a certified life care planner or whether we are practicing as a life care planner, it's the same code of ethics.

Q   And you mentioned practice standards. Did you apply those in your work in this case?

A   Yes.

Q   You're not a doctor, correct?

A   Correct.

Q   In coming up with your life care plan in this case, did you confer with any doctors?

A   When you say confer, what do you mean?

Q   Well, I suppose that's open to interpretation. In coming up with your life care plan that you and I are looking at, did you talk with or meet with any doctor to provide input in giving you the information that you used to come up with that life care plan?

A   Most of the information came from documents that I was provided with, all the different people who evaluated the plaintiff. I, of course, interviewed him, and I did internet research.

This testimony gives rise to many concerns. The "expert" self-servingly dismisses credentialing she lacks—despite her selective use of the profession's vernacular, references to its methods, and specious representations that her work complies with standards and ethical guidelines binding certified life care planners.

Through self-anointed bluster and lip service to an organization of which she is a titular member, she crows she is as qualified and competent as a properly certified life care planner. Her belligerent, deprecatory comments about the professional organization that regulates the practice in which she purports to engage—namely, colloquy that the credential is but a shell to extort money—to legitimize her actions conjure images of another fictitious charlatan making false representations: the Wizard of Oz, hiding behind a thin veneer while boasting of great competence.

Additionally, the brief deposition testimony excerpt calls to mind at least six of ten methodological standard of practice violations (please refer to standards outlined earlier) the "expert" committed:

Standard 1: The life care planner practices within his or her professional scope of practice.
Standard 3: The life care planner performs comprehensive assessment through the process of data collection and analysis involving multiple elements and sources.

Standard 4: The life care planner uses a consistent, valid, and reliable approach to research, data collection, analysis, and planning.

Standard 7: The life care planner seeks collaboration when possible.

Standard 8: The life care planner facilitates understanding of the life care planning process.

Standard 9: The life care planner evaluates.

At best, the "expert" is practicing a perverted version of life care planning, defined by her subjective, self-serving standards and unqualified doublespeak she initiated to blur her lack of credentialing—specifically, the smokescreen discussion she initiated while likening a life care plan to a future needs assessment in an attempt to extricate herself from the mire of not being a legitimately credentialed professional. Her tactics are offensive, denigrate the profession, and cause indignation in all who earnestly attempt to define life care plan damages. Interestingly, later, during her deposition, she volunteered slanderous testimony about the bona fide expert opposing her, even though he had yet to provide any opinions in the case!

The testimony provided the lawyer an opportunity to file a motion to dismiss the "expert," and the opposing expert included in his report the following statement, preserving an opportunity to offer testimony about his counterpart:

> I would be remiss not to comment on testimony Ms. Jones, an expert witness retained by counsel representing the plaintiff, provided on December 12, 2020. Her testimony about credentialing, accepted life care planning methodology, and standards of practice are not consistent with those the professional life care planning community espouses.

Damages Assessments

Economists and accountants typically compute the cost(s) necessary to fund a life care plan. This involves analyses of historical growth/inflation rates for the life care plan's various recommendations (e.g., medications, surgeries, durable medical equipment), projection of the future value of current costs over an evaluee's lifespan, and reduction of future value to present value. In this case, damages are computed within a reasonable degree of economic probability—an exercise beyond the scope of most life care planners and the reason economists and accountants perform this damages assessment.

Since recommendations contained in a life care plan often extend over an evaluee's lifetime, life expectancy is an important variable in computing total damages. In some cases, an injured person's acquired disabling problems—such as some catastrophic cases in which a person is in a persistent vegetative state or sustains severe spinal cord injury—can reasonably be expected to shorten his or her life. Economists rely on qualified medical professionals and, in some cases, actuary studies to determine life expectancies and make necessary adjustments in their computations.

Some life care plans posit one or more scenarios, which require computing multiple valuations. For example, a severely disabled person might have residential options that include living in his home with appropriate in-home nursing care and other essential resources (Option 1) or residing in a skilled nursing facility (Option 2). The dual placement options would necessitate different interventions and involve different costs, requiring the computation of costs associated with both options.

Nonmonetary Damages—Pain and Suffering

As noted at the beginning of this chapter, vocational and life care plan damages lend themselves to being quantified and, accordingly, are referred to as monetary damages. Conversely, pain and suffering damages—related by-products of these monetary damages—do not readily lend themselves to a quantitative analysis. Placing a monetary value on pain and suffering, for example, associated with loss of vision, embarrassment over disfigurement, or loss of ability to perform pleasurable activities cannot be done objectively, within a reasonable degree of scientific probability.

Pain and suffering is the legal term for the emotional and physical stress an injury causes (Law.com Legal Dictionary, n.d.). The award for this damage at trial is typically made at a jury's discretion.

During the assessment of vocational and life care plan damages, of course, experts become aware of how acquired disabling problems have affected an individual overall. It is not uncommon to experience a range of disability adjustment problems secondary to unwelcome postinjury lifestyle changes: to name a few, distress over loss of independence, insecurities over career concerns, and worry about social adjustment and acceptance.

Of course, individual differences and circumstances govern emotional reactions. One person, stoic and cavalier, may take in stride an injury and its associated disabling problems; conversely, another similarly situated person may essentially become nonfunctional. In the context of litigation and assessment of damages claims, experts must consider secondary gain motives and malingering potentially undergirding evaluee presentations.

Figure 1.1 presents a summary of how a plaintiff lawyer proposed to quantify her client's noneconomic damages arising from a motor vehicle accident. This method, presented in a demand letter, simply applied a formula in which counsel imputed an hourly pain, suffering, and mental anguish cost (i.e., $10 per hour) to the plaintiff's waking hours—both postaccident, through the time of the demand letter, and in the future, over the remainder of the plaintiff's life expectancy—resulting in demands for past pain and suffering and future pain and suffering.

Depending on the case at hand, lawyers sometimes compute the value of economic damages and then infer the value of noneconomic damages is some multiple of what can be quantified. For example, in closing arguments at trial, plaintiff's counsel may propose to a jury that the value of pain and suffering damages is twice the value of damages attributable to loss of earning capacity and future care needs.

Scope of Expert Participation

Vocational rehabilitation and life care plan experts can serve as either consulting experts or testifying experts (Shahnasarian, 2015). An expert's case involvement sometimes begins as a consultant and then converts to testifying expert status as evidence is evaluated and litigation strategies evolve.

Figure 1.2 summarizes experts' participation, based on their status as a consulting expert or testifying expert. Lawyers decide on how an expert can best facilitate their objectives.

Figure 1.1 Example of Computation of Noneconomic (Pain and Suffering) Damages

NONECONOMIC DAMAGES:

Timothy Smith's life was abruptly interrupted by the negligence of your insured when he had to seek medical treatment to mitigate the injuries he sustained in this crash. Timothy Smith has consistently suffered and experienced pain caused by the injuries he sustained in the crash. Therefore, Timothy Smith is pursuing both economic and noneconomic damages.

In the event this claim does not resolve in accordance with the terms and conditions of this demand, Plaintiff will present a customary per diem argument to the jury for noneconomic damages.

A fair and reasonable amount to compensate Timothy Smith for his pain, suffering, mental anguish, and inconvenience since 8/23/2019 is $10 per hour for every waking hour he has spent suffering with pain caused by the injuries he sustained in this crash (generally 16 waking hours per day).

PAST PAIN AND SUFFERING:

244 days since the crash × $10/hour × 16 hours per day = **$39,040.00**

Timothy Smith continues to suffer and will continue to suffer from the injuries he sustained in this crash for the rest of his life. Our client will live 42 years into the future. A fair and reasonable amount to compensate Timothy Smith for his future pain and suffering is $10 per waking hour for the remainder of his life.

FUTURE PAIN AND SUFFERING:

Life expectancy 42 years × 365 days/year × 16 hours/day × $10/hour = **$2,452,800.00**

Figure 1.2 Experts' Participation: Consulting versus Testifying

	Consulting Expert	**Testifying Expert**
Expert Examination of Plaintiff	Not Conducted	May or May Not Be Conducted (Typically Conducted)
Disclosure of Expert's Involvement	Typically Not Disclosed	Always Disclosed
Discoverability of Expert's Analysis and Opinions	Not Discoverable	Fully Discoverable
Deposition and/or Trial Testimony	Not Provided	Available on Request

Defense lawyers, most apt to employ experts in consultant roles, do so to facilitate their understanding of damages while not being obligated to disclose to opposing counsel assessments and related evidence potentially disadvantageous to defending their case. Consulting experts typically evaluate the work and opinions plaintiff counsel's experts prepare, offer their critique, and assist in determining options available to defense counsel in using the defense consulting expert's services. These options include (1) maintaining the consulting expert in this capacity, providing input on merits and weaknesses of the opposing expert's assessment and opinions, or (2) converting the consulting expert to testifying expert status, which opens the opportunity to directly counter the opposing expert and introduce new expert evidence.

Shahnasarian (2015) noted lawyers defending cases that involve risk of significant damages awards avoid disclosing their expert's damages assessments when concerned about establishing a "floor" or minimum amount. For example, presume a defense expert computes a $5 million damages estimate compared to the plaintiff expert's assessment of $5.5 million or even up to $10 million. The defense lawyer will need to weigh the following questions in deciding to present the expert's opinion:

- Does the $5 million damages assessment set a "floor" for a jury award that exceeds the amount defense counsel believes is tenable to argue against?
- What is the risk that triers of fact, persuaded by some or all of plaintiff counsel's arguments, will view the $5 million as a "starting point" and adjust this value upward, validating the plaintiff expert's damages assessment?
- Is it better, in terms of suppressing a damages award, not to disclose the defense expert's damages assessment and, instead, concentrate on attacking the plaintiff expert's opinions?

Engagement Details

Once lawyers ascertain a potential expert has not already been retained by opposing counsel and the potential expert does not have a conflict with being retained, it is sometimes helpful for the two to consult before proceeding. Topics for this consultation typically include an overview of case facts including plaintiff's injuries and potential damages; case logistics including venue, deadlines, and potential special considerations (such as need for a translator or accommodations a plaintiff requires); and preliminary fee estimates.

If the lawyer and expert agree the case is appropriate for the expert to accept, the expert forwards information necessary to formalize a retention engagement. The expert's retention materials include the following:

- Retention letter—Appendix B is a sample retention letter. It details the expert's assessment procedures including records review, evaluee examination, and testing; policies on providing testimony; fees; and assorted logistics.
- Retention agreement—Appendix C is a sample retention agreement. It requires a signature by the retention source, which secures the signee's acknowledgment of the expert's retention policies including payment of fees.
- The expert's curriculum vita.

Experts consider themselves retained on a case only after having received a specified retention payment, applicable to fees as they are accrued, and an executed retention agreement. Most experts look askance at lawyers who inappropriately disclose them as a retained expert before a retention has been formalized, a practice known as "pirating" (Shahnasarian, 2015).

A Word on the Adversarial Litigation Environment

Unlike lawyers, expert witnesses do not advocate for a party in a dispute; however, their agreement to participate in a litigated matter requires them to submit to an adversarial environment and to abide by the rules that accompany it. For many vocational rehabilitation and life care plan experts, this environment is far different than the collegial, helping ones in which they trained and practiced before becoming expert witnesses.

Lawyers routinely attempt to portray opposing experts as biased, unqualified, deficient in examination rigor, and financially incented to provide favorable opinions to their retention source while, alternately, presenting their experts as objective, highly qualified, robust methodologically, and upright ethically. After her first deposition—conducted by an aggressive, experienced lawyer in a high-stakes medical malpractice case—the full-time university faculty member seeking to expand her professional work remarked, "No one has ever talked to me like that before." Simply put, work as an expert witness is not for those with thin skin.

Vocational rehabilitation professionals and life care planners should expect to be scrutinized and challenged—sometimes unfairly—throughout their engagement as an expert witness. Experts often encounter attorney bullying, manipulation, and innuendo that they are incompetent, inconsistent, "bought and paid for," or otherwise unsavory en route to formulating and presenting their opinions. These attacks arise through the likes of Boucher Interrogatories, objections to conducting examinations, and attempts to limit the scope of an exam and/or opinions, reaching a crescendo through Daubert challenges and cross-examination.

Of course, skilled experts do not cower or otherwise succumb to illegitimate, harassing ploys aimed to diminish their credibility; they maintain their professionalism, despite depraved tactics to discredit them (Shahnasarian, 2009a). More on these topics appears in Part IV.

PART II

Construction of Opinions
on Claims of Loss
of Earning Capacity

Part II begins with a discussion of methodologies to evaluate claims of loss of earning capacity, including an expanded discussion of Earning Capacity Assessment Theory (Shahnasarian, 2010a) and its adjunct, the Earning Capacity Assessment Form. This foundation provides a basis to detail the processes and mechanics associated with performing an assessment of earning capacity in Chapter 3. Finally, applying the underlying concepts enumerated, Chapter 4 addresses assessments of loss of earning capacity claims in pediatric cases, and Chapter 5 focuses on conducting these assessments in adult cases.

CHAPTER 2

Foundations of Earning Capacity Damages Assessments

According to the Organization for Economic Cooperation and Development (OECD, 2018), workforce participants committed an average of 1,734 hours per year to paid work activity, nearly one-third of their waking hours, engaged in full-time, part-time, and other forms of employment. People often spend five or more decades of their lives pursuing paid employment, with a growing number of individuals extending their careers into their mid-70s. Clearly, for many, work is a major life function, and impairment of one's earning capacity can portend damages beyond a job's remuneration, including potential psychological and social consequences associated with diminished ability to work and earn wages. These latter damages can have implications for another type of damages: namely, pain and suffering—the nonmonetary damages discussed in Chapter 1.

The vocational rehabilitation literature documents peer reviews of methodologies practitioners have propounded to perform evaluations of alleged damages to one's career development. Generally, mainstream methods have a high degree of confluence, procedurally. Nonmainstream methods continue to spark controversy with respect to their procedures and validity of derived results.

Mainstream Methodologies

Van de Bittner, Wallace, Cottle, and Simon (2012) compared vocational experts' methodologies for evaluating employability and earning capacity, citing those published in peer-reviewed professional journals and other publications over a 15-year period. The investigators analyzed 22 methodologies, focusing on their components, and identified the following included in 75 percent or more of contemporary methodologies:

- Records review
- Interview
- Educational assessment
- Work history assessment
- Testing
- Transferable skills assessment

- Labor market research
- Age/work life expectancy assessment
- Rehabilitation plan/assessment of return-to-work options
- Placeability assessment
- Wage or earning capacity comparison
- Production of a written report

Field (2012a) provided a historical review of experts' methods to estimate earning capacity. Others who have reported comprehensive reviews on this topic include Field (2008), Robinson (2014), Robinson and Pomeranz (2011), and Shahnasarian (2010a; 2015).

The methods outlined in *The Valuation of Monetary Damages in Injury Cases: A Damages Expert's Perspective* incorporate the components of the mainstream methods delineated earlier. Chapter 3 describes the processes and mechanics associated with integrating these components to perform an assessment of earning capacity.

Before the Earning Capacity Assessment Theory and its derivative, the Earning Capacity Assessment Form—both expounded on later in this chapter—Weed (2000) presented a method to assess claims of loss of earning capacity that experts continue to regularly use. An acronym, RAPEL, outlines the method's sequential evaluation steps:

Rehabilitation Plan—determination of an individual's functional limitations, vocational strengths, emotional functioning, and cognitive capabilities

Access to the Labor Market—determination of an individual's access to the labor market

Placeability—likelihood that an individual could be successfully placed in a job

Earning Capacity—based on the preceding, comparisons of an individual's preinjury and postinjury capacity to earn

Labor Force Participation—an individual's anticipated work life expectancy

Nonmainstream Methodologies

Vocational assessment methodologies that often stir the most controversy rely heavily if not exclusively on data from statistical sources (such as those the U.S. Department of Labor and professional organizations publish), while incorporating superficial levels of data from a case at hand and overextrapolating inferences from aggregate data to derive opinions. An example occurred in a case involving a mid-career contract truck driver who fractured his nondominant wrist in a single-vehicle accident. His lawsuit spawned several questions about his vocational capacities including his demonstrated earnings history. He documented very low net earnings after expenses ($2,000 to $3,000 per year), along with years when no tax returns were filed, raising significant questions about the legitimacy of his claimed business expense deductions. Among other things, the veracity of the evaluee's reported income to the Internal Revenue Service was called into question.

Asserting the evaluee's demonstrated earnings record was confusing and unreliable, the plaintiff's vocational expert dismissed it and imputed an annual preaccident median wage rate for truck drivers of approximately $60,000, based on a government salary survey. The plaintiff had no documentary evidence of ever generating wages near this level, inviting intense criticism of the expert's methodology under cross-examination while also raising questions about the evaluee's character. Needless to say, these facts provided fodder to deem the wage loss claim baseless, calling into question the integrity of both the expert and evaluee—an unenviable position from which to argue a wage loss claim.

Perhaps the most controverted applications of aggregate data in loss of earning capacity assessments occur when evaluees have resumed their preinjury jobs, maintained or increased their preinjury earnings levels, and have no apparent medical contraindications or prognoses to suggest they will be unable to persist in their career development. Yet a vocational expert cites aggregate data to impugn a loss of earning capacity.

Experts who rely heavily on aggregate data tend to cite studies that people with disabilities experience higher rates of unemployment and earn lower wages than their able-bodied counterparts. Although this may be true at a general level, the commonsense rendering that people with some type of impairment—for a myriad of reasons that range from employer bias to workplace functional difficulties—earn lower wages than those not impaired requires case-by-case discernment. Speaking in platitudes about damages denigrates the science and spirit undergirding vocational rehabilitation.

Assessments of this sort tend to rely heavily on macroeconomic data, superficially integrating case-specific facts. They often occur in cases in which an expert has been retained by counsel representing a plaintiff and the facts are either incomplete or deficient to support a claim of loss of earning capacity opinion, which an analysis performed in line with mainstream methods would likely support.

Invariably, nonmainstream analyses overvalue an evaluee's earning loss claim. Often accompanied with pages of tables with mathematically derived formulae, reports of these sorts may project face validity to a layperson but belie practice standard methodologies, rendering them at best misleading and at worst intentionally manipulative. The adage "garbage in, garbage out" is apropos.

There are occasions when relying on aggregate data, either in part or in toto, is appropriate. Circumstances that might cause an examiner to afford significant weight to aggregate data rather than to an injured person's demonstrated record include

- A younger person who has not yet had an opportunity to establish a reliable baseline earnings record
- One who has been absent from the workplace for an extended period for reasons that may include an illness, need to provide childcare or eldercare services, or lack of financial need to work
- A recent immigrant who has not had an opportunity to fully assimilate into the labor market and appears to have had the potential for advancing to jobs offering higher levels of pay

A comprehensive review and critique of nonmainstream methodologies to evaluate loss of earning capacity claims are beyond this book's scope. Those interested in this subject should refer, for starters, to the annals of *The Rehabilitation Professional* and the *Journal of Forensic Economics*.

This chapter details generally accepted theory and practice that expert witnesses apply to conduct earning capacity assessments in forensic injury cases, including questions relating to how an event(s) in question, allegedly causing an injury, within a reasonable degree of vocational rehabilitation probability, has affected one's ability to work, earn wages, and persist in one's career development. These assessments culminate in an opinion about a loss of earning capacity and, when appropriate, include suggestions for mitigating vocational damages.

In pediatric cases, evaluees typically lack a demonstrated record on which experts can extrapolate deductions as reliable as those they can deduce in cases involving claimants with a long record of career development. Accordingly, they rely on evidence of an evaluee's latent career development potential and integrate into analyses indicators helpful to configure probable career paths before and after an evaluee became injured. Chapter 4 addresses claims of loss of earning capacity in pediatric cases.

The goal of earning capacity assessment cases that involve an adult, of course, are identical to those that involve a child: to determine whether an event(s) in question diminished an evaluee's earning capacity. Along with latent potential, these analyses (1) consider an evaluee's historic earnings and career development record, (2) establish a baseline, preinjury earnings metric, and (3) construct an evaluee's likely career and earnings trajectory in the absence of claimed injuries. The analysis then progresses to ascertain residual, postinjury vocational capacities and, if appropriate, mitigation opportunities. Through a synthesis of these and other factors discussed in the following sections, vocational evaluators derive an opinion, within a reasonable degree of vocational rehabilitation probability, on loss of earning capacity. Chapter 5 addresses claims of loss of earning capacity in adult cases.

Applying Generally Accepted Theory and Practice in Loss of Earning Capacity Assessments

Assessment Objectives

Forensic vocational experts assess how an evaluee's alleged acquired injuries and associated disabling problems may affect his or her earning capacity. This assessment considers ability to work, earn wages, and pursue career development.

If an expert determines an event damaged an evaluee's career development, the analysis expands to incorporate assessments of effects on earning capacity, opportunities to mitigate damages, and, when damages cannot be fully mitigated, the value of the loss of earning capacity over the evaluee's work life. These assessments anticipate career-related damages that may not pose a significant impairment at the time of an examination but may arise, within a reasonable degree of probability, over the course of an evaluee's remaining work life. Figure 2.1 displays the decision-making process using standards of practice that vocational evaluators apply while assessing earning capacity implications associated with an event in question. Robinson (2014) and Shahnasarian (2015) identified other intermittent process questions—such as considering transferable skills, work accommodations, and retraining as means to mitigate damages—that evaluators incorporate in their analyses.

As an example of how acquired injuries might not have near-term earning capacity effects but portend longer-term implications, consider the case of a mid-career drywall installer who sustained multiple lower extremity injuries after a work-related fall from a scaffold. The injured worker resumed his preinjury job, albeit with modifications, and maintained his rate of pay. When considering the physical demands of the evaluee's job along with medical prognostications of progressive degenerative changes and declining functional capacities over time, the vocational expert concluded that, unless the evaluee transitioned to less physically demanding work in the next three to five years, he likely would experience a truncated work life and, by extension, a loss of earning capacity. Hence, transitioning to a less physically demanding occupation presented an opportunity to mitigate anticipated future career damages.

The Valuation of Monetary Damages in Injury Cases: A Damages Expert's Perspective features Earning Capacity Assessment Theory (ECAT) and its derivative, the Earning Capacity Assessment Form (ECAF)—a validated instrument that operationalizes ECAT. In addition to positive peer-reviewed recognition in the realm of loss of earning capacity assessment methodologies, the development of the ECAT and ECAF was predicated on empirical research including studies with subjects composed of practicing vocational rehabilitation

Figure 2.1 Vocational Evaluator Decision-Making Process in Evaluating a Claim of Loss of Earning Capacity

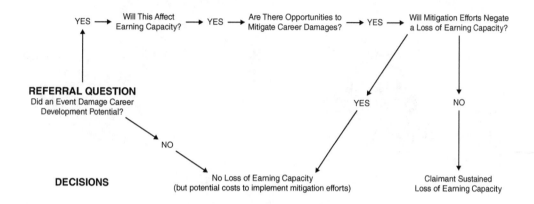

experts, trial attorneys, insurance adjusters, vocational rehabilitation administrators, and graduate students in rehabilitation counseling.

The leading professional forums with an interest in loss of earning capacity claims have recognized the ECAT and ECAF, described next, as invaluable adjuncts to assessing injury damages. The fine points of this methodological base, which incorporates the essential elements of all recognized peer-reviewed methodologies, follow.

Theoretical Foundations: Earning Capacity Assessment Theory

As noted at the beginning of this chapter, peer-reviewed publications recognize multiple methodologies to perform assessments of earning capacity. ECAT (Shahnasarian, 2010a; 2015), predicated on more than three decades of empirical research and reviewed favorably since its inception, ranks among those most prominent. An explanation of its tenets and applications follows.

Earning Capacity Assessment Theory Objectives

ECAT aspires to promote two objectives:

- To offer vocational evaluators systematic, standardized, empirically tested methods to conduct assessments of earning capacity and evaluate claims of loss of earning capacity.
- To offer those not professionally trained and who maintain an interest in claimed vocational damages (e.g., judges and other triers of fact, insurance adjusters, lawyers) a framework to evaluate the merits of evaluators' analyses.

Application of Analytical Processes

Reference to a three-sided pyramid (tetrahedron), shaded to describe concurrent analytical processes, facilitates a discussion of ECAT. Please refer to Figure 2.2 as this discussion unfolds. Each triangle face represents a discrete evaluation process, and the pyramid structure unites the three faces: the shading implies that the like-shaded tasks on each face co-occur and coalesce as the process evolves.

Figure 2.2
Three Faces of the Earning Capacity
Assessment Theory Tetrahedron

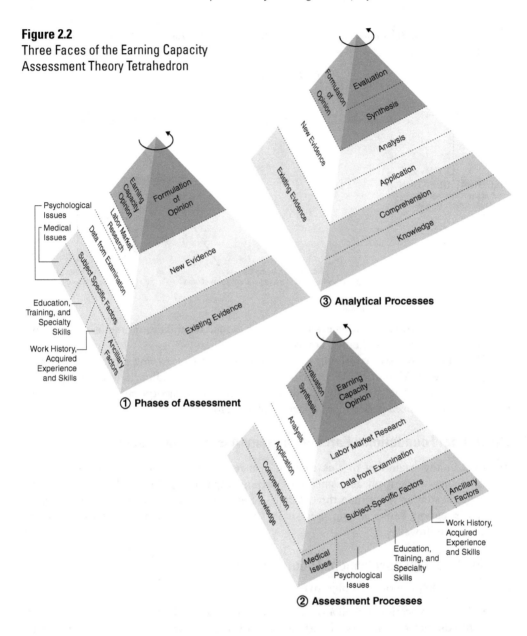

The vocational assessment process begins with an evaluator's attention to tasks and processes described at the pyramid's base. Ascension up the pyramid's sides involves a hierarchical progression in which, appropriately applied, realizing higher levels requires first having accomplished tasks delineated on its lower levels.

First, consider the triangle face at the left side, "Phases of Assessment." It cites three sequential phases of the ECAT assessment process: starting from the bottom, reviews of existing evidence, followed by reviews of new evidence, and culminating in the formulation of an opinion.

Next, refer to the second triangle face, titled "Assessment Processes." At the base, the diagram identifies subject-specific factors necessary to consider at an assessment's onset:

medical issues; psychological factors; education, training, and specialty skills; and ancillary factors, which could include, for example, geographic constraints, family issues, and other pertinent evaluee-specific idiosyncratic considerations. This diagram's midsection implies that an examiner builds on the lower-tiered information by integrating data from an examination and labor market research. Examiners aspire to ascend to the diagram's pinnacle: attaining an earning capacity opinion, stated within a reasonable degree of vocational rehabilitation probability, applying the profession's science, and developed on the undergirding foundation information.

Finally, the third triangle face, "Analytical Processes," as its title implies, describes the analytical processes vocational evaluators undertake while performing earning capacity assessments. Deriving from Bloom (1956), who presented a classic model describing higher-order thinking, this triangle face of the tetrahedron delineates a progression of analytical steps from lower- to higher-order thought processes, each building on one another, leading to evaluation—the goal of science-based, objective inquiry of a claim of loss of earning capacity. The aims of each step are as follows:

- Knowledge—Identifying and/or recalling information
- Comprehension—Understanding and grasping the meaning of information
- Application—Using learned information in new or past similar situations
- Analysis—Taking information apart and exploring new relationships
- Synthesis—Formulating new structures from knowledge and learned information
- Evaluation—Critically examining information and making professional judgments

Regarding the shading on the three tetrahedron faces, note the consistency of shades across them. The coordinated shading conveys the concurrence of assessment processes a vocational evaluator undertakes while performing an assessment. Specifically, the sequential, hierarchical assessment process, beginning at the base of the tetrahedron, involves simultaneously (1) reviewing existing evidence, composed of the subject-specific factors identified, and involving knowledge and comprehension analytical processes (darkest shade); (2) integrating new evidence, including data from an examination and labor market research, involving application and analysis processes (medium shade); and (3) formulating an opinion on earning capacity involving the synthesis and evaluation of information obtained (lightest shade).

The pinnacle of the ECAT pyramid, developing a claim of loss of earning capacity opinion, represents the summation of a vocational evaluator's efforts to address referral questions and assimilate relevant information. This involves reviewing and evaluating facts, evidence, and theories based on reasonably probable judgments—in terms of both internal evidence and external criteria. Internal evidence emanates from a case at hand, which often includes clinically derived data an evaluator generates from an interview, test data, or research. Examples of external criteria include practice standards, codes of ethics, and judicial rules and processes.

ECAT provides a theoretical framework to conduct earning capacity assessments. More than three decades of research and development led to a means to operationalize this theory, providing a systematic, empirically based, peer-reviewed method for practitioners to evaluate claims of loss of earning capacity using the Earning Capacity Assessment Form-2 (ECAF-2). Details on the instrument's development, psychometric properties, and peer reviews and admissibility follow. This discussion on the ECAF-2 concludes with a case study demonstrating its application in a complex case in which a late-career human resources professional sustained both traumatic brain injury and spinal cord injury and nevertheless returned to her preinjury job.

Practice Foundations: The Earning Capacity Assessment Form-2

Introduced in 2001 (Shahnasarian, 2001), the Earning Capacity Assessment Form (ECAF) became commercially available in 2004 (Shahnasarian, 2004a) when Elliott & Fitzpatrick published it. After further validation studies (Shahnasarian, 2008), Psychological Assessment Resources (PAR) published the instrument's second edition, the ECAF-2, in 2010 (Shahnasarian, 2010c). Shahnasarian and Hill (2014) described the instrument's subsequent use in facilitating analyses of claims of loss of earning capacity domestically and abroad.

The ECAF-2 is the only standardized, peer-reviewed instrument developed to facilitate vocational experts' ratings of claims of loss of earning capacity. Early efforts to develop the measure derived from findings that lawyers perceived approaches to assessing claims of loss of earning capacity were neither consistent nor objective (Shahnasarian & Lassiter, 2002).

A four-page document, the ECAF-2 includes 14 factors a vocational evaluator rates with respect to a pending claim of loss of earning capacity. Four statements, arranged in a graduated, hierarchical sequence, accompany each factor.

Within a given cluster of statements, the first statement generally connotes either a high level of vocational functioning or an absence of an impediment to career development. Subsequent statements reflect progressively increasing levels of potential career-related problems that could affect future earning capacity. As an example, ratings from which an evaluator could choose on the cognition factor are

0 Cognitively intact
1 Mild cognition problems, not anticipated to impact future career development
2 Cognitive deficits will adversely impact career development
3 Cognitive deficits preclude gainful work participation

The ECAF-2's graduated rating scheme allows for systematic analysis, assessment, and valuation of phenomena (i.e., factors influencing earning capacity) while incorporating practitioners' clinical judgments. Shahnasarian and Leitten (2008a) emphasized the instrument serves as a resource to facilitate systematic analysis; it is not intended to serve as a stand-alone outcome measure. The ECAF-2's 14 factors and their definitions appear in Figure 2.3, and Figure 2.4 summarizes the ten postulates undergirding its application.

Users complete the ECAF-2 in three steps. First, they rate an evaluee with respect to the nine Inhibitor factors and five Driver factors (see Figure 2.4). Second, they interpret the evaluee's ECAF-2 profile. Third, they apply interpretive guidelines to assign an overall impairment-to-earning-capacity rating. Figure 2.5 shows the Impairment to Earning Capacity Rating Scale—the ultimate point of reference toward which ECAF-2 users develop their analyses.

Some ECAF-2 users complete their item ratings while examining a claimant and then clinically incorporate case-specific data into their assessments. Others defer completing the instrument to their evaluation's conclusion, applying it as a cumulative means to facilitate a loss of earning capacity assessment.

Experienced users complete the ECAF-2 in 15 minutes or less. As users enhance their familiarity and confidence with the ECAF-2's 14 factors, gain skills and confidence in assigning factor ratings, and become adept at interpreting ECAF-2 profiles and applying interpretive standards, they become more competent and proficient instrument users.

Figure 2.3 The 14 ECAF-2 Factors with Definitions

Stability of Career Development: Consists of longevity of employment with previous employers, consistency between types of jobs performed and industries within which subject has worked, eligibility for rehiring with prior employers, and continuity of employment.

Work Propensity: Subject's historical level of work participation including proclivity to pursue overtime work and supplemental employment.

Demonstrated Earnings History: Earnings levels a subject has demonstrated a capacity to attain.

Phase of Career Development: Age, level of career maturity, and vocational accomplishments with respect to status within one of five progressive career development phases—growth, exploration, establishment, maintenance, and withdrawal.

Subject-Specific Issues: Life and/or personal circumstances that may impact a subject's ability to pursue work-related activities.

Motivation: A personality trait affecting work tendencies and productivity. Indicators include record of career accomplishments and work participation, initiatives to enhance existing skill set, reasonableness of job search efforts, attempts to return to work after acquiring disabling problems, efforts to pursue rehabilitation services to overcome work-related obstacles, and use of discretionary time to further career development.

Ability to Apply Prior Skills: Based on transferability of skills—subject's ability to apply previously developed work skills and specialized knowledge to meet the requirements of jobs or occupations other than what subject has performed in the past. Factors such as vocational adjustment issues, physical and cognitive capacity for retraining, and available resources should be considered.

Future Career Development Prospects: A general awareness of what could impact subject's future employability. Dependent on factors such as industry trends, marketplace changes, and modification of management philosophy.

Cognition: Subject's thought processing and mental functioning abilities. Deficits may be congenital, be due to medication, or stem from events such as a head injury, cerebrovascular accident, dementia, or a mental disorder.

Prognosis: Expectancy of how disabling problems and vocational handicaps will impact the subject over the remainder of his or her work life, including future earning capacity.

Need and Capacity for Retraining: Necessity for subject to undergo retraining in order to realize earning capacity; may involve consideration of subject's capacity for retraining.

Preexisting Vocational Handicaps: Includes subject's premorbid medical and psychological history and level of functioning. Unrealized disabling problems may synergize to yield a compounded disabling outcome.

Acquired Vocational Handicaps: Factors that can adversely affect present and future career development, including diminished access to work opportunities, need for workplace accommodations, employer bias in hiring and advancement, and diminished work life expectancy.

Vocational Adjustment Issues: Difficulties subject may realize when career transitioning due to vocationally related and subject-specific characteristics that may inhibit or facilitate positive vocational adjustment. A subject's capacity to make a positive vocational adjustment depends on ability to recover from setbacks posed by newly acquired disabling problems.

Figure 2.4 ECAF-2 Postulates. The ECAF-2 Professional Manual and ECAF-2 instrument can be obtained by contacting its publisher, Psychological Assessment Resources, Inc. (PAR), at www.parinc.com.

Postulate 1: When evaluating loss of earning capacity claims, there are premorbid and postincident factors that could be facilitative (Drivers) as well as detrimental (Inhibitors) to a claimant's vocational rehabilitation. These factors merit analysis.

Postulate 2: ECAF-2 factors that are Drivers include low scores on measures of the following:

- Stability of Career Development
- Work Propensity
- Demonstrated Earnings History
- Career Motivation
- Cognition

Postulate 3: ECAF-2 factors that are Inhibitors include high scores on measures of the following:

- Phase of Career Development
- Subject-Specific Issues
- Ability to Apply Prior Skills
- Future Career Development Prospects
- Prognosis
- Need and Capacity for Retraining
- Preexisting Vocational Handicaps
- Acquired Vocational Handicaps
- Vocational Adjustment Issues

Postulate 4: Drivers and Inhibitors can be quantitatively and qualitatively evaluated by qualified vocational rehabilitation evaluators.

Postulate 5: Drivers and Inhibitors have an interactive effect on vocational rehabilitation potential, presuming an individual is motivated to pursue vocational rehabilitation.

Postulate 6: Positive Drivers can help mitigate earning capacity damages, presuming an individual is motivated to do so.

Postulate 7: The ECAF-2 can be used to generate a quantitative index of Drivers.

Postulate 8: The ECAF-2 can be used to generate a quantitative index of Inhibitors.

Postulate 9: Driver and Inhibitor indices can be used to assess claims of loss of earning capacity with corresponding degrees of loss.

Postulate 10: At times, Drivers can take on Inhibitor qualities and Inhibitors can take on Driver qualities.

A professional user's manual (Shahnasarian, 2010b) accompanies the ECAF-2 and includes instructions on its use, reports of validity and reliability studies, interpretive guidelines, and case study examples. Shahnasarian (2010b) asserted the ECAF-2 can be particularly useful when the assessment of latent or future loss of earning capacity is evident but difficult to quantify. Examples of these cases include

Figure 2.5 The Impairment to Earning Capacity Rating Scale. Adapted and reproduced by special permission of the Publisher, Psychological Assessment Resources, Inc., 16204 North Florida Avenue, Lutz, Florida 33549, from the Earning Capacity Assessment Form-2nd Edition by Michael Shahnasarian, Ph.D., Copyright 2010 by PAR, Inc. Further reproduction is prohibited without permission of PAR, Inc.

- Pediatric evaluees with permanent injuries
- Evaluees early in their careers who have yet to demonstrate an adequate baseline record of vocational attainment
- Evaluees who have not realized their full earning capacity because their career development was interrupted (e.g., a college-educated person who was actively raising children and not employed in the workplace)
- Evaluees who anticipate experiencing degenerative problems and/or other vocational handicaps
- Self-employed evaluees who become compromised in their ability to pursue career development but continue to pursue entrepreneurial activities
- Evaluees who lack a demonstrated earnings record

ECAF-2 Psychometric Properties

Shahnasarian (2004b) reported the ECAF's initial validation study, which involved 78 Florida vocational rehabilitation counselors. Subjects were randomly assigned to either a control group or one of two experimental groups that used the ECAF to help evaluate claims of loss of earning capacity presented in three fact patterns. In all cases, variances within experimental group assessments were significantly less than variances among control group subjects. Further, subjects' ECAF use reduced within-group variance in loss of earning capacity estimates.

Several studies have since examined the ECAF-2's validity and reliability. Briefly, research investigating the ECAF-2's construct validity found vocational rehabilitation experts agreed or strongly agreed that the instrument facilitated analyses of loss of earning capacity claims in 74.5 percent of 70 cases they evaluated (Shahnasarian & Leitten, 2008b). Two Driver factors—career motivation and cognition—emerged most frequently as important in assessing potential loss of earning capacity; a longitudinal study involving claimants who were reevaluated from five to seven years after having undergone an initial evaluation (Shahnasarian & Leitten, 2008b) supported this finding.

Shahnasarian and Leitten (2008c) and Shahnasarian (2010b) reported studies assessing the ECAF-2's internal structure. Given the interdependence of Inhibitor factors and Driver factors, hypotheses that most items would positively correlate have generally proven true. Inhibitor items tend to have stronger positive correlations with other Inhibitor items than with Driver items. Likewise, Driver items tend to have stronger positive correlations with other Driver items than with Inhibitor items (Shahnasarian & Leitten, 2008c).

Regarding the ECAF-2's internal consistency, data from a 2009 study found a coefficient alpha of 0.82 for the 14 items (Shahnasarian, 2009a; 2010b), and interrater agreements among experienced evaluators ranged from 57 percent to 100 percent, with rater agreement on ten items at or above 70 percent.

Shahnasarian and Leitten (2008c) reported results of the ECAF-2's test-retest reliability. The study included 25 graduate students who rated case studies over a two-week interval. Results revealed ECAF-2 Inhibitor items had test reliabilities ranging from 0.74 to 0.96, Driver items had reliabilities ranging from 0.70 to 0.80, and Impairment to Earning Capacity Scale ratings had reliabilities ranging from 0.85 to 0.90.

Shahnasarian, Leitten, and Tremp (2010) reported a study investigating the ECAF-2's interrater reliability. Correlation coefficients significant at the 0.001 levels emerged in analyses of all 14 factors, ranging from 0.71 to 0.90. Analyses of Drivers and Inhibitors and raters' estimates of loss of earning capacity yielded the following correlation coefficients: ECAF-2 Inhibitors, 0.91; ECAF-2 Drivers, 0.92; and loss of earning capacity assessments, 0.94. Subjects agreed or strongly agreed that the ECAF-2 facilitated their evaluations 78.6 percent of the time.

For more information about the ECAF-2's construction and psychometric properties, please refer to the *Earning Capacity Assessment Form 2nd Edition Professional Manual* (Shahnasarian, 2010c). Shahnasarian (2010a) elaborated about the ECAF-2's theoretical bases and research support, and Shahnasarian and Hill (2014) reported on the instrument's use—within the United States, abroad, and by practitioner setting—during the two years and six months after its inception.

ECAF-2 Peer Reviews and Admissibility

Numerous publications have featured the ECAF-2 and its methodological bases, comparing it to other methodologies formulated to conduct assessments of claims of loss of earning capacity. Field (2008; 2012a) reviewed mainstream methodologies vocational experts have been applying during the past 50 years and described the ECAF-2 as a practical approach. He noted it helps vocational experts organize and synthesize information central to assessing earning capacity.

Robinson, Young, and Pomeranz (2009) highlighted the 14 ECAF/ECAF-2 Inhibitor and Driver factors as a means to standardize vocational rehabilitation evaluations, and the California Chapter of the International Association for Rehabilitation Professionals (CA-IARP) Diminished Future Earnings Capacity (DFEC) work group referenced the ECAF/ECAF-2 as a guide to recommend standards for vocational experts in California (Austin et al., 2009).

Reliance on scientifically derived, peer-reviewed methods facilitates vocational rehabilitation experts' efforts to stave off admissibility challenges. In his review of the ECAF-2, while commenting on the admissibility of expert testimony, Field (2012b) concluded the instrument meets the reliability and relevance requirements set forth in the Daubert trilogy (*Daubert v. Merrell Dow Pharmaceuticals*, 1993; *General Electric Co. v. Joiner*, 1997; and *Kumho Tire Co. v. Carmichael*, 1999) as well as challenges inherent to admissibility in federal and state courts. Field went on to cite empirical support for the instrument and noted it has been peer-reviewed in multiple forums since 2001.

Robinson and Pomeranz (2011) noted the focus of the ECAF-2 model "appears to be aimed at satisfying the evidentiary requirements set forth in the Federal Rules of Evidence, Rule 702" (Committee of the Judiciary, 2009). They characterized the model as robust in its focus on examinee-specific factors. Barros-Bailey and Robinson (2012) reviewed labor market information models propounded in earning capacity models during the past 30 or more years and concluded the ECAF-2 model incorporates labor-market search components.

In her review of *Assessment of Earning Capacity 3rd Edition*, including commentary on the ECAF-2, Neulicht's (2011) appraisals were similar to those Field (2012b) voiced. She concluded:

> One of the jewels is Shahnasarian's ability to provide a complete review of his research and the earning capacity assessment form he developed, which has been discussed in prior editions of the book (Assessment of Earning Capacity) and presented/published in multiple peer-reviewed journal articles.

Van de Bittner, Wallace, Cottle, and Simon (2012) applied guidelines from the CA-IARP DFEC work group to evaluate peer-reviewed methodologies published in professional journals and texts during the preceding 15 years. They determined the ECAF-2 methodology addresses central components of an evaluation of employability and earning capacity comparable to other methodologies.

Shahnasarian (2010a; 2011) elaborated on theoretical bases underlying the ECAF-2. Like other models developed to assess claims of loss of earning capacity, the instrument and its underlying theoretical framework focus on evaluator methods and analytical evaluation processes.

Readers are referred to the *ECAF-2 Professional Manual* (Shahnasarian, 2010c) for guidelines on assigning item ratings and interpreting Inhibitor and Driver profiles. The *Professional Manual* also specifies guidelines for translating ECAF-2 profiles to the Impairment to Earning Capacity Scale. An example of how a vocational evaluator applied ECAT and then used the ECAF-2 to develop and quantify a loss of earning capacity opinion follows.

ECAF-2 Case Study Example

The case study presented next involves a senior human resources executive who acquired physical injuries and cognitive impairments after a motor vehicle accident. Of note, her pre-accident medical history includes a lumbar surgery and treatment for mental health issues. She resumed her preaccident job, albeit with difficulties, and continued to perform it through the time of her vocational rehabilitation evaluation.

First, the vocational evaluator presents contextual background information and problems the claimant associates with her accident. Information about her vocational activity follows. The case study concludes with the vocational evaluator's summary and impressions, including an opinion on accident-related loss of earning capacity.

While reviewing the case study, note how the evaluator integrates ECAT into his assessment, including elements that assess the interface between the requirements of the claimant's job—from both exertional and nonexertional perspectives—and her residual capacities. This assessment incorporates an analysis of premorbid factors, parsing them from evidence of newly acquired difficulties affecting vocational functioning. The figures that appear at the end of his analysis show his ECAF-2 item ratings.

Case Study

Background Information and Claimant Presenting Problems

Lynda Smith was referred for a vocational rehabilitation evaluation. A complaint documents allegations of injuries she sustained as a result of a motor vehicle accident on August 31, 2018. Ms. Smith noted Large Corporation A (LCA) employed her as a senior employee relations specialist at the time of her 2018 accident.

Ms. Smith advised me she continues to work with LCA in her preaccident job. She conveyed she was promoted from employee relations specialist to senior employee relations specialist eight months before her accident. "I would never have gotten the promotion if I was performing the way I am now," Ms. Smith said.

Currently, Ms. Smith informed me, she experiences the following problems she relates to her 2018 accident:

- Ongoing neck pain, varied intensity
- Left shoulder pain with diminished range of motion, onsets due to various movements
- Intermittent mid-back pain
- Cognitive dysfunction including difficulties with memory, new learning, concentration, information processing, judgment, and problem solving
- Mood-related problems including anxiety and depression

I referenced documentation of a lumbar surgery in 1990, and Ms. Smith reported experiencing "occasional flare-ups" thereafter. Since her August 2018 accident, she told me, her lumbar pain becomes exacerbated more frequently. I inquired whether her physicians have assessed that her 2018 accident caused additional injury to her lumbar spine, and Ms. Smith responded, "I don't know."

When asked whether she experienced the previously listed problems before her 2018 accident, Ms. Smith replied, "I had an occasional stiff neck before, but nothing like this. I had anxiety and depression before this [2018 accident], as well." I inquired whether she had neck symptoms near the time before her 2018 accident, and she responded negatively.

Concerning her preaccident mood problems, Ms. Smith indicated she was taking psychotropic medication—Wellbutrin and Xanax—for depression and anxiety. "It was nothing that would keep me out of work," she stated. Ms. Smith denied injuring her left shoulder or mid-back or having problems with cognitive dysfunction before her 2018 accident.

When asked about mental functioning, Ms. Smith cited problems with memory, concentration, and speech. "I have difficulty learning new things," she stated, elaborating about her cognitive difficulties. She went on to cite trouble with comprehension. "It's embarrassing, and I do have trouble with remembering things," Ms. Smith added. She referenced her job and participating in meetings. "I get cast aside because I can't keep up, and people don't want to keep explaining things to me," she said.

Ms. Smith also discussed postaccident word retrieval difficulties. "That's difficult in the type of work I do, having to interview people, answer questions in meetings. I'm still constantly mixing up people's names, sending e-mails to the wrong person," she stated.

Elaborating about her problems with judgment, Ms. Smith said, "I've done some really stupid things. I've almost gotten fired a few times." For example, she cited an occurrence when she was reporting the results of an employee complaint, which involved an allegation of a manager bullying an employee. "I revealed confidential information that I shouldn't have. The employee got an attorney, and it was resolved in mediation. They said the employee made reference to specifics of the investigation that he should have never known," Ms. Smith said.

Ms. Smith discussed another example of poor judgment she displayed, postaccident, that involved a complaint of a member of her family, also an LCA employee, about a director's "bad behavior." Ms. Smith informed me she questioned a peer about the complaint's status. "I should have never done that because of a conflict of interest, and I gave my opinions—I shouldn't have done that," she added. Ms. Smith noted the two faux pas she described were not characteristic of her before August 31, 2018. "It will show on my performance reviews. The 2018 has a good review. My 2019 review is not that good," she explained. Ms. Smith apprised me her supervisor made off-the-record comments that he was lenient regarding her overall assessment.

Vocational Activity

Ms. Smith reported she completed high school in 1979 and earned a bachelor's degree in economics in 1983. She told me she also pursued master's level coursework but did not satisfy degree requirements. During Ms. Smith's work career, she indicated, she trained in employee relations and labor relations.

Since 2008, Ms. Smith advised me, her employment has related to human resources with positions concentrating in employee relations and labor relations. She conveyed LCA hired her as an employee relations specialist in May 2016 and that she was promoted to senior employee relations specialist—the job she held at the time of her August 31, 2018, motor vehicle accident—on January 1, 2018. At the time of her accident, Ms. Smith informed me, she worked 40 hours per week, and her annual salary was $99,800.

Ms. Smith described sedentary tasks her senior employee relations specialist job requires. She noted she worked both from her home and from an office in Tampa, preaccident. She apprised me her job requires extensive computer use, interviewing coworkers, making presentations, writing reports, and participating in meetings.

The primary job responsibilities Ms. Smith identified involve investigating employee grievances, advising managers on how to handle sensitive employee situations, researching the merits of grievances and reaching conclusions, and implementing preemptive measures to avoid or mitigate employee problems. Ms. Smith described cognitively complex tasks she performed, preaccident, and reported she interacted with an array of personnel such as legal counsel, scientists, senior executives, and factory workers.

Ms. Smith and I reviewed medical records postdating her August 31, 2018, accident, and she recalled her first treatment was with Dr. Scheffel, a chiropractor, on September 5, 2018. "I was gone for about two months [after the accident]," she said, indicating she resumed her employment with LCA in November 2018. During 2019, Ms. Smith advised me, "I was off for another couple of months," and she conveyed her cognitive difficulties became more apparent to her when she returned to work.

Elaborating about her cognitive difficulties, Ms. Smith cited problems with "thinking straight," which she attributed to both her cognitive impairments and pain distracting her. She advised me her second return-to-work attempt began in mid-November 2019 and has continued to date.

When Ms. Smith initially returned to work, she informed me, LCA extended accommodations that included permitting her to work part-time. Additionally, her employer granted her request to "only focus on my core responsibilities and not be on different team [special] projects." She apprised her immediate manager of her presenting problems, adding, "I'm really nervous about losing my job, so I've been really low-key about this." Currently, Ms. Smith noted, she is not extended accommodations.

Ms. Smith referenced a recent uptick in her work responsibilities. Citing the Phase 2 reopenings in the wake of the COVID-19 pandemic, she said, "Now that the cases are starting to pile up again, I'm starting to run into some problems," and she recounted her cognitive difficulties. Ms. Smith appeared quite distressed during this discussion.

Estimating her cognitive impairments have reduced her work productivity by 20 percent, Ms. Smith stated, "I have to put in at least two more hours a day, and the quality of my work isn't what it was [preaccident]." She went on to say, "My confidence has really been hurt, and I have problems with making decisions. My thinking is really not good."

Ms. Smith reiterated difficulties with tending to details during meetings. "I'm not thinking fast enough to keep up with what's being said," she stated.

I inquired about her preaccident career plans, and Ms. Smith told me she intended to work to at least age 65, possibly to 67. "I was hoping to stick [with my employment with LCA]," she said. Before retiring, Ms. Smith indicated, "I had aspirations about being a manager [with LCA]."

Several times during my clinical interview, Ms. Smith expressed concern about maintaining her employment in light of her cognitive impairments. If not for her August 2018 accident, she assessed, she would have already been promoted to a manager position. "I was very highly regarded," Ms. Smith stated.

As for performance appraisals, Ms. Smith informed me her 2019 performance review was in late February 2019. Again, it was less robust than her prior review. "My immediate manager has had some meetings, coaching with me, just verbally," she said when I inquired about any discipline attributable to her reported postaccident job-performance difficulties.

Ms. Smith denied searching for another job since her August 31, 2018, motor vehicle accident, and she cited no plan to begin a job search "until I have to." Near the end of my clinical interview, she recounted hurt feelings she experiences "when I'm disregarded at meetings. It's like I'm just pushed in a corner."

Summary and Impressions

I.   Ms. Smith completed high school in 1979, earned a bachelor's degree in economics in 1983, and pursued master's degree studies in business and social work but did not earn a graduate degree. She also trained in employee relations and labor relations. Since 2008, her employment has related to human resources, with positions concentrating in employee relations and labor relations. Large Corporation A (LCA) hired Ms. Smith as an employee relations specialist (DOT #166.267-042) in May 2016. She was promoted to a senior employee relations specialist position on January 1, 2018, and she continued to work in this capacity through the time of her August 31, 2018, motor vehicle accident and to date. Based on my understanding of her job responsibilities, Ms. Smith has been performing sedentary, skilled tasks. She described cognitively complex work, requiring her to interact with an array of personnel such as legal counsel, scientists, senior executives, and factory workers. After her August 2018 accident, Ms. Smith recalled, she had an approximately two-month period of work absence, and she resumed her senior employee relations specialist job in November 2018. Accident-related problems subsequently interfered with her work participation, Ms. Smith explained, apprising me that, during 2019,

"I was off for another couple of months." She informed me her second return-to-work attempt began in mid-November 2019 and has continued to date. Previously, Ms. Smith noted, LCA extended accommodations to her, although she currently has none, and she has been working remotely from her home due to the COVID-19 pandemic. Ms. Smith explained that, during periods of heavy work volume, her cognitive difficulties compound her job performance problems. She estimated her cognitive impairments have reduced her work productivity by 20 percent, noting she commits more time to performing her job than she did preaccident. Ms. Smith described several difficulties she has encountered because of her cognitive dysfunction, and she described how her supervisor and coworkers have dismissed her during meetings due to her inability to tend to and contribute to matters being discussed. "I'm not thinking fast enough to keep up with what's being said," Ms. Smith stated. The preaccident career plans she presented were to continue working with LCA through the time of her retirement, assuming advancement opportunities as they availed. She surmised she had been a very attractive candidate for promotion, preaccident. Ms. Smith noted that, since her accident, her job performance has diminished, and she expressed concerns about the viability of her future with LCA. She assessed she would not have been able, at this time, to secure the promotion she earned in January 2018. Disclosing concerns about her job security, Ms. Smith stated: "I'm having trouble keeping up with it [my job], and it's creating all this stress, which causes me a lot of anxiety and depression. If I lose this job, I don't know if I'm going to be able to learn [to perform] another job [because of my cognitive impairments]." Additionally, reflecting on her personal situation, she said, "I'm really worried about my old age. If I lost my job, that would really be bad. I have no children, and my husband (age 78) is going to die before me. I worry about what's going to happen to me. I had always been a strong and independent woman, and now I have this vulnerability I've never felt before." Ms. Smith explained how the COVID-19 pandemic has adversely affected LCA and that her presenting problems make her even more vulnerable to a potential downsizing. She conveyed her 2019 performance appraisal was less robust than her 2018 appraisal, and she indicated her supervisor has been coaching her to facilitate improvement in her job performance. Ms. Smith is approaching her 60th birthday, and she is in the late establishment/withdrawal phase of her career development. She apprised me of several significant work errors and indiscretions she has made postaccident. The job security concerns Ms. Smith voiced appear valid. I am unaware of a reason she would not have been able to pursue her stated preaccident career objectives if not for her presenting problems.

II. Ms. Smith's preaccident medical history includes surgery on her lumbar spine in 1990, a right retina repair procedure in 1994, and a right rotator cuff operation in 2014. She also noted a preaccident history of anxiety and depression. Apparently, her emotional difficulties did not impede her career development. Within a reasonable degree of vocational rehabilitation probability, Ms. Smith's preaccident medical history, as known to me, would not have been a factor in her career development absent her 2018 accident.

III. Ms. Smith is approaching the two-year anniversary of her August 31, 2018, motor vehicle accident, and she remains symptomatic as noted. Medical records provide objective support for her presenting problems. Imaging detected abnormalities throughout Ms. Smith's spine, and Dr. McHugh, a neurologist, determined she is experiencing mild neurocognitive disorder secondary to traumatic brain injury.

Two surgeons—Dr. King and Dr. Labutka—assessed Ms. Smith is a candidate for a C3-C7 anterior cervical discectomy with fusion. Several other treatment interventions, both conservative and invasive, have been recommended. The primary problems Ms. Smith presented to me related to her cognitive impairments and, by extension, implications for her continued employment. She elaborated about problems with new learning, comprehension, memory, word retrieval, judgment, information processing, decision making, and attention to detail. Although Ms. Smith's senior employee relations specialist job currently appears within her capacity from a physical perspective, the cognitive demands associated with it appear at or beyond her cognitive capacities. My prognosis for Ms. Smith's ongoing career development is guarded/fair. Based on information available at this time, it is improbable that she would be capable of securing and maintaining employment with the types of cognitively complex demands her current job requires.

IV. Within a reasonable degree of vocational rehabilitation probability, Ms. Smith's August 31, 2018, motor vehicle accident has caused her a loss of earning capacity. She continues to experience the sequelae of multisystem impairments—including cognitive dysfunction and spinal cord injury—and she is a candidate for a four-level cervical spine fusion and other ongoing rehabilitation intervention. If Ms. Smith were to lose her job with LCA, she would have significant difficulty reentering the workplace, and it is improbable she would be capable of securing employment comparable to her current senior employee relations specialist position. Indeed, Ms. Smith would be fortunate, under this scenario, to secure and maintain a lower-level human resources position offering compensation of $40,000 to $50,000 annually. Even under a best-case scenario, presuming she maintained her employment with LCA, she has acquired several vocational handicaps that likely will diminish her residual earning capacity. These vocational handicaps include increased vulnerability to downsizing, lessened opportunities for promotion and advancement, risk of a truncated work life, increased potential of demotion, and time away from work because of anticipated medical treatments and during periods of symptom exacerbation. Under a best-case scenario that presumes Ms. Smith is fortunate to continue her employment with LCA, I estimate her loss of earning capacity over the remainder of her work life will be approximately 40 percent; this is a conservative estimate.

Figures 2.6a–c and 2.7 display the author's use and application of the ECAF-2 in arriving at his assessment.

Figure 2.6a–c Case Study of ECAF-2 Item Ratings. Adapted and reproduced by special permission of the Publisher, Psychological Assessment Resources, Inc., 16204 North Florida Avenue, Lutz, Florida 33549, from the Earning Capacity Assessment Form-2nd Edition by Michael Shahnasarian, Ph.D., Copyright 2010 by PAR, Inc. Further reproduction is prohibited without permission of PAR, Inc.

Inhibitor Items			
1. Phase of Career Development	0	Able to progress.	
	1	May have difficulty progressing.	Insufficient basis to assess
	②	Difficulty progressing is certain.	
	3	Severely impaired ability to progress.	Not pertinent

Driver Items			
1. Stability of Career Development	⓪	Stable and likely to continue.	
	1	Generally stable.	Insufficient basis to assess
	2	Unstable and inconsistent.	
	3	Erratic with frequent periods of unemployment.	Not pertinent

Comments: _Approaching age 60_
Cog impairments (Mild TBI dx) – very relevant
given complexity of her job
Many physical injuries including candidate for a
4-level cervical
Fortunate to have been promoted preaccident/getting
negative comments about job performance
Significant vocational handicaps

Employee relations/Labor relations – HR specialty
Admirable work ethic/Impressive wage history

Figure 2.7 Case Study Assignment of ECAF-2 Item Ratings to Impairment to Earning Capacity Scale. Adapted and reproduced by special permission of the Publisher, Psychological Assessment Resources, Inc., 16204 North Florida Avenue, Lutz, Florida 33549, from the Earning Capacity Assessment Form-2nd Edition by Michael Shahnasarian, Ph.D., Copyright 2010 by PAR, Inc. Further reproduction is prohibited without permission of PAR, Inc.

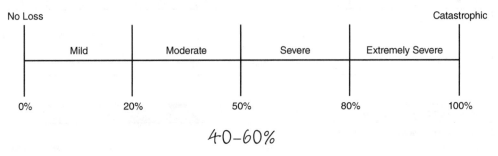

CHAPTER 3

Processes and Mechanics Associated with Performing an Assessment of Earning Capacity

Once engaged to provide vocational assessment services—as either a consulting expert or testifying expert—a vocational evaluator employs the generally accepted theory and practice standards Chapter 2 described. Van de Bittner, Wallace, Cottle, and Simon (2012) delineated general methods and activities vocational experts implement to evaluate employability and earning capacity. Contingent on case-specific facts, referral questions, and both internal and external case factors (please refer to Chapter 2), experts apply methods most apropos to accomplish their work. This chapter provides an overview of the processes and mechanics vocational evaluators undertake to assess a claim of loss of earning capacity in an injury case, consistent with methods and processes professional associations promulgate.

Preexamination Records Review

The sample retention letter included in Appendix B lists the types of records that generally interest vocational evaluators. Because they address damages issues, nonliability records typically have little if any pertinence to the assessments. For example, testimony by those who witnessed a slip-and-fall incident in which a claimant alleged to become injured or a report by an accident reconstruction engineer providing assessments of velocity, collision forces, at-fault, and other details related to a motor vehicle accident rarely have relevance to an evaluation of the merits of a claim of loss of earning capacity.

Vocational evaluators should thoroughly review pertinent records before examining a claimant. Becoming familiar with case-specific facts both optimizes examination time and enables an evaluator to plan pertinent clinical interview questions (discussed in the latter section of this chapter). For example, records reviewed before meeting with an evaluee may identify preinjury gaps between jobs; this advance knowledge enables an evaluator, during a clinical interview, to probe about reasons for interrupted work participation. Further, medical records may reveal issues such as substance abuse, inconsistent reporting of symptoms, and noncompliance with treatment—all fodder for an evaluator's further inquiry.

Of note, experts should remain mindful that a case's facts continue to evolve from the time they become involved in a case through the time a case settles or ends after a jury verdict or bench ruling. Namely, old records relevant to a vocational assessment may be discovered and/or new/additional records postdating a vocational rehabilitation examination may become available. The dynamic nature of the litigation process necessitates experts' awareness of how new records could affect opinions previously rendered.

Experts can and should request updated/additional records throughout their service. They sometimes learn of records during a clinical interview—for example, when a claimant discusses upcoming medical appointments not previously known or by reviewing other records that refer to information that extant records do not fully document. Failure to be aware of or knowledgeable about records with vocationally relevant implications—such as a significant exacerbation of symptoms or onset of a new comorbidity—via provided records threatens to undermine an expert's opinion. Opposing lawyers often leverage their knowledge of records not within an expert's purview to imply bias, prejudgment, or lack of knowledge necessary to provide competent opinions.

Adopting an efficient method of organizing records facilitates experts' efforts to retrieve records. Displaying difficulty locating a record while testifying during a deposition or at trial, for example, can detract from an evaluator's presentation.

Experts are entitled to compensation for costs of copies of records requested. Requests for records typically emanate from a subpoena of the expert's records custodian or at an expert's deposition. State statutes provide guidelines on allowable copying cost. Appendix D is a sample letter explaining an expert's copying costs and associated logistics.

Vocational evaluators maintain records through a dispute's resolution. In most cases, when litigation ends, evaluators purge records they did not create, although attorneys occasionally request that records be returned and maintain records they developed in accordance with regulatory organizations' requirements.

Beyond gathering information, the analytic phase of a records review involves integrating, comparing/contrasting, and synthesizing information that evolves over the course of an analysis. Discovering evidence of invalid test results, learning that a subject's presenting problems lack medical record support, or finding an evaluee noncompliant with prescribed treatment, for example, may cause an evaluator to become suspicious of secondary gain motivation. This suspicion can prepare evaluators to test their theories during a clinical interview and subsequent gathering of information. Evaluators should, of course, avoid prejudging evaluees solely on the basis of information they obtain from records.

In sum, documentary evidence—the foundation on which expert analyses and opinions rest—provides vocational evaluators an important touchstone throughout their assessments. Records enable them to obtain a case's factual bases, apply generally accepted vocational rehabilitation evaluation methodology, and use the tetrahedron model's hierarchical analytical processes (please refer to Chapter 2) to synthesize the science of vocational rehabilitation and systematically derive opinions within a reasonable degree of probability. The integrated application of this methodology facilitates the jurisprudence process and helps experts blunt Daubert challenges, discussed in Chapter 11.

Again, every case is different, and, depending on a case at hand and issues in dispute, documentary evidence germane to a vocational evaluator's assessment will vary. An overview of potential sources of vocationally relevant records and types of information they may provide follows.

Complaint

In addition to specifying the alleged mechanism of a plaintiff's injury, a complaint states the alleged onset date of issues in dispute and damages sought.

Answers to Interrogatories

A plaintiff's responses to answers to interrogatories are akin to sworn testimony. Among other things, they can provide information on work history (including employers, job titles, dates of employment, and earnings history), disabling problems related and unrelated to issues in dispute, and efforts to pursue vocational rehabilitation. It is important to note when the interrogatory responses were submitted and to correlate this information with information generated throughout an evaluation.

Medical Records—Preinjury and Postinjury

Medical records associated with a case can be voluminous, with many having little if any relevance to a vocational evaluator's pending assessment. Nonetheless, it behooves the evaluator to review, at a minimum, the following preinjury and postinjury records: diagnostic records, operative records, assessments, and therapy records. A lack of knowledge of a case's medical assessments exposes an evaluator to cross-examination innuendo portraying the evaluator as uninformed or ignorant about the medical bases undergirding a case and, accordingly, less than competent to proffer valid vocational opinions.

Medical records can provide insight on many vocationally relevant factors including preexisting pathologies and their progression in the absence of issues in dispute; an evaluee's postinjury treatment, functional limitations, and capacities; prognoses; and opportunities to pursue vocational activities. For the sake of this discussion, psychological records comprise a subset of the medical records category. If preparing a life care plan, the evaluator should also request to review bills for rehabilitation interventions rendered to date; this can facilitate the costing of anticipated future treatment (discussed in Part III).

Compulsory Medical Examination Reports

Technically, since a plaintiff is not treating with a healthcare provider who conducts a compulsory medical examination, the reports these examiners generate are not medical records and comprise a class of their own. These exams, performed at the request of defense counsel, depending on the practitioner's specialty and case-specific factors, may include an examiner's taking of a medical history and assessing examination results. The exam conducted will vary by specialty. For example, an orthopedic surgeon would likely perform a physical examination, while a neuropsychologist would likely administer a battery of standardized neuropsychological tests.

Vocational evaluators—whether retained by plaintiff or defense counsel—should consider compulsory medical examiners' opinions in the context of all information amassed during their evaluations, including assessments and opinions they independently derive. For example, a vocational evaluator retained by defense counsel adopting in toto a compulsory medical examiner's opinion that a plaintiff sustained no permanent impairments and has no restrictions, while dismissing contrary opinions of treating doctors, can lead to questions about the evaluator's objectivity.

Without good reason to accept or reject a medical opinion(s) undergirding a vocational opinion, a vocational evaluator becomes vulnerable to aspersions of being biased and beholden to a retention source. Obviously, this association erodes the evaluator's credibility.

An amalgamation of evidence from sources compiled in a case may support a vocational evaluator's decision to ascribe more or less weight to opinions of treating healthcare providers or compulsory medical examiners. Video surveillance showing a plaintiff engaging in physical activities without any overt problems and far beyond those previously represented to be within his or her capacity, for example, could sway an evaluator's decision.

Other reasons a vocational evaluator may choose to adopt one set of medical assessments over another may relate to the time opinions were rendered (giving greater weight to the most current assessments) or methods medical examiners applied to arrive at their assessments (giving greater weight to assessments that incorporated the most robust diagnostic testing). Additionally, sworn testimony provided by a person knowledgeable of a plaintiff may cause an examiner to apportion more weight to this evidence than to a remote record from a person who has outdated or scant knowledge of issues at hand.

When disparate assessments emerge and a vocational evaluator can neither reconcile them nor ascribe more weight to one over another, an option is to develop vocational opinions based on the divergent medical assessments. This involves specifying one or more vocational outcome scenarios, each based on a divergent set of medical opinions. The scenarios should be presented in a nonevaluative manner unless a vocational evaluator has reason to prefer one. Offering options in this manner allows the evaluator to preserve the integrity of the vocational evaluation process and to provide triers of fact technical analyses to consider as they continue to assimilate information contributing to their ultimate disposition.

Excerpts from evaluators' reports involving disparate medical assessments follow. The examples demonstrate how an evaluator can acknowledge differences of opinions and, when possible, reconcile them by integrating information from a vocational rehabilitation evaluation to avert an impasse.

Example 1

The evaluee in the first example, a 41-year-old male who left school during the ninth grade and never attempted the GED exam, pursued self-employment as a landscaper and auto body worker during the approximately 20 years before his motor vehicle accident. He asserted the accident caused injuries to his back and right knee, precluding him from his pre-accident employment. Further, he contended his prior scholastic difficulties made him a poor candidate for retraining. After summarizing the medical records, the vocational evaluator provided the following analysis:

> The medical records I reviewed provide disparate opinions about Mr. Greene's functional capacities and, by extension, his vocational capacities. If assessments Dr. Softe and Dr. Klein rendered are correct, Mr. Greene has no limitation on his vocational functioning, and he has not sustained a loss of earning capacity attributable to his accident. Alternately, if Dr. Albert is correct, Mr. Greene's return to work as a landscaper or auto body worker would be contraindicated from a vocational rehabilitation perspective. Mr. Greene possesses several assets to facilitate his return to work. He is a younger individual who is English/Spanish bilingual and apparently had been successful in entrepreneurial pursuits he described. His work activities enabled him to develop transferable skills as previously delineated. Surveillance I reviewed shows Mr. Greene performing a range of everyday, normal activities including using a lawnmower to maintain his yard, picking up his children at their school, and traversing several public places—all without apparent problems. At a minimum, Mr. Greene appears capable of performing sedentary/light exertion work.

Example 2

A 49-year-old Eastern European immigrant involved in a food import business pursued a claim for injury damages associated with a motor vehicle accident. He presented a myriad of accident-related changes including those associated with his occupational status, earnings, physical condition, psychological and cognitive statuses, functional capacities, family, and lifestyle. The following excerpts provide an example of how an evaluator juxtaposed discrepant medical determinations and overlaid information from her vocational rehabilitation evaluation to weigh the disparate opinions.

> Medical records postdating Mr. Melvin's September 19, 2015, motor vehicle accident include disparate assessments of his presenting problems. Although his treating healthcare providers appear in unison about his accident-related deficits, healthcare providers retained by counsel representing the defendants in his case have alternate, significantly different opinions.
>
> Dr. Mesrop conducted a neuropsychological evaluation on February 14, 2016, and diagnosed cognitive disorder not otherwise specified, along with major depressive episode and severe anxiety disorder. On June 14, 2016, Dr. Milke, a psychiatrist, diagnosed mood disorder due to traumatic brain injury with major depressive-like episode, along with cognitive disorder not otherwise specified. It should be noted Dr. Milke also discerned a history of traumatic brain injury and chronic back pain. In a note dated January 17, 2018, Dr. Nanu, a neurologist, concluded that Mr. Melvin was totally disabled to work as a general contractor due to his neurological problems. Dr. Nanu had earlier identified Mr. Melvin's symptoms and declared his patient had reached maximum medical improvement from a neurological perspective on January 14, 2018.
>
> Regarding healthcare professionals retained by counsel representing the defense in Mr. Melvin's case, on October 28, 2020, Dr. Gausier, a neurologist, concluded that Mr. Melvin was malingering. "I can identify no medical necessity of further medical treatment as would enable significant restoration of functionality—as this patient is entirely and objectively functional. In summary, the patient has suffered no permanent injury within a reasonable degree of medical probability," Dr. Gausier stated. In their November 14, 2020, reports of neuropsychological and psychological examinations, Dr. Gable and Dr. Richards concluded, "There is no objective evidence that Mr. Melvin suffered a brain injury secondary to the September 19, 2015, accident, as the data was inconsistent with the type of injury reported and of questionable validity."
>
> Included in the medical records I reviewed were reports of MRIs of Mr. Melvin's lumbar and thoracic spines. Both reports showed abnormalities.
>
> Although Mr. Melvin presented several functional limitations, he indicated he remains capable of many routine, everyday activities. He assessed he can safely handle 20 pounds, and he noted most hand/arm movements are within his capacity. Walking and standing are generally not a problem for short durations, Mr. Melvin conveyed. He estimated he can sit for approximately 30 minutes, stand five minutes, and walk from ten to 30 minutes before overexerting himself or needing to rest. He did not identify any functional activity from which he is entirely exempt, although he relayed many are challenging.
>
> On a test of mood-related problems I administered, Mr. Melvin scored in the severe range of depression, consistent with my clinical impression. Further, my review

of his responses on the Beck Depression Inventory-II were consistent with information I gathered during my clinical interview and review of his medical records.

Although as noted above there are disparate opinions about the authenticity of Mr. Melvin's presenting problems, my analysis has led me to attribute more weight to the opinions that Mr. Melvin's treating healthcare professionals have ascribed. The remorse Mr. Melvin expressed about his presenting problems and unwelcome lifestyle changes appeared genuine. As noted earlier in this report, several times during my clinical interview, he referenced disappointment in himself because of his compromised ability to provide for his family and pursue his career development.

Deposition Testimony

A plaintiff's testimony can provide a trove of information germane to a vocational assessment, including preinjury and postinjury medical, educational, earnings, and work history details, along with alleged postinjury disabling problems and efforts to pursue vocational rehabilitation. Such collateral information sometimes appears in testimony significant others and employers proffer. The latter source can also provide insight on preinjury and postinjury changes in job performance and related areas.

Other testimony of interest to vocational evaluators can emanate from healthcare providers, along with those who have reviewed records and/or examined the plaintiff but might not have provided treatment. Beyond a recitation of diagnoses, treatment rendered, and responsiveness to treatment, testimony of this ilk sometimes includes prognoses, along with assessments of a plaintiff's exertional and nonexertional capacities on which a vocational evaluator may rely when evaluating work tolerance. The testimony may also include projections of rehabilitation interventions that, when part of an evaluator's retention, can be appropriated into a life care plan.

Academic Records

Especially important in pediatric cases in which children have established little if any work or earnings record before acquiring injuries, academic records provide a partial basis to extrapolate future vocational attainments. Of course, vocational evaluators must integrate other relevant information—including the vocational records of a child's family unit—to supplement available data and to facilitate the development of likely trajectories for a child's career development in the absence of acquired injuries and associated disabling problems. Chapter 4 provides more discussion on culling evidence to establish preinjury baseline earning capacity levels of pediatric evaluees.

Of primary interest to a vocational evaluator when reviewing academic records are an evaluee's record of scholastic achievement and standardized test performance and documentation of any noteworthy aberrant or facilitative vocationally relevant factors. Deductions of the latter sometimes arise from analyses of participation in extracurricular activities, school attendance, and disciplinary action. Academic records can reveal preinjury learning difficulties or, conversely, facts supporting overachievement tendencies. Comparisons of preinjury and postinjury levels of academic progress, with or without accommodations, can also contribute to evaluators' decision-making on future career development issues that could affect an earning capacity opinion.

Information from academic records can also enhance analyses in adult cases. For example, if a vocational evaluator determines an injured person cannot resume preinjury employment, the following questions, presented sequentially, logically follow as the evaluator continues to assess the larger question of earning capacity loss: Does the evaluee possess transferable skills to facilitate work reentry in a position with exertional and nonexertional requirements compatible with his or her capabilities? If not, is the claimant a candidate for retraining? If so, what type of retraining may be indicated? Academic records may shed light in answering these questions.

Additionally, in cases involving alleged claims of an adult's postinjury cognitive decline—such as via multiple sports-related concussions, a cerebrovascular accident, or traumatic brain injury from a vehicular accident—correlating preinjury benchmarks of cognitive functioning from academic records with postinjury markers, such as results from a neuropsychological examination and/or standardized testing an evaluator administers (discussed later in this chapter), can help to determine potential differentials. If an evaluator concludes a claimant acquired cognitive impairments yet remains a candidate for retraining, then the analysis progresses to address the questions posed earlier.

Beyond academic records, documentation of other training a plaintiff might have pursued—including internships, apprenticeships, and employer-sponsored training—can help identify transferable skills. For more information on conducting transferable skills analyses, refer to Weed & Field (2012) and Field & Dunn (2014). Knowledge of any work-related specialty credentials a claimant might have attained further advances this inquiry. This information contributes to a vocational evaluator's assessment of a claimant's transferable skills—especially important when evaluating potential mitigation of claimed vocational damages through retraining.

Employment Records

Employment records greatly facilitate a vocational evaluator's efforts to compare and contrast preinjury and postinjury work records; establish an evaluee's baseline preinjury earning capacity; shed insight on likely career development progress in the absence of alleged disabling problems; and, in some cases, discern indicia of motivation, patterns of adaptive/nonadaptive work behaviors, and general information about knowledge, skills, and abilities developed. The following information from these records is of particular value: job descriptions, performance appraisals, work attendance and payroll records, and documentation related to transitions between jobs. Exertional and nonexertional job requirements, stability of career development, workplace achievement, and reasons for job changes are other areas of inquiry employment records can illuminate.

Earnings Records

Along with academic and employment records, earnings records help establish a foundation essential to develop a plaintiff's baseline, demonstrated preinjury earning capacity level and to address overarching referral questions inherent in evaluating a diminished earning capacity claim. These questions mirror and expand on those cited earlier regarding retraining considerations:

1. Have injuries and associated disabling problems caused an unmitigated differential between preinjury and postinjury earning capacity?
2. If so, can the loss be mitigated?
3. If not, what is the differential between preinjury and postinjury earning capacity?

Surveillance

Mentioned earlier, surveillance sometimes provides what may appear to be real-life evidence incongruent with what an evaluee might have previously relayed and/or what those who have examined an evaluee deduced. Vocational evaluators should place this evidence in the correct context, juxtaposed with other evidence, and weigh surveillance proportionately.

This includes, for example, attempting to reconcile the likes of dates of surveillance with potentially discrepant information, durations and types of activity observed on surveillance, and potential discrepancies between testimonial and documentary evidence.

Social Security Administration File

Although a vocational evaluator rendering an opinion in a civil court or federal court matter is not bound to a disposition the Social Security Administration (SSA) has reached, the information contained in its records sometimes helps to verify, illuminate, and/or develop new theories about a plaintiff's vocational behavior. For example, learning that a plaintiff had been approved for SSA disability benefits several years before a dispute in question and thereafter pursued part-time work until alleging to have acquired new injuries that precluded further employment could cause an evaluator to formulate several damages claims questions such as: Would the progression of preexisting problems have affected the plaintiff's earning capacity in the absence of any newly acquired disabilities? Was the plaintiff suppressing efforts to optimize earning capacity preinjury, in an attempt not to jeopardize the SSA disability award? How do alleged newly acquired disabling problems comport with preexisting problems documented in the plaintiff's SSA disability file?

Other Records

Depending on a case and its facts, many other record sources may facilitate vocational evaluators' analyses. Military records, for example, include information related to military occupational specialty, special training, performance appraisals, service-connected disabilities, and distinctions or lack thereof. Job search records—especially in cases when plaintiffs assert injury-related factors thwarted their initiatives to secure employment—can shed light on alleged mitigation efforts.

As vocational evaluators learn the nuances of a case at hand, they should be mindful of the types of records that may contribute to their synthesis of factual data and advance their analytical processes. The adversarial context in which they perform their work also augurs implications for their credibility: opposing counsel may severely criticize an evaluator who fails to request potentially relevant records for review.

Additionally, a lack of documentary evidence can spur an expert's decision about research to close gaps between documentary evidence and allegations necessary to more clearly address vocationally relevant questions. This could involve research ranging from reviews of regulatory agency registries to verify plaintiff's reported credentials to investigating admission statistics to programs of study a plaintiff reported intent to pursue preinjury. More discussion on conducting labor market research is later in this chapter.

Vocational Rehabilitation Examination

Protocols associated with a vocational rehabilitation examination typically incorporate two components: a clinical interview and standardized test administration. Considering the ECAT model presented in Chapter 2, these components enable evaluators to build on information gathered via records and gather new evidence—specifically, technical evidence not available elsewhere, germane to vocational rehabilitation—to facilitate the analytical processes detailed. More information about clinical interview procedures and the administration of standardized testing appears in the following sections.

Plaintiff lawyers sometimes object to either an examination in toto or its scope. The arguments, of course, mostly emanate from case-specific reasons. Subject matter the evaluator is permitted to inquire about, the need for and appropriateness of proposed tests, and accusations that an evaluator has tainted motives—these are de rigueur objections proffered. Chapter 11 provides more discussion on these topics.

If opposing counsel cannot reconcile differences about an examination's parameters, the court may rule on objections proffered. Vocational evaluators sometimes participate in hearings, explaining the rationale for examination protocols.

Appendix E is a sample affidavit a vocational evaluator prepared to describe the need for a vocational rehabilitation examination. It specifies the examination's scope, logistics, and rationale for procedures.

Plaintiff lawyers often record—via court reporter and/or videographer—exams opposing experts conduct, an opportunity typically foreclosed to defense lawyers. Further, plaintiff lawyers or their proxies occasionally attend the examination; again, this option is typically not available to defense counsel. Shahnasarian (2009b; 2015) discussed methods vocational evaluators can employ to preserve an examination's integrity when third parties attend, and Appendix F is a sample policy statement of an evaluator's guidelines on video-recorded examinations.

Clinical Interview

Jurisdictions within which an examination is being conducted and court rulings can affect methods examiners implement to conduct clinical interviews. For example, some jurisdictions prohibit examiners' use of "lengthy intake forms" for evaluees to complete before a clinical interview. The question of what constitutes "lengthy," of course, is another matter.

Providing an intake form—to either an evaluee, attorney, or other third party—before a vocational rehabilitation exam is strongly advised against, as it invites error into the assessment that could render it invalid. Assistance with and influence on responses from sources other than an evaluee can transmute information undermining empirical examination processes.

For the sake of streamlining an already contentious litigation process, some examiners opt to forgo administering an intake form to an evaluee and, instead, elicit questions from it during a clinical interview. The consequences of this decision, when it is an option, include potentially losing considerable information from an evaluee's written responses that have relevance to an analysis, such as level of detail provided while responding to intake form questions, level of literacy/written sophistication displayed, time required to complete an intake form, legibility of responses and care taken to comply with instructions, and coherency of information provided.

Additionally, orally eliciting basic information from an evaluee—such as medications, names and specialties of doctors, treatment rendered, and educational and work histories—elongates a clinical interview, likely adding to an examination's cost. Opposing counsel, of course, routinely scrutinizes evaluators' fees and cites them during attempts to impeach opinions (discussed in more detail in Chapter 12).

Appendix G presents a sample intake form. Evaluators can obtain as much information as possible from records before a clinical interview and then document on the form new/updated information elicited during the interview. Most intake forms inquire about the following:

- Background information including presenting problems
- Physical condition and medical information
- Physical capacities
- Activities of daily living

- Mental health
- Education and special training
- Work history and career development

During a clinical interview, evaluators typically type or handwrite their notes contemporaneously. They very rarely have access to either a court reporter's transcript or video recordings lawyers (invariably opposing lawyers) commission, if they exist.

In addition to an intake form, abstractions from a review of records made before a clinical interview, and other documents an evaluee might have completed beforehand such as a pain diagram, vocational evaluators compose notes during their exams to facilitate their subsequent reporting of events and analysis. The information captured in clinical interview notes focuses on the following:

- Examination logistics
- Evaluee presentation including gait, use of adaptive aids
- Vocational chronology including differentials between preinjury and postinjury functioning
- Medical/psychological history
- In-depth inquiry of presenting problems
- Assessment of functional capacities/limitations
- Special needs, including services, acquired after the onset of disabling problems
- Expanded assessment of mental health and potential disability adjustment issues, including the examiner's clinical impressions
- Details related to education, special training, skill development, work history, efforts to mitigate contended vocational damages, and preinjury/postinjury changes in career plans

Depending on the complexity of issues under review and associated referral questions, most clinical interviews take two to four hours. Questions posed relate to vocational damages in question. Nonliability issues, including matters of parties at fault, do not fall under the purview of a clinical interview.

Special Considerations When Conducting Nontraditional In-Person Examinations

During the coronavirus pandemic, videoconferencing became a popular medium to conduct vocational rehabilitation examinations. Beyond the obvious safety advantages of this alternative to in-person exams, it can also be more convenient, expedient, and cost effective.

Videoconferencing, typically more accessible and convenient to examination participants than traveling to a designated meeting place, facilitates coordinating and scheduling exams. It also eliminates expert fees incurred during travel to examination sites, along with costs such as lodging and airfare. Evaluees' manner and demeanor when participating in exams from their homes are often more relaxed than when in a formal examination setting; this presents advantages and disadvantages.

The disadvantages to videoconference exams include barriers to an evaluator gathering in-person observations such as greater challenges observing a person's gait, movements, and demeanor. Establishing and maintaining rapport via a computer monitor, television screen, or mobile phone can also prove more challenging than interacting with an evaluee in vivo.

Further, not being physically present with an evaluee causes an evaluator to lose a degree of control of the examination environment. When videoconferencing from their homes, for example, evaluees may become distracted by others entering/exiting the premises, pets, and other extraneous stimuli an evaluator can typically filter and control in a standard exam environment. Additionally, some evaluees lack the technical knowledge necessary to navigate a videoconference's details, which can cause logistical mishaps that interfere with an exam's spontaneity.

Administering standardized tests via videoconference can also be challenging, especially when electronic transmission issues interrupt an examination. For example, departures from standardization can arise in the midst of a timed test when a screen becomes frozen and audio communications are momentarily lost.

Vocational evaluators should take preemptive measures to maintain the integrity of the examination environment under all conditions. Under videoconference conditions, these include providing guidelines at the exam's onset about the presence of others and requests to eliminate or reduce extra-examination influences, for example, mobile phones and other technology, side conversations with others present, and external communications such as texting with lawyers during breaks. To obviate nonverbal communications from others physically present with evaluees—such as their attorneys and significant others—evaluators can request they sit behind the evaluee, in view of the evaluator. Shahnasarian (2020) discussed implications of the coronavirus pandemic on vocational expert assessments.

Despite the aberrations to assessment procedures videoconferencing introduces, some vocational evaluators prefer the medium to in-person clinical interviews in which those in attendance wear masks. In addition to imposing interpersonal barriers between evaluators and evaluees that begin with the visual cue of mask wearing, masks inject a sterile ambiance into the examination environment and are nonfacilitative to building interview rapport and spontaneity. They also prohibit evaluators from viewing facial expressions and related nonverbal cues, contribute to diminished eye contact, and compromise interpretation of nonverbal behaviors that could benefit an assessment. Loss of this information can result in, for example, an evaluator losing opportunities to synthesize an evaluee's verbal and nonverbal communications, contributing to not thoroughly paraphrasing and summarizing evaluee information and, by extension, omitting appropriate follow-up questions.

Further, of course, masks can compromise the oral exchange of information between parties: questions and answers sometimes need to be repeated, due to the muffling of sounds passing through masks and the parties' inability to view mouths as sounds are emitted. This, too, drains the interview of its spontaneity and rapport, contributing to a less desirable exam format.

The problems masks pose, of course, are not restricted to those vocational evaluators encounter. Trial lawyers have commented how masks interfere with some of the most vital tasks they perform, including interpreting jurors' facial expressions and adapting their case presentations accordingly.

Sample Clinical Interview

Presented next are abstractions from a clinical interview stemming from a medical malpractice case in which an evaluee alleged acquiring injuries including ongoing right upper extremity pain and associated functional limitations, intermittent lower extremity pain, and facial drooping. She was unemployed at the time of her incident. "I was working on my [cheesecake] baking business," she said, explaining she was pursuing a startup, home-based business that aspired to sell en masse cheesecakes and other baked goods to a global retailer.

MS: Good morning again, Ms. Randolph.

CR: Good morning.

MS: I am going to be doing two things today in conjunction with my vocational rehabilitation evaluation. First, I'm going to be conducting a clinical interview during
which I will just be learning more about your injuries, how they affect you, what
you can do, what you can't do, treatment you had; I'll be asking how these injuries
affect your ability to do different activities like lifting and bending. I know that you
had a needle sticking incident and that's what we're here primarily to discuss. How
the injuries from that incident affect you.

CR: Yes.

MS: And that incident, I understand, was November 22, 2018?

CR: That's correct.

MS: And I'll also be asking you questions about your ability to do everyday activities:
housework, drive yourself, grocery shopping, things of that nature, and I'll also ask
you about how you've been affected from a psychological perspective—your mental health. I'll be asking you about your schooling and I'll also be asking you about
your work history. I know that you were baking pies and that was your aspiration
at the time, to increase that.

CR: Yes, I was baking cheesecakes.

MS: Now I've had an opportunity to review a number of records, so I have some background of your case.

CR: OK.

MS: And I'm going to be taking a lot of notes and looking at records. I will attempt to
gather information in an organized way so if you can be patient with me . . .

CR: That's fine.

MS: It's a little tedious, but I'd like to get everything in a structured manner.

CR: OK.

MS: So that will be the clinical interview and then the second thing we're going to do is
some testing. This is not a medical exam, so none of the testing will be physical. I'm
going to be giving you some tests, basically, in three different areas—occupational
interests, so we'll be asking you things you like to do, things you don't like to do.
Second, personality, and third, aptitude/abilities.

CR: OK.

MS: OK, so that's the scope of the exam and we'll be very informal. If you need a break
at any time, let me know. I'll prompt you at various times that we are at a good
time to take a break if you'd like one, but if you need one beforehand, obviously,
tell me, and if I say something you don't understand, let me know.

CR: OK.

MS: Otherwise, if you respond, I'll assume you understood that question.

CR: OK.

MS: OK, and you understand that I'm not going to be treating you? I'm going to be
basically seeing you just this one time for purposes related to your litigation.

CR: OK.

MS: OK, so part of the implication of that is that we are not going to have a typical doctor/patient relationship. If you were to see me privately, things you would discuss with me would be privileged/confidential, but in this case, other parties who have an interest in your litigation will have access to information from my exam.

CR: OK.

MS: OK, so do I have your consent to proceed with that?

CR: OK.

MS: OK, and also a paralegal from your lawyer's office is video recording this examination. He has my consent and I assume he has your consent as well?

CR: Yes.

MS: OK, ma'am, I understand from your records that you are having problems with pain.

CR: Yes.

MS: Primarily in your right extremity—right arm?

CR: Yes.

MS: I'm going to ask you to complete a pain diagram and you may have done this before.

CR: Yes.

MS: On the top, if you could put your name and the date and you'll see there's two drawings of a body. The one on your left is labeled front—that is intended to represent the front part of your body, and it's also labeled right side and left side. The drawing on the other side of the page is labeled back—that is intended to represent the back part of your body. At the top of the page there are different symbols to correspond with different types of pain—aching, burning, pins and needles, stabbing, and so forth. So, if you can indicate on the diagram when you have pain, where you have it, and what type of pain you have.

CR: OK. Do you mind if I get my glasses?

MS: No, of course. Anything you need, and, as I said, we are very informal—let me know if there is anything I can do to help you.

CR: Thank you. OK, I think it's complete.

MS: OK. Do you still live in Orlando, ma'am?

CR: Yes.

MS: How did you get here today?

CR: My son drove me.

MS: You came from your home in Orlando, I take it?

CR: Yes.

MS: Do you have a driver's license?

CR: Yes, I do.

MS: Do you have any physician-advised driving restrictions?

CR: No sir.

MS: When did you last operate a motor vehicle?

CR: I believe it was yesterday.

MS: Yesterday . . . do you have any problems with driving?

CR: No, I mainly don't drive very far.

MS: OK. I have your date of birth as August 9, 1965?

CR: Yes.

MS: I noticed you were using eyeglasses when you completed the pain diagram.

CR: Yes, they are reading glasses.

MS: Is your corrected vision clear?

CR: Yes.

MS: Other than eyeglasses, are you using any other adaptive aids today, right now while you're talking to me?

CR: No sir.

MS: I didn't have an opportunity to see you walk very far, but it looks like you very slightly favor your right side. Would that be correct?

CR: I'm sorry?

MS: When you walk, do you feel that you limp a little bit on your right side?

CR: Yes, when I have pain in my knee and foot.

MS: OK. Are the problems with pain in your knee and foot related to the needle stick?

CR: As far as I understand it.

MS: They are. OK.

CR: It's from my knee down to my foot.

MS: Below your knee, below your right knee. That's where the pain is?

CR: Yes, starting from my knee to my foot.

MS: I understand that at the time of the incident in November 2018, you were not employed, is that correct?

CR: I was working on my baking business. Cheesecake.

MS: You were pursuing the start of a business?

CR: Yes.

MS: From your home?

CR: Yes. I was in the midst of looking for a commercial business.

MS: Business that involved selling cheesecakes to Stan's?

CR: Yes.

MS: Stan's Club, right?

CR: Stan's Club.

MS: Have you had any employment since the incident happened?

CR: No, sir.

MS: Did you have a name for your business?

CR: Yes.

MS: What was it called?

CR: Cheesecake Delights.

MS: Did you ever make any money through that business?

CR: No. There was a small amount.

MS: OK, I'm going to ask you about the problems that you're having at this time as a result of the incident that happened in 2018. I know from the records you have problems with pain in your right upper extremity.

CR: Yes, sir.

MS: Is it throughout the right arm?

CR: It's throughout my arm, yes sir. It's through my armpit, I got to mark it on here, but alongside here.

MS: OK.

CR: Right here . . . and my right leg . . . and I have a . . .

MS: Let's start with the right arm.

CR: OK.

MS: You have pain throughout the right upper extremity.

CR: Yes.

MS: From your . . .

CR: Shoulder to my fingers.

MS: OK, ongoing pain?

CR: Yes.

MS: OK. You mentioned pain under your right arm.

CR: In my armpit.

MS: In the armpit.

CR: And alongside this area.

MS: OK, you're pointing to the back of your arm?

CR: Yes, on the site. You want me to mark it?

MS: Sure, take your time. OK, so the pain throughout the right arm, ongoing from the shoulder down to the fingertips, pain in the right armpit area. That's ongoing as well?

CR: Yes, in my armpit.

MS: Then you marked the right knee, pain from the right knee down to the right foot/toes. Is that ongoing as well?

CR: Intermittent, mostly . . . just comes and goes a lot.

MS: OK, you also marked spasms you wrote here, facial spasms? Does it affect your right side of your face?

CR: Yes, my right side of the face now droops.

MS: OK.

CR: That's involuntary, it happens whenever.

MS: OK, let me see what I've identified. Ongoing pain throughout the right arm, from the shoulder to the fingertips; ongoing pain in the right armpit area; intermittent pain in the right lower extremity from the knee to the toes. And you said your right side of your face droops and then spasms affecting the right side of the face.

CR: Correct.

MS: OK, are there any other problems that we haven't identified, any other problems currently as a result of the November 2018 incident?

CR: The eye spasms as well.

MS: Spasms affecting the right side of the face including the eye?

CR: Yes.

MS: What is your most symptomatic body part?

CR: I would say the right arm.

MS: Your right arm?

CR: Yes, and the leg. Yeah, the spasms are involuntary.

MS: In what part of your body is the most intense pain that you have?

CR: Upper extremity.

MS: Right upper extremity?

CR: Yes.

MS: What are the sensations you feel in your right arm?

CR: Sometimes I have a flare up.

MS: What do you feel during the flare up?

CR: Throbbing pain.

MS: OK. Are there any conditions or activities that exacerbate your symptoms . . . your right arm symptoms?

CR: Sometimes it's just the movement of the arm, the position of the arm.

MS: Certain positions and movements?

CR: Yes.

MS: Give me an example of what some of those might be.

CR: Of the movements?

MS: Yes.

CR: Reaching.

MS: Reaching horizontally or overhead?

CR: Overhead.

MS: Both?

CR: Yes.

MS: Any other activities or conditions that exacerbate your right arm symptoms?

CR: If I'm tired, it's having the arm stretched over like in a way where I can't support it.

MS: Like when using a keyboard?

CR: Yes, not being able to fully turn the arm over.

MS: Now let's talk about your right lower extremity problems. You mentioned the pain is more intermittent.

CR: Yeah, it's pretty much started intermittent and it's really bad at night, so it's been my knee to my foot and sometimes my right foot swelling.

MS: So you tend to develop increasing levels of pain over the course of the day?

CR: Yes.

MS: Do you have any problems with inflammation in your right foot?

CR: Yes, and right ankle.

MS: During the evening that's when it develops?

CR: Well, I'm not quite sure if it's just the pressure of walking that the foot and ankle swells so I believe it's just the weight on the leg.

MS: . . . and that tends to happen near the end of the day?

CR: Swelling of the ankle, it depends on how much weight is on it.

MS: Secondary to weight-bearing, how is that?

CR: Yeah.

MS: . . . and then I think you used on this diagram a symbol for burning pain, that's what you feel in your right leg?

CR: I really don't know how to describe that constant pain.

MS: What do you feel in your right leg?

CR: Oh, in my leg. It's just aching, it's . . . I wish I had a better word for it.

MS: Anything else that's important for me to know about your right leg symptoms?

CR: No, it's usually thick in the morning.

MS: Your leg feels thick.

CR: My foot. Yeah, it feels tight and that's when the back of the heel tightens up and feels achy at times.

MS: OK. No problems with your facial . . . you said spasms?

CR: Yes.

MS: How often do you feel facial spasms?

CR: I really don't know, they are involuntary.

MS: Approximately how many times per day would you say, if there is a range?

CR: To be honest, I really can't tell you, they can come at any time.

MS: Throughout the day?

CR: Oh yeah, any time.

MS: Are they painful?

CR: The only time it's painful is at a time when I get a bigger one. It's a pulling sensation on the neck area.

MS: It's a pulling sensation that affects your neck?

CR: Yeah.

MS: The right side of your neck?

CR: Yeah.

MS: How long do they last when you have these spasms?

CR: Few minutes I would say.

MS: Have we discussed all of the problems you're experiencing now as a result of the November 2018 incident?

CR: Yes.

MS: Have you had any of these problems before the incident?

CR: No, sir.

MS: Did you ever sustain any injury to your right arm or leg before this incident?

CR: Uhhhh, I guess it's been many years before, I fell and bruised my shoulder.

MS: OK.

CR: That was it.

MS: How long ago was that?

CR: I guess it was about nine or ten years ago.

MS: That's your best estimate. What injury did you sustain to your right shoulder?

CR: It was bruised.

MS: What type of treatment did you have at that time?

CR: None.

MS: None, OK, no medical treatment?

CR: I went to the emergency room.

MS: Were you prescribed any medication?

CR: I don't remember.

MS: You don't recall what treatment you had if any?

CR: Other than going there, I'm not sure if they prescribed something. I can't remember.

MS: Had you made a full recovery from that injury?

CR: Yes.

MS: So no prior injury to either your leg or your arm?

CR: No, sir.

MS: What about any problems with facial drooping, spasms?

CR: No sir.

MS: Do you know what the doctors are diagnosing in terms of the cause of your symptoms?

CR: CRPS.

MS: Which doctors made that diagnosis?

CR: Dr. Bulroy.

MS: He's the only one who made the diagnosis?

CR: Yeah.

MS: Near the time before this happened, did you have any medical problems at all? You stopped smoking cigarettes?

CR: No, I was going to try a new product that they were going to put on the market.

MS: For smoking cessation?

CR: For, uhhh, like an e-cigarette.

MS: Did you have any medical problems near the time before the incident occurred?

CR: No, sir.

MS: No restrictions of any type either?

CR: No, sir.

MS: Do you have any problems with your mental function, memory, concentration, attention span—any of those types of problems?

CR: Not really, but my medication can make me a little forgetful. Maybe not concentrate.

MS: It dulls your memory and concentration?

CR: Sometimes it's more a concentration thing.

MS: Memory as well or just concentration?

CR: It's a little of both.

MS: OK. Can you give me some examples?

CR: For example, when I first take OxyContin . . . I take OxyContin 40 mg per day and I also take the Percocet.

MS: How does that affect your memory and concentration? Give me some examples.

CR: I like to read, but when I do some reading, really short, I don't finish it . . .

MS: Because you have difficulty comprehending or is it . . .

CR: I don't think I'm concentrating or focused, I would say focused.

MS: You are right-handed, right?

CR: Yes.

MS: I have your height at five feet five inches.

CR: That should be right.

MS: What is your current weight?

CR: 152 lbs.

MS: What was it at the time of the incident?

CR: About 142 lbs.

MS: So you gained about ten pounds, what do you attribute that to?

CR: I don't know.

MS: OK.

CR: I was concerned about the weight gain, but I believe it's the lack of being able to exercise, participate in an activity.

MS: Diminished level of activity postincident?

CR: Oh, it's definitely that, for sure.

MS: I know you had three marriages, right?

CR: Yes.

MS: When did your most recent marriage commence?

CR: Five years ago.

MS: That's to Jose Randolph?

CR: Yes.

MS: What does your husband do, what is his job?

CR: He's a foreman for a construction company.

MS: I see you have two children?

CR: Yes.

MS: Lloyd, how old is Lloyd?

CR: 29.

MS: Ralph is your other son?

CR: Yes, he's 26.

MS: Does your husband or your children have any disabling problems?

CR: I'm sorry?

MS: Do either your husband or your children have any disabling problems?

CR: No.

MS: The place that you live in in Orlando, is that a house, apartment, condo, what type of dwelling is it?

CR: It's a house.

MS: One story or two?

CR: It's two stories.

MS: Do you know how many square feet it is?

CR: No.

MS: How many bedrooms and bathrooms?

CR: It's three bedrooms and one and a half baths.

MS: Is it in a residential area?

CR: Yes.

MS: How long have you lived there?

CR: 20 years.

MS: Do you own the dwelling?

CR: Yes.

MS: Any plans to leave your home?

CR: No sir.

MS: Have you made any disability modifications to your home?

CR: No sir.

MS: Do you have any problems with accessibility within your house?

CR: Sometimes it's difficult going up steps.

MS: What problems do you have with that?

CR: Pain in the leg going up the steps.

MS: With whom do you live there?

CR: My husband and my two sons are there.

MS: So there's four people living there?

CR: Yes.

MS: Any animals, pets?

CR: I have one dog and my son has a puppy, so two dogs.

MS: I'm going to ask you a couple more questions about your medical history before November of 2018. Had you ever had surgery, before the needle stick incident?

CR: No, just the C-section.

MS: Both children?

CR: . . . and tubal ligation. One was a C-section.

MS: What year was that, how old were you at the time?

CR: 23 or 24 . . .

MS: 23 or 4, for both of those procedures?

CR: Yes.

MS: Any other surgeries or operations you've had, any other procedures?

CR: No.

MS: Anything else remarkable in your medical history before November 2018?

CR: No.

MS: I saw one record from 2008 that indicated you had some gastrointestinal problems, a cyst to your liver?

CR: No, not that I'm aware of. I've had my stomach ache a lot, but not a cyst in my liver that I'm aware of.

MS: It says a cyst or some other problem in the liver, but you don't recall that. Did that resolve in any event?

CR: I don't recall any of that.

MS: OK.

CR: Are you sure those are my records?

MS: It's not uncommon to sometimes have an error, I'll double check that. In any event, you haven't had any subsequent problems, right?

CR: No, not really. The main thing was I hurt my back on the steps outside and it was resolved.

MS: You had a slip accident?

CR: Yes.

MS: When was that?

CR: Can't remember the year, it has to be somewhere around, I can't remember the year.

MS: Approximately how long ago was that?

CR: I would say anywhere between seven or eight years ago.

MS: You injured your lower back?

CR: I slipped on the steps and they just gave me ibuprofen and it resolved.

MS: It was your lower back that was affected?

CR: Yes.

MS: . . . and you fully recovered?

CR: Yeah, they gave me ibuprofen 500 mg and that was it.

MS: OK. Anything else you can think of in your medical history that we haven't discussed prior to November 2018?

CR: No, other than migraines.

MS: OK. Since the incident happened in November 2018, going forward from then through today, have you had any unrelated problems . . . like car accident, slip and fall, disease, illness, anything like that?

CR: No sir.

MS: Apart from hospitalization associated with childbirth, no other hospitalization prior to November 2018 other than what you told me?

CR: No.

MS: Regarding the problems we've been discussing this morning, what is the major problem affecting you?

CR: My arm.

MS: Your right arm?

CR: Yes, and my leg. I don't know how you separate those, they're all together.

MS: If you had to rate the pain intensity in your right arm, zero to ten, zero is no pain at all, one is a minor distraction, tolerable, to a ten, which is excruciating and intolerable, the upper end of the pain scale, how would you rate your right arm pain?

CR: I would say about a five.

MS: OK, and the right leg?

CR: About the same.

MS: OK, and then the facial spasms? When they occur?

CR: As far as pain?

MS: Yes.

CR: Generally, no pain unless I'm having a harsh spasm.

MS: During the harsh spasm, what is your pain intensity, on the same scale, zero-to-ten scale?

CR: I would say about a two.

MS: Are you still treating with Dr. Bulroy?

CR: Yes.

MS: Is he a neurologist?

CR: Yes, sir.

MS: When did you last see him?

CR: I saw him last week on Wednesday.

MS: So about one week ago?

CR: Yeah, I think it was before.

MS: How often do you see him?

CR: Monthly. At times I've seen him more than once per month, a couple times.

MS: Are you treating with any other doctors right now?

CR: For just my general health?

MS: Let's start with any other doctors for incident-related reasons.

CR: Oh, incident . . . uhhh, right now I'm seeing Dr. Gust. I just started seeing him.

MS: What is his specialty?

CR: He's a neurosurgeon.

MS: When did you last see him?

CR: I don't have the exact date; I'm going to say April.

MS: April of 2019?

CR: Yes.

MS: Anyone else with whom you're treating for incident-related reasons?

CR: Yes. Dr. Plano.

MS: What is his specialty?

CR: I believe he's a pain specialist.

MS: Pain management?

CR: Yes.

MS: When did you last see Dr. Plano?

CR: That was in April as well.

MS: How often do you see him?

CR: I've seen him once.

MS: OK, one time. Do you see any other doctors on a recurrent basis other than Dr. Bulroy?

CR: For the incident, no.

MS: Are there any other doctors with whom you're treating currently for incident-related reasons other than the three that you just identified?

CR: No, not that I can recall.

MS: Those are the three for the medical incident that you're treating with currently?

CR: Right, I'm going to rehab for some therapy for my leg right now.

MS: Who are the physicians with whom you're currently treating for reasons not related to the incident?

CR: Not related would be Dr. Sanders, my general doctor.

MS: Like a primary care doctor?

CR: Yes.

MS: Anyone else?

CR: No sir, that's it.

MS: Do you have any scheduled appointments with physicians?

CR: The only scheduled one would be Dr. Bulroy.

MS: When is your next appointment with him?

CR: I think the end of the month.

MS: Since the incident happened . . . you want to take a break?

CR: Yes, can I?

MS: Anytime you need to.

CR: OK, thanks.

MS: Have doctors discussed with you any future surgeries?

CR: Yes.

MS: OK, who was a doctor that discussed that with you?

CR: Dr. Gust.

MS: Is there a timeframe for that, any timeframe?

CR: No.

MS: What would be the purpose of that?

CR: To help with pain.

MS: OK. I know you have physical therapy and occupational therapy. Have you had occupational therapy for your hand?

CR: I tried to have therapy, but she doesn't take my insurance.

MS: OK, that was the person who did the functional capacity evaluation, that was Sue Walenko?

CR: Yeah, I did do therapy, I'm sorry.

MS: Those are the only therapies you had, physical therapy and occupational therapy?

CR: Yes.

MS: Are you currently in any treatment or therapy?

CR: Yes, therapy now for my face.

MS: Is that physical or occupational?

CR: Physical.

MS: How often do you have that?

CR: Right now, once per week.

MS: Where do you go for your therapy?

CR: Ability Rehab.

MS: Who is prescribing your physical therapy?

CR: Dr. Bulroy.

MS: Did he tell you what his future treatment protocol was going to be?

CR: What do you mean? I'm sorry I misunderstood the question. Do you mean the gentleman that's doing the therapy?

MS: No, Dr. Bulroy. Did he tell you what his future treatment protocol is going to be for you, for the physical therapy, like the duration of it or the intensity of it?

CR: No.

MS: Have you had any other treatment or therapy other than what we discussed?

CR: Yes, I had physical therapy back in 2018.

MS: How about any injections, have you had any injections?

CR: Yes, I had nerve blocks.

MS: How many nerve blocks have you had?

CR: Best I can recall, maybe three.

MS: Where were they, in your right arm?

CR: No, in my throat.

MS: When was your last nerve block?

CR: I believe it was 2018.

MS: None since then?

CR: No. The nerve block didn't do it for me.

MS: Now I know you're not using any adaptive aids today other than glasses. Do you have any adaptive aids that you use at home or anywhere else?

CR: No sir.

MS: Your medication, as you told me, you're taking OxyContin?

CR: Yes.

MS: And that's for pain, right?

CR: Yes.

MS: You mentioned 40 mg three times per day?

CR: Correct.

MS: You said Percocet you're taking. That's also for pain?

CR: Yes.

MS: Do you know the frequency and dosage of that?

CR: Ten mg twice per day.

MS: Ten mg twice per day. Any other medications?

CR: Prescription-wise, I have MiraLAX for constipation.

MS: Do you know the dosage and frequency?

CR: Not really, I use the cap.

MS: Once per day?

CR: Yes, it's a powder you mix with water.

MS: OK, anything else?

CR: For migraines I take sumatriptan. I'm taking the brand Imitrex.

MS: Imitrex. How long have you had problems with migraines?

CR: I have migraines in my history.

MS: You have a longstanding history of migraines?

CR: For a long time, I didn't have any migraines, I had migraines and they went away.

MS: When did your migraine problems begin?

CR: You mean age-wise?

MS: Yes.

CR: I can't remember exactly the age. I remember teens definitely having migraines.

MS: How long do you have migraines now?

CR: Varies, sometimes the medication gives me a headache, so I make sure I take the medication before it gets out of hand.

MS: At this time, what would you say over an average month how many migraines do you have?

CR: Headaches are different, but for migraines couple of times per week.

MS: OK. Is that your entire medication protocol that we just reviewed?

CR: Yes, prescribed, yes.

MS: What else do you take?

CR: Other than vitamins that the doctor said I must take like vitamin C, magnesium, and B12.

MS: Were you taking medications near the time before the incident, for example, Imitrex?

CR: Before the incident?

MS: When you have migraines, did you take any medication for it?

CR: No.

MS: You start taking Imitrex after the incident?

CR: Yes. I've been prescribed it. I had to use tramadol acetaminophen or something . . . it's a long name . . . Fioricet.

MS: You took Fioricet before the incident?

CR: No, after the incident I had Fioricet and I was switched to the Imitrex.

MS: Before the incident you took Tylenol, was it over the counter?

CR: Yes, over the counter.

MS: To control your migraine problem?

CR: Yes. That was ibuprofen.

MS: You mentioned the medications you take cause you constipation and headaches, both side effects?

CR: Yes.

MS: Any other side effect with your medications?

CR: Let's see . . . no.

MS: Did you take all your meds in the last 24 hours?

CR: No, I didn't take Imitrex. I only take that when I get migraines. I haven't had Mira-LAX in 24 hours.

MS: OK, now I'm going to ask you what you can and can't do physically. With your left hand and arm, do you have any lifting limitations with your left hand and arm?

CR: No sir. I mostly use my left.

MS: How much are you able to safely handle with your right upper extremity? Lift and carry with your right upper extremity again, safely?

CR: I don't know, weight safely ten pounds, I'm guessing.

MS: Have doctors given you any lifting instructions?

CR: Yes, Dr. Benezette gave me restrictions.

MS: What did he tell you to limit lifting to?

CR: Well, the instructions were no heavy lifting, pushing . . .

MS: But did he tell you specifically a pound limit?

CR: No.

MS: But he advised you to be cautious with your right upper extremity lifting?

CR: I would say that, generally. That's why I lift as much as I can, light things.

MS: When you use your right upper extremity to lift objects, what does that do?

CR: I'm not sure. It causes pain in my arm.

MS: It causes your pain to worsen?

CR: Definitely aggravates it.

MS: I assume with your left hand you're not limited. For example, you can extend your arm horizontally, would that be true?

CR: Yes.

MS: You can supinate left upper extremity?

CR: Yes.

MS: You can touch your thumb to each of your left-hand fingers?

CR: Yes.

MS: Make a fist with your left hand?

CR: Yes.

MS: You can extend it overhead?

CR: Yes.

MS: No limitations with your left upper extremity. How about fine motor function in your left-hand fingertips like fastening buttons, picking up something little with your fingertips? Any problems with those activities?

CR: Yes.

MS: Now with your right hand, can you touch the fingers on your right hand to your right-hand thumb?

CR: Yes.

MS: Can you close your right hand into a fist?

CR: Yes.

MS: Can you extend your right arm horizontally?

CR: Yes.

MS: How about overhead, can you extend your right arm overhead?

CR: Certain limits, not fully.

MS: OK, what about the fine motor functioning in your right hand and fingertips? Is that impaired or is that intact?

CR: I would say impaired.

MS: Can you give me some idea what the degree of impairment is, from your view?

CR: I can touch my fingers, I'm slow . . .

MS: You're slower than you were before the incident, moving your right-hand fingers?

CR: Yes. I also have problems touching my ring and pinky fingers to my thumb on the right hand.

MS: Your fourth and fifth right-hand digits?

CR: Yes.

MS: Any problems moving your neck, left, right, up, down?

CR: No.

MS: How about your legs, any limitations in moving your legs? Do you have the full range of motion in your legs?

CR: I can move my legs, yes.

MS: OK, but your right leg and foot are less fluid in movements, isn't that what you told me? Left leg is OK. No problems with the left leg?

CR: My left leg is fine. I have the pain in my right leg.

MS: Walking, standing for short durations like you have been today, you're OK with that, would you say?

CR: Yes.

MS: OK, and bending at the waist, any problems with that?

CR: No.

MS: How about movements below the waist level, such as squatting, climbing stairs, getting on hands and knees, any difficulties with those?

CR: I have difficulty doing the stairs in my house, somewhat pain in my foot. I can squat. What was the others?

MS: Getting on hands and knees.

CR: That's OK.

MS: OK, what is within your tolerance in terms of, for example, walking—how long are you able to walk before you overdo it, need to rest, overexert yourself?

CR: I can definitely walk about 15 to 20 minutes at a time.

MS: What about standing—what is within your tolerance standing?

CR: Maybe half an hour or more, I haven't timed it. Maybe more.

MS: How about sitting?

CR: I would say more than half an hour or so, about how long we've been sitting today.

MS: And about driving?

CR: Good question, you mean how long can I be driving a car?

MS: Yes, how much time, the duration, how long?

CR: 15 to 20 minutes, maybe 30 minutes.

MS: About 30 minutes. The vehicle you operate, is it automatic or manual transmission?

CR: It's manual.

MS: How often do you drive?

CR: Maybe a couple times per week.

MS: Two times per week?

CR: A little more than two.

MS: Two or three?

CR: Yes.

MS: Do you have a disabled person parking placard?

CR: No sir.

MS: Any problems with your balance?

CR: As far as I can recognize, no.

MS: How about hearing?

CR: No.

MS: Sense of smell or taste, any problems with those?

CR: No.

MS: Breathing, any problems with that?

CR: No.

MS: Bowel or bladder problems?

CR: No. Just constipation.

MS: How about fatigue? Any problems? You did mention feeling tired.

CR: Yeah.

MS: Have you had any falls since the incident occurred, falling?

CR: No.

MS: Does the weather or any other environmental condition affect your symptoms, like hot, cold, dampness, humidity, anything of that nature?

CR: Cold.

MS: How does that affect you?

CR: For me I think it can make my pain worse.

MS: Do you think you're getting better, worse, staying the same, what would you say about the stability of your condition?

CR: I would say, I'm not quite sure what the progression, so . . . right now probably about the same. I don't know the uncertainty of it, though.

MS: Do you know what stage of CRPS has been diagnosed?

CR: No. As far as I mentioned, the lifting and carrying . . .

MS: From what I understood you said they didn't specify a pound limit, but they said to be cautious.

CR: He said no heavy lifting.

MS: What other restrictions were imposed?

CR: Just a sedentary life.

MS: Do you have problems with sleeping?

CR: I would say that I do.

MS: Did you have any problems with sleep before your 2018 incident?

CR: I would say I generally got maybe eight hours of sleep before.

MS: So you say you had no sleep problems before the incident?

CR: Not that I can recall, no sleep issues.

MS: How often do you have sleep problems now?

CR: I go to bed at 11 p.m. and get up around 8 a.m.

MS: Do you wake up at that time?

CR: Yes.

MS: How often do you have sleep problems?

CR: Since the accident.

MS: Every night you have sleep problems? What's the cause of the sleep problems?

CR: I know pain wakes me up, that's for sure. Any other, I'm not sure if any of the medications have an effect.

MS: Do you take naps during the day?

CR: Yes.

MS: How often do you nap?

CR: Maybe once a day.

MS: How long is a typical nap?

CR: Usually I take a short nap. More than 30 minutes, maybe 30 to 45 minutes.

MS: Do you take any medication to help you sleep?

CR: No.

MS: Do you have problems with nightmares?

CR: No.

MS: Regarding your self-care, are you able to bathe yourself, dress yourself, take care of your personal needs?

CR: Yes, at the time I do as much as I can without needing assistance.

MS: You can do all your self-care?

CR: I need help with my hair care.

MS: OK. Who helps you there?

CR: Sometimes the young lady that does hair care generally does that. Depends on what she's doing to my hair, how long it lasts, sometimes I get my hair done every couple months.

MS: Is this a hairdresser?

CR: Yes.

MS: She's a hairdresser you see how often?

CR: Every couple months.

MS: OK. I think I read in your deposition your husband shaves your legs for you.

CR: Yeah, he washes my hair.

MS: Does he shave your legs too?

CR: Yeah.

MS: Does he continue to provide those services, too?

CR: Yes.

MS: Are you able to prepare light meals for yourself?

CR: Light meals, yes.

MS: Do you do any baking now, any cheesecakes?

CR: No. Any meals I do doesn't require chopping, slicing.

MS: You no longer bake or make cheesecakes?

CR: No.

MS: What's the reason?

CR: Am I able to . . .

MS: What is the reason you're not making cheesecakes now?

CR: Because they are handmade . . . mixing . . .

MS: Both hands are required.

CR: I would say I'm pretty dominant on my right hand, but you need both hands, you need to . . .

MS: You're unable to mix products with your left hand.

CR: From beginning to end of the process, I was referring to.

MS: OK. Do you do any housekeeping chores?

CR: Yes, if there are small items, cups, plates, I would do a few of those dishes.

MS: You wash small stuff.

CR: Yes. Generally, I work more with my left, whatever I can do with my left. I do try to use my right because I know I have to use it.

MS: Do you do things like sweeping or vacuuming?

CR: No.

MS: Do you have anybody that you pay to provide services for you, like a housekeeper, yard maintenance person, pool person, anybody like that?

CR: No.

MS: Who provide services to you, your husband does?

CR: Yes.

MS: He provides housekeeping services to you?

CR: Yes, he cleans the home.

MS: How about your sons, do they as well?

CR: They take care of their . . . you know, they keep their area clean.

MS: So is your husband the only person who actually does things for you?

CR: They help from time to time.

MS: . . . but it's mostly your husband. Anyone else besides your husband?

CR: No, he does lawn.

MS: Before you became injured, what types of recreational or leisure activities did you have?

CR: I pretty much exercised, I went to the gym.

MS: How often did you do that?

CR: Usually about four times per week I would go to the gym. First, we'll go to the gym and do some cardio and then we'll go and do some weights.

MS: Any other leisure activities that you had?

CR: I enjoyed cooking, taking time with recipes.

MS: You still exercise at a gym or anywhere else?

CR: No.

MS: How about cooking, is that still a leisure activity? You don't find cooking pleasurable?

CR: No.

MS: What else do you do for your leisure activity? You said something about reading earlier.

CR: I read. I try to do some walking to keep moving.

MS: I think you were asked during your deposition about your average day, and you said sometimes you're up before 7 a.m., and, depending on how you're feeling, your activities vary by taking a walk just a couple blocks from your house depending on how your legs are doing. If they're swollen, you lie down, put them up. You might answer email, small tasks in the house, maybe wash a few dishes, glasses, coffee cups. You may or may not have lunch. If it is a good day you take another walk, if you can. And when your husband gets back from work, you prepare a meal. After dinner you watch TV, read until about 11 p.m. Is there a change, is it the same, has there been a change in your routine since then?

CR: No, I generally try to keep to walking. On a good day I'll try, depending on pain in my foot. Go to doctor's appointment, I do pay the bills and I do go to the store, that's generally my walk to Publix.

MS: How about anything else you do? Do you socialize, go to any organizational meetings, church services, or anything like that?

CR: No.

MS: OK, I'm going to ask some questions now that are in the mental health area.

CR: OK.

MS: Have you had any mental health treatment the year before or after the November 2018 incident?

CR: No.

MS: Any family history of mental illness?

CR: No, none that I'm aware of.

MS: Have you ever been prescribed any medication for mental health–related problems like depression, anxiety?

CR: No.

MS: Have you ever had any trauma to your head or lost consciousness before the incident?

CR: No sir.

MS: Do you feel you need any mental health treatment at this time?

CR: No sir.

MS: Have you had any problems with depression recently?

CR: No sir.

MS: How about anxiety?

CR: No sir.

MS: Thoughts of self-harm?

CR: No sir.

MS: Any type of mental health concerns or problems that you currently have?

CR: No.

MS: You are concerned about your physical condition, I assume, from what you told me.

CR: Yes.

MS: How about financial difficulties, any problems there?

CR: No, we seem to be OK.

MS: OK. Any problems in your marital relationship?

CR: Uhhh, I would say my husband is affected by what's going on with me.

MS: Anything else you feel is relevant for me to know in assessing your mental health condition?

CR: No.

MS: Do you feel . . . overall psychologically, do you feel you're a well-adjusted person, or are you having any difficulties with your adjustment?

CR: I would say there are some coping strategies to learn as I go through this process here. I would say I'm OK overall.

MS: OK, now we're going to move on to your schooling . . . I believe I saw in the records that you finished high school?

CR: Yes.

MS: What year did you graduate?

CR: 1983.

MS: Then you went on to Daytona Community College?

CR: Yes.

MS: Did you finish your paralegal degree?

CR: Yes, I got a paralegal degree, AS degree and an AA degree.

MS: Associate of Science and Associate in Arts. What was the AA in?

CR: Just general stuff.

MS: Oh, I see, and the AS was a paralegal?

CR: Yes.

MS: What year did you get the Associate in Arts degree? You completed a Bachelor of Science in sociology degree, that was in 2000, I believe?

CR: Yes.

MS: Do you have any other formal educational training?

CR: No sir.

MS: Your baking skills . . . did you have any culinary training for that? Any restaurant work or anything like that?

CR: No sir.

MS: You were self-taught . . . your baking skills?

CR: Yes. I had to take the Food Management certification.

MS: Was that a course you take?

CR: It was for the state.

MS: Did you have a course to prepare you for the . . .

CR: Yes.

MS: How long was the course?

CR: Self-study.

MS: Self-study. It's for Food Service Manager?

CR: Food Safety, Management certification.

MS: When did you obtain that credential?

CR: 2014.

MS: Is it still valid?

CR: From what I know right at this moment, yes. There was a time expiration and it may be this year, I believe it's good for five years.

MS: Do you have any other working credentials other than that certification?

CR: No.

MS: Have you ever been a certified paralegal?

CR: I wasn't certified.

MS: What else did you do in the past?

CR: Lease expense agent.

MS: You were certified?

CR: Well, I guess it's sort of like licensing to sell, for sale, marketing.

MS: What kind of products?

CR: At the time it was for Prepaid Legal Services.

MS: Prepayment of legal services?

CR: Prepaid Legal Services. I was hired as an independent contractor.

MS: Did you acquire any other credentials?

CR: No sir.

MS: How about employers? Let me go through your work history. Cheesecake Delights you were self-employed; I think that was from 2014 to 2018.

CR: Yes, that's for baking.

MS: You were a cheesecake maker. Did you make nothing else other than cheesecakes?

CR: Yes, I made cupcakes.

MS: OK, and then prior to that I have the prepaid legal services.

CR: Before the baking?

MS: Yes. What job did you have before the baking?

CR: Prepaid came before the baking. The baking was the last thing I did before.

MS: Let's go in reverse order, before Cheesecake Delights, what was the job you had before that?

CR: To be honest, I'm going to tell you I might not know all of them in order.

MS: Yeah, that's fine, do the best you can do.

CR: I did Prepaid Legal Services that's for sure, sales and marketing.

MS: What was your job title with them?

CR: I guess they would call that legal expense agent, I guess that's why you had to get state licensing for that.

MS: How long did you do that work?

CR: That was a little over a year maybe.

MS: I have Clifton Financial Services?

CR: Yes sir.

MS: What was your job title for that organization?

CR: Receptionist.

MS: How long did you do that work?

CR: About six months.

MS: Before that Choice Paralegal?

CR: Pretty much my own business helping people fill out forms.

MS: So an administrative assistant?

CR: Yes.

MS: How long did you do that job?

CR: It was really for myself, so it was ongoing back and forth.

MS: You were a contractor?

CR: Long period of time.

MS: Approximately how long would you say?

CR: Maybe four, five . . .

MS: Months?

CR: Throughout the years.

MS: Years, I see you were an administrative assistant/paralegal.

CR: Yes.

MS: Then Oceanside Inn, tell me your job title with them.

CR: I was the clerk.

MS: Like hotel clerk.

CR: Front desk.

MS: How long did you work at Oceanside Inn?

CR: If I can remember, maybe one year.

MS: Prior to that I have Jackson Hewitt Tax Service?

CR: Yes, I did that seasonal, so I may have done it maybe two or three times you know meaning each year, so it's seasonal work.

MS: What was your job title?

CR: The last time I worked with Jackson Hewitt I was the office manager.

MS: About before Jackson Hewitt, do you remember what you did?

CR: Not in order. I know some of those jobs I had. At the time I worked for Serenity House as the TANS case manager.

MS: How long did you perform that work?

CR: I was hired temporarily, so I'm going to say at least six months.

MS: What other jobs have you had historically?

CR: Historically I worked as a hostess.

MS: Where was that at?

CR: I can't recall the name right now, but when I do . . .

MS: OK, any other type of work that you can recall?

CR: Yeah, throughout the years I worked in restaurants, just mainly cashier.

MS: Cashier.

CR: Yes.

MS: The jobs we just discussed, did you have any employer-sponsored training in any of those jobs?

CR: Yes. I worked for Smothers Law offices here in Orlando, and I was doing a paralegal degree, so they sponsored me to come and work there.

MS: So some employer-sponsored training in managing legal records . . .

CR: Oh yeah, research.

MS: Conducting research.

CR: It was the Smothers Law Firm.

MS: So you were a paralegal at the time?

CR: Yes. During my time I was obtaining the paralegal degree, not the entire time, so I believe it was.

MS: Did you have any sales training when you worked for Prepaid Legal Services?

CR: Yes, I would say we did a lot of training.

MS: Customer services and sales?

CR: Yes.

MS: Any other type of employer training that you had?

CR: None that I can recall.

MS: How about general office administration? I know that you had a lot of office types of jobs, receptionist, administrative assistant.

CR: Those jobs, I'm not sure if I would consider them employer-sponsored training. They just hire you, well you have to know the system.

MS: They teach their computer systems, generally how the office works?

CR: Yeah.

MS: How did you do in school? How was your academic performance?

CR: It was better than average, sometimes average, but most likely better than average.

MS: Do you recall how you did on any standardized testing, like SATs or any achievement test?

CR: No, I don't recall that.

MS: Did you ever repeat a grade in school?

CR: Not that I can recall.

MS: When you were in school, were you in regular classes, accelerated or remedial classes?

CR: As far as I can recall, it's always been regular classes.

MS: Do you have any second language skills?

CR: No sir. I've taken Spanish I and II, required courses, but no, nothing fluent.

MS: OK. You wouldn't claim to have Spanish language skills?

CR: No.

MS: I take it you've had on-the-job training at some of these jobs you perform. You've learned by doing the job?

CR: You mean working for the attorney? That was definitely on the job.

MS: That was conducting legal research and organizing legal records?

CR: Yes.

MS: Any other on-the-job training?

CR: I would say Jackson Hewitt.

MS: Completing tax returns?

CR: Well, for the management position at the time, it required a lot more how to run an office.

MS: You had on-the-job training in completing tax returns?

CR: At the time when I was managing the office, it required a lot more than just tax returns, so there was a training that we had to attend.

MS: Office management?

CR: Yes.

MS: But you also did learn how to do tax returns, like individual and corporate?

CR: No. Individual.

MS: OK. Looks like you've had several jobs that involve cash handling.

CR: Yes.

MS: You have a computer at home, I take it. You mentioned something about typing on the computer.

CR: Yes.

MS: Do you know how to use Microsoft?

CR: Yes.

MS: Any other software that you're able to use?

CR: No.

MS: Do you know how to use Excel, PowerPoint, those are all Microsoft applications?

CR: Yes, I can get through it some.

MS: What is your typing speed? What was it before you hurt your right arm?

CR: I'm not quite sure.

MS: Do you know how to type?

CR: I have typing skills, but I don't remember the last time I had a typing test.

MS: But you're able to type using all your fingers, other than your physical problems?

CR: Right, right.

MS: I take it over the years you've had proprietary systems, for example, when you're working for the law firm or the tax return systems.

CR: Yes.

MS: Like database management where you put data in and the software sorts and stores data for different uses?

CR: As far as the law firm, generally they're really into their systems, I can tell you that. I've always been more into their research in cases, client interviews, etc.

MS: You'd have to input information into the system?

CR: Yeah, sure.

MS: The skills you've developed through your different work and training, let's talk about that. You mentioned conducting client interviews, you've done that?

CR: Yes, a couple.

MS: How about your case manager, did your job involve that, too?

CR: Oh yeah.

MS: So you have some skills you developed in that area from a few different jobs.

CR: Yes.

MS: What about supervising, have you had supervisory experience?

CR: Well, I would say when I worked with Jackson Hewitt, being an office manager, I have a couple of employees.

MS: What type of people were they?

CR: Well, they were tax preparers, but it was a short time.

MS: Well, you mentioned a certification in Food Safety, so you have food handling experience and skills?

CR: Yes.

MS: What other work-related skills have you developed?

CR: I would say the legal research. At the time I was working on legal writings as well and I was good at teamwork, working with others.

MS: Team building.

CR: Yes.

MS: Do you have some cash management skills? Cashier.

CR: Sure.

MS: Did you prepare deposits and so forth?

CR: Actually, no.

MS: Do you have other general office administration skills, like scheduling, ordering office supplies?

CR: Ordering office supplies, yes. Scheduling, I had to do scheduling.

MS: You've done that too?

CR: Yes, Jackson Hewitt as well.

MS: Then of course you have food preparation skills.

CR: Yes.

MS: So what I've identified is conducting client interviews, supervision, you mentioned tax preparer, you did that for a short time, food handling and storage, conducting legal research, legal writing, client service, team building, cash handling, general office administration including scheduling and ordering office supplies, and food preparation. Can you think of any other skills that you've acquired, or did we pretty much define the major skills?

CR: I think you've pretty much defined . . .

MS: OK, have you considered any other training you might be interested in pursuing?

CR: Yeah, I've considered obtaining my master's degree.

MS: In what field?

CR: I haven't decided yet. But as far as the work related, I haven't quite pinned that down.

MS: You want to take another break? I can stop if you'd like to.

MS: So, we were just talking about your educational background, your work history, and now I'm focusing a little bit more on the years near the time before the November 2018 incident. When did you last have employment in which you earned income prior to November 2018? Would that have been Prepaid Legal Services?

CR: Are you saying earned income as an independent contractor or are you saying working for someone for an hourly rate?

MS: Good question. Any income at all where you were paid wages for what you did labor-wise, whether you were a W-2 employee or a 1099 contractor.

CR: I would say Prepaid was the last, although with the baking, it was family and friends that bought the cheesecakes, that's how I got started in that, but it wasn't enough to report.

MS: It was not enough income, you'd sell a cake for $10 here and there, from what I understand, reading your deposition?

CR: I was just getting it off the ground.

MS: Apart from nominal income.

CR: Right. So I would say Prepaid.

MS: That was when you were a legal expense agent.

CR: Yes.

MS: I know you said you worked there a little over a year. When did that end, the best of your recollection?

CR: I want to say the beginning month of 2011. That's my best guess.

MS: OK. The work that you did, let's say the ten-year period predating the last time you were active in the workplace, looks like you performed pretty much office space sedentary work, would that be correct? You told me you did a receptionist job, worked as an administrative assistant, front desk clerk, office manager. Would that be correct?

CR: I would say most of my jobs have been in that area. The marketing was, I would say, part sedentary, but it would require you to do sales presentations.

MS: The Prepaid Legal?

CR: Yes, I would do sales presentations, set up meetings. I was pretty active. So I wouldn't say it was all sedentary.

MS: What types of legal services were they?

CR: We call it legal shield; it was sort of like a policy but not really a policy itself.

MS: Put into some type of program?

CR: Contractual, so I would say that they had to pay memberships, more on the line of a membership.

MS: Is that what you were selling, was protection memberships?

CR: They call it legal sales, so it was an individual having access to attorney office work, general.

MS: General legal. OK. You made sales presentations, where did you go to make these?

CR: Different businesses, we set up appointments for the employees, different businesses.

MS: Local.

CR: Yes.

MS: So throughout Central Florida. What other job responsibilities did you have?

CR: I would say team building for team training.

MS: You trained other salespeople.

CR: Yes.

MS: Did you have administrative responsibilities too?

CR: Yes, order supplies, make appointments, generally keep a file on customers, customer service.

MS: So basically sedentary and light exertion because you had to travel out of your office and drive to different locations.

CR: Yes.

MS: How many miles per week would you say you had to drive?

CR: I don't recall.

MS: OK, what would be the heaviest amount of weight that you'd have to handle at that job?

CR: I can't recall.

MS: Nothing over 20 pounds, would you say?

CR: I would say, yes, that would be my best guess.

MS: Was that a full-time job or were you a contracted employee?

CR: I was an independent contractor; I did full time.

MS: You worked full-time as an independent contractor.

CR: Yes, for myself I worked full time.

MS: Do you recall how you were paid?

CR: Yes, at the time they would make a monthly deposit into your account based upon your sales.

MS: You were paid commission; you were 100 percent commission?

CR: Yes.

MS: OK, let me see if I have any earnings records here. . . . I don't think I have any earnings records going back that far. Do you recall what your compensation was when you left Prepaid Legal Services?

CR: No, I don't recall.

MS: Do you have a general idea, like was it $5–10k, $10–20k, more like $20k?

CR: I would say less than that for sure.

MS: Less than what?

CR: $5k maybe.

MS: You generated less than $5k per year?

CR: I would say probably. I don't know, I can't really recall the exact amount.

MS: All right, $5k or less, best of your recollection.

CR: I'm not sure.

MS: That's OK.

CR: I know I didn't make a lot of money during that commission sales work.

MS: What would be the last year that you actually reported any income that you generated? Would it have been after 2011, did you report any income?

CR: No.

MS: So 2011 would be the last year you reported employment income?

CR: I believe so.

MS: I know you reported a loss for Cheesecake Delights in 2016.

CR: That's the baking.

MS: That's a little over $2k loss in 2016 and then the other income, would that be your husband's income that would be on your tax return?

CR: Which tax return are you looking at?

MS: 2016, then 2017 there was another loss that was recorded.

CR: That's Cheesecake Delights.

MS: That would be Cheesecake Delights again. Then all of the other wages would be his wages.

CR: That's correct.

MS: Then 2018 that would be the same too as far as wages would be his?

CR: That's correct.

MS: Which was another loss.

CR: Right.

MS: You reported business losses in 2016, 2017, and 2018—correct?

CR: Correct. I also wanted to correct when we were speaking about the question you asked me about where we stand with the financials, so I wanted to make sure I clarify that.

MS: OK, just one second here.

CR: OK.

MS: You mean when I asked you about any financial difficulties you might have. Is that what you are talking about?

CR: Yeah.

MS: You want to clarify that?

CR: Yeah, I was saying we were doing OK, but the OK is not really OK because with all the medical, it's just created a real hardship.

MS: You are having financial difficulties?

CR: Oh yeah.

MS: I understand. When did you start Cheesecake Delights, was that in 2016?

CR: Yes.

MS: You work out of your home?

CR: Yes.

MS: Did you have any commercial food preparation equipment or license at the time?

CR: No, because at the time we started looking for a commercial kitchen, so we didn't have any commercial equipment or anything.

MS: Did you have any customers?

CR: Family and friends and just the offer from Stan's.

MS: So the offer from Stan's was to put on roadshows?

CR: Yes. They would like to have my cheesecake on their roadshows.

MS: You baked, you said, cupcakes, cheesecakes, right?

CR: Yes.

MS: You had your own recipe?

CR: Yes.

MS: Did you have a website?

CR: Actually my son was working on that at the time. I can't remember if he had a website up.

MS: Do you have one now?

CR: No.

MS: What do . . . well, I guess the tax return speaks for itself in terms of what you generated in terms of sales and all that.

CR: With cheesecake?

MS: Yes.

CR: I would say it was pretty much seasonal unless I'm going to make cupcakes for a special occasion, birthday, or something like that.

MS: How many hours would you commit to Cheesecake near the time before the needle stick incident?

CR: Well, I don't know the hours. I know that in the time I had to do management certification, I had to get approval to bake cakes, and . . .

MS: Generally, how many hours on an average week did you commit to the business? I mean, that was a one-time deal where you had to get a certification, but other than that, actually baking or selling things or talking to people trying to promote the business.

CR: My best guess out of a day, I would say up to four hours. And it depends on the baking itself, could have been a little longer. But yes, promoting, I went out and promoted. Talking to people generally.

MS: How would you get your customers?

CR: Through my husband's coworkers, family, friends, and there was actually one company that would buy my cakes from time to time.

MS: When did Stan's approach you for an opportunity?

CR: I believe it was 2017, month, day, I don't know exactly.

MS: 2017 they approach you, how did they learn about you?

CR: Well, I was shopping in the store and a gentleman walked over and asked what I do with the products I have in my basket.

MS: He was an employee?

CR: No, he was actually the manager. I come to find out during the conversation.

MS: He asked you when he saw the products you were purchasing, asked you why was there like a large quantity?

CR: No.

MS: Then you said I was going to make some cheesecakes, how did that evolve to the point where you . . .

CR: I told him I bake cheesecakes and I offered to bring him a sample because primarily if I wasn't making any money off of cheesecakes, I was giving away cheesecakes. So I would bake for free samplers a lot.

MS: He tried it and liked it.

CR: Yes, he called me on the phone and said I'd like to have these cheesecakes on a roadshow and he would work with me.

MS: Was it a contractor or how would that have worked?

CR: No, it wasn't a contract at the time.

MS: So when you do a roadshow, what's involved in a roadshow? Are there people who give samples out on the floor?

CR: You go from store to store selling your product. You would be selling cheesecake products at different locations.

MS: A roadshow involves traveling to different stores, Stan's Club stores, and you're on the floor and you sell your product?

CR: Correct.

MS: And you get to provide samples there too?

CR: Yes.

MS: Would you have been paid solely on commission?

CR: I really don't know; we didn't actually have that contract. So until I got to that point, everything . . .

MS: You're aware of the compensation terms?

CR: I'm unaware of the compensation.

MS: Did you actually do any roadshows?

CR: No.

MS: It was all in discussion phase?

CR: All in discussion, and I was actually out looking for a commercial kitchen, a place to bake.

MS: So you as a self-employed cheesecake/cupcake maker, you purchased your own products?

CR: Yes.

MS: . . . and made baked goods and sold them.

CR: Yes.

MS: Those were the major job responsibilities.

CR: Well, I'm sure with, perhaps I know that would have changed because I would be moving to a commercial kitchen.

MS: It would have changed, but at that point that's what you did. You would have maybe . . .

CR: Family and friends mostly, I was selling to at that point.

MS: You would have leased some place like that.

CR: That's what I was going to do is try and find a commercial kitchen.

MS: That you would have probably leased. More than likely.

CR: The church I belong to just built a church hall, and we leased the hall as a commercial kitchen in it just to caterers, they don't use anything but the kitchen.

MS: You aspired to grow your business.

CR: Absolutely. I thought it was a great opportunity, so . . .

MS: So you stood for long periods of time while you were baking?

CR: Yes.

MS: You used both upper extremities?

CR: Yes.

MS: You have to handle pots, especially if you're in a commercial area, those are quite heavy.

CR: Yes.

MS: You do the cake decorating, too, you know how to make all the different types of designs and people's names if it's a birthday cheesecake?

CR: I forgot about that now that we're talking about it, I did take the cake decorating course as well.

MS: How long would you stand when you're doing this work?

CR: Definitely more than a couple hours, because you're doing different things. I would say a few hours.

MS: You would handle up to how much weight?

CR: Lifting?

MS: Yes.

CR: Again let's just say my best guess would be maybe up to that point we spoke about in a normal capacity.

MS: What would that be?

CR: Not a tray, I didn't say it would be 20 lbs. I didn't have any difficulty lifting anything heavy.

MS: Typically, would it be up to 20 pounds? What would that be like, a tray?

CR: I would say I believe I had the capabilities of lifting it.

MS: I understand. Anything else physically demanding? Did you use the mixers?

CR: I used the mixers; you have to be pretty much exact on the timing and ingredients or it came out wrong. Having the order ready on time, promoting it, knocking on doors.

MS: When did you stop baking? When was the last time you did any baking?

CR: I haven't done any since I've been injured.

MS: That would have been November 2018, right?

CR: Yes.

MS: You haven't had any other employment either?

CR: No.

MS: OK. Do you think you could perform your baking activities in a modified manner? For example, maybe slower, let's say relying on your left hand, not using your right hand, or just using it as a helper hand?

CR: I'm not sure of that, I haven't tried or anything for that, movements in my arm I would say my best guess is no baking. I do decorate them, so my arm requires a lot of movement.

MS: You don't believe you could do it even in a modified manner?

CR: No.

MS: OK. Are any doctors restricting you from working right now?

CR: I just have a physical restriction and . . . you'll have to ask Dr. Bulroy that.

MS: Let me ask you, are you able to brush your teeth with your right hand?

CR: Yes. I use a battery-operated brush, electrical. So generally I use my left.

MS: You can use it, though—your right hand, to brush your teeth?

CR: Yeah, I can use it, but I generally use my left. I can brush my teeth with a battery-operated one.

MS: How long are you able to use a keyboard with your right hand?

CR: 20 minutes, I'm guessing . . .

MS: That's your best estimate.

CR: I don't do a lot of work, so . . .

MS: What else are you able to do with your right hand? I know you're restricted, but I'm trying to better understand what you can and can't do. I know you can write a little bit.

CR: Yeah, I do some writing. You know it flares or gets aggravated, and that's when I stop.

MS: How long are you able to write?

CR: My best guess, a few minutes, five minutes. I don't do a whole lot of writing.

MS: We have some writing for you today, but it's not going to be like writing an essay. You're going to be checking boxes, circles. If you have problems let me know, because I don't want to push you beyond your limits. You're able to cut meat?

CR: I have my husband do generally any performance with a knife.

MS: I am not talking about chopping an onion or something like that, but if you're having let's say a piece of chicken, you're able to cut it.

CR: Yes. I can.

MS: What about performing other types of work that would involve no significant amount of lifting, like sedentary work that would involve primarily communicating and nominal hand use? I'm thinking of jobs like a cashier in a movie theater or some other cashier job where someone gives you a credit card and you give customers tickets, you swipe the card, you know, nominal hand use that you could do even with your left hand. Or like an information clerk, where you're just talking to people; people ask you where's the food court, where's the restroom, where's this, where's that. No real manual activity or maybe even something like a light delivery driver like a process server, somebody who just drives, or when people come to my office and give me a subpoena for something, that's all they handle. Things like that that would be nominal and no manual activity. Would those be within your capacity?

CR: Uhhh . . . well, all things are possible, that's for sure. Ummm, meaning . . . would that capacity also be within my skill set?

MS: You have a bachelor's degree and the types of jobs I just mentioned are pretty unskilled jobs, like an information clerk.

CR: You said an unskilled job . . .

MS: Unskilled is defined as something you learn from a short demonstration up to 30 days of on-the-job training to perform a job at an average level. That's technically what an unskilled job is, according to the United States Department of Labor.

CR: So what are you thinking?

MS: I'm just asking: do you think those jobs would be physically within your capacity? I think mentally, I'm pretty sure you could do those jobs in just speaking with you today.

CR: I understand what you're saying. I was just asking as far as the skilled versus unskilled, what you're thinking in that capacity for my level of education, training . . .

MS: You're overqualified from a skill level; you have a bachelor's degree, right, and two associate degrees. How about a job as a realtor? You've developed sales skills, you have good interpersonal skills.

CR: I don't know what the requirements are for a realtor, do you—and that would require a lot of driving.

MS: That's correct; well, it depends on the real estate you handle, you could be selective in what you represented. It often involves driving customers, there's no question about that.

CR: What else does it require to be a realtor?

MS: You show real estate, sometimes there's an open house. You have to have a license, you would have to pass the realtor's license exam, and there's typically like a 30-day course you would take to prepare for it. You would get the license and then you affiliate with a real estate company and, like I said, yes. In some cases there is driving and some like you're doing an open house and you're showing the same property and people come to you. You arrange details, like closing details. People get mortgages with lenders; you coordinate in some cases inspections like with appraisers and other people. It's a lot of telephone work, it's a lot of coordination, sales.

CR: Is that commission?

MS: In some cases there is a salary, but generally it is commission based, but some do pay salary. Does that interest you at all?

CR: No. There's not a market for that right now.

MS: Right now, in Florida, it seems to be a pretty good market—both commercial and residential.

CR: Is it?

MS: In my area it is actually.

CR: In your area?

MS: Tampa, St. Petersburg. Did you like the baking work that you did?

CR: Yes. I enjoyed it.

MS: Have you applied for Social Security disability?

CR: Yes.

MS: What was the disposition on your application?

CR: My husband's income.

MS: OK. You were denied.

CR: Yes.

MS: Because your husband earns too much money.

CR: Yes, I think so. Don't realtor and paralegal sort of have similar job responsibilities?

MS: Paralegal is more working with records.

CR: Well sure, when you're looking at commission based versus . . .

MS: You mean does the income compare?

CR: Well sure, I would think . . . I was just trying to figure out how you were coming up with a realtor.

MS: I'm thinking jobs that don't have as much manual activity—due to your right hand injury. Of all the jobs you've had, what would you say was the most skilled or challenging job that you held?

CR: That I've had?

MS: Yes, that you've had.

CR: I would say the paralegal, well I don't know, I believe the office manager job was up there, too.

MS: Have you ever had a job termination?

CR: Yes, I've been terminated.

MS: Tell me about that.

CR: Let's see, I was terminated from the tax place.

MS: What was the reason for that? Was that Jones & Family Tax Service?

CR: Yes.

MS: Do you know the reason they terminated you?

CR: Yes. They had a reason. For me, I didn't accept the paycheck that they had given me. So it was a question about the hours.

MS: Due to reported hours?

CR: Yeah, because I worked overtime and they didn't pay me.

MS: There was a dispute involving hours that you worked.

CR: Yeah, I would say that.

MS: Have you ever had a workers' comp claim?

CR: No.

MS: Now the income you have, is it solely your husband's income?

CR: Yes.

MS: No other income you have from any other source?

CR: No.

MS: Do you recall the highest wages that you ever reported to the Internal Revenue Service? Per year.

CR: That I've earned?

MS: Yes.

CR: My best recollection is maybe eight something . . .

MS: Eight thousand dollars.

CR: Yearly? Are you asking a yearly income?

MS: Yes.

CR: I've earned less than . . . I don't recall.

MS: You said $8k, would that be the highest that you . . .

CR: No, I was thinking hourly wage.

MS: So on an annual basis, what would be the highest amount that you ever reported to the IRS?

CR: I don't recall.

MS: Do you have any plans to pursue rehabilitation at this time? You know, to try and go back to work basically. What plans do you have?

CR: I don't have any concrete plans as of yet. I know I have medical to continue on top of it.

MS: Have you made any job applications since November 2018?

CR: No.

MS: Do you have any plans to begin a job search at this time?

CR: I will see what the doctors have to say.

MS: OK. Just about done here.

CR: You've done a lot of writing.

MS: OK, I think I have everything needed for the interview. Let's take a break before we move on to the testing portion of my examination.

Vocational Evaluator's Summary and Impressions Based on Clinical Interview and Case Assessment

After the clinical interview presented previously, the evaluator implemented the ECAT methodology Chapter 2 outlined. The evaluator's summary and impressions follow. Additionally, subsequent opinions generated after a review of updated/additional information are presented.

Readers are encouraged to focus on the evaluator's assimilation of existing evidence from records with new evidence—including information from the clinical interview, standardized testing, records including surveillance, consultations with healthcare professionals, and labor market research. The case study further illustrates how the evaluator applied the ECAT model's higher-order analytical processes—in particular, analysis, synthesis, and evaluation—to arrive at an opinion.

Summary and Impressions

I. A 1987 high school graduate, Ms. Randolph reported she earned an associate in arts degree in general studies in 1998 and an associate of science degree in paralegal studies in 2000. Additionally, she advised me she earned a bachelor's degree in sociology in 2004. The last employment Ms. Randolph reported to have had before she pursued self-employment was in 2011, when she worked as a legal expense agent with Prepaid Legal Services. She informed me her earnings were commission based and her job responsibilities involved selling identity-theft protection memberships and general legal services. Based on my understanding of her work, Ms. Randolph performed sedentary/light exertion tasks. Regarding her self-employment, she indicated she worked from her home and prepared baked goods. On her 2012 through 2014 tax returns, Ms. Randolph indicated her self-employment generated no income; however, she reported losses during all of these years. She informed me she baked cupcakes and cheesecakes and had planned to engage in a "roadshow" with Stan's Club. Ms. Randolph had no formal contract and was not aware of any compensation terms. As a self-employed baker, she indicated, she performed sedentary/light exertion tasks that involved bimanual activities and at times extended periods of bearing weight. "I haven't done any [baking] since I've been injured," Ms. Randolph stated. Further, she noted she has not held alternate employment. She assessed she has not been able to perform her former baking work, even in a modified manner. I discussed with her alternate employment including sedentary work that would involve nominal right-hand use, such as employment as an information clerk at a shopping mall, process server, and realtor. Ms. Randolph informed me she has considered retraining, and she expressed interest in pursuing master's degree studies.

II.   After her November 22, 2018, medical incident, Ms. Randolph pursued treatment at Horizon Medical Center. Her complaints were related to right-hand pain. Dr. Bulroy examined Ms. Randolph and described difficulties his patient had with right upper extremity use. "I would restrict this patient to sedentary activities regarding the use of her right upper extremity pending follow up with me in one month," Dr. Bulroy stated in a spring 2019 office note. He suspected complex regional pain syndrome (CRPS) affecting Ms. Randolph's right upper extremity on April 3, 2019, and he restated his prior sedentary activity restrictions. An August 19, 2019, note Dr. Khan authored documents difficulties with facial palsy Ms. Randolph manifested. Ms. Randolph subsequently underwent stellate ganglion blocks, which Dr. Malik indicated on November 20, 2019, provided some symptom relief. An addendum to a functional capacity evaluation an occupational therapist, Sherry Young, performed on November 3, 2019, notes Ms. Randolph is "permanently and totally disabled." As a basis for her opinion, Ms. Young made a general reference to her clinical experience and studies of people with "severe physical and cognitive limitations." In my opinion, the standard Ms. Young apparently applied does not relate to Ms. Randolph, based on my clinical examination of her and review of records. On May 5, 2020, a nurse practitioner restricted her to sedentary activities with her right upper extremity. In a June 25, 2020, progress note, Dr. Sastry stated: "Consider trial spinal cord stimulator to reduce right upper extremity pain." In his July 1, 2020, report, Dr. Bulroy noted Ms. Randolph remains restricted with the use of her right upper extremity in terms of reaching, pushing, pulling, heavy lifting, and carrying. "I restrict her to sedentary activities regarding the use of her right upper extremity," Dr. Bulroy said. Dr. Steig authored an "Independent Medical Evaluation" on August 19, 2020. He concluded Ms. Randolph was experiencing a type-II chronic [sic] regional pain syndrome caused by a peripheral nerve injury during the course of a venipuncture on November 22, 2018, and he elaborated on his analysis and assessment of Ms. Randolph's symptomatic body parts. I reviewed Dr. Bulroy's May 4, 2020, report in which he concluded Ms. Randolph "remains permanently and totally disabled with regard to the use of her right upper extremity as a result of the injury she sustained November 22, 2018." The most recent medical record I reviewed is Dr. Triggs's May 4, 2021, assessment in which he cited Ms. Randolph's use of large doses of opioid pain medication. He concluded, "Neither clinical examination nor extensive testing has provided convincing evidence of a neurological injury to account for this lady's complaints." The records I reviewed included surveillance of Ms. Randolph taken on December 13 and 14, 2019, and March 20, March 26, April 13, and April 15, 2020. Among the activities she can be seen performing during the period she was surveilled are smoking an electronic cigarette with her right hand, handling (unfolding and counting) paper currency with her right hand, playing lottery scratch-off tickets repeatedly with her right hand, holding a cell phone and texting with her right hand, and manually unlocking a vehicle door with keys using her right hand.

III. On a measure of intellect, Ms. Randolph scored in the low-average range, commensurate with my estimate of her level of mental functioning before her November 22, 2018, medical incident. She appears cognitively intact. Ms. Randolph does not use adaptive aids. She denied having problems with driving, and she informed me she operates a manual transmission vehicle. She repositioned normally while seated. Ms. Randolph denied having lifting limitations with her left arm/hand. With her right/dominant upper extremity, she indicated, she has some functional use. For instance, Ms. Randolph estimated she can safely handle "maybe a pound or two," and she noted she can operate a keyboard for up to 20 minutes. No cervical spine problems were cited. "I can write somewhat," Ms. Randolph stated. She is able to cut meat she eats. No problems with walking or standing for short durations were noted, and she denied having trouble with bending her waist, squatting, or getting on her hands/knees. Ms. Randolph estimated she can drive approximately 30 minutes, walk "more than half an hour," stand at least 30 minutes, and walk from 15 to 20 minutes before overexerting herself or needing to rest. Ms. Randolph assessed she does not need mental health treatment; I concur. On a personal level, I found her pleasant and likable. She has education, training, work experience, and skills as previously delineated. These factors are assets to Ms. Randolph in her vocational rehabilitation.

IV. I fully appreciate the extent of Ms. Randolph's stated symptoms that affect her dominant/right upper extremity and right lower extremity. Additionally, she is presenting problems with facial spasms. Her most intense pain is in her right upper extremity. Based on information available at this time, I recommend Ms. Randolph restrict her work activity to sedentary/light exertion. To the degree possible, she should abstain from repetitive right upper extremity use and repetitive activities that involve bimanual functioning. Within a reasonable degree of vocational rehabilitation probability, Ms. Randolph is a candidate for vocational rehabilitation. She should be able to resume her former employment as a legal expense agent. Regarding her self-employment as a baker, any projection of earnings she might have been able to realize in the absence of her medical incident is speculative. Ms. Randolph's demonstrated earnings as a baker during the time before her incident are unimpressive. Of course, there are several alternate occupations she could pursue at this time, including various sales-related jobs and work that mainly involves providing information. The evidence I have had an opportunity to consider to date does not support a claim of loss of earning capacity attributable to Ms. Randolph's November 22, 2018, medical incident.

V. It would be reasonable to provide Ms. Randolph some assistance to facilitate her vocational rehabilitation.

Updated Summary and Impressions

During my clinical interview of Ms. Randolph, she mentioned Dr. Gust had discussed with her implanting a neurostimulator; however, Dr. Rauck, an anesthesiologist/pain management specialist with whom I consulted on December 21, 2020, ruled out this intervention. While discussing future care needs, Dr. Rauck opined Ms. Randolph's symptoms do not relate to a diagnosis of CRPS.

The updated information I have had an opportunity to consider has not caused a change in my opinions about Ms. Randolph's vocational capacities. Specifically, the evidence I have had an opportunity to consider does not support a claim of loss of earning capacity attributable to her November 22, 2018, medical incident.

Standardized Test Administration

Standardized testing can provide objective input to supplement vocational evaluators' assessments. The selection and prescription of evaluators' test batteries often vary, based on facts and contingencies idiosyncratic to a case at hand, including features of an evaluee's profile.

For example, if English is not an evaluee's first language and an evaluator desires to obtain a measure of the evaluee's intellect, the evaluator should ensure language issues do not confound test results, potentially invalidating them. Options to remedy this problem include securing versions of tests printed in the evaluee's first language, employing a translator, and administering a nonverbal measure, such as the Test of Nonverbal Intelligence, in place of a standard IQ test printed in English.

Of course, tests administered to pediatric evaluees differ from those administered to adult evaluees. Many other factors can affect the selection of tests, including the nature of an evaluee's alleged disabling problems, testing that might have already been performed contemporaneous with a pending examination, an evaluee's preinjury and postinjury vocational activities, and types of impairments.

In some cases, courts impose restrictions on testing. Additionally, since standardized tests are regulated, evaluators' credentials have implications for the types of tests they qualify to procure and administer.

Shahnasarian (2015) described specific tests from which vocational evaluators can choose. The test batteries vocational evaluators prescribe generally derive from three psychometric domains: intellect and abilities, occupational interests, and personality. A description of each domain along with a discussion on how the respective test data can facilitate assessments follows.

Intellect and Abilities

Needless to say, employment in the wide range of occupations that comprise the world of work requires highly varying skillsets and cognitive demands, and individuals' cognitive capacities, among other things, affect the types of occupations accessible to them. Generally, earnings correlate with skill levels required of job incumbents (i.e., higher-skilled occupations generally are more remunerative than lower-skilled jobs). The following table, from the U.S. Department of Labor (1991), specifies skill levels with associated time required to learn to perform work tasks at an average level.

Skill Level	Amount of Learning Time Needed to Develop the Facility for Average Performance in Job/Worker Situation
Unskilled	From a Short Demonstration to Up to 30 Days
Semiskilled	From 30 Days to Up to 6 Months
Skilled	From 6 Months to 4 Years
Highly Skilled	From 4 Years to More Than 10 Years

Objective measures of evaluees' general intelligence and aptitudes can facilitate analyses of many issues evaluators investigate en route to rendering opinions on claims of loss of earning capacity. These measures include career development potential before and after an evaluee became injured, test performance with respect to overachievement/underachievement tendencies, unrealized career development potential, capacity for new learning and career growth, and prospects for retraining.

Regardless of whether an individual sustained a cognitive impairment, all vocational evaluations merit an assessment of an evaluee's intellect and abilities. Means to promote this assessment beyond standardized testing include analyses of evaluees' demonstrated scholastic and career development records.

Cognitive dysfunction can result from many mechanisms such as traumatic brain injury, cerebrovascular accident, degenerative neurological disease, and history of substance abuse, to name a few. In some cases, cognitive impairments arise secondary to medication side effects. Neuropsychological evaluations that assess degrees of impairments, intact and impaired cognitive functioning, and prognoses can be invaluable adjuncts to vocational evaluators' assessments.

When relevant, comparisons of preinjury and postinjury cognitive functioning may assist in discerning impaired mental abilities that, in turn, may adversely affect earning capacity. Further, when impairments manifest, measures of residual cognitive functioning can serve manifold purposes such as assessing differentials between preinjury and postinjury levels of functioning, identifying accommodations and compensatory techniques that could benefit an injured worker, and identifying occupational alternatives and retraining opportunities that remain viable.

Occupations require varying skills and aptitudes for incumbents to demonstrate and master to progress. Skilled trades, for example, largely involve aptitudes related to mechanical reasoning and manual functioning, while behavioral science occupations typically require incumbents to be skilled in areas related to social insight and interpersonal communications. Aptitude testing can help to define strengths and weaknesses within an evaluee's skill set, thereby facilitating an evaluator's ability to thoroughly evaluate a claim.

Aptitude testing can also be very specific. For example, in a case involving a hand injury to a surgeon, dentist, or jeweler, a test of manual speed and dexterity may be in order; or, for a clerical worker, an evaluator may consider administering a typing test.

Occupational Interests

Occupational interest inventories represent a class of psychometric tests that measure expressed and latent vocational interests. Test items often inquire about likes/dislikes and preferences in areas such as school subjects, work activities, and occupations. Some tests also include evaluees' self-assessments of skills and aptitudes and inquire about historical vocational objectives.

Most interest inventories incorporate a database to facilitate an evaluator's interpretation of an evaluee's test results. For example, The Self-Directed Search (Holland & Messner, 2017) applies trait-factor personality principles to organize occupations in the world of work into related families and subfamilies. After scoring an evaluee's interest profile, evaluators can process and interpret results with assistance from a computer-generated interpretive report. Referencing its database of thousands of occupations, academic pursuits, and avocational activities, the report identifies matches compatible with the evaluee's interest profile.

Occupational interests correlate positively with many career-related factors, thereby meriting consideration in a vocational assessment. These include job satisfaction, job performance, stability of career development, and work life longevity—all of which can affect earning capacity.

Personality

Information derived from personality tests adds another important consideration to an evaluator's assessment: the compatibility between an evaluee's disposition and temperaments with work tasks inherent in an occupation. For example, those prone to introversion may not be well suited for occupations that involve sales, adversarial encounters, making group presentations, and leadership.

Some personality traits, such as perseverance and high levels of frustration tolerance, can be quite adaptive to one's career development and potential earning capacity. Conversely, clinically significant levels of depression and anxiety, in some cases, can have profound implications for one's ability to secure and maintain employment. Factors such as low self-esteem and low self-confidence, likewise, can inhibit ability to realize career potential and to optimize earning capacity.

Assessing personality-related issues during a vocational rehabilitation evaluation can also be advantageous when contemplating initiatives to mitigate countermanded factors. Part III of *The Valuation of Monetary Damages in Injury Cases* elaborates on this.

Shahnasarian, Kaiser-Ulrey, and Lassiter (2006) discussed the use of the Minnesota Multiphasic Personality Inventory-II and other personality measures in vocational rehabilitation evaluations. Skilled integration of personality variables into a vocational assessment can facilitate an evaluator's analysis of reasons underlying an evaluee's achievement or lack thereof and, in the latter case, make recommendations and/or evaluate interventions to diminish maladaptive personality-related factors. Personality assessment also facilitates identifying occupations well suited for evaluees.

Postexamination

After an examination, vocational evaluators' work includes reviewing additional/updated records, interpreting test results, and gathering relevant supplemental information necessary to complete an assessment. Of course, these efforts culminate in the preparation of a report, which describes methods employed to derive damages-related opinions. The remainder of this chapter describes postexamination activities involved in preparing a report that often becomes evidence—in part or in whole—throughout the adjudication process.

Review of Additional/Updated Records

During a clinical interview, evaluators often learn new information that prompts them to request additional/updated records relevant to their assessments. For example, questioning could elicit a gamut of previously unknown evaluee information—from job search efforts to recent onset of new presenting problems and previously unknown unrelated trauma or illness.

Vocational evaluators should alert their retention sources when they discover new information germane to their assessments and request pertinent documentation of it. Failure to do so both deprives the retention source of information potentially important to prosecute their cases and places evaluators at peril of criticism and associated loss of credibility in their methodology and, by extension, opinions derived.

Along with information extracted from an evaluee during a clinical interview, vocational evaluators should correlate information from additional/updated documentation with information from records previously reviewed. Discrepant information, of course, should be identified and handled in accordance with guidelines discussed earlier.

Interpretation of Test Results

At times, vocational evaluators score some tests—mostly brief screening tests—during an examination. In conjunction with information from a clinical interview, preliminary test data can facilitate decision-making on other measures that may benefit a vocational assessment. For example, surprisingly low scores on measures of basic skills may cause an evaluator to add to a test battery more robust measures of general mental abilities; however, evaluators generally score and interpret the majority of tests comprising a selected test battery after an examination.

Many tests are computer scored, requiring more complex logistics than hand-scored tests. Along with raw test scores and associated statistical reference point data, automated interpretive reports typically accompany the test results. An evaluator should rely on these reports cautiously, mindful that their interpretations compare evaluees' scores with normative data based solely on demographic characteristics similar to the evaluee, devoid of the breadth of ancillary, often critical information available to an evaluator, which must be carefully synthesized when interpreting test results.

As an example, consider a case involving a college-educated woman in her mid-20s who sustained abdominal gunshot injuries resulting in a plethora of disabling problems including chronic abdominal and lumbar pain, psychological adjustment problems, and a host of unwelcome lifestyle changes such as inability to bear children—a stated preinjury objective. Unabashed comparisons of results from her personality test profile with her demographic group cohorts, obviously, would lead to many spurious findings. Her interpretive report cited extreme psychological difficulties including depression, paranoia, social avoidance, and posttraumatic stress disorder—understandable when interpreted in the context of her injuries and associated disabling problems but atypical of her able-bodied cohorts. When synthesizing test results and related findings with case-specific fact patterns, evaluators must consider objective bases for an evaluee's symptom presentation and trauma-related psychological sequelae.

Automated test scoring programs process data and make deductions based solely on scoring of an evaluee's responses on an answer sheet and subsequent mechanical cross-references to a clinical database, drawing statistical comparisons. This is among the reasons standardized tests are restricted, not available to the public, and require advanced training to procure and interpret. The evaluator must perform higher-level analyses that require the integration and synthesis of important supplemental case information beyond what computer-processed data provides.

Competent evaluators apply many layers of analysis when interpreting test data beyond raw test scores from individual instruments. The primary level of analysis involves determining whether test results are valid. Results from invalid profiles should not necessarily be discarded, and, when they arise, reasons for them should be explored and factored in the analysis. Reasons for invalid test results include evaluee mental confusion, problems with reading comprehension, and, in some cases, lack of cooperation with the examination process, symptom exaggeration, and malingering.

Some tests include validity scales sensitive to malingering and symptom exaggeration. Additionally, evaluators can gain insight into an evaluee's test motivation by inspecting completed test protocols to assess an evaluee's level of effort and response consistency. To perform these analyses, an evaluator could, for example, review an evaluee's responses on an intelligence test. The design of most intelligence and aptitude tests includes presenting items in order of progressive difficulty; that is, initial items are relatively easy, and subsequent items become increasingly difficult. Inconsistent response patterns can be detected when evaluees tend to incorrectly respond to easy questions yet correctly answer more difficult questions. Sometimes a "Christmas tree" response pattern emerges, where it is evident the evaluee did not seriously attempt test items, and even random responding would have generated a higher score.

Evaluators also analyze results between tests in their batteries to develop a composite profile. Further, they correlate their data with test results from other examinations and related measures, such as an evaluee's scholastic records and records of work achievement; clinical correlation of this information lends insight into ECAF-2 factors such as Need and Capacity for Retraining, Cognition, and Motivation (please refer to Chapter 2).

Consideration of Supplemental Information

Evaluators sometimes determine a need to obtain supplemental information after completing a vocational rehabilitation examination. Most often, this includes collateral source information and labor market research.

Collateral Source Information

Sources from which vocational evaluators most often obtain collateral information include evaluees' healthcare providers, family members, friends, caregivers, and employers. Of course, an evaluator must secure proper permission and authorization before initiating any communication.

Evaluators may find input from collateral sources helpful when they detect evaluees lack insight into the extent of their deficits, appear reluctant to disclose the scope of their disabling problems, or exhibit cognitive dysfunction that precludes them from providing comprehensive and accurate accounts during a clinical interview. Interviews of collateral sources also provide opportunities to verify and further investigate information an evaluee provided.

In addition to providing observations of an evaluee before and after the onset of disabling problems, collateral sources sometimes reveal new, undocumented information. A healthcare provider, for example, could enlighten an evaluator about an evaluee's prognoses or comorbidities not specified in treatment records, or an employer may describe a diminution in an evaluee's postinjury work productivity not documented in performance appraisals, despite extraordinary accommodations being extended.

Labor Market Research

Labor market research can add value to vocational rehabilitation evaluations when an evaluator requires supplemental information to refine opinions about (1) an evaluee's residual earning capacity after concluding an evaluee has sustained a loss of earning capacity, and (2) vocational rehabilitation interventions necessary to mitigate earnings damages, after determining such interventions are required.

In some cases, an evaluator may determine an evaluee possesses a residual postinjury earning capacity; however, the residual amount is less than the evaluee's preinjury capacity, which results in a loss of earning capacity. Labor market research in these cases often concentrates on identifying occupations that remain within the evaluee's capacity, along with associated compensation levels. In other cases, when concluding evaluees can continue their career development—albeit in a modified manner and with intervention—without sustaining a loss of earning capacity, evaluators may propose retraining or implementing workplace accommodations. Labor market research in these cases tends to focus on specific accommodations and details related to programs of study suited for an evaluee.

Briefly, evaluators undertake labor market research for reasons that include obtaining the following information:

- Occupation-specific wages
- Occupation-specific job responsibilities, along with exertional and nonexertional requirements
- Job openings, with associated requirements and wage rates
- Labor market projections specifying anticipated growth in various industries and occupations
- Programs of study suitable for an evaluee—including costs, duration, and earnings on program completion and workplace reentry
- Workplace accommodations

Preparation of the Vocational Rehabilitation Evaluation Report

A vocational evaluator's report describes work undertaken in conjunction with an evaluation, explains how facts and evidence evaluated contributed to an assessment, and culminates in a presentation of opinions and the bases for them. At times, depending on the status of a case, preliminary reports will proceed a final report.

Final reports should contain all opinions an evaluator foresees presenting during a trial. Failing to do so often contributes to judges' decisions to exclude testimonial evidence not disclosed before a preestablished evidence discovery deadline, as opposing counsel invariably argues at trial that the presentation of delinquent, not previously disclosed opinions creates an unfair "ambush," depriving them of their entitled opportunity to learn and evaluate all expert opinions beforehand.

Multiple audiences—each with varied perspectives and interests—review, consider, and critique reports of vocational rehabilitation evaluations. The audiences include trial lawyers prosecuting and defending torts, damages experts (including experts opposing the evaluator and those relying on the evaluator's opinions), insurance adjusters, triers of fact, and judges. Careful documentation of methods applied, bases undergirding analyses, and comprehensive presentation of supportable opinions hallmark reports that pass their inevitable scrutiny.

Vocational evaluators should reflect on their reports to ensure they comply with guidelines enumerated in Chapters 1 and 2—namely, answering three major questions: (1) Does the work comply with standards of practice? (2) Are methods employed and opinions presented complete and defensible? (3) Is the work sufficiently constructed to defend a Daubert challenge? More discussion on this latter question is in Chapter 11.

Generally, the contents of a vocational rehabilitation evaluation report include the following:

- Mechanism of an evaluee's injuries and vocational activities at time of injury
- Evaluee's injury-related presenting problems

- Scope of examination, including clinical interview and other assessment measures (e.g., interviews of family members/others, evaluator observations, standardized testing)
- Index of records reviewed
- Report of information obtained during clinical interview, including the evaluee's pre-injury and postinjury medical history, functional capacities and limitations, activities of daily living, mental health, education, and effects of acquired disabling problems on ability to work and earn wages
- Presentation and interpretation of test results
- Presentation of opinions including assessments of alleged vocational damages

If an evaluator's opinions change as a case evolves, based on new information that emerges after a report's publication or a case's developments, the evaluator must disclose the new opinions and reasons for them. This usually involves writing an updated report and sometimes providing a deposition/updated deposition during which questions posed focus on reasons for new opinions. As noted earlier, failure to make known new opinions before a preestablished discovery deadline risks their disqualification.

Vocational evaluators typically present their opinions sequentially, as outlined next. The denouement of an evaluator's efforts, the ECAF factors described in Chapter 2 guide the process of presenting the assessment, including the assembly, synthesis, and evaluation of available information, integration of new information, and development of opinions via the higher-order ECAT analytics.

Summary of Evaluee's Vocational History

The presentation begins with an overview and consolidation of an evaluee's education and work history—focusing on skills and vocational themes (e.g., assessment of exertional and nonexertional requirements associated with work performed, stability of career development, and overachievement/underachievement tendencies). Evaluators highlight irregularities they detect, including those related to work participation and earnings. Additionally, they note the evaluee's phase of career development.

Assessment of an Evaluee's Relevant Preinjury Medical Problems

Although vocational evaluators focus on alleged damages relating to an issue in dispute, they must also consider an evaluee's medical history including any preexisting injuries. This information can become highly relevant when evaluating an evaluee's long-term work capacity in the absence of alleged acquired disabling problems and merits consideration before addressing the relationship between alleged postinjury medical problems and claimed vocational damages.

The progression/degeneration of preexisting injuries, independent of allegations of newly acquired disabling problems, sometimes presages career-related outcomes for an evaluee. These could include the imminent need to pursue less physically demanding employment or anticipation of an eventual truncated work life. Simply put, evaluators should impose proper context in their damages assessments by bifurcating preexisting injuries and claimed injuries.

For example, a mason with a history of chronic back pain alleged acquiring functional limitations from a motor vehicle accident and asserted the accident prohibited him from continuing to work in his physically demanding chosen profession. A vocational evaluator's review of preaccident medical records and consultations with orthopedic surgeons revealed the evaluee's preaccident back problems had a progressive, degenerative course. Further, medical support led the evaluator to conclude the evaluee's continued work as a mason likely would have eventually exacerbated his underlying injuries, leaving no recourse other than an occupational change. This contributed to the evaluator's conclusion that, regardless of any new injuries the evaluee might have acquired, his preaccident injuries were incompatible with his job's physical requirements, and his career as a mason would have been short lived—even if the motor vehicle accident had not occurred.

In some cases, evaluees understate or omit fully disclosing to an evaluator their histories of prior medical problems and/or treatment. The omissions may not be intentional and sometimes emerge as artifacts of an evaluee's disabling problems (e.g., cognitive dysfunction, medication side effects); conversely, evidence sometimes leads an evaluator to conclude an evaluee calculated the understatement or omissions of relevant medical history. Evaluators should note their observations in their assimilation of case information, along with instances when medical evidence supports or refutes what an evaluee conveyed. These contingencies underscore the necessity for evaluators to prepare well for their clinical interviews via preinterview records reviews along the lines described earlier in this chapter.

Assessment of an Evaluee's Relevant Postinjury Medical Problems

Evaluators clinically correlate evaluees' presenting problems with medical assessments. This level of analysis is central to answering questions of whether issues in dispute can reasonably be held responsible for claims of loss of earning capacity.

A review of an evaluee's postinjury medical problems, treatments, and assessments facilitates an evaluator's presentation when opining on the interface of an evaluee's residual capacities and capacity to perform past relevant work. If the evaluator concludes that resuming prior work—with or without accommodations—exceeds the evaluee's capacity, the analysis advances to address the examinee's vocational rehabilitation options. These could include the likes of applying transferable skills to alternate occupations, retraining, or becoming employed in a modified manner, such as working part time (please refer to items IV and V in the Summary and Impressions section of the sample report later; these components of the sequential process include evaluating facilitative and nonfacilitative factors to pursuing vocational rehabilitation and arriving at a loss of earning capacity opinion).

Ideally, when evaluators provide their final assessments of vocational damages, evaluees will have attained maximum medical improvement, the point in time during the postinjury recovery period when healthcare professionals rule out the likelihood of further substantive functional gains or improvements. If an evaluee has yet to attain this state, the evaluator should consider declaring that the pending assessment remains in a formative state, with final opinions on vocational damages deferred to near or at the time the evaluee reaches maximum medical improvement. An exception to this provision is when evaluees have sustained extremely severe or catastrophic injuries, rendering improvement to the point of becoming a vocational rehabilitation candidate highly improbable.

Providing premature final opinions can undermine an evaluator's credibility. Consider, for example, a final opinion on work capacity rendered during the acute phase after an evaluee's recovery from traumatic brain injury (TBI). In cases of mild and moderate TBI, some people continue to realize gains in their cognitive functioning up to two or three years after becoming injured. A premature opinion, rendered when an evaluee was functioning at a very low level and incapable of resuming preinjury employment before realizing significant cognitive functioning gains, can lead to erroneous work capacity prognostications.

Other considerations when evaluating how relevant postinjury medical problems affect an evaluee's vocational functioning include the aggravation of a preexisting disabling problem that might have previously had nominal effects on an evaluee's vocational functioning but has since become prominent, as well as unrelated postinjury medical problems. Regarding the latter, evaluators should always inquire about any medical problems evaluees might have experienced after issues in dispute occurred, such as motor vehicle accidents and other traumas, along with illness or disease. Obviously, permanent injury from these could have implications for an evaluee's damages claim.

Facilitative and Nonfacilitative Factors to Pursuing Vocational Rehabilitation

After providing an overview of an evaluee's vocational chronology and reviewing preinjury and postinjury medical problems, the summary and presentation of damages opinions continue with an assessment of an evaluee's facilitative and nonfacilitative factors to pursuing vocational rehabilitation. Reference to ECAF-2 Inhibitor and Driver factors particularly relevant to a pending evaluation can facilitate this presentation (please refer to Chapter 2).

Generally, evaluators address the following while inventorying factors that bear on an evaluee's prospects for vocational rehabilitation: cognitive capacities, preserved and impaired physical capacities, evaluee personal qualities, education, training, work-related credentials, work experience, and transferable skills. This assessment enables an evaluator to define residual capacities that may be parlayed into vocational activity, establishing a foundation to respond to the overarching referral question: Within a reasonable degree of vocational rehabilitation probability, have an evaluee's injuries caused a loss of earning capacity?

Opinion(s) on a Claim of Loss of Earning Capacity

Arriving at an opinion(s) about a claimed loss of earning capacity, the apex of the ECAT tetrahedron presented in Chapter 2, requires the analytical progression described previously, enabling an evaluator to perform a systematic assessment of damages in question. With a proper foundation, evaluators most often address the following questions in their determination of a claim's monetary value:

- Can the evaluee resume prior work with or without accommodations?
- If not, is the evaluee a candidate for retraining? Presuming a successful retraining outcome, will an evaluee be able to generate earnings commensurate with historical levels?
- Will injuries impair career development progress (e.g., ECAF-2 Inhibitor factors including Phase of Career Development, Prognosis, and Acquired Vocational Handicaps)?
- Did the evaluee have an opportunity to fulfill career development potential before becoming injured?
- Presuming an evaluee sustained a loss of earning capacity, what if any opportunities exist to mitigate the loss?

Presuming an evaluator concludes an evaluee sustained a loss of earning capacity, the final task necessary to complete the evaluation is to quantify the loss. This involves providing opinions of differentials between an evaluee's preinjury and postinjury earning capacity, derived from analyses idiosyncratic to the evaluation at hand.

For example, if an evaluator concludes an evaluee cannot resume prior employment but can retrain to mitigate career-related damages, the analysis will expand to identify appropriate training programs and anticipated wages on program completion and workplace reentry. Or, if an assessment results in a determination that an evaluee sustained significant cognitive and/or physical impairments that preclude returning to an occupation offering high-paying wages but retains the capacity to perform less cognitively complex, sedentary work offering lower pay, the evaluator will compute the difference between the evaluee's demonstrated preinjury earnings and anticipated postinjury earnings. In both cases, the assessments should also consider anticipated preinjury and postinjury career trajectories along with associated earning capacity differentials.

The Impairment to Earning Capacity Rating Scale from the ECAF (see Figure 2.5) provides another means to quantify preinjury and postinjury earnings differentials. Based on assessments of its nine Inhibitor and five Driver factors, vocational evaluators determine an evaluee's injury-related degree of impairment to earning capacity (none, mild, moderate, severe, extremely severe, or catastrophic) that they then apply to the scale. The sample report presented next provides an example of how an evaluator synthesized case information to arrive at an opinion on an evaluee's claim of loss of earning capacity.

Sample Report of a Vocational Rehabilitation Evaluation

A sample report of a vocational rehabilitation evaluation follows. Briefly, the evaluee, an attorney, presented cognitive dysfunction and physical injuries arising from a motor vehicle accident.

The evaluator identifies the report as "preliminary" for reasons that include the accident's relative recency (approximately seven months before the examination) and significant case-specific facts: primarily, the evaluee's tenuous, remote work situation during the COVID-19 pandemic, which she suggested had enabled her to conceal her accident-related impairments. The evaluee had yet to reach maximum medical improvement and the evaluator notes his opinions remain in a formative state.

While reviewing the sample report, consider how it incorporates the methodology this chapter described—namely, review of records, examination protocol (including clinical interview and standardized test administration), and presentation of opinions—while applying the methods and analytical processes Chapter 2 outlined. Additionally, note the evaluator's preliminary determination that the evaluee sustained a "moderate" loss of earning capacity; use of this term corresponds with the ECAF-2 nomenclature used to describe degrees of loss of earning capacity (i.e., a 20 to 50 percent loss). The evaluator's preliminary opinions integrated assessments of ECAF-2 Inhibitor and Driver factors particularly relevant in this case, including the evaluee's cognitive impairments, stability of career development, and phase of career development, contributing to the determination that the evaluee's career development trajectory was rising when she became injured and she had yet to realize her full earning capacity.

Sample Report

Overview

Kathy Round was referred to me for a vocational rehabilitation evaluation. A complaint documents allegations of injuries she sustained as a result of a motor vehicle accident on January 6, 2020. Ms. Round noted she was employed as a partner/lawyer with Gentry Spicer (GS) at the time of her accident.

On August 12, 2020, I conducted an examination of Ms. Round via Zoom videoconferencing; the COVID-19 pandemic led to my use of this medium. My exam included a clinical interview, which required 4 hours and 20 minutes, and the administration of a battery of tests that required an additional 2 hours and 45 minutes for her to complete. Mary Pallat from my office assisted with the testing portion of my exam. Ms. Round apprised me she was speaking to me from her home in Tampa, Florida.

Ms. Round reported she holds a valid driver's license and does not have doctor-advised driving restrictions. I inquired about problems with driving, and she replied, "Since the accident, I really struggle with driving at nighttime. I see a lot of halos. I have anxiety when driving [since January 6, 2020]." Ms. Round told me that, because of injury to her neck, she also has greater difficulty turning her head when driving, causing her to turn her whole body rather than just move her neck to either side when, for example, changing lanes.

Describing her employer as a Philadelphia-based firm with approximately 55 lawyers nationally, Ms. Round said, "My main specialty is nursing home defense." She indicated she has continued to work with GS in the same capacity, albeit with modifications because of her injuries and the pandemic.

As for her January 2020 accident, Ms. Round advised me she struck the back of her head on her seat's headrest. I inquired whether she lost consciousness, and she replied, "I didn't lose consciousness, but I don't remember everything." Dr. Mercer's July 14, 2020, report notes the following injuries Ms. Round sustained because of her January 2020 motor vehicle accident:

Cerebral concussion grade 2 with postconcussive syndrome

Posttraumatic cephalalgia

Chronic pain syndrome

Chronic insomnia secondary to chronic pain syndrome

Chronic intractable cervical, thoracic, and lumbosacral strain with palpable fibromyositis

Disc bulges at L4-5, L5-S1 level, central disc protrusion/herniation at C3-4 level, C4-5 level, C5-6 bulge, C6-7 disc protrusion/herniation, small disc protrusion/herniation at T3-4 through T7-8 level

Currently, Ms. Round conveyed, she experiences the following accident-related problems:

- Headaches, exacerbated by extended computer use and exposure to lights
- Concentration and memory difficulties
- Diminished frustration tolerance
- Ongoing neck pain radiating into shoulders, worse on left side, with restricted range of motion
- Ongoing mid-back and lower back pain radiating into lower extremities

Ms. Round denied experiencing any of the aforementioned problems before her January 2020 accident. On further inquiry, she denied previously injuring her head, neck, or back. Ms. Round informed me she led an active lifestyle preaccident, including vigorous exercise and participating in energetic Cub Scout activities with her children. I asked about any pre-accident cognitive or emotional difficulties, and she responded negatively. "I was at a point in my career where my work came very easily to me," she stated, referencing her professional experience.

Concerning mental functioning, Ms. Round cited problems with memory, concentration, and speech. She noted frequent occurrences of entering rooms and not remembering her intentions and also forgetting items she intended to purchase. "Last week, I completely forgot about [taking] a medication, which is something I've never done before," Ms. Round stated.

Ms. Round discussed her efforts to compensate for her memory deficits. These included sending herself reminder text and email messages and making notes to herself. She elaborated how background noise distracts her, contributing to attentional difficulties. "I think I have some auditory sensitivity now," Ms. Round added.

Regarding speech, Ms. Round described word retrieval difficulties and cited instances of being unable to recall medical and legal terms. "During one mediation, I forgot the name of one of my nursing homes," she said.

Vocational Activity

Ms. Round apprised me she completed high school in 1990 and earned an undergraduate degree in political science in 1994. She reported she completed law school in 1997. After law school, Ms. Round told me, she worked as an assistant state attorney/prosecutor for approximately three years and then pursued her career development with various law firms. She indicated her practice has specialized in nursing home defense. She advised me her current employer, Gentry Spicer (GS), recruited her in October 2003 and that she has continued her tenure with the firm through the time of her January 6, 2020, motor vehicle accident and to date.

On July 1, 2019, Ms. Round conveyed, GS promoted her to partner. At the time of her January 2020 accident, she informed me, she was working from 40 to 60 hours per week and earned an annual salary of approximately $155,000 plus a bonus. Ms. Round described her bonus pay as discretionary, "and any work I brought in, I would get a percentage back." She noted her promotion to partner status was accompanied by an expectation that her marketing efforts would generate revenues for her firm. "That's where you make your money, because you get a percentage of the work [billings] you bring in," Ms. Round explained.

Ms. Round described cognitively complex work she performed. "I was never in my office five days a week," she said, citing work she performed throughout Florida, much of which occurred in South Florida. She discussed her work in her firm's office, courthouses, and various other locations to participate in hearings, take unsworn statements, or take depositions, for example. Ms. Round estimated "more than half" of her time was spent out of her firm's office before her January 2020 accident.

The essential functions of Ms. Round's job, she advised me, required sedentary and light exertion tasks; however, she conveyed she often stood for more than one hour while in court, walked long distances from parking areas to courthouses, and often transported heavy luggage/boxes of documents while traveling. Ms. Round elaborated about the coordination associated with making lengthy documentation presentations. "That's a lot of standing and performing and reaching," she explained.

Ms. Round recalled a three-week absence after her January 6, 2020, accident. We reviewed documentation of her postaccident treatment. When she returned to work, she said, "I was not working full hours at all. I was exhausted at work. I was in pain. I was uncomfortable."

Elaborating about her cognitive difficulties when she returned to work, Ms. Round described how she reconfigured her work environment because of her photosensitivity. "I couldn't concentrate as long. I was in pain, and I was making errors. I had to proofread things much more. It took me longer to do things," she said. Ms. Round informed me her employer accommodated her with a special chair and workplace ergonomic modifications before she began working remotely in March 2020 due to the COVID-19 pandemic. Additionally, she noted she has been relying more on her paralegal and legal assistant since her January 2020 accident.

Because she fears losing her employment, Ms. Round apprised me, she has been close-mouthed about disclosing all of her accident-related problems. She reiterated how her work takes considerably more time to complete because of her cognitive difficulties. Ms. Round stated:

> They [management and coworkers at GS] know of my neck injury. They know of my concussion. They don't know about the shearing injury to my brain. They don't know about the mistakes I make and how much longer it takes me to complete my work. They know I need more help with the lifting and moving of documents. I don't want others to know about my cognitive stuff [problems] because that's what they pay me for—my brain.

Ms. Round went on to report the pandemic conditions—including courts being closed, no jury trials occurring, and her remote work status—enable her to conceal her cognitive difficulties from her employer. She expressed worry about changes to her current working conditions and the implications for her career development. Ms. Round reckoned her accident-related injuries and associated disabling problems require her to spend from 40 to 50 percent more time to complete her work. Further, she surmised her productivity would be more impaired if she were required to travel. "I'm working a lot more [hours] than they [my employer] know I'm working," Ms. Round said.

The preaccident career plans Ms. Round identified were to continue her work with GS. "My long-term goal, when my kids were in college, was to open up my own mediation practice," she told me.

Again, Ms. Round expressed concern about her ability to resume the full scope of her preaccident job responsibilities in the manner she performed them before January 2020. "It's going to be very difficult for me. I don't know how I'm going to do it," she stated. She conveyed how making coherent legal arguments in front of judges, among other things, will be more challenging. "I don't feel as sharp and as confident as I used to," Ms. Round added.

Records Reviewed

Records from the following sources were reviewed with this evaluation:

- Florida Traffic Crash Report
- Complaint
- BayCare Health System
- Florida Orthopaedic Institute
- Independent Diagnostic Radiology
- Premier Internal Medicine
- Mease Countryside Hospital
- St. Joseph's Hospital
- Sunshine Medicine Associates
- University Diagnostic Institute
- Westchase Orthopaedic and Rehabilitation
- Faisal Collins, MD
- Mark D. Hill, MD, PhD
- Chris N. Ian, MD
- Samia Michelle, MD
- Robert Mercer, MD
- Brett Milky, MD
- Michael V. Smith, MD
- Alexandra Zayre, MD

Assessment Measures

The following assessment measures were used in this evaluation:

- Clinical Interview
- Wahler Physical Symptoms Inventory
- Shipley Institute of Living
- Beck Depression Inventory-II
- Self-Directed Search Form R
- Minnesota Multiphasic Personality Inventory

Background Information

The following background information was obtained from records and my clinical interview:

FULL NAME:	Kathy Round
DATE OF BIRTH:	July 14, 1976
ONSET OF DISABLING PROBLEMS:	January 6, 2020, motor vehicle accident
RACE:	Black
DOMINANT HAND:	Right
HEIGHT:	5 feet 8 inches
CURRENT WEIGHT:	165 pounds
PREACCIDENT WEIGHT:	Approx. 170 pounds
MARITAL STATUS:	Married, Christopher Rich, age 48

CHILDREN:	Daughter, born in 2005
	Son, born in 2008
RESIDENCE:	Tampa, Florida
PRESENTING PROBLEMS:	• Headaches, exacerbated by extended computer use and exposure to lights
	• Concentration and memory difficulties
	• Diminished frustration tolerance
	• Ongoing neck pain radiating into shoulders, worse on left side, with restricted range of motion
	• Ongoing mid-back and lower back pain radiating into lower extremities
PROCEDURES SINCE ACCIDENT:	Two epidural steroid injections to cervical spine, administered by Dr. Collins
TREATMENT SINCE ACCIDENT:	• Pain management with injections, most recently in March 2020
	• Physical therapy
PRESENT TREATMENT:	None due to COVID-19 pandemic
TREATING DOCTORS:	Dr. Collins, pain management
	Dr. Slough, orthopedic surgeon
MEDICATIONS:	• Ibuprofen, daily
	• Turmeric, daily
	• Advil, daily
	• Hemp oil, daily
	"Prescribed meds with side effects that I do not like and take as needed":
	• Tramadol
	• Tizanidine hydrochloride
	• Meloxicam
	• Methocarbamol/Robaxin
	• Ondansetron/Zofran, nausea
	• Naproxen
	• Percocet, "did not like how I felt"
EDUCATION:	High school diploma, Massachusetts, 1990
	Bachelor's degree, political science, minors in philosophy and psychology, Calvin University, 1994
	Juris doctorate degree, Southwest State University School of Law, 1997
	Admitted to the Florida bar, 1997
EMPLOYER AT TIME OF ACCIDENT:	Gentry Spicer, PC
JOB TITLE AT TIME OF ACCIDENT:	Partner/Lawyer
RATE OF PAY AT TIME OF ACCIDENT:	Approx. $155,000 per year plus bonus
PRESENT WORK STATUS:	Partner/Lawyer, Gentry Spicer, approx. $155,000 per year plus bonus

Clinical Interview

Introduction

Kathy Round presented as a Black female who had shoulder-length brown hair and brown eyes. She appeared her stated age of 44. I inquired about corrective lenses, and Ms. Round said, "I have reading glasses, and that's it." She informed me her corrected vision is clear. She repositioned frequently while seated and appeared to become more uncomfortable as my clinical interview progressed.

Although Ms. Round assessed her gait is normal, she noted she experiences pain and numbness in both shoulders, especially her left one, which can affect her gait when carrying a purse or a work briefcase over her shoulders. "I don't wear heels anymore," she added, apprising me she has modified her footwear to avoid exacerbating her symptoms. Ms. Round did not use adaptive aids during my exam.

Ms. Round reported she is right-hand dominant, 5 feet 8 inches tall, and weighs 165 pounds. She told me she and Christopher Rich married in 2003 and that this has been her only marriage. She reported Mr. Rich is a self-employed financial advisor and is 48 years old. When asked about children, she indicated she has two.

As for her home, Ms. Round informed me she lives with her spouse and two children in a two-story, approximately 4,000-square-foot house with a detached two-story garage/guesthouse she owns in a residential area, in which she has lived six years. Although she denied having near-term plans to relocate, she said, "We have looked at a few homes."

Ms. Round noted she has not modified her home for disabilities. "We've talked about moving to a one-story home," she said, apprising me that ascending/descending stairs exacerbates her lower back symptoms. She went on to reference her daughter's diabetes insipidus, reporting she frequently becomes dehydrated. "She needs me a lot. I bring her water a lot. She has trouble at nighttime and trouble during the day. Her bedroom's on the second story, and mine is on the first story," Ms. Round said. Concerning pets, she has two guinea pigs.

Physical Condition and Medical Information

Ms. Round denied having any medical problems or restrictions near the time before her January 6, 2020, motor vehicle accident. "I was very active," she said, citing a lifestyle inclusive of hosting large dinner parties, working full time, performing volunteer work, and participating in extracurricular activities with her children.

When asked about preaccident operations and procedures, Ms. Round reported an appendectomy in 1989, cesarean section deliveries in 2005 and 2008, and a hysterectomy in October 2017 or 2018. "I had a nodule in my thyroid," she said, indicating she takes Armor for hypothyroidism. "I didn't start the medication until after the accident," Ms. Round added, although she does not relate her thyroid problems to her January 2020 accident. We reviewed Dr. Zelenka's March 26, 2018, office note.

I inquired about the reason for a brain MRI in August 2014, and Ms. Round responded, "It turned out to be caffeine-related headaches from drinking too much caffeine. Once I quit the espresso, it went away."

Ms. Round denied having preaccident fracture injuries, apart from "a big toe fracture. I stubbed my toe." She told me about a "minor car accident" she was in from 25 to 30 years ago, although she denied acquiring any injury from it. Ms. Round did not recall any other significant preaccident medical problems.

Regarding unrelated postaccident problems, Ms. Round advised me an MRI showed "an incidental finding in my heart. They followed up, and it turned out to be nothing."

As for her understanding of diagnoses physicians have rendered, Ms. Round expressed abnormalities have been detected in her cervical, thoracic, and lumbar spines. "I think I have seven herniated discs, several bulging discs," she said. Concerning her cognitive difficulties, Ms. Round stated, "I have postconcussive syndrome." She conveyed her understanding that a brain MRI detected a shearing injury.

When asked about the primary problem she attributes to her accident, Ms. Round said: "It's the cognitive, struggling with work, and then the neck pain. It's the combination of the neck and the head." Because of her concentration difficulties, she recounted, work tasks take her longer to accomplish, and she gave an example of proofreading documents.

Additionally, Ms. Round informed me she experiences dizziness and headaches due to extended computer use. She went on to cite trouble with memory that elongates the time necessary for her to recall and organize facts as required, for example, when preparing for and participating in mediations.

Further, Ms. Round referenced scrolling on computer monitors and viewing a television. "Moving screens bother me, and I'm very sensitive to light," she said. Ms. Round expressed her preference to be in dimly lit areas. "Sometimes my family will tell me I've become very forgetful," she added.

Describing how her ability to multitask has become impaired since January 6, 2020, Ms. Round also noted she has difficulty with information processing, especially new information that requires analysis and synthesis. She apprised me about difficulties in a recent project involving a motion to dismiss for lack of jurisdiction that required her to request an extended deadline. "I was struggling to put together something I could easily put together [preaccident]," Ms. Round stated.

Ms. Round reported her neck is her most symptomatic body part. She told me maintaining her neck in a position exacerbates her pain. To manage her symptoms as best as possible, she indicated, she repositions frequently. Ms. Round advised me she traveled by air in February 2020—a requirement of her job—and that this greatly exacerbated her neck symptoms. She expressed concern about her ability to travel by air or make long car trips as required in her job. Because of the pandemic, Ms. Round conveyed, she has not traveled by air since February 2020, although she added, "At some time, I'm going to have to start doing that again."

Discussing her mid-back and lower back pain distribution, Ms. Round described ongoing pain with bilateral radicular symptoms. "Shooting pain, some numbness," she said about the sensations she feels. Activities and conditions that exacerbate her mid-back and lower back symptoms, Ms. Round informed me, include bending her waist, maintaining a position, reaching overhead, and exertion.

Generally, Ms. Round noted, her symptoms worsen when she increases her activity. She described her participation in play activities with her children that worsen her symptoms; accordingly, she apprised me, she has restricted her participation in these types of activities. Ms. Round went on to lament she and her husband canceled a March 2020 ski vacation because of her injuries.

Regarding headaches, I inquired about triggers. Ms. Round recounted her problems with photosensitivity and movement of objects on computer and television screens. "I got a hard time reading. I used to be somewhat of a speed reader. Now I have to take more breaks," she said. I inquired about distractibility due to background noise, and Ms. Round responded negatively.

Ms. Round reported she experiences headaches "just about every day. Weekdays are worse than weekends," and she told me how computer use and driving contribute to the onset of her headaches. She indicated her typical headaches last up to a full day and that she prefers to seek a dark place when headaches begin.

Using a 0-to-10 scale, with 0 indicating no pain and 10 representing the worst pain possible, she rated her pain intensities as follows:

- Headaches—0 to 8
- Neck—3 to 10
- Mid-back—2 to 5
- Lower back—3 to 6

Ms. Round advised me her current treating doctors are Dr. Collins (pain management) and Dr. Slough (orthopedic surgeon). She conveyed she most recently saw both doctors in May or June 2020. Ms. Round informed me she is no longer treating with Dr. Milky (orthopedic surgeon).

As for postaccident operations and procedures, Ms. Round apprised me Dr. Collins administered two epidural steroid injections under anesthesia to her cervical spine. I asked about future surgery, and she reported Dr. Slough's physician assistant discussed a two- or three-level anterior cervical discectomy with fusion. Concerning other operations, Ms. Round said, "They're focusing on the neck because that's where the most pain is. Dr. Collins said, 'Let's focus on the neck and then move down.'"

When asked about treatment and therapy since her January 2020 accident, Ms. Round indicated she has had physical therapy and pain management with injections. She advised me her most recent injection was in March 2020. No current treatment or therapy was identified, and she again conveyed the pandemic has caused her to restrict her participation in treatment.

Dr. Mercer's July 14, 2020, note states:

> She has now reached maximum medical improvement, and she has suffered a permanent injury from the accident January 6, 2020, with an overall 23 percent permanent impairment rating to the body as a whole. She is permanently restricted from lifting greater than 20 pounds from a bent position, 10 pounds repetitively.

> She . . . periodically will require therapy and in the future will require surgery.

Ms. Round informed me she uses the following adaptive aids: heating pads, hard cervical collar, soft cervical collar, and a reacher. She noted her doctors have recommended purchasing a TENS unit. Additionally, Ms. Round apprised me she has purchased various pillows and a lap desk.

Regarding medications, Ms. Round sent my office a list, which indicates she takes the following daily: ibuprofen, turmeric, Advil, and hemp oil. Additionally, she noted the following "prescribed meds with side effects that I do not like and take as needed": tramadol, tizanidine hydrochloride, meloxicam, methocarbamol/Robaxin, ondansetron/Zofran for nausea, naproxen, and Percocet, about which she reported, "Did not like how I felt." She denied taking any of the preceding medications before her January 2020 accident. "I was on an estrogen patch for the hysterectomy," she said.

As for medication side effects, Ms. Round reported her pain medications interfere with her concentration and make her feel dizzy. She discussed her aversion to taking pain medications. During the 24 hours before my exam, Ms. Round advised me, she had taken only her thyroid and cholesterol medications.

Concerning physical capacities, Ms. Round conveyed her job typically requires her to walk with large volumes of documents "and carry them to court, depositions, and mediations." She described how she sometimes works with multiple banker boxes of documents and how handling them exacerbates her symptoms. Ms. Round went on to convey difficulties she experiences handling heavy suitcases and briefcases of records when traveling. She assessed she can safely handle less than 20 pounds. She cited problems with essentially all cervical spine movements. Ms. Round informed me she has full range of motion in all extremities.

During my clinical interview, Ms. Round demonstrated she could touch each finger to her thumb on either hand, make a fist with either hand, and extend her arms horizontally and overhead. She complained that overhead arm extensions exacerbate her neck and shoulder pain. She also described how twisting movements exacerbate her neck and back symptoms, so she has modified the type of bra she wears. Ms. Round went on to note bending over to tie shoelaces is problematic.

When asked about physical, everyday activities, Ms. Round apprised me she feels lower back pain when transitioning from sitting to standing. "I try to go on short walks to get my body moving. I feel it, but I have to do it," she said. Ms. Round reported bending her waist and movements below her waist—such as squatting, kneeling, and climbing stairs—exacerbate her neck and lower back pain.

Ms. Round told me she is able to stand ten minutes and walk from 20 to 30 minutes before overexerting herself or needing to rest. She estimated she can sit comfortably up to one hour, with movement, depending on the seating surface.

Approximately four days per week, Ms. Round indicated, she operates a motor vehicle. She advised me her commute to her place of employment is up to one hour. She conveyed she obtained a parking placard for persons who have disabilities "shortly after the accident."

Ms. Round identified the following additional physical problems:

- Balance—"When I get numbness [in my legs]."
- Hearing—"I'm sensitive to noise, which I was not before the accident. I do get an occasional ringing sound [in my ears]."
- Fatigue—She complained about difficulty sleeping that contributes to fatigue.

Ms. Round denied injuring any teeth in her January 2020 accident. No postaccident falls were identified.

Regarding the status of her physical condition, Ms. Round stated, "I feel like I'm the same. I feel like, if I don't do the surgery, my neck is not going to get any better." She said about her cognitive status, "At this point, I think it's stable." The sole physician-advised restriction Ms. Round identified was her 20-pound lifting limit.

Activities of Daily Living

We reviewed Dr. Zayre's August 2018 office note documenting insomnia, and Ms. Round assessed it might have related to her high caffeine intake at the time. She did not recall having difficulty sleeping near the time before her January 6, 2020, motor vehicle accident.

Currently, Ms. Round conveyed, she has nightly difficulty sleeping due to interrupted sleep caused by pain three or four times per night. Once awake, she informed me, she has problems falling asleep again. "Sometimes I'll move to a couch. Sometimes I'll move to a different bed," Ms. Round said.

Usually, Ms. Round noted, she goes to sleep at 10:00 p.m., and she recounted her problems with interrupted sleep. She apprised me she typically awakens between 7:00 and 7:30 a.m. She denied napping or taking sleep aid medication.

Ms. Round described prior postaccident problems with nightmares with a recurrent theme of riding over a bridge. "Now, I wake up abruptly," she said, citing themes of being unable to respond promptly to her children's needs.

Although Ms. Round reported she is independent in grooming and self-care, she told me her daughter has been clipping and painting her toenails, "because that's more difficult for me." She went on to cite problems with bending her waist and twisting, indicating this makes shaving her legs more challenging. Ms. Round also advised me she has trouble styling and blow-drying her hair, and she referenced pain associated with overhead movements. She conveyed she had her hair cut shorter postaccident "to make it easier to maintain."

I inquired about her ability to perform housekeeping chores, and Ms. Round responded, "That's a big source of anxiety for me, stress for me." She informed me her home is less tidy now than it was before she became injured. "Beds aren't being made. Surfaces aren't being cleaned. Floors have dust on them," Ms. Round explained. She went on to state, "The laundry's been piling up. I've been having a hard time keeping up with the laundry."

Ms. Round elaborated about problems accessing her microwave oven and cleaning areas below her waist. "My husband's been doing more of the cooking [since my January 2020 accident]," she said. Ms. Round noted difficulty handling heavy pots and accessing cupboards overhead and below her waist. She indicated she can prepare light meals.

When asked whether she employs a housekeeper, Ms. Round responded negatively and referenced the COVID-19 pandemic. "We don't want to have anyone in the house [during the pandemic]," she said, recounting her daughter's health vulnerabilities. She apprised me her family members have assumed responsibility for many chores she previously performed. Additionally, Ms. Round reported many chores either go undone or are not performed to her satisfaction. "That gets me very stressed out," she said, citing adaptations including using disposable cutlery.

Ms. Round told me she continues to employ a yard maintenance service, as she did before her January 2020 accident. Occasionally, she indicated, she participated in planting and weeding around her yard, although she said, "I can't do that anymore."

As for hobbies and leisure pursuits before her January 2020 accident, Ms. Round advised me she served as a den leader in her son's Cub Scout pack. She conveyed she had been quite active in camping and community service projects. "I was also a homeroom mom for my kids' classes, and I had a leadership position with the business sponsors," Ms. Round said. Additionally, she informed me she taught Sunday school. Because of her cognitive difficulties and the elongated time required for her to complete work tasks, she noted, "I just can't do the volunteering work like I used to."

Other preaccident avocational pursuits Ms. Round identified included paddle boarding, kayaking, boating, and participating in community fundraising activities such as half marathons and walkathons. She also apprised me she enjoyed swimming and participating in sports with her children. "Our vacations were very active vacations. We would go to Colorado, hike up to seven miles a day," Ms. Round said. She reported she also went zip lining, snow tubing, and skiing. She told me she participated in a triathlon as recently as four or five years ago.

Concerning her average day, Ms. Round recounted she has been working remotely from her home since March 2020. "I've been given the leeway to work remotely. The Florida office was never really closed down. We're considered essential workers. I've just tried to avoid the subject [of returning to work at my office]," she stated.

Ms. Round went on to discuss how working remotely provides an opportunity to conceal her accident-related problems from her employer. "I suspect it's going to be more difficult with my kids going back to school, the driving to and from [school]. I think when school starts is the unspoken anticipation of when I'll have to go back [to work in my office]," she said. Ms. Round elaborated about concerns of performing the full scope of her job responsibilities including traveling as needed and participating in courthouse events.

I inquired about her daily work schedule, and Ms. Round replied, "All day, on and off. Up until 10:00 p.m., I'll have spurts of working and not working. I work more hours [now than I did before January 6, 2020], but short-spaced." Further, because of her requirement of more time to complete work tasks due to her cognitive difficulties, she said, "I work on weekends, too."

Other activities of daily living Ms. Round identified included playing board games with her children. She indicated she participates in light housework as her condition permits. Approximately every two weeks, she advised me, she goes to the beach with her family.

Mental Health

Ms. Round denied participating in mental health treatment, experiencing head trauma, or losing consciousness before her January 6, 2020, motor vehicle accident. I inquired about prescriptions of psychotropic medications, either before or after her accident, and she conveyed she was prescribed Xanax for anxiety after her daughter was diagnosed with migraines. Ms. Round informed me she took the medication for only one week, approximately. No other prescriptions of psychotropic medications were identified. She denied having a family history of mental illness.

Since her January 2020 accident, Ms. Round noted, she has not treated with any mental health professional or undergone a neuropsychological evaluation. I asked whether she believes she currently needs mental health treatment, and she responded equivocally. Ms. Round cited problems with stress and anxiety, and she added, "I can get a little short tempered."

When asked about her overall psychological status, Ms. Round stated, "I think I'm very stressed out, and I'm very worried about that [cervical spine] surgery. My daughter needs me, and my son needs me, too." She also discussed concerns about her presenting problems adversely affecting her career development. "I'm afraid at some point it's going to catch up with me, and I'm going to get terminated, or something that's never happened before—I'll get [a] poor performance [rating]," Ms. Round said.

The primary mental health concerns Ms. Round identified related to anxiety and stress management and her physical health. She attributed her anxiety/stress to frustration and unwelcome lifestyle changes, and she discussed how her frustration tolerance has diminished since January 2020. Ms. Round apprised me her husband has brought to her attention multiple instances when she became impatient.

I inquired about feeling depressed, and Ms. Round replied, "I miss my old life. I get sad. It's heartbreaking when my kids ask me to do something with them, and I can't." She referenced her accident-related injuries and assorted disabling problems.

When asked about her marital relationship, Ms. Round responded, "I get very frustrated with my husband for not doing more." Ms. Round specifically denied having problems with finances or thoughts of suicide.

Ms. Round was pleasant, likable, and interpersonally skilled. Her affect ranged from generally normal to occasionally anxious/depressed. Her memory was good/fair, and her concentration was good. Ms. Round spoke clearly and coherently, although her speech was somewhat pressured. She did not display problems with either expressive or receptive language, and she did not evidence a thought disorder.

Education and Special Training

Ms. Round described her scholastic performance as strong throughout her education. She did not recall her scores from prior standardized testing. Ms. Round reported she graduated from high school in 1990. She relayed she participated in her college's volleyball team.

In 1994, Ms. Round told me, she earned a bachelor's degree in political science, with minors in philosophy and psychology, at Calvin University. She indicated she earned a juris doctor degree at Southwest State University School of Law in 1997, the same year she was admitted to the Florida bar. No other formal education or training was identified.

Ms. Round advised me she began her law career as a prosecutor. She cited on-the-job training in nursing home defense litigation. No second language skills were presented.

Regarding computer use skills, Ms. Round said, "I'm good with the computer," although she recounted her difficulty with computer use because of her presenting problems related to her January 6, 2020, motor vehicle accident. "It's easier for me to read documents on paper now rather than on a computer," Ms. Round stated.

Through training and work experience, Ms. Round conveyed, she developed the following skills:

- Conducting legal research and writing briefs
- Taking depositions
- Questioning experts in damages hearings
- Defending employment law cases including race, ethics, background, disability, and retaliation cases
- Human resources knowledge
- Advising employees on human resources actions—for example, union cases, discharge decisions, and reasonable accommodations
- Practice development

Ms. Round denied considering retraining.

Career Development

The following work history was obtained from records and my clinical interview:

Job Title	Name of Organization	Dates
Partner/Lawyer	Gentry Spicer, PC	10/2003–present
Associate Attorney	Carter Smith	2002–2003
Associate Attorney	Franklin and Company	6 to 8 months
Assistant State Attorney/ Prosecutor	State of Florida	1997–2000

I inquired about her job satisfaction as a partner/lawyer with Gentry Spicer, and Ms. Round replied, "My job was my second home. It's my family. I couldn't have a more perfect job." Currently, she assessed, her job is secure; however, she added, "When life goes back to normal [after the COVID-19 pandemic], then I'm very concerned." Ms. Round informed me she has not searched for another job since her January 6, 2020, motor vehicle accident. The only source of income she identified at present was her employment.

Review of Medical Records

Results of Diagnostic Testing

01/16/20 *Jerry Church,* MD

Lumbar Spine Limited

Impression:

> Pars defect at the L5 level. Most of the time this is congenital. However, it could also be secondary to trauma. Correlation with patient's symptomatology is advised.

Rich P. Richards, MD

CT C-Spine without Contrast

Impression:

> No acute osseous abnormality.

Greg Singh, MD

CT Head Brain without Contrast

Impression:

> No acute intracranial abnormality.

01/25/20 **Dean G. Stallworth, MD**

MR Lumbar Spine without Contrast

Impression:

> 1. There are disc bulges with facet hypertrophic changes at L4-5 and L5-S1 causing impingement of the thecal sac. The foramina are narrowed bilaterally.
> 2. No focal protrusion or acute osseous abnormality is noted. Multiple vertebral body hemangiomas are noted.

02/11/20 **Dean G. Stallworth, MD**

MR Brain without Contrast

Impression:

> Unremarkable MRI brain without contrast.

MR Cervical Spine without Contrast

Impression:

> 1. MRI of the cervical spine demonstrates multilevel noncalcified central disc protrusions at C3-4 and C4-5 causing mild to moderate canal stenosis.

2. At C5-6, there is a diffuse disc bulge with bilateral facet hypertrophy causing canal and bilateral foraminal stenosis.

3. At C6-7, there is a left paracentral protrusion causing mild canal stenosis and left lateral recess narrowing with impingement of the left C7 nerve root.

4. No acute osseous abnormality is appreciated.

02/12/20 Gregory M. Carlson, MD

MR Thoracic Spine without Contrast

Impression:

1. Multilevel small disc protrusion from T3-4 through T7-8 results in canal narrowing or stenosis without definite impingement.

2. Osseous degenerative change and scoliosis without acute osseous abnormality.

3. Prominent fat overlying the anterolateral right side of the heart likely represents a lipoma. Correlation with any prior chest imaging or follow-up chest CT should be considered. Subcentimeter fluid signal structure in the left lobe of the thyroid is most consistent with a cyst, which could be confirmed with ultrasound.

02/21/20 Greg Singh, MD

CT Chest with Contrast

Impression:

Diffuse mild prominence of the pericardial fat. No discrete focal lesion is identified on the examination. Recommend correlation with images from prior MRI examination.

No acute cardiothoracic abnormality.

Robert Christopher, MD

US Thyroid Parathyroid Head Neck

Impression:

Simple cyst left lobe of thyroid is stable from 3/29/2018 exam—2 sub cm hypoechoic nodules, 1 within each lobe, have developed since prior study.

07/26/20 Mark D. Hill, MD, PhD

CT Brain without Contrast

Impression:

Mild bilateral frontal lobe volume loss (atrophy), unchanged from 1/16/20.

CTMRPT Brain Correlation

Impression:

1. Frontal lobes—correlating findings: Bilateral atrophy, bilateral frontal lobe bright T2 and FLAIR spots near the gray-white junction, bilateral prominent perivascular spaces, bilateral decreased tracts from the internal capsules and brain stem, increased glucose uptake on the right, decreased fractional anisotropy.

2. Right parietotemporal lobe—increased glucose uptake.

3. Right temporal lobe and posterior left cingulate gyrus—decreased glucose uptake.

MRI Brain without Contrast

Impression:

1. Frontal lobes—mild bilateral atrophy, unchanged from the 1/16/20 CT and the 2/11/20 MR.

2. Bilateral frontal lobes—Bright T2 and FLAIR spots near the gray-white junction, consistent with traumatic axonal injury, also seen on the prior study of 2/11/20.

3. C-FAST score = 4 (normal = 0; range = 0–6).

4. Internal capsules—decreased tracts in the mid and anterior tracts on the left and the posterior tracts on the right from the internal capsules and the brain stem, correlating with the regions of decreased FA in the internal capsules (IC) above.

5. Occipital lobes—mild bilateral periventricular ischemic changes, unchanged from 2/11/20.

6. Bilateral frontal lobes—prominent perivascular spaces.

PET Brain

Impression:

1. Clusters of abnormally decreased glucose uptake in the right temporal lobe and the left posterior cingulate cortex, consistent with areas of the brain that are damaged and unable to perform their functions normally.

   right inf lat ant Temporal Cortex = –1.7091 SD
   left pos Cingulate Cortex = –1.8985 SD

2. Clusters of abnormally increased glucose uptake in the right parietotemporal lobe and right frontal lobe, consistent with areas of the brain that are working harder than normal because they are damaged themselves, or because they are not damaged but are compensating for other areas that are damaged and cannot perform their functions normally.

   right Parietotemporal Cortex = 1.9567 SD
   right mid Frontal Cortex = 1.8343 SD

Assessments

01/14/20   *Pinellas County Emergency Medical Services*

Narrative:

> SunStar 490 dispatched emergent with FD reference multiple vehicle MVC. UAF 44 y/o F with chief complaint of anxiety and dizziness. Pt was driver of 4-door SUV. Pt was traveling northbound in second from the right through lane at approximately 60 mph. Pt was rear-ended by an SUV merging from the right through lane. Both vehicles sustained minor damage and pulled to the right side of the road. No airbag deployment was noted in pt's car. Pt reports that she was restrained with lap and shoulder belt. Pt denies LOC but says she hit the back of her head on the head rest. Pt reports some soreness to the back of her head and neck, beginning since the accident. Pt denies headache, weakness, visual changes, fatigue, numbness, tingling, paresthesia, N/V/D, or SOB. GCS 15.

Michael V. Smith, MD/St. Joseph's Hospital

History of Present Illness:

> The patient presents following motor vehicle collision. The onset was 3 hours ago. 44-year-old female states that she was driving between 70 and 80 miles an hour on the road when she was rear-ended by another car. She states that she was pushed back against her seat but did not lose consciousness. She states that, at that point in time, she believes she had a panic attack and hyperventilated resulting in her feeling dizzy.

Diagnoses:

> Evaluation after motor vehicle collision.
>
> Acute cervical strain.
>
> Cephalgia.

Disposition:

> To home.

01/16/20   *Chris M. Ian, MD/Mease Countryside Hospital*

Chief Complaint:

> Pt states involved in an MVA x 2 days ago. Pt c/o head pain, back pain, neck pain, nausea, dizziness, lightheadedness. Pt states seen at St. Joseph's ED. Dx whiplash.

History of Present Illness:

> Feels dizzy, back is hurting worse (low back and neck and shoulders), now photophobia, nausea started Tuesday. Vomiting since yesterday, more today.

Past Medical History:

Endocrine, other, cyst on thyroid.

Genitourinary, other, fibroids.

Anxiety, situational.

Diagnoses:

Postconcussive syndrome.

L5 pars defects.

Disposition:

Discharged to home.

Plan:

Ultram 50 mg.

Zofran 4 mg.

Motrin 600 mg.

Robaxin 500 mg.

01/21/20 *Samia Michelle, MD*

History of Present Illness:

She went to St. Joseph's North. She was told she had concussion. She went to Mease Countryside Hospital, vomiting, headache. She has CT scan of head and cervical spine, an X-ray of lumbar spine.

Social History:

Living with: Yes, husband.

Power of attorney: Yes, husband.

Comments:

Height: 5.00 feet 8 inches. Weight: 170.0 pounds.

Impression:

Headache.

Postconcussive syndrome.

Plan:

Ordered MRI brain cervical and lumbar spine.

Light physical exercise.

01/24/20 **Brett Milky, MD**

Impression:

1. Cervicalgia induced by the motor vehicle collision.

2. Cervical sprain strain induced by the motor vehicle collision.

3. Preexisting disc degeneration of the cervical spine aggravated by the motor vehicle collision.

4. Preexisting disc degeneration of the thoracic spine aggravated by the motor vehicle collision.

5. Lumbago induced by the motor vehicle collision.

6. Lumbar sprain strain due to some other motor vehicle collision.

7. Pars defect L5-S1 preexisting aggravated by the motor vehicle collision.

8. Preexisting disc degeneration of the lumbar spine.

Plan:

1. Voltaren 75 mg tablet twice a day.

2. Patient will follow up after the MRI.

3. Physical therapy will begin. We will do this 2–3 times a week for the next 6 weeks.

01/30/20 **Lauren Miller, PT/Westchase Orthopaedics & Rehabilitation**

Plan:

2 x week for 4 weeks.

02/17/20 **Alexandra Zelenka, MD**

Past Medical History:

C-Sect—2005, 2008.

Appendectomy—1989.

Fractured right foot—2010.

Daughter—diabetes insipidus, ddavp, hearing loss.

Attorney.

Married with 2 children.

02/24/20 **Faisal Collins, MD**

Comments:

Wt: 175 lbs.

Plan:

Multimodal pain management was discussed.

Will schedule for C7-T1 interlaminar ESI.

Impression:

1. Low back pain.

2. Lumbar radiculopathy.

3. Radiculopathy due to lumbar intravertebral disc disorder.

4. Cervical radiculopathy.

03/11/20 *Faisal Collins, MD*

Plan:

Schedule for right paramedian C6-C7 interlaminar ESI.

The patient may benefit from future PT—acute pain limiting at this time.

07/14/20 *Robert Mercer, MD*

Neurological Impression:

1. Cerebral concussion grade 2 with postconcussive syndrome.

2. Posttraumatic cephalalgia.

3. Chronic pain syndrome.

4. Chronic insomnia secondary to chronic pain syndrome.

5. Chronic intractable cervical, thoracic, and lumbosacral strain with palpable fibromyositis.

6. Disc bulges at L4-5, L5-S1 level, central disc protrusion/herniation at C3-4 level, C4-5 level, C5-6 bulge, C6-7 disc protrusion/herniation, small disc protrusion/herniation at T3-4 through T7-8 level.

Recommendations:

1. In my opinion, she has now reached maximum medical improvement.

2. Do not believe any further neurodiagnostic testing is indicated.

3. In my opinion, she suffered a permanent injury from the accident January 6, 2020. She will have symptoms indefinitely. She has to learn to live with her symptoms, adjust her lifestyle accordingly, periodically will require palliative therapy, and in the future may require surgery.

4. She is permanently restricted from lifting greater than 20 pounds from a bent position, 10 pounds repetitively.

5. My opinion that this is a permanent injury is based on her prolonged clinical complaints, positive findings of muscle spasm, restricted range of motion, and review of medical records and MRI scans.

6. If she develops underlying or worsening of underlying arthritis, the patient's symptoms may deteriorate.

7. In my opinion, this represents at least an overall 23 percent permanent impairment rating to the body as a whole.

8. Williams' exercises for neck and back three times daily and after hot showers.

9. Avoid high impact such as jogging, jumping, bouncing, basketball, volleyball, racquetball, horseback riding, soccer, golf, or tennis.

10. May do walking, aqua therapy, core, plank, yoga, Pilates stretching exercises, elliptical, StairMaster, and tai chi.

11. Periodic use of muscle relaxers and anti-inflammatory drugs.

12. Continued medical care costs will be approximately $4,000 to $5,000 per year to include doctor visits (approx $150 per visit), medications (approx $200 per month), physical therapy (approx $125 per visit), TENS unit (approx $684 device), epidural blocks (approx $15,000 per injection), and home therapy (approx $150 for equipment). If there is a need for laminectomy, discectomy, or fusion, the total inclusive cost ranges from $80,000 to $110,000. The approximate cost for an updated MRI every three years ranges from $2,000 to $2,500. Physical therapy costs would be between $125 and $250 per session, which is expected to take two to three sessions per week for a term of three to six weeks depending upon the severity of the exacerbation. The approximate cost of epidural steroid injections is $1,500. The approximate cost of radio frequency ablations is $20,000 to $25,000.

13. In my opinion, she has now reached maximum medical improvement, and she has suffered a permanent injury from the accident January 6, 2020, with an overall 23 percent permanent impairment rating to the body as a whole. She is permanently restricted from lifting greater than 20 pounds from a bent position, 10 pounds repetitively. She will have symptoms indefinitely, has to learn to live with her symptoms, adjust her lifestyle accordingly, and periodically will require therapy and in the future will require surgery.

14. In my opinion, she does meet the criteria for serious emergency medical condition per Florida Statute 627.732 with serious jeopardy to her health, serious impairment of bodily function, and serious dysfunction of a bodily organ if not taken care of.

07/26/20 Mark D. Hill, MD, PhD

Conclusions:

In summary, the radiographic findings of scarring in the brain, abnormal sugar uptake, and abnormal water movement in the axons of the brain are consistent with traumatic brain injury.

Results of Preinjury Diagnostic Testing

09/25/13 Gary Michael Smith, MD

US Thyroid Parathyroid Head Neck

Impression:

Complicated cystic nodule lower pole of left thyroid lobe. Six-month follow-up ultrasound recommended for reassessment.

No significant thyroid enlargement.

07/22/14 Gary Michael Smith, MD

US Thyroid Parathyroid Head Neck

Impression:

Stable appearance complex cystic nodule lower pole left thyroid lobe. Continued serial ultrasound follow-up recommended in 6–12 months' time.

08/11/14 Anil Gordhanbhai Patel, MD

MRI Head Brain without Contrast

Impression:

Unremarkable noncontrast brain MRI.

07/12/17 Rhonda Kay McDowell, MD

US Transvaginal

Impression:

1. Uterine fibroids noted in the right fundal region.

2. The right ovary is not visualized.

3. There is thickening of the endometrial stripe. The endometrial stripe measures 1.6 cm, which is too thick even for a premenopausal patient. Additional evaluation may be helpful.

US Thyroid Parathyroid Head Neck

Impression:

> The single complex cyst at the lower pole of the left thyroid gland is stable to slightly smaller in size than previous exam.

03/29/18   *Ryan Telford, MD*

US Thyroid Parathyroid Head Neck

Impression:

> Simple-appearing cyst in the left lobe today measures up to 7 mm, previously measuring up to 12 mm on the original ultrasound of 9/25/2013. Overall, this has a benign appearance.

Preinjury Assessments

07/21/14   *Alexandra Zelenka, MD*

History of Present Illness:

> Had 1 episode of "almost syncope" 1 wk ago.
>
> Has gained about 30 lbs in the last 5 years.
>
> Unable to lose weight.

07/31/14   *Alexandra Zelenka, MD*

History of Present Illness:

> Continued vertigo.
>
> Headaches, pressure behind the eye.

07/12/17   *Alexandra Zelenka, MD*

Comments:

> Cold since May; red marks on legs.

History of Present Illness:

> Also has had purple dots small section x 5 days on right lower leg, no longer there now, concerned possible platelet issue; requesting lab work.
>
> Weight loss since 2/2017, 30 lbs weight watchers.

03/26/18   *Alexandra Zelenka, MD*

Assessment:

> Weight gain.
>
> Vertigo.
>
> Insomnia.
>
> Thyroiditis.

Results of Testing

On the Wahler Physical Symptoms Inventory, Ms. Round generated a score of 2.4. This score placed Ms. Round at the ninth decile in relation to a comparable normative group.

The Shipley Institute of Living Scale was used to assess Ms. Round's intellectual skills and abilities. Ms. Round attained an estimated WAIS-R IQ score of 109. This performance placed her in the average range of mental functioning.

On the Beck Depression Inventory-II, Ms. Round generated a total score of 38, which corresponds to the severe range of depression.

Results of personality testing on the MMPI-2 were mixed. Ms. Round demonstrated some inconsistencies in her response style. Test administration difficulties should be considered, along with her cognitive difficulties.

On the Self-Directed Search Form R, Ms. Round scored highest on the Enterprising occupational theme. This theme is most often associated with self-gain occupations. Ms. Round rated her managerial skills as very high. She also assessed her teaching and sales abilities, understanding of others, and office skills as above average. The occupations she noted interest in pursuing most recently were "lawyer," "marine biologist," "professor," and "small business/shop owner." Among the occupations from the Self-Directed Search Form R that correspond with Ms. Round's test results are entrepreneur, director of institutional research, business manager, financial planner, employment manager, legislator, labor relations specialist, city manager, social worker, and appeals referee.

Summary and Impressions

I.   A 1990 high school graduate, Ms. Round earned an undergraduate degree in political science in 1994 and a juris doctorate degree in 1997. Gentry Spicer, PC (GS), recruited her in October 2003, and her tenure with the firm continued through the time of her January 6, 2020, motor vehicle accident and to date. Ms. Round informed me her practice has specialized in nursing home defense. On July 1, 2019, GS promoted her to partner, and she worked in this capacity from 40 to 60 hours per week through the time of her accident. As a partner, Ms. Round explained, the scope of her job responsibilities became enlarged and broadened to include expectations that her marketing efforts would garner billable work, in turn offering her opportunities to enhance her compensation. Based on my understanding of the essential functions associated with her employment with GS, she performed sedentary/light, skilled/very skilled tasks. Of note, she apprised me she performed much of her job outside her firm's office—often in courthouses and other venues. Ms. Round noted much of her practice was in South Florida, which required travel via commercial aircraft or motor vehicle. When traveling, she noted, she often transported large volumes of documents, audiovisual devices, and luggage, requiring her to handle objects in the light/medium range. After her January 6, 2020, accident, Ms. Round recalled, she had a three-week absence from GS. On her return to work, she conveyed, her work participation was irregular and less than full time. Ms. Round described postaccident difficulties—including problems with photosensitivity, cognition, and pain—that interfered with her ability to perform her job. GS accommodated her through the time she began working remotely in March 2020, due to the COVID-19 pandemic. She has continued to work remotely to date. In addition to accommodations GS has extended, Ms. Round reported, she has been relying more on her paralegal and legal assistant. She elaborated about her accident-related presenting problems and ill effects on her job performance and productivity. She noted tasks take her from 40 to 50 percent longer to complete, and, to compensate, she works far more hours than she did preaccident. Ms. Round described problems with errors, forgetting important information, and several difficulties performing the cognitively complex tasks inherent in her job. Understandably, citing concerns about her job security, Ms. Round apprised me she has been close-mouthed about disclosing the totality of her accident-related problems. In this vein, the pandemic has permitted her to work remotely and unobtrusively and has exempted her from travel, court appearances, and other events at which the manifestations of her accident-related problems would more likely be exposed, thereby enabling her to conceal her impairments. Ms. Round mentioned several times her worry about her impaired work capacity, need to resume the full scope of her job responsibilities as she performed them before the COVID-19 pandemic, and implications of inferior performance for her career development. My analysis has led me to conclude Ms. Round's expressed concerns are valid. The preaccident career plans she presented were to continue her work with GS, and she described long-term career objectives that included establishing a mediation practice. I am unaware of a reason Ms. Round would not have been able to pursue her stated preaccident career objectives if not for her acquired disabling problems. "I'm afraid at some point it's [my presenting problems are] going to catch up with me, and I'm going to get terminated, or something that's never happened before—I'll get [a] poor performance [rating]," Ms. Round stated, describing her imminent career concerns. Although she assessed her employment with GS is currently secure, she stated, "When life goes back to normal [after the pandemic], then I'm very concerned." Ms. Round is in the establishment/maintenance phase of her career development. Ironically, the timing of the COVID-19 pandemic appears to have been fortuitous to her in her vocational rehabilitation. The information I have thus far had an opportunity to consider indicates Ms. Round's career development trajectory was rising when she became injured, and she had yet to realize her full earning capacity.

II.   Ms. Round denied injuring her head, neck, or back before her January 6, 2020, motor vehicle accident. Likewise, she denied having any preaccident problems with cognitive dysfunction. I am unaware of any documentary evidence that refutes Ms. Round's representations.

III. Approximately seven months have elapsed since Ms. Round's January 6, 2020, motor vehicle accident, and the full extent of her injuries and associated disabling problems has yet to be fully discovered. Medical records provide objective support of her presenting problems. Imaging of Ms. Round's cervical spine, thoracic spine, and lumbar spine detected abnormalities, as have scans of her brain. Regarding the latter, on July 26, 2020, Dr. Hill found problems associated with atrophy and traumatic axonal injury, which led to his conclusion that Ms. Round experienced traumatic brain injury. On February 24, 2020, Dr. Collins diagnosed problems with cervical radiculopathy and lumbar radiculopathy; Dr. Mercer imposed permanent light-duty restrictions on Ms. Round on July 14, 2020. Further, the neurologist prognosticated his patient will require intensive, multimodal future care. In response to my query about her primary problems, Ms. Round said: "It's the cognitive, struggling with work, and then the neck pain. It's the combination of the neck and the head." She conveyed her neck is her most symptomatic body part. Ms. Round elaborated about her limitations with essentially all cervical spine movements and ongoing pain with radicular symptoms. She described how various movements, such as twisting and bending, exacerbate her neck and back symptoms, and she described adjustments in her everyday activities she has implemented to manage her pain. Movements below Ms. Round's waist—such as squatting, kneeling, and climbing stairs—exacerbate her neck and lower back pain, as does transitioning from sitting to standing. Other problems she presented related to several unwelcome postaccident lifestyle changes she has encountered. Ms. Round scored in the severe range of depression on testing administered during my exam; her score was consistent with my clinical impression. On a test of mental functioning, she scored in the average range; considering her vocational profile, her testing performance was much lower than my estimate of her preaccident level of intellect.

IV. On a positive note, Ms. Round is a younger individual (age 44) who has managed to maintain her preaccident employment, albeit with accommodations and highly unusual COVID-19 pandemic conditions. She has education, training, work experience, and transferable skills as previously described.

V. The evidence I have thus far had an opportunity to review has led me to conclude, within a reasonable degree of vocational rehabilitation probability, the work difficulties Ms. Round described are consistent with her objective medical records, healthcare professional assessments, and results from my exam. As noted earlier, the full extent of her injuries and associated disabling problems are continuing to be evaluated, and the aberrant COVID-19 pandemic conditions under which Ms. Round has been working preclude a full assessment of her impaired work capacity. Under a best-case scenario, based on information available at this time, I estimate her loss of earning capacity secondary to her January 6, 2020, motor vehicle accident will be in the moderate range. Again, this is a preliminary, conservative estimate. I recommend Ms. Round undergo an updated vocational rehabilitation evaluation when pandemic restrictions have abated, providing an opportunity to assess her capabilities under conditions in sync with those customarily required.

Date _____

_____
Michael Shahnasarian, PhD
Certified Life Care Planner #258
Certified Rehabilitation Counselor #3701
Certified Vocational Evaluator #58360
International Psychometric Evaluator Certification #985
Licensed Psychologist PY5644
Fellow, American Psychological Association
Fellow, International Academy of Life Care Planners
Fellow, National Career Development Association

CHAPTER 4

Pediatric, Youth, and Young Adult Cases

Even though they might have never worked a day in their lives before experiencing an injury, of course, children, youth, and young adults who acquire injuries and associated disabling problems possess an earning capacity that might have since eroded. Cases involving young people with injuries task vocational evaluators with both applying the science of their profession and meeting legal standards when establishing measures of evaluees' preinjury and postinjury earning capacity levels, thereby providing expert guidance to those determining and awarding monetary damages for differentials.

Cases with children and youth, and sometimes young adults, typically have scant vocational documentation on which evaluators can rely. In some cases, such as those with babies, no vocational history exists; in cases with older children, limited and/or incomplete information of demonstrated achievements may emerge. Accordingly, evaluators gather and integrate available harbingers of information providing insight into an evaluee's vocational capacities and likely career trajectory—both before and after becoming injured—from primary and secondary sources, often relying heavily on the latter.

The lack of evidence to reference when assessing the vocational capacities of children and young adults requires evaluators to construct models based on available data and to extrapolate from them, within a reasonable degree of probability, assessments of loss of earning capacity attributable to injuries and associated disabling problems. This sometimes involves deducing multiple scenarios of likely preinjury and postinjury career trajectories.

Since children and many young adults have not had an opportunity to enter the workplace and establish reliable earning capacity indicators, one of an evaluator's primary challenges becomes determining these metrics with little or no documentary support from evidence specific to an evaluee. These data points become central to addressing questions about earning capacity in the absence of an evaluee's injuries and acquired disabling problems. Considering an evaluee's disabled state, what is his or her residual earning capacity? The variance between the values these questions elicit, multiplied by the evaluee's work life expectancy, becomes the basis for a claim of loss of earning capacity.

To many laypeople considering an evaluation of a person with little or no vocational history, these questions are unanswerable. Yet vocational evaluators must apply the science of their profession to answer these and related questions, within a reasonable degree of vocational rehabilitation probability, facilitating the resolution of disputed earning capacity damages. After all, triers of fact and others charged with resolving a real-time damages claim cannot, of course, reassemble in five, ten, or 20 years, awaiting facts and history to guide their decision-making. Their dispositions are rendered in the here and now, relying on facts on hand and sage expert witness input.

Case-specific factors and issues involving mitigation often add further levels of analysis to damages questions. After having determined a baseline preinjury earning capacity level, an evaluator can assess other aspects of a loss of earning capacity claim, such as alleged delays in workplace entry secondary to acquired disabling problems. For example, a case involving a college student who experienced burn injuries to a dominant upper extremity included a claim that the injury required extensive treatment, causing a two-year delay in completing her studies and furthering her career development. Accordingly, damages sought included lost wages for the period of alleged delayed workplace entry, and the evaluator's retention included assessing both the claim's merits and the evaluee's mitigation efforts.

The evaluation models and methods the two preceding chapters outlined apply to both children and adults. Neulicht and Berens (2005) introduced a similar widely used pediatric evaluation method, PEEDS-RAPEL. The PEEDS acronym derives from five domains fundamental to evaluating a claim of loss of earning capacity in a pediatric case:

- Parental/Family Occupation
- Educational Attainment
- Evaluation Results
- Developmental Stage
- Synthesis

The RAPEL part of the acronym was discussed in Chapter 2. Neulicht and Berens (2015) discussed the application of PEEDS-RAPEL in pediatric cases involving acquired brain injury.

Of course, an evaluator must make case-specific adjustments to assessment protocols when performing pediatric and young adult evaluations. Common adjustments, described next, help to assure evaluators apply best practices to configure comprehensive, reliable, and valid information in the assumptions they develop and on which they rely.

Sources of Evaluation Information

Like adult assessments, pediatric assessments incorporate reviews of records, an examination consisting of a clinical interview and sometimes testing, and input from collateral information. This latter source can be especially effective since children often cannot aptly communicate the scope of their disabling problems, lack insight and maturity into them, and/or present in a reticent, nondisclosing manner.

Records

The following sources, depending on a child's age and records that exist, may provide insight into preinjury and postinjury matters vocational evaluators assess. Despite abbreviated documentary evidence, evaluators can assemble and integrate the best indicators, along with information from traditional evaluation sources and research-based evidence, to develop reasonable theories that evolve to opinions presented within a reasonable degree of vocational rehabilitation probability.

- Academic records including documentation of scholastic achievement, standardized testing performance, and development of Individualized Education Plans
- Extracurricular activities
- Unrelated comorbidities if applicable
- Employment and earnings records if available
- Family-related vocational information as available

Evaluators' records reviews should focus on indices like underachievement/overachievement, behavioral and disciplinary problems, and signs of precocious behavior and, contrarily, special needs. Information from these records may provide insight useful to honing a model(s) of an evaluee's career trajectory(ies) both before and after becoming injured.

Additionally, documentary and other evidence sometimes identifies problems unrelated to issues in dispute, and evaluators parse them accordingly, including considering how an aggravation of preexisting problems may affect vocational functioning. For example, a child diagnosed with attention-deficit disorder, oppositional defiant disorder, or special needs before an incident in dispute has risk factors independent of new trauma causing injuries, and a vocational evaluator must consider this when assessing overall damages.

Like all assessments, those that involve children and young adults should consider opportunities to remediate identified impairments threatening vocational damages. Identified deficits in learning, naturally, would include determinations of how tutoring, school accommodations, and other interventions might offset scholastic difficulties.

Clinical Interview

Depending on a child or young person's impairments, age, attention span, and maturity level, the duration of a clinical interview will vary from less than 15 minutes to up to several hours. This upper limit requires cooperation from higher-functioning adolescents and young adults and a facilitative clinical interview environment.

Some evaluee impairments prohibit any meaningful clinical interview—including rudimentary interactions when an evaluator holds an evaluee's hand and instructs, "Squeeze once for yes and twice for no," to answer questions that include "Can you hear me?" and "Do you hurt?"

Successful clinical interviews of pediatric and young adult evaluees require an environment in which evaluators establish rapport-optimizing opportunities to elicit meaningful information to advance an assessment. Despite an evaluator's best efforts, attaining these conditions is not always tenable—especially when overshadowing tensions from the litigation environment affect evaluees' behaviors.

Evaluators should also remember young evaluees may perceive them as imposing authority figures; reducing this barrier can help diminish inhibitions that limit disclosures. One evaluator, for example, uses a large aquarium in his office as a prop to initiate non-threatening conversation before proceeding with questioning that a youth may initially be unwilling to answer in toto. His practice, after greeting a child evaluee, is to draw attention to fish in the aquarium, discussing them and other topics far from the examination before posing substantive clinical interview questions.

The subject matter of clinical interviews with children, youth, and young adults varies and again depends on the types of conditions and issues described earlier. Generally, to the degree an evaluee can provide relevant information, the interviews include the topics Chapter 3 outlined, absent of course areas such as work experience, earnings, and skills developed.

Younger evaluees sometimes ascribe little importance to information evaluators value and often require prompting. For example, after asking an eighth-grade evaluee about his school grades and receiving "Good" as an answer, the evaluator followed up by referencing her records review; it identified a marked postinjury decline in certain school subjects. The evaluator provided her observations and probed for reasons underlying the changes.

Eventually, the evaluee yielded, disclosing concerns over his facial disfigurement and attempts to avoid drawing attention to himself. He elaborated on tendencies to dislike and withdraw from participating in classes involving oral discourse as a primary mode of instruction, such as speech and foreign language courses. This, the evaluee reckoned over the course of the evaluator's query, accounted for the variances in his postinjury scholastic performance.

Evaluators' interviews of children and young adults should include inquiry about their favorite and least favorite school subjects along with the respective reasons, scholastic performance, role models, relationships with teachers and peers, and near-term/long-term plans. Of course, evaluees' age, maturity, and extent of disabling problems will govern the depth and quality of information elicited. Evaluee disclosures reveal wide ranges of sophistication in evaluee responses, which can also be instructive. With cognitively intact mature youth and young adults, more detailed discussion about career decisions, plans for developing skills, and pursuing education and training is in order.

Evaluators should explore reasons for young people's career ambitions; this inquiry may provide insight about their work values, role models, career maturity, and knowledge of the world of work. Exploring reasons a middle schooler aspires to become a professional athlete or an about-to-be high school graduate opts to forgo extended college scholarships, for example, offers a window into the evaluee's worldview.

Quite often, children and young adults who underwent extensive medical treatment develop bonds with treating healthcare providers and aspire to emulate them; they often express career interests that parallel those they admire. Conversely, others with similar experiences develop aversions to anything associated with their treatment experiences and strongly voice their opposition to occupations related to healthcare. Again, probing into evaluees' reasons for their occupational interests and career plans may provide insight to further an evaluator's assessment.

Evaluators should, of course, tailor to an evaluee's presenting problems and clinical profile inquiries that address the classic question that we encounter as children, that we ponder as we pursue our education and make career decisions, and that remains in our unconscious during the formative years of our career development: What do you want to be when you grow up? Responses promise to illuminate, among other things, evaluees' career maturity, self-esteem, career values, and ability to make valid translations of their personal situations to workplace realities.

Clinical observations derived from interacting with a young evaluee can also facilitate the assessment process. For example, some young children, barely audible, respond nominally to questions and exhibit a paucity of interpersonal skill development. The reasons for their reticence and manner could relate to issues at hand, and evaluators should correlate their observations with other evidence as they develop their damages theories.

Conversely, some children and young people present precociously, while others exhibit atypical behaviors. Examples of the latter include attention-seeking behaviors; violations of interpersonal space with an evaluator; inappropriate, disinhibited behavior; and social regression. Again, evaluators should clinically correlate their observations with documentary and other evidence, including collateral sources and results from standardized testing, to discern relationships between presenting problems and diagnosed conditions as they evaluate vocational implications.

Observations of family and caregiver dynamics can also further an evaluator's analysis. Interacting with parents who repeatedly talk over their children or present information that appears to overstate preinjury capacities, for example, could prompt an evaluator to delve further into measures of evaluees' aptitudes, personality, and social development.

In some cases, such as serious motor vehicle accidents where, in addition to personal injuries, a child or young adult might have also experienced the death of a parent, an evaluator's inquiry should expand into indicators of the evaluee's ability to cope with the loss and, by extension, implications for career development. Evaluators' interviews sometimes elicit information about regressive behavior after a child's loss of a parent, such as bedwetting after having previously mastered the milestone and playing with non-age-appropriate objects (e.g., a child in early adolescence playing with dolls or toy trains).

Children who prematurely lose a parent or significant person in their life, of course, react in myriad ways. Some may appear well adjusted, although they may disclose an exacerbation of mental health distress secondary to triggers such as Mother's Day/Father's Day or the absence of a parent during an important developmental milestone, such as a first menstrual cycle or high school graduation. Again, evaluators should inquire about surrogate parental figures and role models.

The following excerpt presents an evaluator's impressions of a teenage boy who lost his father in a car accident. In this case, the evaluee developed troublesome psychological behaviors that had widespread deleterious effects. In addition to the clinical interview, the evaluator integrated in her assessment information from collateral sources, school and mental health treatment records, and results from standardized testing. Her work culminated in a life care plan with recommendations to facilitate the evaluee's vocational rehabilitation through mental health intervention, case management, a life skills coach, and tutoring (Chapters 6 through 9 address life care plan development).

> Rodrigo Sanchez was ten years old and about to begin the fifth grade when his father died in 2016. He is now a 15-year-old, ninth-grade student. The information I have had an opportunity to consider indicates Rodrigo strongly identified with his father, and he enjoyed a close relationship in which he respected and admired him.
>
> I am not aware of any mental health, scholastic, or interpersonal difficulties Rodrigo experienced before his father's untimely, horrific death. At a very young age, he has displayed disturbing psychological symptoms leading to intensive mental health intervention. These interventions include four inpatient psychiatric admissions (most recently three to four months before my exam), psychotherapy, and prescribed psychotropic medication with psychiatric monitoring.
>
> Records document antisocial behavior and scholastic, familial, and interpersonal difficulties Rodrigo has experienced since his father died. Reports I prepared in conjunction with my assessments of his mother and brother discuss complex family dynamics also applicable to Rodrigo.
>
> Only 15 years old, Rodrigo is the "man of the house," a burden made more challenging considering the absence of his father and lack of significant surrogate role models. Characteristics of his surviving family members further complicate his situation: Rodrigo has a younger, special-needs brother about to enter puberty and a modestly educated mother, marginally employed, who does not speak English and has had cultural assimilation difficulties compounding her grief reaction and challenges of raising, alone, two sons who have special needs.
>
> Rodrigo will likely require ongoing, significant rehabilitation intervention related to the loss of his father. On a positive note, he is cognitively intact, and he

scored in the lower end of the average range of intellect on testing administered during my exam (Full Scale IQ = 92). Additionally, personality testing suggests Rodrigo has motivation to succeed.

Damages claims emanating from injuries to young people must be discerned from evaluees' perspectives—perspectives sometimes much different than those of adults and healthcare professionals. Shahnasarian and Hilby (2020) discussed the use of the ECAF-2 in young adult cases, noting how the instrument can facilitate evaluators' assessments of nuanced, emergent vocationally relevant behaviors.

Impaired ability to engage in age-appropriate activities sometimes can spawn maladaptive secondary problems, foreshadowing negative vocational implications. An example follows.

Example of Anticipated Interaction of Primary and Secondary Disabling Problems in a Case Involving a Young Adult

Presented next are abstractions from a report involving a teenager who sustained injuries to his vocal cords, prohibiting him from speaking above a whisper. His physical limitations were nominal and essentially irrelevant in consideration of his career development. The evaluator learned through her clinical interview, however, about significant psychological sequelae the evaluee acquired secondary to his speech production problems. Applying the ECAF-2, the evaluator arrived at an opinion of how the conjoint effects of these disabling problems would reduce the evaluee's earning capacity over his work life.

Evaluator's Findings and Opinions

I.   Mr. Salmon was 15 years old and in the ninth grade at the time of his May 15, 2013, motorbike accident. He recalled his accident occurred near the time he was completing the ninth grade, and he remained hospitalized through the end of the school year. Mr. Salmon returned to his parochial school during the fall 2013 academic year, and his injuries did not delay his academic progress. No accommodations were extended to him. Mr. Salmon and his parents compared and contrasted Mr. Salmon's preaccident and postaccident dispositions, noting he became considerably more reticent after his accident. He disclosed postaccident social inhibitions he developed because of his vocal projection problems, noting he became far less participatory in class discussions and sought to diminish drawing attention to himself. "I usually sat more toward the back [of my classes]," Mr. Salmon stated, describing his postaccident behavior and socially reclusive tendencies. He went on to cite difficulties with his expressive language and making himself understood and concerns about others' perceptions of him. Mr. Salmon described how these factors interacted, contributing to adversely affecting his self-image and social behavior. Of note, his acquired disabling problems began during the formative period of his adolescence, likely affecting his personality development. Mr. Salmon had not yet formulated career plans before his 2013 accident, and he had no work experience. His only paid employment since his accident, which he has maintained to date, is employment as an oil change technician with Midway Motors—a job he secured after completing high school in spring 2016. Based on my understanding of his job responsibilities, Mr. Salmon performs unskilled/semiskilled tasks that require medium/heavy exertion. Although he conveyed he can perform the full scope of his job responsibilities, he noted difficulties with demanding exertional tasks. Additionally, he cited communication difficulties he experiences with his employers' customers. Mr. Salmon is uncertain about his career plans, and he informed me he is "not right now" considering resuming his education. He was in the growth phase of his career development at the time of his May 2013 motorbike accident, and he remains in this phase. Within a reasonable degree of vocational rehabilitation probability, Mr. Salmon's accident has delayed his career development progress. He disclosed concerns about his opportunities for career growth and advancement secondary to his acquired disabling problems. From a vocational rehabilitation perspective, Mr. Salmon's concerns are valid. Unfortunately, lifelong underemployment is a significant risk he acquired. This risk is accompanied by psychological and psychosocial sequelae, posing further damages.

II.   Medical records document Mr. Salmon's tracheal injuries after his May 15, 2013, motorbike accident. He has been diagnosed with bilateral vocal cord paralysis. During the acute period after his accident, Mr. Salmon experienced a seizure. He has undergone multiple bronchoscopy and laryngoscopy procedures, and, apparently, such procedures will be required for him during the remainder of his life. The primary problems he noted experiencing because of his 2013 accident are "the [impaired vocal] projection, because that affects the mental part, too." Mr. Salmon spoke in a whisper during my clinical interview, and I had difficulty hearing him. In addition to expressive language difficulties, he cited breathing difficulties, exertional limitations, and significant psychological sequelae. Mr. Salmon's self-esteem and self-concept have been adversely affected by his acquired disabling problems. This portends deleterious consequences on his career development and ability to realize his potential. Additionally, Mr. Salmon's presenting problems, in my opinion, have caused him to develop social anxiety issues. Social inhibition tendencies appear to be plaguing him in all spheres of his life, including his school, dating, vocational, family, and personal behaviors. He characterized himself as "more shy" since his accident—an attribution his parents corroborated. Mr. Salmon's impaired ability to engage in oral communications will obviously be quite limiting in his future career development. Coupled with the associated psychological consequences—including his admitted tendencies to avoid oral communications—these qualities are damaging to his career development. Mr. Salmon is at risk of lifelong career underachievement, which, within a reasonable degree of vocational rehabilitation probability, will compound his psychological distress.

III. On a positive note, Mr. Salmon is a younger individual (age 19) who is cognitively intact. He scored in the average range on a test of mental functioning and scored well on measures of attention to detail and general fund of information. Additionally, Mr. Salmon demonstrated good performance on a test of manual speed and dexterity. He has a normal gait, does not use adaptive aids, and has functional capacities as previously delineated. On a personal level, I found him pleasant and likable. Although Mr. Salmon undoubtedly has significant limitations in his vocational functioning, in my opinion, he will be capable of ongoing employment for the duration of his work life expectancy. Of course, his acquired vocational handicaps—including employer bias, need for accommodations, compromised prospects for advancement, and increased vulnerability to reduction in workforce—will further erode his residual earning capacity.

IV.   It is reasonable to presume that, if not for Mr. Salmon's presenting problems, he would have attained levels of education comparable to or greater than what his parents attained. Conservatively, it is also reasonable to presume he had the potential to attend college and earn a bachelor's degree. Although I cannot rule out his ability to pursue his education, clearly, his acquired disabling problems would make it quite challenging for him to apply knowledge he gained from his education in his career development. Within a reasonable degree of vocational rehabilitation probability, the vocational handicaps Mr. Salmon acquired because of his May 15, 2013, motorbike accident caused him a loss of earning capacity. Applying the Earning Capacity Assessment Form-2 to my analysis, I estimate this loss will be in the range of 30 to 40 percent over the remainder of his work life.

Standardized Test Administration

Depending on their age and cognitive capacities, some children can and should undergo standardized testing during a vocational evaluator's assessment; of course, the same is true for adolescents and young adults, contingent on their presenting problems and referral questions. The types of tests administered to children differ from those administered to adults.

The selection of an evaluator's test battery for young people should begin with appreciation that, in many instances, their attention may be limited and their participation in taking tests is often reluctant. This is also true of many adults but especially noteworthy when assessing a younger population. Accordingly, evaluators should plan their selection of tests and timing of test administration to optimize the likelihood of enlisting evaluee cooperation and obtaining valid results.

Vocational testing for children, youth, and young adults, like that for adults, derives from three domains: interests, aptitudes, and personality. Evaluators should ensure the selection of a test battery suits the evaluee's level of development; reference to test user manuals and normative data obtained during test validation can provide the necessary guidance on test selection.

Some vocationally relevant measures are especially apropos for evaluees between the ages of six and 18. For example, the Culture Free Self-Esteem Inventory (Battle, 2002) assesses five domains of a child's self-esteem (academic, general, parental/home, social, and personal) and provides normative data by age group: middle childhood, ages six through eight; late childhood, ages nine through 12; and adolescence, ages 13 through 18. These assessments can help identify opportunities to remediate personal factors that threaten to suppress vocational achievement, such as low academic self-esteem. Regarding measures of basic skills for this cadre, the Wide Range Achievement Test-4 (Wilkerson and Robertson, 2006) provides grade-level equivalent scores on measures of arithmetic, reading, and spelling. Metrics of these basic abilities, especially when correlated with scholastic performance data, can help to prognosticate a young person's capacity for educational achievement—a factor that correlates positively with earning capacity.

An exhaustive review of measures available to assess claims of loss of earning capacity in cases involving children, adolescents, and young adults exceeds the scope of *The Valuation of Monetary Damages in Injury Cases: A Damages Expert's Perspective*. Shahnasarian (2015) provided an overview of aptitude, personality, and occupational interest tests most often used in vocational rehabilitation evaluations.

Like all information evaluators integrate into their analyses, they should cautiously interpret children's test results, which can be affected by age-related attentional difficulties, levels of maturity, and a host of extraneous factors. Generally, the younger the evaluee, the greater the variance of normative group test data. The integration and synthesis of cumulative, systematically gathered expert evidence, guided by the analytical ECAF-2 processes Chapter 2 described, can advance evaluators' assessments of test result validity and reliability. Clinical correlation of all evidence at hand, including results from standardized testing, facilitates evaluators' initiatives to develop empirically based inferences from new evidence.

In cases in which children have continued their education after becoming disabled, comparisons of preinjury and postinjury scholastic performance, school accommodations or lack thereof, and Individualized Education Plans that specify special needs, accommodations, and learning interventions facilitate an assessment of how injuries and associated disabling problems have affected and could affect an evaluee. Evaluators should compare/contrast this foundation information with pertinent test results; such clinical correlation helps evaluators draw valid and reliable inferences from objective test measures.

Collateral Source Interviews

Quite often, especially in cases involving very young children, collateral source information contributes significantly to evaluators' assessments. This includes interviewing parents and others influential in evaluees' lives and appropriating relevant vocational data to construct models predictive of vocational scenarios ranging from young persons' projected level of educational attainment to earnings they likely would have realized devoid of acquired injuries and associated disabling problems.

Parents and family members, caregivers, and sometimes a young person's teachers and role models can provide insightful information that advances evaluators' assessments of an evaluee's preinjury and postinjury capacities. Beyond details related to scholarship, occupational interests, and motivation, evaluators should also probe these sources on topics such as bullying, teasing, and postinjury behavioral and discipline problems.

Preferably, evaluators interview collateral sources in the absence of evaluees. Overhearing trusted loved ones, guardians, and others elaborate to a professional detailed accounts of their impairments—ranging from personality defects to physical, emotional, social, and intellectual deficiencies—obviously can adversely affect anyone's psyche, let alone those of children, youths, and young adults. Additionally, evaluees' presence tends to inhibit collateral source disclosures of sensitive observations and assessments.

In concert with data from the sources this chapter previously identified, data extracted from human collateral sources can hone a vocational evaluator's objective to construct a model(s) of an evaluee's likely career trajectory in the absence of injury-related disabling problems. The proverb "The apple does not fall far from the tree" has support in behavioral science longitudinal studies pertinent to assessing vocational achievement. For example, Annette, Dubas, and Gerris (2010) reported positive correlations between values transmitted from parents to children and career development, and Fans, Benson, and Kaestle (2013) found parent resources influenced adolescent children's education and career development. A longitudinal study Orth reported (in press) found support for the premise that the family environment during a person's early adulthood has long-term effects on self-esteem.

When gathering information about family, extended family, and others influential in an evaluee's development, evaluators should consider their levels of educational attainment, scholastic achievement, skill development, and career paths. Parental, home, and other social influences affecting an evaluee—to name a few, familial expectations and attributions of achievement or lack thereof to ability or effort—are also relevant. Further, evaluators should consider role models available to an evaluee, both preinjury and postinjury, and supplemental interventions available to remedy an evaluee's acquired disabling problems, including tutors, school resources, accommodations, and technological applications.

Of course, the complexion of the world of work will continue to evolve with the advent of new technologies and global events. Recently, the COVID-19 pandemic introduced major workplace changes as workers socially distanced and electronic technologies facilitated opportunities for masses of people worldwide to work remotely—a work environment often more conducive to people with disabilities.

Undoubtedly, new technologies will evolve, including ones from robotics, bioscience, and space development. Major advances in prosthetics, for example, have emerged during recent years amid the escalation of armed conflicts worldwide and corresponding unfortunate needs of those who have lost limbs.

Along with technological advances, enlightened people entrusted with governance decisions will hopefully advocate for people who have disabilities, which promises to further revolutionize the world of work as we know it. These factors, likewise, should reckon in an evaluator's rendering of an evaluee's preinjury and postinjury vocational scenarios. Of course, such anticipation must remain within a reasonable degree of probability to avoid the risk of being discarded as speculative.

Following is an example of collateral family background information an evaluator derived and factored into an assessment of an evaluee's likely preinjury vocational course. It illustrates how information about an evaluee's family constellation, coupled with other evidence, can contribute to deducing reasonable educational and vocational scenarios in the absence of an evaluee's acquired disabling problems.

Case Example

A baby experienced a medical incident at birth and has since been catastrophically disabled. To facilitate a determination of loss of earning capacity damages, a vocational evaluator provided an estimate of the evaluee's likely level of educational attainment in the absence of her disabling problems. An economist then used this opinion as a predicate to apply earnings estimates from U.S. Department of Labor salary surveys to the levels the evaluator deemed reasonable.

In addition to interacting with the evaluee and reviewing her and her family's records, the evaluator pursued his assignment by interviewing the evaluee's mother and stepfather to obtain family background information, which provided important foundational details for his assessment. Excerpts from the evaluator's report follow.

Case Information

Five-year-old Janice Rachel was referred to me for a vocational rehabilitation evaluation. A complaint documents allegations of injuries she sustained due to a birth-related medical incident. Answers to interrogatories assert injuries and damages as follows: "Permanent brain damage along with physical impairments that require continuous medical and nursing care."

Janice's mother, Deborah Allett, reported Janice experiences the following incident-related problems:

- Severe cognitive impairments
- No speech production
- Seizure disorder—most recent seizure on November 25, 2020
- Nonambulatory
- Totally dependent in all activities of daily living
- Intermittent skin breakdown problems
- Derives nutrition through a gastrostomy tube

- Spasms
- Labored breathing
- Ongoing gastroesophageal distress
- Sleep disorder
- Impaired vision

Ms. Allett apprised me Janice has never attended school or participated in homebound education. She expressed her understanding that, if not for the medical incident, Janice would have been a healthy baby, and she would not have any of the aforementioned disabling problems. I inquired whether she believes her daughter is realizing any cognitive gains, and Ms. Allett replied: "Not at all. I don't see any improvement at all."

Family Background Information Provided by Janice's Mother and Stepfather

Ms. Allett noted she was born in Haiti and immigrated to the United States when she was 14 years old. She apprised me she completed high school and earned an associate degree in criminal justice at Palm Community College in 2016. Ms. Allett also reported she attended one semester of paralegal studies and one semester of business administration studies. She told me she does not have disabling problems.

Regarding employment, Ms. Allett indicated the city of White Forks currently employs her as a customer service representative. She advised me she works 35 hours per week and earns $13.99 per hour. Additionally, Ms. Allett conveyed, she works as a deli clerk at a Valley Super Market ten hours per week and earns $14 per hour.

Ms. Allett informed me she secured her job with the city of White Forks in June 2019. Other employment she has held, she noted, includes jobs as a legal assistant with a law firm and as a front desk supervisor at a hotel.

As for Janice's biological father, Ms. Allett cited Simon Rachel, also born in Haiti. She apprised me they currently live apart, married in 2009 and divorced in 2019. "We were separated since 2016," she stated.

Ms. Allett told me Mr. Rachel graduated from high school in Haiti and pursued college studies in the United States. She was uncertain whether he satisfied college degree requirements. To the best of her knowledge, she indicated, Mr. Rachel has no disabling problems. Ms. Allett advised me she was not aware of her ex-husband's current employment status. While they were married, she conveyed, Bell Communications Systems employed Mr. Rachel as a customer service representative. "He did that for a long time," Ms. Allett added.

In addition to Janice, Ms. Allett informed me, she had one other child with Mr. Rachel—Donald Rachel, who is ten years old. She noted her son is in the fourth grade and has no disabling problems. I inquired about Donald's scholastic performance, and his mother replied: "Very good. He made the honor roll again. He's doing great in school."

Concerning Ms. Allett's current husband, Samuel Pinson, she apprised me he, too, was born in Haiti, and he has been living in the United States since July 2018. "He's in transition, [converting] to permanent resident status," she said about Mr. Pinson's immigration status. Ms. Allett reported Mr. Pinson completed high school and some college studies in Haiti. "He wants to [study] law enforcement," she told me, citing her husband's plans to continue his education.

Mr. Pinson advised me he last worked as a police officer in Port-au-Prince, Haiti, in 2018, and he conveyed he had 14 years of experience as a law enforcement professional. He informed me he plans to earn a college degree and secure a law enforcement job in the United States.

Summary and Impressions

Janice Rachel is an unfortunate five-year-old child who is experiencing multisystem, catastrophic disabling problems. Records indicate she experienced hypoxic ischemic encephalopathy and has global, profound developmental delay. Janice is unable to walk or talk, and her ongoing disabling problems have included recurrent seizures, daily problems with emesis, and spasms. Indeed, her rehabilitation intervention needs are intensive.

Ms. Allett informed me Janice has never attended school including homebound education. She is researching educational opportunities for her daughter. Janice's disabling problems, within a reasonable degree of vocational rehabilitation probability, will preclude her from employment. It is reasonable to presume that, if not for her disabling problems, Janice would have attained a level of education akin to her family members and would have pursued her career development in employment commensurate with her education. Conservatively, and within a reasonable degree of vocational rehabilitation probability, if not for her disabling problems, Janice likely would have had the capacity to earn either an associate degree or a bachelor's degree.

Sample Report: Pediatric Case

This chapter concludes with a full sample report that involves a late-adolescent male who sustained a permanent injury. Despite acknowledging the evaluee acquired a permanent injury with associated disabling problems, the evaluator concluded he did not sustain a loss of earning capacity. The report illustrates how an evaluator applied ECAT and the procedures this chapter enumerated—namely, records review, clinical interview, standardized testing, and integration of collateral source information—to address referral questions and arrive at expert opinions.

Rehabilitation Evaluation
of Mark Rosetti

Michael Shahnasarian, PhD
July 13, 2020

Overview

Mark Rosetti (born February 20, 2005) was referred to me for a rehabilitation evaluation. Medical records describe injuries he sustained as a result of a left ankle incident on May 4, 2017. Mark noted he was 12 years old and completing the sixth grade at the time of his incident.

On June 2, 2020, I conducted clinical interviews of Mark and his parents—John and Ann Rosetti—via Zoom videoconferencing; the COVID-19 pandemic led to my use of this medium. Mark apprised me he was communicating with me from his home in Pensacola, Florida, and my interview of him required 2 hours and 50 minutes.

Mark told me that he holds a restricted driver's license while learning to drive and that he plans to obtain a regular driver's license at age 16. He reported he operates an automatic transmission vehicle with standard equipment, and he denied having doctor-advised driving restrictions.

I inquired about problems with driving, and Mark referenced his left foot. He indicated driving more than 30 to 45 minutes causes his foot to "stiffen up." After driving 60 to 75 minutes, he advised me, his left foot becomes painful, although he conveyed it is painful "earlier if I've had an activity before I started driving."

I asked Mark about his current education status, and he replied, "I just finished the ninth grade." He informed me he is not attending summer school.

Regarding his 2017 left ankle incident, Mark denied striking his head or losing consciousness. In his March 13, 2019, answers to Landscape's interrogatories, when asked to describe each injury for which he is claiming damages in this case, he noted:

> Mark's peroneal nerve was completely severed and the nerve endings were evulsed from his anterior tibialis. He will never recover. The damage is permanent. His left foot drops and hangs down, causing him to have a "stepping gait" and "foot slap." Mark will never wiggle his toes again. He will never be able to put on a pair of socks and shoes like everyone else because his toes curls under his foot. That makes it hard for him to walk when not wearing a brace. His left leg is permanently scarred. Mark will require bracing and future painful surgeries in order for him to be able to walk. Mark permanently lost the function of his peroneal nerve in his left lower leg, ankle, and foot. Mark has abnormal sensations from the scar down his left leg and foot. Mark will always walk with a limp, even with braces. He has instability as a result, which causes imbalance, stumbling, and occasional falling. Mark gets intermittent jolting neuropathic pains down his left lower leg and foot. The

antalgic gait will likely lead to back, hip, leg, and other problems for the rest of his life. Mark has to wear a brace to walk, run, and play with his friends or participate in sports. The injury causes pain and limitations of movement for Mark's left lower leg, ankle, and foot.

Currently, Mark apprised me, he experiences the following problems he relates to his 2017 incident:

- Left foot weakness with intermittent pain, exacerbated by activity
- Altered gait, more pronounced when fatigued or in pain
- Limited in physically demanding activities such as playing lacrosse
- Inability to move toes of left foot
- Onset of left knee pain such as after performing squat or lunge exercises
- Left foot pain secondary to activities such as driving and running for extended periods or "running hard a much shorter period of time, sprinting"

Mark denied experiencing the previously noted problems before his 2017 incident. I referenced records from January 2012 documenting preincident injury to his left lower extremity. He recalled that his leg was cast and that he fully recovered, "to my knowledge." Mark reported his left foot/leg had been asymptomatic near the time before his May 4, 2017, incident.

No problems with mental functioning were identified, and Mark specifically denied having trouble with memory, concentration, or attention span. I referenced preincident documentation of a concussion, and he told me he has had "possibly" two concussions. "I made fine recoveries from both of them," Mark stated.

Vocational Activity

Mark indicated he underwent the first of three left foot surgeries the day of his May 4, 2017, incident. "I was at the end of my sixth grade year," he said. Mark advised me he wore an immobilizing brace on his knee after the surgery. Conveying his strong preincident scholastic performance exempted him from completing several outstanding requirements, he said, "I had to do some assignments [to complete the sixth grade]."

After his 2017 incident, Mark informed me, he resumed school on schedule, on campus, and began the seventh grade in August 2017. Although he noted he has had periods of absence due to postincident medical treatment, he apprised me his academic progress has not been interrupted. "I missed a fair amount of school because of this," Mark said, referencing surgeries and medical treatment.

I inquired whether his left foot injury affected his scholastic performance, and Mark replied, "I've maintained straight As since the injury." He reported no accommodations were extended to him after he began the seventh grade, although he told me he was permitted to use an elevator after surgeries. "Other than that, no [accommodations]," he said. I asked whether any accommodations will be extended when he begins the tenth grade, and Mark responded negatively. As for his affinity for school, he stated, "I enjoy school."

Concerning career ambitions before his May 2017 incident, Mark said, "I was 12 [years old], so I wasn't thinking that far ahead." He indicated about his current career objectives, "I'm thinking something with engineering," and he elaborated about interest in biomedical engineering. Because Mark's parents are lawyers, operating their own commercial litigation practice, I inquired whether he is interested in pursuing law, and he replied, "Not particularly, no."

I asked Mark about any colleges he has considered, and he responded, "Some engineering school, most likely." He advised me he has not considered specific institutions of higher education.

Regarding concerns that his injuries will inhibit his career plans, Mark conveyed he had been considering a career as a surgeon. He surmised, however, he would be unable to perform lengthy surgeries due to limitations with standing because of his left foot injury. Mark said that, with "biomedical engineering, I don't know [if I would be limited]."

Mark reckoned that jobs requiring him to bear weight for extended periods would exceed his capacity. "Construction worker, doctor, like I said," he added. We discussed outpatient surgeries that would involve limited periods of bearing weight. Additionally, while meeting with Mark's parents, I noted an increased trend in robotic surgeries, and I discussed with the Rosettis considering career counseling for their son.

Since his March 2019 surgery, Mark assessed, he has lost opportunities to earn income through refereeing lacrosse, part time. He informed me his left foot injuries would preclude him from becoming a professional lacrosse player. "It was a small possibility [to become a professional lacrosse player before May 2017]. Now it's a zero possibility," Mark said.

Mark was not aware whether he reported his earnings as a part-time lacrosse referee to the Internal Revenue Service. He estimated his cumulative earnings have been $800.

Mark noted he had also considered pursuing his career development as a military medic. "Now that's impossible due to my [left] foot injury," he stated. He apprised me he had considered this option during the eighth and ninth grades. Mark did not identify any other adverse effects he anticipates on his career development caused by his left foot injury.

Records Reviewed

Records from the following sources were reviewed with this evaluation:

- Plaintiff's Verified Answers to Defendant Greenscape Landscape Services, Inc.'s, Interrogatories, November 18, 2018
- Plaintiff's Amended Verified Responses to Defendant Greenscape Landscape Services, Inc.'s, Interrogatories, March 22, 2019
- Plaintiff's Amended Verified Responses to Defendant Ocean View Park No. 1 Condominium Association, Inc.'s, Interrogatories, March 22, 2019
- Plaintiff's Unverified Responses to Defendant Greenscape Landscape Services, Inc.'s, Updated Interrogatories, November 4, 2019
- Deposition of Scott Willard, MD, treating neurosurgeon, March 10, 2020
- Deposition of Gregg Fike, MD, defense neurosurgeon expert, April 24, 2020
- Deposition of Eric Bose, DPM, treating podiatrist, May 20, 2020
- Deposition of Ann Rosetti, mother, March 10, 2019
- Deposition of John Rosetti, father, March 10, 2019
- Deposition of Mark Rosetti, March 10, 2019
- Deposition of Carrie Baker, physical therapist, April 22, 2020
- Centra Care, includes billing
- Child Neurology Center of Pensacola, PA
- Electrostimulation Associates
- Pensacola Hospital for Children/Kids Urgent Care/Advent Health, includes billing
- Pensacola Hospital Medical Center
- Pensacola Hospital Sports Medicine and Rehabilitation
- Pensacola Otolaryngology Group, PA, includes billing

- Pensacola Pedi Assoc., LLC, includes billing
- Foot and Ankle Associates of Pensacola
- Jamison Clinic, billing only
- Madison Orthopedic Clinic, PA
- Johns Hopkins Medicine, includes billing
- Mason Clinic, billing only
- Park Place
- NeuroSkeletal Imaging of Pensacola
- Neurosurgical Associates of Pensacola
- Pensacola Fire Department
- Pensacola Orthopaedic Center
- Publix Pharmacy, includes billing
- Trauma Physician's Service of Pensacola, includes billing
- Richard Appleton, MD
- Chris Barnett, MD
- Scott Willard, MD
- Scott Bookman, MD
- Eric Bose, DPM
- Diana Brennan, MD
- Gregg Fike, MD
- James Herman, MD
- Doug Constantine, ATC
- Janice Edwards, MD
- Dennis Hooks, MD
- Samuel Hutchison, MD
- Henry Howard, MD
- David Green, MD
- Eric Greer, MD
- Deborah Peterson, MD
- Loren Laney, MD
- Michael Leonard, MD
- Jack Moody, MD
- Samuel McGill, MD
- Myra Stevens, MD
- Warren Richards, PhD, January 14, 2020
- Randy Richardson, MD
- Jena Ryan, MD
- Karen Samuelson, MD
- Dean Stanley, MD
- Brian Tomlinson, MD
- Colin Tripp, MD
- Allen Zimmerman, MD
- Orange County Public Schools
- Bodily injury photos
- MetLife, billing statement
- Blue Cross Blue Shield, payment summary

Background Information

The following background information was obtained from records and my clinical interview:

FULL NAME:	Mark Rosetti
DATE OF BIRTH:	February 20, 2005
ONSET OF DISABLING PROBLEMS:	May 4, 2017, left ankle incident
RACE:	Caucasian
DOMINANT HAND:	Ambidextrous: writes with left hand and throws with left hand
HEIGHT:	5 feet 9 inches
CURRENT WEIGHT:	Approx. 127 pounds
PARENTS:	John Adam Rosetti, born June 15, 1969
	Ann Newsom Rosetti, born October 14, 1976
SIBLINGS:	Josh, 10
	Nikki, 6
RESIDENCE:	Pensacola, Florida
PRESENTING PROBLEMS:	Left foot weakness with intermittent pain, exacerbated by activity
	Altered gait, more pronounced when fatigued or in pain
	Limited in physically demanding activities such as playing lacrosse
	Inability to move toes of left foot
	Onset of left knee pain such as after performing squat or lunge exercises
	Left foot pain secondary to activities such as driving and running for extended periods or "running hard a much shorter period of time, sprinting"
PROCEDURES SINCE INCIDENT:	Primary repair, left traumatic common peroneal nerve laceration with nerve tube. Irrigation and debridement and laceration, left traumatic leg laceration, Henry Howard, MD, May 4, 2017
	Left prone common peroneal nerve release and graft repair left. Neurolysis of left common peroneal nerve (unusual difficulties). Neurolysis left deep peroneal nerve (unusual difficulty). Neurolysis left superficial peroneal nerve (unusual difficulty). Excision of previous skin scar. Intraoperative neurophysiology, Scott Willard, MD, January 16, 2018
	Left posterior tibial tendon transfer to middle cuneiform, Dennis Hooks, MD, March 18, 2019

TREATMENT SINCE INCIDENT:	Physical therapy, multiple protocols
PRESENT TREATMENT:	Physical therapy, twice per week, approx. one hour per session
TREATING PROFESSIONALS:	Dr. Bose, podiatrist
	Dr. Youman
	Todd Ferman, physical therapist
MEDICATIONS:	Over-the-counter Tylenol and Advil, occasionally for left foot pain
EDUCATION:	Kindergarten through fifth grade, Audubon Park Elementary School
	Sixth through eighth grade, Glenridge Middle School, 4.00 state GPA and 5.00 district GPA
	Ninth grade, Winter Park High School
VOCATIONAL STATUS AT TIME OF INCIDENT:	Sixth grade student
PRESENT VOCATIONAL STATUS:	To begin tenth grade in August 2020

Clinical Interview

Introduction

Mark Rosetti presented as a clean-shaven Caucasian male who had brown hair and brown eyes. He appeared his stated age of 15. I inquired about any problems with his vision, and Mark responded negatively, noting he does not wear corrective lenses.

When asked about his gait, Mark stated, "There is a slight limp," and he apprised me he tends to favor his left side, which is "more prominent" after activity. He reported bearing weight on his left side is painful, "if I'm tired and if I used my foot a lot." Mark told me he was not using an adaptive aid while conversing with me, although he added, "When I wear shoes, I have orthotic inserts within my shoes." He indicated his physical therapist, Mr. Ferman, prescribed his orthotics.

Mark advised me he is ambidextrous, writes with his left hand, and throws with his left hand. He conveyed he is 5 feet 9 inches tall and weighs approximately 127 pounds. "I don't eat that unhealthy. I eat protein all meals of the day," he stated. Mark informed me he is not in a significant other relationship. He described his previous use of an AFO brace and said, "People thought that was kind of weird." He noted his participation in physical therapy and other byproducts of his injuries have "prevented me from being normal" and, by extension, inhibited his social life.

As for siblings, Mark apprised me he has a younger brother and younger sister, who are both healthy and do not have disabling problems. "My dad has some torn muscles," he said, referencing his father's "shoulder and pec."

Concerning his home, Mark reported he lives with his parents and two siblings in a single-story house that has "a single step in it." He told me his parents own the dwelling and that he has lived there "my whole life." He denied planning to relocate or that his home has been modified for disabilities.

I inquired about accessibility limitations within his home, and Mark indicated he has difficulty maneuvering the single step "when I'm tired." He went on to say, "I fall on my face," and he advised me the step does not have a railing near it.

During Mr. Rosetti's 2019 deposition, he conveyed that he is a self-employed commercial litigation and bankruptcy attorney and that he owns the Rosetti Law Firm, PA. Ms. Rosetti noted during her 2019 deposition that she is an attorney and assists her husband with the Rosetti Law Firm. When asked about Mark's future career plans, Ms. Rosetti stated, "He mentioned, 'Mom, wouldn't it be cool if one day I could cure paralysis.' He has mentioned biomedical engineering, but if you ask him now, he'll probably say he doesn't know."

Physical Condition and Medical Information

Mark denied having any medical problems or restrictions near the time before his May 4, 2017, left ankle incident. No preincident surgeries were identified. We reviewed medical records predating his 2017 incident. Mark apprised me his February 2010 brain MRI was initiated to evaluate problems with migraines. I inquired about current migraine problems, and he replied, "I haven't had any recently." He reported his migraines tend to occur after not eating or drinking for extended periods.

When asked about his 2009 left wrist injury, Mark told me he fully recovered. He indicated his gait was normal, "to my knowledge," after he recovered from his preincident left lower extremity injury. Mark did not recall injuring his left hand in 2017 or his left knee in April 2017. He recalled fracturing his left upper extremity "when I was pretty young." He did not recollect any other preincident medical problems.

Regarding unrelated postincident problems, Mark indicated he experienced a left wrist injury in 2019. "You could technically say it was related to my [2017] injury," he stated, advising me that he was "boarded" while playing lacrosse and that his left foot injury precluded him from protecting himself from the impact his left wrist sustained. "It wouldn't have been as bad because I would have been able to stop myself from falling," Mark explained. He advised me his left wrist was cast. I asked him whether he fully recovered, and he replied, "My wrist still hurts when I take a harder shot in lacrosse." No other unrelated postincident medical problems were identified.

As for his understanding of diagnoses physicians have rendered, Mark said, "My peroneal nerve was severed." We discussed his three postincident surgeries.

Concerning the primary problem Mark attributes to his 2017 incident, he stated, "My left foot pain." He apprised me that the only body part injured in his incident was his left lower extremity and that his left foot is his most symptomatic body part. He referenced his last surgery and reported the top part of his foot, "closer to my ankle," is particularly troublesome.

At 8:30 a.m., when I inquired whether he was experiencing any pain, Mark responded negatively. "I haven't done anything strenuous today," he explained. He assessed his symptoms worsen when he increases his activity, causing his left foot to feel "super tight." Mark went on to describe aching and burning sensations. "I used to get electrical shocks," he said, indicating the sensations have "since gone away."

When asked about activities and conditions that cause his symptoms to flare up, Mark cited, "Any activity where my left foot is in heavy use. It seems to be quicker when I'm playing lacrosse."

Mark recounted his left foot pain intensity varies, depending on his activity. Using a 0-to-10 scale, with zero indicating no pain and ten representing the worst pain possible, he rated his left foot pain intensity after vigorous activity from seven to eight, and he referenced playing lacrosse. After a lacrosse game, Mark advised me, he sits in the locker room "to wait for my foot to stop hurting." Before the COVID-19 pandemic, he conveyed, his pain intensity on a typical school day was "maybe a one or a two."

The medical professionals treating Mark, he informed me, are Dr. Bose (podiatrist), Dr. Youman, and Todd Ferman (physical therapist). He noted he had seen all three of his treating providers within a few weeks before my exam. He apprised me that he last saw Dr. Hooks "a good time ago" and that the surgeon discharged him, as did Dr. Belzberg. Mark reported he continues to treat with Mr. Ferman, and no other scheduled medical appointments were identified.

Please see the Review of Medical Records, Operations/Procedures section of this report for details about Mark's postincident operations and procedures. He denied that future surgery has been scheduled or anticipated for him, to the best of his knowledge.

Regarding treatment and therapy since his 2017 incident, Mark cited multiple protocols of physical therapy. He denied undergoing pain management injections. Mark expressed his belief that Dr. Hooks had prescribed his current physical therapy protocol. He told me he participates in physical therapy twice per week, with each session lasting "give or take an hour." He was not aware of the cost of the therapy.

As for adaptive aids, Mark said, "At the moment, I only have orthotic inserts in my [left] shoe. I used to have an AFO until this most recent surgery." He indicated he last used an AFO before his March 18, 2019, operation. Occasionally, he advised me, he uses a left ankle sleeve, "and I have orthotic inserts built into my skate." No other adaptive aids were identified. While meeting with me privately, Mr. Rosetti conveyed his son has expensive, customized shoes.

Mark informed me he is not taking any prescribed medications. "I'll sometimes take two Tylenol or two Advil if my foot pain is really bad," he said when I inquired about taking over-the-counter medications. Mark noted he most recently took an analgesic "a few days ago because my tooth was giving me pain." He apprised me he last took Advil for left foot pain "a week or two ago" after exercising.

Concerning physical capacities, I asked Mark whether he is exempt from any functional activity because of his left foot injury, and he replied, "Any sport that requires a lot of running." He went on to cite difficulties with lateral movements, and he reported playing lacrosse and participating in track and field events are problematic.

When asked about the amount of weight he can safely lift and carry, Mark told me that, before the COVID-19 pandemic, he performed squat exercises with a barbell on his back and approximately 65 pounds of weight, three sets of ten repetitions. He indicated he does not currently have a physician-advised lifting restriction. Mark expressed he is "nervous" when exercising because of his left foot injury.

Mark denied having problems with any cervical spine movements or being limited in using either upper extremity. "A slap shot in lacrosse causes my left wrist to hurt," he stated, citing his aforementioned postincident left wrist injury. Mark denied having problems using his right foot/leg.

During my clinical interview, Mark reported he is able to touch each finger to his thumb on either hand, make a fist with either hand, and extend his arms horizontally and overhead without problems. He advised me his fine motor functioning is intact in both hands.

Regarding physical, everyday activities, Mark cited no problems with bending his waist. He conveyed his left knee is painful when squatting, "if my form isn't perfect." He described climbing stairs as problematic.

Generally, Mark informed me, he can run from 30 to 45 minutes, stand from two to three hours, and walk from 60 to 90 minutes before overexerting himself or needing to rest. He denied being limited in the duration he is able to sit comfortably.

I inquired how often he operates a motor vehicle, and Mark replied, "I'm driving fairly consistently in relation to COVID." He denied having a parking placard for persons who have disabilities.

Mark identified the following additional physical problems:

- Balance—"My balance isn't really as good," he said, citing his left foot injury.
- Fatigue—He noted his left foot tires more easily than his right foot.

Mark discussed falling and noted his most recent fall was approximately four days before my exam, while playing lacrosse. He did not recall his last fall due to an unprovoked reason. He apprised me he is cautious about his activities to preempt further injuring himself. As an example, Mark cited his abstinence from an aggressive soccer match. I asked him about his most recent fall within his home, and he replied, "I cannot recall." He denied that any of his postincident falls caused him permanent injury.

I inquired whether his symptoms change when exposed to various environmental conditions, such as hot or cold/damp conditions, and Mark responded, "I don't know. I haven't experienced enough."

As for the status of his condition, Mark stated, "I am slowly improving." On further inquiry, he said, "Strength-wise and form, when I'm doing things." He was not aware of any current physician-advised restrictions.

Activities of Daily Living

Mark denied having problems with sleeping. Usually, he told me, he goes to sleep at 10:00 p.m. and awakens at 8:00 a.m. Mark denied napping, taking sleep aid medication, or having problems with nightmares. He indicated he is independent in grooming and self-care.

Concerning household chores, Mark advised me he can prepare meals, "unless it's right after a lacrosse game." I inquired about any limitations with routine household chores such as making his bed, sweeping, or vacuuming. "It would be the same scenario," Mark replied, conveying light chores are generally within his capacity, apart from when he is recovering from a period of overexertion. He denied that outside services are employed for incident-related reasons.

Mark informed me his parents employ a yard maintenance service. "I take out the trash, do the dishes, occasionally cleaning," he said when I inquired about other types of household chores he performs.

During Mark's April 2019 deposition, he noted that, before his March 2019 surgery, he could jog with his brace on, ski, and rock climb and that he did not participate in volleyball, kickball, or other activities during physical education class. He stated, "I can't run or sprint. Like move fast and moving side to side. I can't do it." He indicated he plays lacrosse on two different teams: recreational and travel teams. Mark testified he had missed lacrosse games because of his left leg injury. He noted that, before his May 4, 2017, incident, he played lacrosse and also enjoyed soccer, basketball, and football. He further reported he likes to read, play video games, and spend time with his friends. Mr. Rosetti's April 2019 deposition indicates Mark took band class and played the saxophone.

During my clinical interview, Mark said, "I'm not in band anymore. I do play guitar, though, in a guitar class." He apprised me he previously participated in a concert band, not marching band, and he did not associate his left foot injury with ceasing playing the saxophone.

I asked Mark about present hobbies and leisure pursuits, and he advised me he participates in competitive lacrosse in the Central Florida Lacrosse League. "I play defense," he said, conveying the season spans from fall through March, followed by a spring season—from April through May/June. Mark informed me the COVID-19 pandemic has interfered with his participation in lacrosse.

During lacrosse season, Mark noted, he practices two or three times per week. "Then I have lacrosse games every other weekend. I was playing lacrosse every day until this injury happened, and now I obviously can't," he stated. Due to his left foot injury, he apprised me, lacrosse is the only sport he is "able to play."

Because of the pandemic, Mark reported, he began attending school remotely in mid-March 2020. He told me the spring 2020 academic term concluded in late May. Mark indicated he plans to vacation in North Carolina with his family during summer 2020 and resume school in August 2020. He was not aware when lacrosse will resume. "Once it starts, I'm in it," Mark stated.

Mark advised me he plans to continue his participation in competitive lacrosse when the season resumes. "I'm playing at the same [league] skill level, but my personal skill level isn't as good [because of my left foot injury]," he said. He elaborated on movements that he is unable to perform, such as stopping with his left foot and moving it to his left side. Referencing prescribed home exercise, Mark surmised he will be required to perform "in-home physical therapy the rest of my life [to preserve my left foot functioning]."

Mental Health

Mark denied ever participating in mental health treatment or being prescribed psychotropic medications. Referencing his treatment for migraines, he said, "Other than that, not that I remember, no."

I inquired whether he believes he currently needs mental health treatment, and Mark responded, "There have been times when it may have been [advisable to treat with] a mental health professional [postincident]." He added, "I try to be as stoic as possible."

When asked about his overall psychological status, Mark said, "Other than movements where I'm not doing that well, I think I'm doing fine due to my personality." Overall, he assessed he is psychologically well adjusted.

Regarding mental health concerns, Mark said, "There have been times when I've been frustrated and upset." On further questioning, he cited difficulties turning to the left side while playing lacrosse. He went on to note exercising and occurrences "when I have to stop due to my foot."

I asked about any problems with anxiety/stress, and Mark replied, "Nothing out of the ordinary." He specifically denied having trouble with alcohol, drugs, or thoughts of suicide. No other mental health concerns were presented.

Mark was pleasant, polite, likable, and interpersonally skilled. He projected a normal affect. His cognition was intact, and his memory and concentration were good. Mark spoke clearly and coherently. He did not display problems with either expressive or receptive language, and he did not evidence a thought disorder.

Education and Special Training

Again, Mark was completing the sixth grade at the time of his May 4, 2017, left ankle incident. He apprised me he plans to continue his studies at Winter Park High School in August 2020. Mark reported his school attendance during the 2019/2020 academic year was "fine. I only missed a couple of days of school."

A July 31, 2012, record from Orange County Public Schools reports:

Mark was referred for evaluation of his cognitive ability as it relates to eligibility for the Gifted Program.

Current evaluation results indicate that Mark's intellectual functioning is in the Significantly Above Average category of cognitive ability. His Composite Intelligence Index Score of 133 exceeds approximately 99 percent of the scores of other students in the same age group who have been administered this test. The chances that the range of scores from 126 to 137 includes Mark's "true" CIX are approximately 95 out of 100.

According to Mark's 2019 deposition and school records, he is a straight-A student, and his last B grade was during fifth grade. His school transcript indicates he earned 4.00 state and 5.00 district grade point averages during eighth grade. Mark made similar statements during my clinical interview.

An April 2019 Orange County School District educational plan notes Mark is enrolled in the gifted program until April 2022. The record states, "Mark is an exemplary student. He understands new ideas quickly; he is a class leader and is always asking questions." Ms. Rosetti noted her son participates in an International Baccalaureate program.

During my clinical interview, Mark affirmed he has had strong scholastic performance, both before and after his 2017 incident. "I do well," he stated. Mark apprised me that he took the SAT exam during the seventh grade to qualify for the Duke Tip Scholar Program and that he plans to take the exam again during the upcoming school year.

Mark told me math and science are his best subjects in school. "To my knowledge, I'm in the highest classes I could be taking," he stated when I inquired whether he participates in advanced placement (AP) classes.

As for special skills, Mark said, "I'm in a Spanish class. I'm not bilingual. I'm decent at music." Concerning credentials, he indicated he is a certified lacrosse referee, level II, which required him to pass a skills test and exams (open and closed book) and complete a course that required "a couple of hours." He advised me he obtained the credential in fall 2019. Mark conveyed his medical treatment previously interfered with his ability to referee lacrosse games.

I asked Mark about his computer use skills, and he replied, "They're passable." He informed me he can use a variety of software.

Work History

Job Title	Name of Organization	Dates
Part-Time Lacrosse Referee	Central Florida Lacrosse Officials, Sean Corbid	Fall 2019— March 2020, "before COVID"
Car Cleaner		

Interview of Mark Rosetti's Parents, John and Ann Rosetti

I verified that Mr. and Ms. Rosetti were educated as lawyers. "Our firm practices commercial litigation," Mr. Rosetti said.

We reviewed Mark's presenting problems as he presented them to me. Ms. Rosetti noted Mark has difficulty putting on socks and shoes. "It strikes me every time I see it," she said about her observations. Ms. Rosetti elaborated about her son's left foot functional limitations including his inability to wiggle his toes and adaptations he has made.

Mr. Rosetti apprised me his son uses both feet to drive due to problems with moving his left foot. He went on to cite trouble Mark has operating brake and accelerator pedals when fatigued. Mr. Rosetti also reported his son overestimates his ability to run, and he estimated a correct duration is from 15 to 20 minutes. "He's a prideful kid," Mr. Rosetti stated, and Ms. Rosetti added, "As parents, we've never focused on what he can't do." She suggested they employ can-do, encouraging guidance with Mark.

Mr. Rosetti said, "He didn't make his high school varsity lacrosse team," citing Mark's functional limitations because of his left foot injury. Mr. Rosetti elaborated about lacrosse drills his son is unable to perform. He also told me Mark's athletic options have been curtailed.

Ms. Rosetti discussed her son's attempt to play tennis this year. She indicated Mark desired to participate in a sport that his high school sponsors. "Tennis was something he was going to try again," Ms. Rosetti said, advising me Dr. Hooks approved of this. After two lessons, Ms. Rosetti conveyed, her son's left knee pain became "excruciating," and he experienced considerable symptom exacerbation. She elaborated about Mark's limitations with participating in sports, which she suggested is distressing for a 15-year-old athletically inclined youth who is attempting to assimilate socially with his peers.

Referencing her son's participation in prescribed home exercise, Ms. Rosetti said, "It's with him forever," assessing that his participation will be lifelong and that much self-discipline is required. "I'm confident that's a mental toll on him," she added.

Ms. Rosetti informed me Dr. Youman is a local family practice physician specializing in sports medicine. "He's now our home base," she said, noting he is treating Mark for his tendon transfer injury in Dr. Hooks's absence. Ms. Rosetti apprised me Dr. Hooks practices at Johns Hopkins.

Mr. Rosetti affirmed that his son's scholastic performance has not been impaired by his left foot injury. "He's spectacular, and he's so self-driven," Ms. Rosetti added. Mr. Rosetti said, "He's focused on getting good grades in school and his extracurriculars," surmising Mark has the potential to be the valedictorian of his high school class.

Ms. Rosetti offered that Mark was never bullied after his May 4, 2017, left ankle incident; however, she discussed her son's prior need to wear a brace and noted the ill effects on him socially. She reported Mark has missed several of his peers' activities, "and some of the things he doesn't tell us."

The Rosettis verified Mark had no residual problems after his preincident left lower extremity injury. They went on to indicate that all of their son's preincident injuries had fully resolved.

Review of Medical Records

Results of Diagnostic Testing

05/04/17 **Mathew Swinson, MD**

Left Tibia/Fibula

Impression:

Normal left tibia/fibula.

08/07/17 **Larry S. Finkel, MD**

Electromyography

Impression:

A severe lesion in the left common peroneal nerve is present, localized to the region of the fibular head. The prominent acute denervation and lack of reinnervation at 3 months post injury and anastomosis procedure are relatively poor prognostic signs for a good functional recovery. Clinical correlation is advised.

08/17/17 **Arthur Mathews, MD**

Tib-Fib without Contrast

Impression:

1. Enlargement of and abnormal signal intensity within the peroneal nerve just below the level of the fibular head extending into the peroneal tunnel.

2. Edema-like signal and enlargement of the anterior and lateral compartment musculature of the leg, consistent with denervation changes.

10/26/17 **Barry Howell, MD**

US Extremity Nonvascular Complete Left

Impression:

Marked enlargement and heterogenicity of the repaired segment of the left common peroneal nerve. Several individual enlarged fascicles can be identified in continuity throughout the length of the repair, without a residual full-thickness transection demonstrated.

10/27/17   Tom Young, MD

Electromyography

Impression:

> There is electrophysiological evidence of a severe common peroneal neuropathy with no evidence of renal vacation of the deep peroneal innervated muscles. There is modest early innervation of the peroneus longus.

01/05/18   Oscar Crenshaw, MD

Electrodiagnostic Testing

Impression:

> This study demonstrates a complete left deep peroneal neuropathy and partial severe left superficial peroneal neuropathy with distal axonal degeneration.

03/18/19   Emily Dunlap, MD

Left Foot

Impression:

> Splint material obscures evaluation of osseous structures.

> Subcutaneous emphysema on the dorsal and plantar aspects of the mid and forefoot. Surgical changes of medial cuneiform related to tibial split posterior tendon transfer.

05/10/19   Charles Blake, MD

Left Foot

Impression:

> Cast material removed since 3/18/2019 with resolution of immediate postoperative changes such as soft tissue swelling and subcutaneous emphysema. Lucency in the intermediate cuneiform related to surgery demonstrates progression of healing. Mild residual dorsal soft tissue swelling. Osseous demineralization of the foot has developed likely related to disuse. Borderline elevated calcaneal pitch although the talar-first metatarsal angle is preserved.

Operations/Procedures

05/04/17   *Henry Howard, MD*

Procedure:

1. Primary repair, left traumatic common peroneal nerve laceration with nerve tube.

2. Irrigation and debridement and laceration, left traumatic leg laceration.

01/16/18   *Scott Willard, MD*

Procedure:

Left prone common peroneal nerve release and graft repair left.

Neurolysis of left common peroneal nerve (unusual difficulties).

Neurolysis left deep peroneal nerve (unusual difficulty).

Neurolysis left superficial peroneal nerve (unusual difficulty).

Excision of previous skin scar.

Intraoperative neurophysiology.

03/18/19   *Dennis Hooks, MD*

Procedure:

Left posterior tibial tendon transfer to middle cuneiform.

Assessments

05/04/17   *Pensacola Fire Department*

History of Present Illness:

Pt was struck in left leg by lawn mowing edger while riding his bicycle. Pt was sitting on ground on arrival, wound was to left calf, about 2 inches in length, minimal bleeding. Parents on scene stated that they would transport child to hospital.

Plan:

Parents wanted to transport POV, and refused medical transport.

Diana Brennan, MD/Pensacola Hospital

History of Present Illness:

> The patient presents with left lower leg laceration. 12 y/o male with no PMHx and vaccines UTD presents to the ED with left lower leg laceration happening just PTA. Pt was riding his bike in the neighborhood when his lower leg was lacerated by an edger. Mom says she was concerned because pt was not able to move foot well. The location where the incident occurred was neighborhood.

Diagnoses:

> Nerve injury (peroneal).

Disposition:

> Admit.

Richard Appleton, MD/Pensacola Hospital

History of Present Illness:

> Pt was not able to dorsiflex his left foot well. Ortho consulted and pt transferred to OR and repair done. Peroneal nerve laceration, left lower extremity I and D, peroneal nerve repaired.

> He had intermittent urticaria on his upper extremities, upper chest and forehead postop. So we start Benadryl. He is athletic boy.

Assessment:

> Complaining of pain and refuses to drink.

Henry Howard, MD/Pensacola Hospital

History of Present Illness:

> There was a landscape worker with an edger that was working around him. Apparently, the landscaper moved the edger exposing the blade, and made contact with Mark's L lateral leg causing a laceration. Since the injury, parents have noticed the patient's inability to mobilize ankle and toes.

05/04/17   Henry Howard, MD/Pensacola Hospital

Plan:

> PT and AFO order.

> Knee immobilizer on at all times when ambulating.

> FU outpatient.

> DC tomorrow after completion of IV abx.

05/15/17   *Loren Laney, MD*

History of Present Illness:

He is immobilized for 3 weeks. Planned PT. Now with rash under his brace. + itchy and + red. Has tried hydrocortisone/aquafor.

Past Medical History:

1. History of chronic adenoiditis.
2. History of chronic otitis media.
3. History of concussion.
4. History of diaper rash.
5. History of eczema.
6. History of jaundice.
7. History of migraine headaches.
8. History of upper respiratory infection.
9. History of urticaria.
10. History of viral exanthem.
11. History of lisping.
12. History of LSOM (left serous otitis media).
13. History of left wrist injury.
14. History of roseola.

Comments:

Weight 85.2 lb. Percentile 34%.

05/23/17   *Henry Howard, MD*

Plan:

At this time, we recommend to the patient and the patient's mother he may discontinue use of knee immobilizer. We recommend gentle knee as well as ankle range of motion. A prescription for physical therapy was given to the patient. We also recommend the patient may ambulate with use of crutches and then transition slowly without crutches to walk independently. We discussed with the patient to avoid any extreme knee flexion until two weeks from today's office visit.

The patient may also benefit from a customized internal as well as external ankle/foot orthosis to the left lower extremity. A prescription was given for an internal as well as external customized ankle/foot orthosis.

Given his peroneal nerve injury, we recommend obtaining the nerve conduction study at six to nine months postoperatively.

We would like to see the patient back in the office in two to three months for repeat evaluation.

We will contact the patient's mother in terms of referral of a pediatric neurologist.

05/26/17   *Carrie Baker, PT/Pensacola Hospital Sports Medicine and Rehab*

Physical Therapy Lower Extremity Evaluation

Plan:

3x3-6 weeks.

06/22/17   *Carrie Baker, PT/Pensacola Hospital Sports Medicine and Rehab*

Plan:

2-3 x 8 weeks.

07/10/17   *Chris Barnett, MD*

History of Present Illness:

Mark had juvenile migraines when he was five years old.

Before this incident Mark played travel ice lacrosse. He would like to find a way to play again.

Social History:

Patient is in the seventh grade.

Plan:

Recommend talking to Dr. Finkel, Dr. Kane, or Dr. Rathinam for NCV's/EMG studies for prognosis and treatment. Mom prefers Dr. Finkel.

Plan to order a referral with EMG.

Continue bracing and physical therapy.

07/24/17   *Henry Howard, MD*

History of Present Illness:

In the interim, the patient has been wearing two types of ankle foot orthosis. He wears an internal as well as external brace. He has been able to return to activities such as rock climbing. He has been approved to play lacrosse with the use of an external ankle foot orthosis and he is excited to start lacrosse in the fall. The patient would also like to proceed with lacrosse in the future and he is getting cleared to wear an ankle foot orthosis. The patient's mother has been in contact with a brace fabricator to allow the patient to use these external braces. The patient reports no significant pain in his left ankle.

Plan:

We are pleased that the patient is returning to activities as tolerated at this time. We recommend the patient to follow up with Dr. Finkel, a pediatric neurologist, for his peroneal nerve injury.

08/17/17 *Eric Greer, MD*

Assessment:

He had an MRI done of the peroneal nerve. I am waiting on the results of this. He also had an EMG nerve conduction test done, which showed poor conduction across the fibular head and a lot of muscle fasciculation activity in the extensors of the foot and small muscles of the foot.

Impression:

Common peroneal nerve injury, probably distal to the sensory branch. He probably has a neuroma. Whether or not fascicular migration has occurred properly is not clear, but at 3½ months, I would be hopeful that he would start to have some return of function and he has none. At this point, the MRI results have become available and it looks like he does have evidence of thickening of the peroneal nerve just below the fibular head, which may be indication of a neuroma.

Plan:

Dr. Finkel suggested that reexploring the nerve would be in his best interest, based on the EMG nerve conduction results, and I explained to the parents that this is most likely going to be necessary. We talked about neurolysis and neurectomy, as well as grafting, and how all of this is done, including sural grafting versus an AxoGen graft. The parents, right now, really would like to wait and give him a little more time. I explained to them that if there is no improvement by 6 months from the time of injury, then definitely reexploration would be in order. I explained to them that the only concern about waiting is atrophy within the muscle and he has a little bit of atrophy there already, but he is doing his best to keep the muscle active by doing therapy, etc. He does not have any ability for spontaneous movement of the muscles, but he is doing stretching exercises, etc. He is also stretching his Achilles tendon.

Thus, the parents do want to wait, so they will come back and see me in the beginning of October and if he does not show any evidence for even a minor amount of motor improvement, then he will need another operation with neurolysis and/or grafting. Parents are happy with this plan. I will see him back in the beginning of October.

10/20/17 *Carrie Baker, PT/Pensacola Hospital Sports Medicine and Rehab*

Diagnosis:

L peroneal laceration, repair, foot drop.

10/24/17   *Henry Howard, MD*

History of Present Illness:

He does continue to wear an ankle foot orthosis custom brace on the left lower extremity. Both the patient and his mother state that he has not regained active dorsiflexion yet. The patient has no loss of sensation and strictly has motor deficits.

The patient did have an electromyography performed, which revealed the tibialis anterior muscle had prominent denervation without evidence of reinnervation. Again, this was performed approximately three months postoperatively. The patient saw another surgeon at Johns Hopkins who recommends waiting at least six months postoperatively and then follow up with a repeat electromyography study. The patient will be getting a new electromyography and an ultrasound next week while he is at the Mason Clinic.

The patient has been able to play lacrosse with a custom ankle-foot orthosis brace.

Plan:

Dr. Howard does recommend continuing to wait and see if the nerve does regrow function and it is still too soon to tell from our standpoint. The patient may require a nerve transfer, which would be performed by one of these specialized physicians at Johns Hopkins or Mason Clinic. Eventual tendon transfer may be needed. The patient was given a prescription for physical therapy to work on range of motion and strengthening if he does choose to attend.

We will see the patient back in approximately three months for repeat evaluation.

10/26/17   *Brian Tomlinson, MD*

Chief Complaint:

Left foot drop.

Impression:

Left common peroneal nerve laceration, status post direct repair. At this point, I would hope for some clinical recovery. His EMG is scheduled for tomorrow. If there is no recovery on the EMG, one could consider a secondary nerve procedure, which would entail resecting the neuroma in continuity and performing a secondary reconstruction. This would most likely need interpositional grafting. Alternatively, one could give it further time and then consider a tendon transfer. The tendon transfer could be done locally or at Mason with one of my pediatric orthopedic colleagues.

11/26/17 **Samuel Hutchison, MD**

Assessment:

Patient accidentally bumped the left side of his face on the granite wall in the swimming pool, started bleeding from the left side under the eyebrow. No N/V, no visual disturbance.

Diagnosis:

Eyelid laceration, left.

11/27/17 **Chris Barnett, MD**

Assessment and Plan:

Since our last visit together the patient has undergone an EMG nerve conduction study. This was performed at the Mason Clinic in Rochester. This showed a couple of motor unit potentials in the peroneus longus muscle. There were no active motor units in the tibialis anterior.

We discussed at length the concept of a possible surgical exploration versus a wait and watch approach. Our recommendation at this point is to have the EMG nerve conduction study repeated 2 months after the last one. We would be looking for nascent potentials in the tibialis anterior muscle. That would suggest a good prognosis. If that muscle remains without any motor units then we would consider a surgical reexploration with a possible nerve graft repair. Family is in agreement with this approach.

01/05/18 **Scott Willard, MD**

Assessment and Plan:

Patient underwent a nerve conduction study today. There is no response in the motor conduction on the peroneal nerve. There is no response on sensory supply of the left superficial peroneal nerve. There were no motor units in the anterior tibialis. There are reduced motor units present in the peroneus longus.

Plan:

Given that the patient had a primary anterolateral repair in May and he still has no motor units in the tibialis anterior, this carries a very poor prognosis for spontaneous recovery. We have recommended a surgical exploration with intraoperative nerve conduction studies. We will want to demonstrate a compound nerve action potential across the area of grafting. If it does not conduct across the neuroma then we would opt for a nerve graft repair. If there is good conduction across the neuroma then we would consider simply neurolysis. Parents are in full agreement. Arrangements for surgical exploration are underway.

01/17/18 **Scott Willard, MD/Johns Hopkins Hospital**

Discharge Summary

Hospital Course:

On 1/16/2018, Dr. Belzberg performed neurolysis of the peroneal nerve. Intraoperative monitoring was performed and the nerve was functioning across the prior area of repair so further grafting was not done. Some portion of the nerve was noted to be avulsed from the muscle. There was still some fascicles entering the muscle so there was not a clear repair that could be done for this. Wound was dressed, the patient was extubated and taken to the recovery room in satisfactory condition. The patient remained neurologically stable and was discharged to home on 1/17/18.

Work/School Excuse Letter:

S/he is excused from work/school from 1/16/18 until 1/24/18 and should return for follow-up/further treatment.

02/13/18 **Myra Stevens, MD**

History of Present Illness:

Hit his head to the chest of another player during ice lacrosse practice. No LOC and no vomit. He is forgetting what happened after the incident and what he did afterwards. Currently states that he feels fine.

Diagnosis:

Concussion.

02/15/18 **Randy Richardson, MD**

Chief Complaint:

About 2½ years ago, he was diagnosed with a mild concussion. His dad is an assistant coach and did a baseline on him.

07/06/18 **Scott Willard, MD/Johns Hopkins Hospital**

Assessment and Plan:

Patient has been making minimal recovery since the time of surgery. He has a tiny bit of eversion but has not regained any dorsiflexion. He has not regained any sensation.

There is a strong Tinel's on percussion of the common peroneal nerve at the level of the fibular head and then it starts to die off distally. Patient does have grade 3 (3 eversion power). Dorsiflexion however 0-1. There is no sensation in the common peroneal nerve distribution.

Patient underwent a nerve conduction study today. The EMG portion of this shows clear innervation to the tibialis anterior but only a small portion of the muscle. That is consistent with the intraoperative finding of a partial evulsion injury of the nerve from the muscle.

Patient is over a year out from his injury. There was no clear sprouting from the current EMG that would suggest he is going to have a significant change over time. I think he should consider a tendon transfer and will consult with orthopedics for the timing of this and whether it is a worthwhile intervention for him.

08/03/18   *Dennis Hooks, MD*

Impression:

Patient would be a good candidate for tendon transfer but is fairly young, which may pose a problem with tendon tension balancing during the transfer and good postoperative compliance. There is currently no literature to strongly suggest an appropriate age for such a transfer. At this time, they have decided to proceed with a posterior tibialis tendon transfer. He has adequate dorsiflexion and will not need a TAL.

Plan:

Plan for surgery.

11/07/18   *Eric Bose, DPM*

Chief Complaint:

The chief complaint is: pt mom states that he has drop foot due to an accident that happened in 2017. States that since he is prone to stubbing his toe. States that once every few weeks it happens. States that a significant toe stubbing happened and it's still painful and swollen.

Past Medical History:

Foot trauma due to twisting.

Left foot trauma.

Assessment:

Compression arthralgia of the ankle/foot.

The gait demonstrated a left foot drop.

02/22/19   *Dennis Hooks, MD*

Impression:

Patient and family would like to pursue plan for PTTT transfer. A thorough conversation was held between Dr. Hooks, the patient, and the patient's mother discussing all options. At this time, they have decided to proceed with a posterior tibialis tendon transfer and surgery scheduled. He has adequate dorsiflexion and will not need a TAL.

Plan:

Follow up care for first 2 weeks in Baltimore then return to Pensacola.

04/01/19 Gregg Fike, MD

Record Review

Impression and Plan:

> Mark Rosetti has suffered a permanent injury as a result of this incident. He has significant and near-complete peroneal nerve injury. The records seem to reflect that he had a complete foot drop. This is not expected to recover at this point.

05/10/19 Dennis Hooks, MD

Assessment:

> Mark Rosetti is 7 weeks s/p left posterior tibial tendon transfer to middle cuneiform on 3/18/19, doing well and progressing appropriately at this interval postoperatively. We will transition to a short CAM walking boot and start his course of physical therapy as scheduled.

11/18/19 Gregg Fike, MD

Letter Addressed to Ms. Conte

> I have reviewed the MRI of the tibia and fibula on Mark Rosetti. This does not alter the opinions I have expressed previously.

12/09/19 Dennis Hooks, MD

Assessment:

> He has returned to running and playing lacrosse with help of orthotics and PT BIW. His gait, stride, and cadence have felt mostly normal from what he can tell. He does however complain of persistent discomfort when walking barefoot. The off-ice practices for lacrosse are difficult for him as he has weakness with running.

01/29/20 Eric Bose, DPM

History of Present Illness:

> Patient presents today to follow up on foot drop surgery done in Baltimore March 2019.

Assessment:

> Left foot drop.

02/11/20 Dean Stanley, MD

History of Present Illness:

> The patient is a 15-year-old male seen today for the left knee. Patient's description of how the problem occurred: patient started having anterior left knee pain a few weeks ago, NSI. Patient's pain is also located along the medial border of the patella. He and his mom feel this is due

to increased physical activity now that he is almost one year postop from tendon transfer, which was done in March of 2019.

He is in the 9th grade at Winter Park High School and plays travel lacrosse at the RDV. He would like to play tennis, but feels he can't with his knee pain. On average, the patient's pain level is 5/10.

He is a lacrosse player. He had an acute movement and pain from an event at lacrosse practice. He was not able to walk on it. He felt better the next day.

He goes to P.T. at OH for posterior tibial transfer. He notes that he started more plyometrics at P.T. 2-3 weeks ago.

He also did harder plyometrics with his trainer.

His pain is anteromedial. It hurts with running and longer walking. He is practicing with his lacrosse team right now.

Impression:

Left patellofemoral pain.

Treatment Plan:

The patient was educated on patellofemoral pain syndrome.

I have recommended amending his P.T. to accommodate the patello-femoral pain.

2-3 per week for 4-6 weeks. Naprosyn 500 mg tablets were prescribed.

03/03/20 Gregg Fike, MD

Compulsory Medical Examination

History of Present Illness:

Today Mark reports pain associated with the tendon following the tendon transfer. The tendon transfer was apparently performed nearly one year ago. He reports that that leg and foot continue to become tired. He used to have electrical shocks and could not walk, but he now has some dysesthetic pain that remains, but is more intermittent. It is not constant. He may still be improving strength-wise, with continued technique as regards the posterior tibial tendon transfer. He plays ice lacrosse. He enjoys working out. He has tried tennis, but he has had some troubles with knee pain. No further surgery is planned at this time. He has used an ankle and foot orthosis in the past, but not now. He reports that running causes the transferred tendon to tighten up, as does standing for a length of time.

He has had to hobble off the ice rink before he has to be carried off of it. He continues with physical therapy twice a week.

Impression and Plan:

Mark Rosetti is suffering a peroneal nerve section/avulsion. He is left with a permanent injury in the sense that he has had multiple surgeries, and still has disordered function of the distal left lower extremity. He is undergoing physical therapy, but these injuries will remain permanent and will not resolve fully. Future medical costs should be somewhat limited and related principally to physical therapy. No further surgery or treatment is indicated. He is unrestricted in his activities from my standpoint with the obvious qualification that again, the foot is not normal.

03/23/20   Gregg Fike, MD

Letter Addressed to Ms. Conte

This is the deposition of Alan Belzberg. The attachments to the deposition are very helpful. They have the Johns Hopkins records.

These records do not alter any opinions I have expressed in my prior correspondence.

Results of Preinjury Diagnostic Testing

02/04/10   Janice Edwards, MD

Electroencephalogram

Impression:

This is normal EEG for age. Clinical correlation is recommended.

02/12/10   Marc Stapleton, MD

MRI Scan of the Brain

Impression:

1. No focal intraparenchymal abnormality is identified.

2. There is no area of restricted diffusion.

3. There is no evidence of diminished fractional anisotropy on the diffusion tensor images.

4. Note is made of moderate inflammatory changes in the paranasal sinuses and minimal inflammatory changes in the mastoid air cells.

01/12/12   Peter Grand, MD

MRI Left Foot without Contrast

Impression:

1. Stress fractures of the head and neck of the visualized talus and the navicular bone. There is a bone bruise or stress reaction seen in the inferior proximal cuboid bone. The fifth metatarsal bone appears normal.

2. Strain or partial tear of the visualized quadratus plantae muscle.

3. Reactive or posttraumatic changes in the subcutaneous fat anterior to the bones of the midfoot.

Preinjury Assessments

04/06/09 *James Herman, MD*

History of Present Illness:

He injured his left wrist yesterday when he apparently fell out of a bounce house.

Impression:

Buckle fracture of the metaphyseal/diaphyseal junction of the distal radius, left wrist x one day.

Plan:

At this point, we have agreed to place him in a long arm cast for immobilization.

05/06/09 *James Herman, MD*

Plan:

At this point he may discontinue the splint and gradually return to normal activities as tolerated. We will see him back on an as-needed basis.

02/04/10 *Jena Ryan, MD*

Letter addressed to Gregory D. Gordon, MD

Comments:

As you know, Mark is a 4½-year-old boy who has been referred to our office for evaluation of headaches.

Mark started complaining of headaches at 2 years of age. He describes his headaches as bifrontal headaches. Over the last few months, there has been significant increase in frequency and severity of headaches. Mark had 3 bad headaches around Christmas time relieved by emesis.

Intermittently, Mark complains of retroorbital pain. Some of the headaches have been severe enough to the point that Mark looks pale and has photophobia. Typically, headaches are relieved by vomiting, Tylenol, and sleep.

With several headaches Mark woke up in the morning and looked pale and complained of headaches. On average they have been occurring at least once a week over the last month.

Social History:

> Mark is currently at JCC. He received speech therapy for 1 or 2 years just for mild lisp. Lisp has corrected. Mark lives at home with parents and 1-year-old brother.

Impression:

> Mark Rosetti is a 4½-year-old boy with 2-year history of intermittent headaches that have worsened over the last 2 months especially around Christmas time. Some of the headaches are associated with vomiting, nausea, and photophobia.
>
> I believe that most likely Mark has migraine headaches; however, secondary causes of headaches should be ruled out first.

Plan:

> At this time, I requested brain MRI, CBC, CMP, TSH, ANA, and ESR along with EEG.

04/07/10 Jena Ryan, MD

Impression:

> Mark Rosetti is a 5-year-old boy with history of migraine headaches. Routine EEG, brain MRI, and blood work have all been within normal limits. Headaches have significantly decreased since his last visit with us. Overall, he is doing well, and mother has no other neurological concerns.

05/27/10 Scott Bookman, MD

Impression:

> Possible allergic rhinitis.

12/13/11 Michael Leonard, MD

History of Present Illness:

> The patient is a 6-year-old male here for evaluation of his left foot pain. He states approximately three to four days ago, he was playing on the playground. He was tripped and thinks he may have hit or injured his left foot on a rock. After the injury, he had pain over the lateral aspect of the foot. He states since that injury he has had difficulty bearing weight and has been walking on the inside part of his foot with a slight limp.

Impression:

> The patient has a left foot fifth metatarsal bone contusion versus occult fracture.

Plan:

We will place him in a short-leg walking cast. He can be weight bearing as tolerated. We will have him avoid any high-impact running or twisting activities.

May return to school on 12/13/2011.

01/12/12 *Eric Bose, DPM*

Chief Complaint:

The chief complaint is: pt mom states that Leonard put him in a cast on his L foot. States that he was sensitive on his L lateral foot. States that they since did not find a fracture but put him in a cast anyways. States that when the cast came off (after Christmas) there was one time that his foot felt "flat." Mom states that nothing is consistent. States that right now he is walking funny.

History of Present Illness:

Mark M. Rosetti is a 6 year old male. Past medical history reviewed— lateral left foot soft tissue swelling.

Assessment:

Possible closed fracture of the base of the fifth left metatarsal.

Plan:

An MRI.

01/31/12 *Eric Bose, DPM*

Assessment:

Closed fracture of the navicular bone of the left foot.

Closed fracture of the left talus.

Plan:

Continue walking boot.

02/21/12 *Eric Bose, DPM*

Chief Complaint:

The chief complaint is: recheck L ft talus fx after rwc, Pt states it is not painful anymore.

Plan:

PRN.

02/28/12   Eric Bose, DPM

Chief Complaint:

> The chief complaint is: pt mom states Mark has been limping since he stopped using RWC last week.

03/05/12   Randy Moody, PT

Physical Therapy Lower Extremity Evaluation

History of Present Illness:

> Patient reports that he fell on his foot and it hurt but he was not taken in to the doctor until he began limping. He fractured talus, navicular and 5th metatarsal. He has been out of the boot for 2 weeks and mother states that he is continuing to walk on the outside of his foot and with a limp.

Plan:

> 2 x a week for 4 weeks.

07/31/12   Karen Gardner, MA, NCSP/Orange County Florida Public Schools

Psychoeducational Report

Reason for Referral:

> Mark was referred for evaluation of his cognitive ability as it relates to eligibility for the Gifted Program.

Summary and Conclusions:

> Current evaluation results indicate that Mark's intellectual functioning is in the Significantly Above Average category of cognitive ability. His Composite Intelligence Index Score of 133 exceeds approximately 99 percent of the scores of other students in the same age group who have been administered this test. The chances that the range of scores from 126 to 137 includes Mark's "true" CIX are approximately 95 out of 100.

11/30/15   Sarah Kemron, MD/Pensacola Hospital

Chief Complaint:

> Injury to head x 2 yest in lacrosse tournament.

Impression:

> Concussion.

01/23/17 *William Spinner, MD*

History of Present Illness:

Mark Rosetti is an 11-year-old young man with a left hand injury after playing with ice balls when they were on vacation. The patient got an impact injury over the hand. He had a lot of pain and swelling, and now three weeks later the swelling persists, so he is here with his mother wondering if anything can be done.

Assessment:

X-rays taken of the left hand show evidence of a healed probable neck metacarpal fracture of the index with near anatomic alignment, slight volar angulation, and no evidence of any pathology or pathologic fracture or bony tumor is noted.

Impression:

Healing left hand metacarpal closed fracture compatible with an impact injury about a month ago.

Plan:

Return to normal activities.

04/01/17 *Jack Moody, MD*

History of Present Illness:

This is a very pleasant and cooperative male, who comes in today concerning his left knee. He is 12 years of age. He tells me on or about 03/19/2017, he tripped and fell and he hit his knee on the stairs. He is having pain in the area of the left tibial tubercle that has persisted. His mother brings him in for orthopaedic evaluation and care at this time.

Assessment:

Contusion of tibial tubercle, left knee.

Plan:

1. Use over-the-counter ibuprofen.

2. Activities as tolerated.

Summary and Impressions

I.   Mark Rosetti was 12 years old and completing the sixth grade at the time of his May 4, 2017, left ankle incident. He is now 15 years old, and he recently completed the ninth grade. Mark underwent the first of three surgeries on his left lower extremity the day of his May 4, 2017, incident. Records document subsequent surgeries on January 16, 2018, and March 18, 2019. Since he became injured, Mark returned to school and his academic progress has not been interrupted; however, he has had periods of absence because of medical treatment. Records indicate he has maintained robust scholastic performance, and his preincident and postincident scholastic performance is comparable. Indeed, Mark has established a very impressive scholastic record. He indicated no accommodations are extended to him at his school. "I only missed a couple of days of school [during the 2019/2020 academic year]," Mark stated. Mr. Rosetti informed me his son has the potential to be the valedictorian of his high school class. Mark is in the growth phase of his career development. The career ambitions he is currently considering include pursuing studies in biomedical engineering. When discussing occupations he has contemplated pursuing, Mark expressed concern his problems with bearing weight would limit his options—including a career as a surgeon. We discussed outpatient surgeries that would involve limited periods of bearing weight, and I discussed with his parents the increasing trend in robotic surgeries. I recommend that Mark pursue career counseling in the upcoming years to facilitate his career decision-making and planning.

II. Preaccident medical records document abnormalities detected in imaging of Mark's left foot in January 2012. On February 1, 2012, Dr. Bose indicated that Mark experienced a left foot talus fracture. He subsequently participated in physical therapy. Mark told me he fully recovered from his preincident left lower extremity injury "to my knowledge," and his leg was asymptomatic at the time of his 2017 incident. His parents conveyed similar information to me, and I am not aware of any contradictory evidence.

III. As noted earlier, Mark underwent three left lower extremity surgeries after his May 4, 2017, incident. His most recent surgery was in March 2019. The most recent records I reviewed are from Dr. Fike. The orthopedic surgeon assessed Mark is "suffering a peroneal nerve section/avulsion. He is left with a permanent injury in the sense that he has had multiple surgeries, and still has disordered function of the distal left lower extremity." Dr. Fike determined Mark does not require further surgery and stated Mark "is unrestricted in his activities from my standpoint with the obvious qualification that again, the foot is not normal." The primary problem Mark presented related to his left foot pain. He told me he was pain-free when I inquired about any pain he was feeling. Mark qualified his comment by noting we were speaking early in the morning, and his activity level had been nominal. He went on to explain that his left ankle area becomes more painful when he increases his activity. Generally, when engaged in sedentary/light activities, Mark suggested, he experiences scant pain problems. He conveyed participating in vigorous physical activity, such as a competitive lacrosse game, causes his pain to occur. He told me he has a "slight limp" that becomes more prominent after activity. Mr. and Ms. Rosetti discussed their son's presenting problems and indicated he tends to understate them because of his character and pride.

IV. Mark possesses several assets facilitative to his ongoing rehabilitation. He is a younger individual (age 15) who is cognitively intact. Again, he has demonstrated very superior scholastic performance, and records from Orange County Florida Public Schools include testing that indicates Mark's intelligence is approximately at the 99th percentile. Apart from orthotic shoe inserts, he does not use adaptive aids. He derives from an advantaged family background; both of his parents have advanced degrees as lawyers who have established their own practice. Further, they appear to be exemplary role models, providing resources and support to their son. From a functional perspective, Mark advised me he regularly exercises and trains for lacrosse. He informed me that, before the COVID-19 pandemic, he performed squat exercises with a barbell on his back and approximately 65 pounds of weight, three sets of ten repetitions. Mark denied having any problems with his right foot/leg. He reported his fine motor functioning is intact. Mark denied having any problem with bending his waist. He estimated he can generally run from 30 to 45 minutes (Mr. Rosetti opined this is an overstatement), stand from two to three hours, and walk from 60 to 90 minutes before overexerting himself or needing to rest. He denied having any limitations with sitting. When I inquired about the stability of his condition, Mark stated, "I am slowly improving." He did not identify specific physician-advised restrictions, and I am unaware of any documentation of this sort. Mark responded negatively when I inquired about difficulty sleeping. He told me he plans to continue playing competitive lacrosse, as he has postincident. Mark assessed he is psychologically well adjusted, and I concur. On a personal level, I found him pleasant, polite, likeable, and interpersonally skilled. He projected a normal affect. Mark also impressed me as mature, poised, and self-confident.

V. I appreciate Mark has sustained a permanent injury affecting his left ankle area. Fortunately, he possesses several assets that bode well for his career development. I also appreciate that the preincident theoretical universe of occupations available to him has become constricted; however, within a reasonable degree of vocational rehabilitation probability, Mark's injuries and associated disabling problems have not caused him a loss of earning capacity. My prognosis for his career development is very good.

VI. The injuries Mark sustained to his left lower extremity on May 4, 2017, will require future rehabilitation intervention, and I am preparing a life care plan to this end.

Date _____

Michael Shahnasarian, PhD
Certified Life Care Planner #258
Certified Rehabilitation Counselor #3701
Certified Vocational Evaluator #58360
International Psychometric Evaluator Certification #985
Licensed Psychologist PY5644
Fellow, American Psychological Association
Fellow, International Academy of Life Care Planners
Fellow, National Career Development Association

CHAPTER 5

Adult Cases

Earning capacity assessments of adults vary widely from those involving children, youth, and young adults. To begin, adults typically possess higher levels of maturity and knowledge of the world of work, and they have (1) implemented decisions that have shaped to varying degrees their career development and (2) established a record that reflects their successes, challenges, capacities, and potential.

Additionally, in some cases, adults' medical histories, predating what motivated a pending vocational evaluation, merit consideration, since adults have lived longer than young people with potential concomitant life experiences and vocationally relevant implications. These histories sometimes include medically relevant factors, such as a progression of preexisting medical problems. In the absence of an issue in dispute, along with unrelated postincident injuries and medical problems an evaluee might have acquired, these factors can complicate an earning capacity assessment. Evaluators must parse related and unrelated disabling problems and their likely effects on evaluees' career developments and earning capacities. In some cases, the assessment also requires a consideration of the effects of new injuries on preexisting conditions and, by extension, effects on earning capacity.

Further, adults' backgrounds sometimes include personal factors—unique family responsibilities, dual career issues, criminal histories, drug and alcohol problems, or patterns of work-related underachievement/overachievement, to name a few—that can hold vocational implications. Some voluntarily cede their ability to work and earn wages, for example, while raising children, providing eldercare, or choosing to undergo a hiatus from the workplace. Additionally, some adults lack monetary-based motivation to work and/or optimize their earning capacity for reasons that include inheritances and trust funds that reduce their financial work incentives, decisions not to work to avoid jeopardizing disability and insurance benefits, and perceived entitlement of monetary benefits being pursued through litigation (i.e., secondary gain). Such factors, of course, also become relevant when assessing preinjury and postinjury vocational behavior and claims of loss of earning capacity.

Another difference between cases involving young people and adults are case-specific questions that often arise due to adults' established educational and work histories. For example, in some cases, injuries and associated disabling problems preclude adult evaluees from resuming their former jobs and career paths, yet they remain capable of alternate employment. These cases generally require assessments of factors that include their transferable skills, retraining potential and retraining options, need for and viability of implementing workplace accommodations, and potential job placement challenges. Diminished work life expectancy in light of injury-related problems also may become a relevant consideration.

In cases that involve young adults with difficult beginnings in their career development, evaluators should place proper perspective on vocationally relevant facts to discourage improper stereotyping. A good example derives from a case involving a 23-year-old male who left school during the 11th grade, pursued employment as a laborer, and had not attempted the General Educational Development (GED) exam before sustaining injuries that reduced him to light-duty functional capacities. An excerpt from the evaluator's report appears next.

> Mr. Tonto suggested he was raised in a disadvantaged household, which adversely affected his educational pursuits. During the 11th grade, he explained, he left school due to scholastic difficulties and confusion about his academic status. His parents divorced when he was in elementary school, and he lived mostly with his father as a child and teenager. "I had problems with my dad, so it caused other issues growing up," Mr. Tonto said. He conveyed his father "had issues with both [drugs and alcohol]," and he suggested he was raised in a less-than-stable home environment. "That's why everything didn't go as planned with getting my diploma and GED," Mr. Tonto stated. He told me he plans to further his education through employee benefit resources available to him with his current employment as a senior stocker with National Supermarkets.

Background information along these lines adds to the context necessary to suppress prejudgments of the evaluee as a high school dropout with little career development potential. The evaluator extracted evidence from her examination—including results from testing and observations of adaptive behaviors indicative of positive work motivation—to describe how the evaluee's upbringing stifled his ability to realize his potential, which his injuries have further challenged. Sizemore and Walker (2020) discussed potential manifestations of adverse childhood experiences on occupational functioning during adulthood.

Chapter 2 described conceptual processes essential to analyzing a claim of loss of earning capacity, and Chapter 3 detailed the mechanics necessary for an evaluator to employ while synthesizing theoretical bases and processing case-specific facts. The foundational bases these chapters specify apply to all cases—pediatric and adult. Chapter 4 outlined special considerations when evaluating pediatric claims of loss of earning capacity, and the remainder of this chapter addresses outcome decisions evaluators most often reach in their assessments of adult claims of loss of earning capacity, namely:

- The evaluee did not experience a loss of earning capacity.
- The evaluee did experience a loss of earning capacity, and the loss can be quantified.
- Retraining and/or other interventions are necessary to mitigate earning capacity damages.

Detailed case examples, presented later, describe evaluators' integration of factual and analytical considerations to formulate one of the three types of conclusions just listed. Examples of complex situations that sometimes arise while evaluating an adult's claim of loss of earning capacity follow. This chapter concludes with a sample full report of a vocational rehabilitation evaluation in a case involving an adult evaluee.

Conclusion of No Loss of Earning Capacity

As noted in Chapter 1, all analyses of claims of loss of earning capacity ultimately address a central question: Is there a differential between an evaluee's preinjury and postinjury earning capacity? If the evaluator determines the answer to this question is no, the analysis concludes. Alternately, the analysis expands with assessments of viable interventions to mitigate vocational damages and the valuation of any differential in earning capacity that cannot be reconciled.

Like all opinions pertaining to claims of loss of earning capacity, opinions that an evaluee has not sustained a loss consider contemporary and future vocationally relevant factors. While an evaluee might have resumed employment offering compensation comparable to preinjury levels, for example, an evaluator must also consider questions related to the evaluee's future career development, such as:

- Will the evaluee experience problems with symptom exacerbation and functional decline that threaten to impair future employability?
- Do injuries imperil career advancement and opportunities to realize higher earnings levels?
- Is there a likelihood that an evaluee's work life will be shortened, secondary to a progression of injury-related problems?

In cases where an evaluator concludes an evaluee's injuries preclude a return to preinjury employment and career development options, the assessment then focuses on the evaluee's residual capacities, efforts made to mitigate claimed damages, and viability of the evaluee assuming alternate employment that offers compensation comparable to preaccident levels. Labor market research sometimes facilitates this analysis. Injuries may prohibit an evaluee from resuming prior employment; however, this does not necessarily lead to a conclusion that the injuries have caused a loss of earning capacity.

Further, in some cases, such as the following example, an evaluator may conclude that an evaluee is underemployed postinjury (i.e., underachieving career and earning capacity potential) but has not experienced a loss of earning capacity. The state of underemployment may be self-selected and attributable to factors that include convenience and job satisfaction. That is, evaluees sometimes accept employment offering lower pay in exchange for greater job satisfaction, less stress, and enhanced quality of life—factors that appear operative in the following case example.

Case Example

In the following example, the evaluee had been performing sedentary, office-based work when she sustained injuries to her neck, shoulders, and spine in a motor vehicle accident. The evaluee's employer severed her employment when she did not return to work following the expiration of her Family and Medical Leave Act benefits. Afterward, the evaluee reentered the workplace, having secured a job that made use of her transferable skills and involved exertional demands comparable to those of her preaccident job. The evaluee's new employment, however, offered compensation of approximately 20 percent less than her preaccident pay, and she pursued a claim of loss of earning capacity. In addition to her diminished postaccident rate of pay, the evaluee's rationale included an assertion that postaccident driving-related anxiety and discomfort with lengthy travel restricted the universe of jobs accessible to her. By extension, she contended her current rate of pay represented her earning capacity.

The evaluator ultimately concluded the evaluee was underemployed, and a claim of loss of earning capacity was unmerited. His determination included an assessment of relevant Earning Capacity Assessment Form-2 factors guided by the Earning Capacity Assessment Theory analytical process (please refer to Chapter 2). The evaluation process included labor market research that identified pending work opportunities within the evaluee's self-defined travel confines. Implicit in the evaluator's opinion is that no mitigation interventions—such as worksite accommodations or retraining—are in order, and the evaluee is voluntarily underemployed, which is her prerogative.

Of note, the evaluator learned of significant unrelated postaccident medical problems the evaluee encountered, including a myocardial infarction that necessitated a quadruple bypass operation. The evaluator reckoned preexisting and unrelated postaccident medical problems were relevant in evaluating claimed damages, which also included a claim for future accident-related treatment. Excerpts from the evaluator's report appear next.

Summary and Impressions

I.   A 1984 high school graduate, Ms. Minchin noted she had employer-sponsored training in professional underwriting, effective collections, and legal collection procedures. During summer 2019, she reported, she completed a six-week QuickBooks course. The work history Ms. Minchin presented included several credit and collection positions. Superior Autos hired her as an accounting clerk (DOT #2143482-010) in June 2012, and she maintained this employment through the time of her December 6, 2017, motor vehicle accident. Based on my understanding of her job responsibilities, Ms. Minchin's job involved sedentary, semiskilled tasks. She earned $19.50 per hour and worked 40 to 45 hours per week in a traditional office environment, which was a 19-mile drive from her home. The first postaccident treatment Ms. Minchin pursued was the following day, when she saw Dr. Baynes, a chiropractor; these records document complaints of neck, shoulder, and spine symptoms Ms. Minchin presented. She told me her symptoms worsened, and she underwent procedures on her left shoulder on April 6, 2018. After her accident, Ms. Minchin assumed a short-term disability leave of absence on January 10, 2017. She said Superior Autos "terminated me [in April 2018] because I went beyond the allowed [Family and Medical Leave Act] time." According to Ms. Minchin, Dr. Baynes had been restricting her from returning to her accounting clerk job, and Superior Autos "never gave me any notice. They just terminated me." The only subsequent employment Ms. Minchin reported has been her current job as a billing clerk with All American Solutions, Inc. (AAS). Her current job requires exertion comparable to her former accounting clerk position with Superior Autos, albeit less cognitively complex. Ms. Minchin informed me she works 37 hours per week and earns $16 per hour. She has had two pay increases—most recently in October 2020—since her employment with AAS commenced. Ms. Minchin apprised me her current job responsibilities are within her capacity. No accommodations are extended to her, and she has not requested any. Ms. Minchin provided the following response when asked whether she believes she is capable of resuming her former accounting clerk job with Superior Autos: "I have no interest to go back to the firm—too much work. Poor management, and too much stress." Reflecting on her experience and skillset, Ms. Minchin assessed she is underemployed. "With my QuickBooks certification and my experience, I should be making more money," she explained. She opined that jobs for which she is qualified and offer compensation greater than she is currently generating would require her to commute beyond a radius she feels comfortable driving. Ms. Minchin advised me she is restricting her universe of prospective employers to a radius of ten to 15 miles from her home, "due to my anxiety of driving, and wear and tear on me physically." The preaccident career plans she presented were to maintain her employment with Superior Autos. "Just work through retirement age at this point. I don't have career plans," Ms. Minchin stated, responding to my query about current career plans. She has not sought alternate employment since she began her tenure with AAS, and she denied planning to begin a job search. Ms. Minchin conveyed her current commute to AAS is a 15-minute drive from her home. She denied having any absences because of medical problems during 2020. Additionally, she assessed her employment with AAS is secure. Ms. Minchin noted her performance appraisals have been positive. She reported no doctor has restricted her from working since she returned to work. She is 56 years old and in the maintenance phase of her career development.

II. Ms. Minchin's medical history before and after her December 6, 2017, motor vehicle accident is significant from a vocational rehabilitation perspective. She was diagnosed with diabetes at age 39 and has a history of multiple miscarriages. Ms. Minchin's problems with depression and anxiety predate her 2017 accident, and she had pursued psychotherapy and psychotropic medication to address her mental health concerns. Ms. Minchin's psychotherapy records document problems in her marital relationship, and she apparently characterized her husband as a "drug addict who is demanding of her" to her psychotherapist (please reference the February 5, 2021, record noted on page 25). Also of note, unrelated to Ms. Minchin's December 2017 accident, she experienced a myocardial infarction on May 20, 2020, and she underwent a quadruple bypass operation on June 9, 2020. Ms. Minchin's medical history unrelated to her December 6, 2017, accident is important to consider when evaluating damages claims she associates with her accident.

III. As noted earlier, Ms. Minchin initially presented complaints related to her neck, shoulders, and spine, and she underwent left shoulder surgery on April 6, 2018—an arthroscopy with labral tear repair and other procedures. Ms. Minchin reported to me that her lower back and left shoulder restrictions are her primary accident-related problems. Her lower back is her most symptomatic body part. Ms. Minchin underwent bilateral lumbar radiofrequency ablations in October 2020. She noted the intervention has yet to relieve her pain. From a functional perspective, she advised me she has no lifting restrictions with her right upper extremity, and she can lift from five to seven pounds with her left upper extremity. Ms. Minchin denied having problems with any cervical spine movement, using her right hand/arm, or using either lower extremity. Her fine motor functioning is intact in both hands, Ms. Minchin reported. She estimated she can walk 30 minutes and sit approximately one hour before exceeding her tolerance. She responded negatively when asked about problems with driving, although she expressed feeling uncomfortable after periods in excess of 45 minutes. My analysis has led me to conclude that her former position as an accounting clerk and her current position as a billing clerk remain within her capacity.

IV. Ms. Minchin possesses several assets facilitative to her vocational rehabilitation. She is cognitively intact, and she scored in the average range on a measure of intellect administered during my exam. Apart from eyeglasses, Ms. Minchin does not use adaptive aids. Further, she is not taking any medications for accident-related reasons, and she is not participating in treatment or therapy. Ms. Minchin did not identify specific physician restrictions, and I am unaware of any documented. She demonstrated her postaccident capacity to secure and maintain a position making use of her transferable skills. Ms. Minchin has work experience and transferable skills as previously delineated.

V. My work in Ms. Minchin's case included conducting labor market research to identify positions in her locale for which she is qualified. Specifically, my research focused on current employment opportunities within a 20-mile radius of her home in Carmel, Indiana. My efforts successfully identified several positions that offer compensation greater than what Ms. Minchin is generating and commensurate with or greater than what she earned when Superior Autos employed her. The opportunities I identified include:

- QuickBooks Bookkeeper, Indiana Commercial Care
- Accounting Manager, Village Jewelry and Gift Shop
- Insurance & Billing Specialist, Smeltzer and Associates
- Remote Financial Controller, ENT Associates
- Payroll Accountant, CFS of Central Indiana

Again, Ms. Minchin has not sought other employment since she began her current billing clerk job with AAS in October 2018. I concur with her assessment that she is underachieving her earning capacity; however, this appears to be a product of her choice. There are work opportunities Ms. Minchin could pursue that meet her self-imposed commute criteria. My analysis has led me to conclude that her December 6, 2017, motor vehicle accident did not affect her earning capacity.

Conclusion That the Evaluee Did Experience a Loss of Earning Capacity, and the Loss Can Be Quantified

One or more of the following criteria must be met for an evaluator to conclude an evaluee's injuries have caused a loss of earning capacity: (1) an evaluee cannot resume prior employment or alternate employment offering levels of compensation commensurate with demonstrated preinjury levels, (2) viable interventions to mitigate vocational damages fail to fully restore an evaluee's work capacity to its preinjury level, (3) there is a reasonable basis to project future decline in work capacity, which will adversely affect an evaluee's earnings, or (4) injuries have reduced an evaluee's ability to realize latent career development and earning capacity potential. The rationale for reaching this conclusion could have exertional and/or nonexertional bases.

Once loss of earning capacity has been determined, the evaluator's next task is to quantify the degree of the loss. In some cases, mitigation efforts vis-a-vis workplace accommodations or retraining may diminish the loss, and evaluators consider in their damages calculations the costs associated with these interventions. For example, a carpenter—unable to resume physically demanding construction work he performed before both of his lower extremities were amputated—pursued a two-year retraining program to become a computer-assisted drafter. The earning capacity damages in this case include tuition costs associated with retraining, lost wages while retraining, and differentials between preinjury and postinjury earning capacity on the evaluee's workplace reentry.

An evaluee's degree of earning capacity loss can be quantified in various ways; a synthesis of case-specific factors can guide the evaluator's determination of the best method(s) for a case at hand. In all cases, evaluators should conform to scientific precepts and implement the most parsimonious yet comprehensive methods.

A case example follows and involves an evaluee who acquired cognitive deficits that impaired his work capacity. In accord with the law of parsimony and case-specific factors, the evaluator selected methods to comply with standards of practice specific to the case's nuances to quantify an assessment of loss of earning capacity.

Case Example

Unequivocal evidence of permanent cognitive deficits arising from a medical incident prompted this claim of loss of earning capacity evaluation. The evaluee's presenting problems included difficulty with processing, memory, and maintaining focus, along with some trouble with speech production.

Briefly, the 49-year-old evaluee held jobs as a full-time security agent and part-time customer service agent at an airport when he became disabled after multiple cerebrovascular accidents. He also had been intermittently pursuing college studies. The evaluator learned the evaluee had no physical limitations; however, the evaluator determined that, although the evaluee was a candidate for vocational rehabilitation, his cognitive deficits precluded a return to his former employment.

Assessing the evaluee's residual nonexertional capacities via a review of records, clinical interview, interpretation of test results, and consultation with a neurologist who also examined the evaluee, the evaluator discerned the evaluee's work ability. Specifically, he determined the evaluee remained capable of unskilled, sedentary/light exertion work in a low-stress environment. After identifying occupations that met these criteria, the evaluator then applied the law of parsimony and conducted labor market research to identify pending employment opportunities and corresponding rates of pay for which the evaluee qualified. This led to the evaluator concluding the evaluee had an earning capacity ranging from the minimum wage rate to $11.00 per hour, a reduction from his preinjury earning capacity of approximately $70,000 annually. An economist computed differences between preinjury and postinjury earning capacity. Excerpts from the examiner's report follow.

Summary and Impressions

I.   Born in Jamaica, where he completed high school, Mr. Gowster informed me he passed the GED exam in the United States in 2000, earned an associate degree in general management in 2010, and pursued bachelor's degree studies in airport operations from January 2015 to April 2017; he did not satisfy degree requirements. A complaint indicates Mr. Gowster was involved in three vocational activities in 2015: full-time employee with The O'Hare Aviation Department (he worked as an airport operations agent), part-time employee with Midwest Airlines (he worked as a customer service agent), and student pursuing bachelor's degree studies. Mr. Gowster apprised me his preaccident career development plans were to "progress my career at the airport. I was looking at positions at FEMA." Based on my understanding of his responsibilities as an airport operations agent and part-time customer service agent, he performed semiskilled, light/medium exertion tasks. If not for his disabling problems, Mr. Gowster surmised, "I would've been finished by now [with my undergraduate education]." He described postincident difficulties with retention and new learning, and he reckoned he is unable to resume his education. Likewise, Mr. Gowster assessed his presenting problems prohibit him from resuming his former employment with O'Hare and Midwest Airlines. I discussed with him alternate employment such as work as an information clerk at an airport or other public venue and as a cashier at a movie theater. Such employment, Mr. Gowster opined, remains within his capacity. A review of his employment record indicates several work-related concerns were voiced. His employment records from O'Hare also include references to positions he pursued after his February 2016 cerebrovascular accident (CVA). After Mr. Gowster's initial CVA, Dr. Killibratt determined on March 24, 2016, that he was "cleared to return to work on Monday 03/27/2016 with no restrictions." Mr. Gowster responded to a request for production, stating he "decided to stop working on 8/20/2017 and then had another [CVA] on 10/13/2018. I continue to have cognitive problems and speech problems." Mr. Gowster went on to cite other difficulties he assessed would interfere with his work capacity. He has not had subsequent employment. O'Hare documentation indicates he submitted requests for accommodations; apparently, the organization determined none was viable. Mr. Gowster responded negatively when asked whether he has plans for vocational rehabilitation. He denied searching for a job since his employment ended. The Social Security Administration deemed Mr. Gowster disabled. He was in the establishment phase of his career development at the time of his February 2016 CVA.

II.   Mr. Gowster's medical history before 2015 is significant from a vocational rehabilitation perspective. Records document ongoing cardiac problems he experienced since circa 2003, including congenital heart disease. Additionally, he had problems with diabetes (determined uncontrolled in September 2015), hypertension, and other comorbidities as noted. I defer to a qualified medical professional for an assessment of how the progression of Mr. Gowster's underlying comorbidities would have affected his career development and future care needs in the absence of issues in dispute.

III.   As noted earlier, Mr. Gowster experienced CVAs in February 2016 and October 2018. He provided his understanding that his presenting problems are residuals of his CVAs. Interestingly, in July 2017, Dr. Ensole surmised his patient's CVA in February 2016 might have "caused some learned helplessness." Dr. Ensole's records cite references to complex partial epilepsy (please refer to his July 23, 2018, office note). Mr. Gowster underwent a neuropsychological evaluation with Dr. Lydell in September 2019. Dr. Lydell concluded there was "unequivocal evidence of a very significant reduction in Mr. Gowster's high-level mental abilities." He went on to describe his assessment of Mr. Gowster's emotional sequelae. After his second CVA in October 2018, Dr. Ensole opined on November 12, 2019, Mr. Gowster was unable to engage in work activity at that time. The most recent record I reviewed is Dr. Ensole's response to questions posed in December 2019; the neurologist again determined his patient was not capable of work activity. The primary problems Mr. Gowster presented to me on March 22, 2021, were "focusing and memory, processing information." Mr. Gowster assessed his mental acuity has diminished. My analysis has led me to conclude he is not capable of resuming his former preincident vocational activities including his airport operations agent job, his customer service agent job, and advanced bachelor's degree studies.

IV.   On a positive note, Mr. Gowster, age 49, has a normal gait and does not use adaptive aids apart from eyeglasses. He is not participating in any active treatment or therapy. Mr. Gowster responded negatively when asked about problems with pain. He also assessed his reflexes/responsiveness have not slowed. From a functional perspective, Mr. Gowster denied having any physical limitations or problems with lifting/carrying, and he assessed he can safely handle 20-pound objects. He responded negatively when asked about difficulties with cervical spine movements or using any of his limbs. Further, Mr. Gowster denied having problems with bending his waist or initiating movements below his waist, including squatting, kneeling, and climbing stairs. Likewise, he denied being limited in the duration he can sit, stand, or walk comfortably. No problems with balance, hearing, breathing, bowel/bladder, fatigue, or falling were noted. Mr. Gowster assessed his problems with cognitive dysfunction and speech were continuing to improve. Regarding his activities of daily living, he denied having problems with grooming and self-care. Other than transportation, Mr. Gowster conveyed, he does not rely on others for any services. He said he did "not at all" have problems exercising at a fitness center. Mr. Gowster assessed he does not need mental health treatment. On a personal level, I found him pleasant and polite. He has education, work experience, and transferable skills as previously delineated.

V. Although Mr. Gowster is not able to resume his preaccident vocational activities, within a reasonable degree of vocational rehabilitation probability, he remains a candidate for vocational rehabilitation. At this time, unskilled, sedentary/light exertion activities appear within his capacity, with restrictions that include not working in an overstimulating environment. His work environment should also be relatively low stress. Again, Mr. Gowster responded affirmatively when I presented alternate occupations to him (please refer to the earlier discussion), and I am unaware of a reason he would be unable to perform such work. The activities of daily living he identified appear to be consumed with considerable idle time. I recommend he consider taking an online course to facilitate his vocational rehabilitation. It should be noted that Mr. Gowster did not score well on two measures of intellect I administered. His prospects for retraining are limited. Pursuing vocational rehabilitation, in my opinion, would be therapeutic for him from a mental health perspective, and I support his efforts to this end. My preliminary assessment of Mr. Gowster's earning capacity has led me to conclude that he is capable, at this time, of generating hourly employment income ranging from the minimum wage rate to $11.00.

Conclusion That Retraining Is Necessary to Mitigate Earning Capacity Damages

Evaluators consider retraining when they surmise evaluees' injuries and associated disabling problems, unremedied, have caused or could cause an erosion of earning capacity. Retraining can offer the most efficacious way to restore and preserve an injured evaluee's residual earning capacity. This intervention tends to be most viable for those who become injured early in their career development.

Of course, an evaluator must ascertain that an evaluee is a good candidate for retraining. Several factors govern this decision, including the evaluee's age, phase of career development, motivation to pursue retraining, cognitive capacities, developed preinjury transferable skills, and functional capacities. Further, in cases of an affirmative decision, the evaluator should consider types of retraining feasible to facilitate an evaluee's ability to regain preinjury earning capacity.

Information derived from a clinical interview and vocational testing can be particularly helpful in discerning appropriate retraining considerations. An evaluee's prior scholastic record and work history can also provide insight.

Presuming an evaluator concludes retraining is in order, the evaluator's focus shifts to researching retraining opportunities with attention to details that include training venues, admission requirements, curricula, time required to complete retraining, costs, and placement and anticipated earnings on completion of retraining. These considerations are then distilled into a comprehensive retraining plan specific to the evaluee and ultimately address questions of how the proposed retraining will affect postinjury earning capacity.

Case Example

Orthopedic injuries a 27-year-old evaluee sustained rendered him incapable of resuming the full scope of his preinjury carpenter job. A vocational evaluator concluded it was unlikely he could attain earnings commensurate with his preinjury earning capacity without developing an enhanced/new skillset, and, accordingly, she researched and recommended retraining programs.

The evaluator's subsequent analysis included applying numerous vocationally relevant metrics as described in the previous section and qualifying the evaluee as a candidate for retraining. She then reported results of her research, viable retraining/career options, and information necessary to quantify retraining-related damages including costs of retraining, lost earnings while retraining, and differentials between earnings before and after retraining. Excerpts from the evaluator's report follow.

Summary and Impressions

I.   Mr. Goosini reported he left school during the 12th grade and passed the GED exam in 2012 or 2013. He pursued employment as a food preparation worker with fast food restaurants before securing a job as a laborer with Joe & Frank's Builders, Inc. (J&F), circa 2013. Mr. Goosini advised me he was subsequently promoted to positions as a carpenter and crew manager, and his employment with the organization continued through the time of his August 4, 2019, motor vehicle accident, until March 2020, when he was "laid off." Mr. Goosini did not associate his severance from J&F with the COVID-19 pandemic. Payroll records indicate he was paid $19 per hour. Based on my understanding of his job responsibilities, Mr. Goosini performed semiskilled/skilled tasks that required medium/heavy exertion. He performed the full range of body movements, maneuvered uneven surfaces, and worked at heights. Medical records document procedures Mr. Goosini underwent on his right lower extremity and ankle the day of his August 4, 2019, accident, and he recalled an approximately three-month period of work absence afterward. When he returned to work, he conveyed, he was extended considerable accommodations; nonetheless, the tasks he performed contributed to symptom exacerbation. He continued to work until his layoff. Mr. Goosini surmised his impaired postaccident job performance contributed to the demise of his employment. He has not had subsequent employment. "When I got laid off is when COVID started to really hit, and everything started shutting down," Mr. Goosini said, explaining why he has not sought alternate employment. The preaccident career ambition he presented was to "be my own contractor, eventually." I am unaware of a reason Mr. Goosini would not have been able to pursue his stated preaccident objective if not for injuries and associated disabling problems he acquired in August 2019. His surgeon, Dr. Hoffer, apparently recommended an occupational change due to the inherent hazards of his job and their incompatibility with Mr. Goosini's deficits and residual functional limitations. Mr. Goosini assessed he is unable to resume the full scope of his preaccident job responsibilities; however, he assessed he is capable of performing light exertion work. He expressed uncertainty about his current career plans. "I'm trying to figure out which direction to turn my life to next," Mr. Goosini stated. He advised me he has considered pursuing retraining and employment as a welder in a metal fabrication shop. "Things on flat ground where I could sit down when I needed to, and I would have dollies and carts [to move materials]," he said about his thoughts. Mr. Goosini also noted interest in computer-assisted drafting, and he responded affirmatively to other precision handwork occupations I presented to him. He responded positively when asked about his former job satisfaction as a carpenter. During the interim, Mr. Goosini informed me, he plans to pursue handyman work. He is in the exploration phase of his career development. He impressed me as motivated to pursue vocational rehabilitation. Mr. Goosini demonstrated a stable preaccident work history.

II. Mr. Goosini reported he had no medical problems or restrictions near the time before his August 4, 2019, motor vehicle accident, and I am unaware of any records that refute his representation. Again, he underwent open reduction and internal fixation procedures on his right ankle on August 4, 2019—the day of his accident. Dr. Hoffer placed Mr. Goosini on a non-weight-bearing lower extremity status the following two months. Mr. Goosini is approaching the one-year anniversary of his accident, and he remains symptomatic as noted. The primary accident-related problems he presented pertained to his right leg and ankle—specifically, problems with pain and functional limitations. Mr. Goosini conveyed his symptoms worsen when he increases his activity. My analysis has led me to conclude that, from a vocational rehabilitation perspective, returning to work in his former crew manager/carpenter occupation is contraindicated.

III. On a positive note, Mr. Goosini is a younger individual (age 27) who is cognitively intact. From a functional perspective, he estimated he can safely lift and carry from 20 to 30 pounds, depending on the distance. No cervical spine or upper extremity limitations were noted. Mr. Goosini informed me his fine motor functioning is intact. He denied having problems with bending his waist. He estimated he can generally stand 30 minutes and walk 60 minutes before overexerting himself or needing to rest. Mr. Goosini does not have limitations in the duration he can sit comfortably. He assessed he is psychologically well adjusted and does not need mental health intervention. On a personal level, I found him pleasant and likeable. He has experience and skills as previously delineated.

IV. Although resuming his prior crew manager/carpenter occupation is contraindicated, Mr. Goosini is capable of alternate employment. I recommend he limit his future vocational activities to those that involve sedentary and light exertion tasks. Further, I recommend he avoid work tasks that require more than infrequent climbing, balancing, stooping, kneeling, crouching, crawling, and maneuvering uneven surfaces. Mr. Goosini impressed me as possessing average intellect, and I believe he is a good candidate for retraining. This would enable him to optimize his residual vocational rehabilitation capacity and preserve his work life. I recommend a budget of approximately $10,000 to $15,000 for vocational guidance services, applied to assistance with career decision-making and planning, retraining costs, and job placement. The types of retraining programs Mr. Goosini noted considering are appropriate in terms of his vocational profile and include computer-assisted design and drafting (CAD), welding, and prosthetist certification programs. As a welder, Mr. Goosini's work opportunities would be limited due to his accident-related injuries and associated problems. The training programs I reviewed at State College of Texas, Brazos Valley Technical College, and St. Martin's College require from 1.25 years (drafting program) to two years (program of studies in orthotics and prosthetics technology) to complete. For reference, following are May 2019 median hourly wage data published by the Texas Bureau of Labor Statistics. This data is specific to the Bryan/College Station metropolitan area. After Mr. Goosini completes retraining, I estimate it would require from three to five years for him to realize the median wage rates cited.

- Mechanical drafter, $24.14
- Architectural and civil drafters, $23.78
- Welders, cutters, solderers, and brazers, $19.74

Regarding employment as a prosthetics/orthotics fabrication technician, my research indicates that median annual wages in Bryan/College Station are $41,700. I was able to identify pending job openings within a 50-mile radius of Mr. Goosini's home for the following positions: architectural drafter, TIG welder/fabricator, and structural welder.

Complex Cases

Noncompliant/Uncooperative Examinees and/or Lawyers

Life care planners sometimes encounter far-less-than-cooperative evaluees. These occurrences tend to arise when evaluees undergo compulsory examinations requested by opposing counsel and, fortunately, are infrequent.

Evaluee behaviors during these instances can range from willful to involuntary noncompliance and, on rare occasions, abuse—usually verbal but sometimes implicitly or explicitly threatened physical. If evaluators have any suspicion from reviewing records before an exam that inappropriate examination behavior could arise—for example, after reviewing documentation of an evaluee's history of violent psychiatric or other reckless behavior—they should request appropriate safeguards before the exam, such as having security people and/or others present during evaluee/evaluator interactions. Another alternative is to request an examination via videoconference.

In some cases, such as when an evaluee has a documented traumatic brain injury and/or mental health difficulties that affect exam behavior, the overt lack of cooperation may be involuntary, an artifact of acquired disabling problems. This calls for incisive clinical judgment. Whenever a significant evaluee-caused aberration to customary in-progress examination protocols occurs—especially when a security concern arises—the evaluator should temporarily adjourn the exam and alert the retaining source about the abnormality while seeking guidance before proceeding.

Evaluators sometimes confront a dilemma when deciding whether an evaluee's examination behavior crosses a line that justifies aborting an exam: Is there sufficient justification to terminate the examination that will cause the court to side with the termination decision? Keen insight and judgment of issues at hand guide this decision. The evaluator's task in these situations requires discernment of the aberrant issues and their etiologies, assessment of whether they can be reasonably dealt with and reconciled, and ability to cull demonstrative evidence and document sufficient justification about decisions made.

When deciding to terminate an exam because of an evaluee's behavior—or sometimes the behavior of the evaluee's lawyer—the evaluator risks a court decision that disagrees with the merits of the evaluator's decision, potentially leading to a ruling that the evaluator forfeited the opportunity to gather evidence the aborted examination would have afforded. Additionally, there is the possibility that the court will disqualify the expert.

An evaluator's decision to abort an exam must be well founded, accompanied with well-documented rationales justifying the action. Accurate and incisive documentation of unjustified interference with examination protocols and other exam anomalies facilitates a judge's ruling on whether to validate an evaluator's decision and, by extension, has important implications that include granting subsequent opportunities to reexamine the evaluee and determining issues related to recovering fees and costs from an aborted examination.

Figure 5.1 presents a letter an evaluator composed following an exam he aborted, after having determined continuing under extant conditions would prove fruitless, likely yielding invalid outcomes, at best. The evaluator's documentation includes references to the lawyer's recalcitrant, interfering behavior, a consultation with the lawyer who retained him, and references to the offending lawyer's unjustified standards of practice violations.

A challenging exam, due to an evaluee's defiant examination approach and lack of cooperation, occurred in a case in which an evaluee was pursuing concomitant claims of loss of earning capacity and the need for future medical care due to a motor vehicle accident. The evaluator determined the evaluee's noncompliance, although not abusive, was willful and calculated. Excerpts from the evaluator's report, presented next, document selective presentation of responses to clinical interview questions.

The evaluator carefully documented clinical interview happenings that support the premise that the evaluee deliberately initiated behaviors to subvert the process of discovering evidence necessary to opine on claims in dispute. Such documentation is important for reasons that include pursuing a court order that the evaluee provide better answers, fending off criticisms that the evaluator lacked evidence to fully assess issues at hand, and exposing the evaluee's self-serving noncompliance.

Of note, while considering the evaluator's account, readers should know the evaluee had a preaccident medical history of injuries similar to those she alleged to have sustained in her motor vehicle accident, and she had been unemployed for several years before it. The evaluator reported this history to provide context when describing the evaluee's disingenuous examination participation.

> Ms. Appleton was unemployed at the time of her 2021 motor vehicle accident, and her last employment was approximately four years earlier. She claimed to have been seeking employment when her accident occurred. Ms. Appleton declined to provide an answer to my query about her preaccident career plans, and she did not present any plan to pursue vocational rehabilitation. I found Ms. Appleton uncooperative, refusing to answer questions clearly related to her claim of loss of earning capacity and need for future rehabilitation intervention such as whether she has searched for work since her 2021 motor vehicle accident, whether any physicians are restricting her from working, whether she believes she is capable of performing sedentary work that would permit her to reposition at will, and whether she believes she is able to perform part-time sedentary work. Additionally, Ms. Appleton declined to answer my questions about her preaccident medical history and unrelated postaccident medical problems. She refused to answer basic questions about her functional capacities such as the duration she can walk before overexerting herself or needing to rest. Ms. Appleton stated, "I really don't know," in response to my query about the duration she is able to sit. I also found her noncompliant in questions I posed about any work-related credentials she attained such as kitchen sanitation certification while working as a server, her computer-use skills, and other work-related skills. Multiple times during my clinical interview Ms. Appleton referred me to her records rather than choosing to comply with my standard clinical interview structure and answer my questions that conform to standards of practice in vocational rehabilitation. For example, she made this type of reference when I inquired about any physician-advised restrictions. Ms. Appleton even referred me to her records

Figure 5.1 Sample Letter Documenting the Need to Abort an Examination, Pursuant to Inappropriate and Irreconcilable Lawyer Interference

Dear Mr. Guileppe:

As you know, I was scheduled to conduct a full-day vocational rehabilitation evaluation of Michael Beitten on May 5, 2021. Unfortunately, due to interference I encountered from Kevin MacPort, Esq., counsel representing Mr. Beitten, I was unable to complete my exam. In fact, the total examination time was approximately ten minutes.

I began my exam approximately 25 minutes late, due to technical difficulties Mr. MacPort reported experiencing with the videoconference he attended with his client. At the beginning, while providing my introductory comments, I asked Mr. Beitten to let me know if he did not understand a question I posed; he acknowledged my request and conveyed he would act accordingly. During the brief time I had to interview Mr. Beitten, Mr. MacPort interfered three times, despite my request that he refrain from participating.

Mr. MacPort's first interference was after I asked Mr. Beitten whether he has problems with driving, and he responded negatively. Mr. MacPort told me I would need to explain what "problems" mean, and Mr. Beitten then said he did not understand my question. I restated it, and Mr. Beitten changed his initial response. I asked Mr. MacPort to abstain from participating in the exam, noting that Mr. Beitten acknowledged he understood he was to apprise me of any questions he did not understand. Mr. MacPort raised his voice and made a long statement, informing me I was not to govern him.

The second occurrence of Mr. MacPort's interference was just a few minutes later, when I inquired about Mr. Beitten's rate of pay during his tenure with Pacific Theme Parks. Mr. Beitten said his rate of pay was "$15 something per hour," and Mr. MacPort interjected, "Look it up in the interrogatories. We're not going to let you take another deposition."

At this time, Mr. MacPort again raised his voice when I requested he not interfere with my exam, and he aggressively responded that he would conduct himself as he felt the need. Before I could proceed, Mr. Beitten's transmission to the videoconference dropped, and Mr. MacPort adjourned the interview to tend to the technical difficulty at hand.

During the previously noted break, I called you and described the difficulty I was experiencing with Mr. MacPort's recurrent interference and his less-than-professional behavior toward me. I understand you and Mr. MacPort then spoke by telephone, and, on completion of your conversation, I attempted to resume my interview of Mr. Beitten. Less than two minutes later, after I asked Mr. Beitten whether he experienced a loss of consciousness in his January 2, 2017, motor vehicle accident, Mr. MacPort interjected before his client could answer: "We're not going to answer that question, Mike. This is not a deposition." Again, Mr. MacPort raised his voice. At that time, I advised Mr. MacPort I would not be able to continue my exam with his interference, and I aborted the exam.

I have been conducting vocational rehabilitation evaluations since the late 1980s, and, over the years, I have authored multiple peer-reviewed articles and books related to methodologies for conducting a vocational rehabilitation evaluation, including a textbook, *Assessment of Earning Capacity*, which is in its fourth edition. I have also lectured on this topic at universities and professional association meetings throughout North America. My efforts over the years have been widely recognized as having advanced the state of practice in vocational rehabilitation (please refer to my curriculum vitae).

Although I complied with the court's order on my exam and standards of practice in vocational rehabilitation, the interference I encountered from Mr. MacPort is, to say the least, highly unusual and difficult to understand. I have conducted several thousand exams during my career and can recall only one other occurrence of the sort I had with Mr. MacPort.

Please let me know if you have questions.

Sincerely,

Michael Shahnasarian, PhD
President

when I asked whether she has problems with grooming, self-care, housework, and her activities of daily living. The lack of cooperation I encountered is both highly unusual and suspect. In addition, it should be noted Ms. Appleton was discerning in selecting questions to which she would and would not respond. For example, she declined to answer questions related to her preincident medical history and unrelated postaccident medical history. I also found it interesting that, despite her reported memory difficulties, she several times referenced questions she believed I had already posed, indicating she would not again respond to them.

Loss of Earning Capacity Opinions in Cases of Postinjury Career Advancement and Earnings Gains

The fact patterns in most cases in which evaluees pursue claims of loss of earning capacity typically include evidence of postinjury career decline. Work absences (sometimes for extended periods), job loss and difficulties securing new employment, diminished postinjury earnings, and recurrent periods of symptom exacerbation—these are among the more common markers of postinjury career difficulties. Occasionally, however, evaluees demonstrate the opposite: they advance their career development postinjury and realize earnings higher than their preinjury levels.

Opinions that individuals who have made postaccident career gains and realized increased earnings have experienced a loss of earning capacity are atypical and counterintuitive. These assessments require considerable evaluator insight and explanation to justify a loss of earning capacity opinion.

The case example presented next features an evaluee who, postinjury, successfully maneuvered several vocational rehabilitation challenges—weaning herself from Social Security Administration disability benefits, earning a bachelor's degree, and securing employment offering wages higher than what she earned preinjury, to name a few. Yet the evaluator concluded the evaluee sustained a loss of earning capacity.

In arriving at his opinion, the evaluator cited medical records providing objective support for the evaluee's injury-related complaints consistent with the types of postinjury vocational difficulties the evaluee presented. The evaluator clinically correlated data gathered from his clinical interview, test results, consultations with the evaluee's physicians, and records while using the ECAF-2 to arrive at an opinion that the evaluee's injuries caused her to experience a mild to moderate loss of earning capacity; the evaluator quantified the loss as a 20 to 35 percent diminution over the remainder of the evaluee's work life. Excerpts from the evaluator's report follow.

Summary and Impressions

I.   A 1985 high school graduate, Ms. Sainz reported her employment with Health Wise commenced in 1987, when the organization hired her as a respiratory therapist. Records indicate her tenure continued through the time of her January 13, 2015, work-related motor vehicle accident. During the time of her service with Health Wise, Ms. Sainz completed an associate of science degree in nursing in 1996, passed the registered nurse license exam circa 1996, and enrolled in a bachelor of science degree in nursing in 2014. She completed degree requirements after her 2015 accident, in May 2018. Education records document accommodations extended to Ms. Sainz after she became injured. She conveyed Health Wise employed her as a case manager at the time of her 2015 accident. Based on my understanding of her job responsibilities, she performed skilled tasks that required sedentary/light exertion, though at times she performed tasks requiring higher levels of exertion. Copies of W-2 wage and tax statements indicate Health Wise paid Ms. Sainz wages of $68,884 in 2013 and $67,302 in 2014. She discussed physical and cognitive difficulties she experienced after her July 13, 2015, work-related accident, and she assessed she was not capable of resuming her preaccident job. Because she did not return to work, Ms. Sainz explained, Health Wise terminated her employment; records document a July 30, 2015, termination date. The Social Security Administration (SSA) subsequently approved her application for disability benefits, establishing a starting day of January 13, 2015. After her termination from Health Wise, Ms. Sainz persisted in her education, disengaged her participation in disability benefits with the SSA, and reentered the workplace in November 2018, when Mid-State Healthcare hired her as a case manager. "I never wanted to be on [SSA disability benefits]," Ms. Sainz stated, discussing her postinjury vocational rehabilitation efforts. She apprised me her job responsibilities with Mid-State were the "same exact thing" as those she performed with Health Wise. Ms. Sainz informed me her annual compensation with Mid-State was in the range of $80,000 to $90,000, and she noted she voluntarily separated from Mid-State in 2019 "because I wanted to be closer to my kids and family." During her tenure with Mid-State, Ms. Sainz relayed, she experienced job performance difficulties, especially when she began it. "I quit, and they asked me to come back. They gave me more time, and, after a while, I was able to function," Ms. Sainz conveyed. When she relocated from Colorado to Oklahoma, Ms. Sainz reported, she secured a supervisor job with her current employer, Wellness Health Systems. "I was making $39 to $40 an hour," she said, noting she was "never released by my doctor to be a supervisor" due to learning difficulties secondary to her cognitive deficits. In lieu of a supervisor position, Ms. Sainz explained, Wellness extended her a case manager position similar to the ones she performed with Health Wise and Mid-State. She has maintained this position to date. Currently, Ms. Sainz earns approximately $36 per hour. When asked whether her job responsibilities are within her capacity, she responded: "It's stretching me far. My concerns are forgetting stuff. A case manager is someone who follows someone all through their care. I'm just doing admission stuff right now." Ms. Sainz described considerable problems with memory, and she discussed concerns about the viability of her ongoing employment. The preaccident career plans Ms. Sainz presented were to continue her education and become a nurse practitioner. I am unaware of a reason she would not have been able to attain her stated preaccident career objectives if not for her injuries and associated disabling problems. Ms. Sainz elaborated about problems with new learning and retention, assessing her cognitive impairments render her preaccident career plans untenable. She informed me she now plans to persevere in her case manager position with Wellness as best as she can, although she prefers her former longtime employer, Health Wise. Ms. Sainz assessed she would have been able to become a nurse practitioner in 2022 if not for her presenting problems. Although she has not disclosed her presenting problems to her employer, she noted, she had divulged her cognitive difficulties to a trainer who observed her to have difficulty learning a computer program. Ms. Sainz is in the maintenance phase of her career development. She demonstrated a stable preaccident work history. Ms. Sainz impressed me as motivated to continue her vocational rehabilitation as best as her condition allows.

II. Approximately five and one-half years have elapsed since Ms. Sainz's January 13, 2015, work-related motor vehicle accident, and she remains symptomatic as noted. Medical records provide objective support for her presenting problems. Ms. Sainz presented at Ben Franklin Hospital the day of her accident with neck, back, and headache complaints. Imaging subsequently detected abnormalities throughout her spine. Dr. Fischer diagnosed mild neurocognitive disorder due to traumatic brain injury on July 23, 2015, and Dr. Detweiler and Dr. Talas have since rendered similar diagnoses with respect to Ms. Sainz's cognitive status. Ms. Sainz is continuing to be prescribed medications for pain and mental functioning difficulties. She has undergone injections in her cervical spine and lumbar spine, and she has also participated in conservative treatment. "Patient has failed conservative treatment with injections and NSAIDs," Dr. Bellow determined on September 7, 2018. Postaccident records include recommendations for rehabilitation interventions to address Ms. Sainz's physical and cognitive impairments. During my clinical interview, she said her primary disabling problems are "[my] memory and the pain in my neck, and problems getting up sometimes, and my legs." She also presented challenges with bladder and bowel incontinence. Ms. Sainz conveyed her neck is her most symptomatic body part. From a physical functioning perspective, she complained that lifting aggravates her neck and back symptoms, and she assessed she can safely lift and carry ten pounds. Ms. Sainz informed me she is "absolutely" less proficient in performing fine motor tasks, noting she frequently drops objects. Additionally, she described difficulties transitioning from sitting to standing, especially after extended sitting, and she noted performing movements below her waist is problematic. Before overexerting herself or needing to rest, Ms. Sainz noted, she can sit approximately 30 minutes and stand or walk from 15 to 20 minutes. When opportunities during her workday avail, Ms. Sainz reported, she naps. She assessed her physical condition and cognitive status are worsening. My analysis has led me to conclude her current employment as a case manager with Wellness is at the limit of her capacity.

III. In addition to her work motivation, Ms. Sainz possesses other assets to facilitate her vocational rehabilitation. She has education, training, work experience, and skills as previously documented. Additionally, postaccident, Ms. Sainz has demonstrated the capacity to advance her education, albeit with accommodations, attain impressive scholastic results, and secure employment comparable to employment she held at the time of her 2015 work-related motor vehicle accident.

IV. Despite her postaccident successes, my analysis has led me to conclude, within a reasonable degree of vocational rehabilitation probability, Ms. Sainz's January 13, 2015, motor vehicle accident has caused her a loss of earning capacity. As previously indicated, she has had difficulties performing tasks more complex than those she historically performed, and, despite the passage of time and considerable treatment she has undergone, she continues to experience many difficulties performing her job. Indeed, her accident-related injuries and associated disabling problems will likely continue to plague her over the remainder of her work life. Among the vocational handicaps Ms. Sainz acquired are increased vulnerability to layoffs and downsizing, constricted opportunities for advancement and promotion, need for accommodations, potential employer bias, and risk of a shortened work life expectancy. My analysis has led me to conclude, conservatively, Ms. Sainz has realized a mild to moderate loss of earning capacity, which I am quantifying as a 20 to 35 percent diminution over the remainder of her work life.

Full Sample Report of a Vocational Rehabilitation Evaluation

This chapter concludes with a full sample report of a vocational rehabilitation evaluation arising from a case in which a 32-year-old auto mechanic sustained lower back and other injuries in a motor vehicle accident. Although the evaluee continued to work in his preinjury occupation and secured employment offering compensation greater than his preaccident level, the evaluator opined that continued physically demanding work as an auto mechanic would jeopardize his work life. Accordingly, he proposed a retraining plan and specified a budget for it in a life care plan developed under separate cover.

While reviewing the report, note the evaluator's references to various accident-related unwelcome lifestyle changes the evaluee has encountered. These include descriptions of the evaluee's diminished postaccident self-esteem, sensitivity about disfigurement, inability to engage in activities with his four-year-old son as he desires, significant financial problems that have caused his family many hardships, and difficulties in his intimate relations. This documentation helps to address damages beyond those associated with earnings and earning capacity: it facilitates the evaluator's identification and justification for interventions to address the noted problems via a life care plan and also illuminates pain and suffering damages that transcend the evaluee's physical injuries.

Sample Report

Overview

David Smith, Jr., was referred to me for a vocational rehabilitation evaluation. A complaint documents allegations of injuries he sustained as a result of a motor vehicle accident on April 14, 2018. Mr. Smith noted Tradition Auto employed him as a mechanic at the time of his accident.

On December 7, 2020, I conducted an examination of Mr. Smith via Zoom videoconferencing; the COVID-19 pandemic led to my use of this medium. My exam included a clinical interview, which required four hours, and the administration of a battery of tests that required an additional four hours and 50 minutes. Myra Pierce from my office assisted with the testing portion of my exam. Mr. Smith apprised me he was conversing with me from his lawyer's office in Orlando, Florida.

Mr. Smith reported he drove to the place from where he was speaking with me, and he told me he commuted from his home in Jensen Beach to Orlando the day before we met "so I could be fresh for you." He indicated he holds a valid driver's license and does not have doctor-advised driving restrictions.

I inquired about problems with driving, and Mr. Smith responded affirmatively. He described postaccident driving-related anxiety he has developed. "I get jittery a little bit," he said, advising me he becomes more anxious when driving near trucks. Further, Mr. Smith conveyed his lower back stiffens after driving from 45 to 60 minutes.

Mr. Smith informed me he did not resume his preaccident job with Tradition Auto "because they said I was a liability." Currently, he noted, Scott's Automotive & Golf Car Repair, Inc., in Fort Pierce employs him as a mechanic.

Regarding his April 2018 accident, Mr. Smith apprised me he struck his head. I asked him whether he lost consciousness, and he replied, "All I remember is hearing glass shattering and my wife saying, 'Oh my God, move!' and hearing my son screaming in his car seat."

In his January 20, 2020, answers to interrogatories, when asked to describe each injury for which he is claiming damages in this case, Mr. Smith responded:

> My injuries include but may not be limited to the following: fractured upper jaw subsequently causing me to lose my two front teeth, headaches, left ear tinnitus, neck pain, back pain, and numbness and weakness in my legs. I have also been suffering from anxiety, posttraumatic stress disorder, and depression. Due to injuries sustained from the subject incident, I underwent cervical and lumbar epidural steroid injections. On or about July 27, 2018, I had to undergo a laminotomy with microdiscectomy at L5-S1 performed by Dr. Johnston. Due to continued pain, I underwent a series of injections without much relief. On or about January 16, 2019, I had to undergo another surgery procedure, sacroiliac joint fusion bilateral, which was performed by Dr. Donald Dunlap.

Currently, Mr. Smith told me, he experiences the following accident-related problems:

- Dental injuries to three top/front teeth
- Occasional headaches, decreased
- Ongoing left ear tinnitus
- Intermittent neck "stiffness," prominent in morning and evening
- Ongoing lower back pain with left lower extremity radiculopathy
- Difficulty sleeping
- Anxiety
- Depression
- Trouble with sexual activity
- Short-term memory loss

Mr. Smith denied experiencing any of the preceding problems before his 2018 accident. On further questioning, he denied injuring his neck or back before April 14, 2018. Similarly, Mr. Smith denied having preaccident problems with tinnitus, memory, or mood.

As for mental functioning, Mr. Smith cited problems with memory and speech. He described difficulties with recalling where he has placed items. I inquired about speech problems, and he indicated he has been having trouble with word retrieval. Mr. Smith expressed his understanding that he experienced a concussion.

Vocational Activity

Mr. Smith advised me he left school during the tenth grade and passed the GED exam at age 18. He conveyed that most of his work experience during the past 12 years, approximately, has been as an auto mechanic. "I've always wanted to be a mechanic since I was a kid," Mr. Smith stated.

According to Mr. Smith's June 18, 2020, answers to interrogatories, he had the following employers, wage history, and reasons for leaving his employment:

Name of Organization	Dates	Pay	Reason for Leaving
Tire Kingdom	5/2020–	$13 per hour	
Limitless Auto Service	10/2019–5/2020	$600 per week	"Pay scale and on the books."
Auto Performance Center	8/2019–10/2019	$600 per week	"Missed work because dog bit by snake."
Tradition Auto	eight months	$600 per week	"Injuries due to subject accident."
Roosevelt Bridge Tire & Auto, Inc.	two years, 2016–2017	$500 per week	"Better employment opportunity."
JDM Acquisition Company, LLC	2015–2017	$15–$18 per hour	"Better employment opportunity."
Advantage Ford of Stuart	2013 to 2015	$750 per week	"Better employment opportunity."
Treasure Coast Toyota	five months in 2014	$12.50 per hour	"Better employment opportunity."
Tire Kingdom	two years	$11.50 per hour	"Better employment opportunity."

Name of Organization	Dates	Pay	Reason for Leaving
Auto Air & More	eight months in 2010	$400 per week	"Disgruntled employer."
Cartenders of Stuart	five months in 2009	$350 per week	"Terminated due to personal phone calls."
Treasure Coast Irrigation	2006–2008	$11 per hour	"Religious discrimination."
Enterprise Plumbing Services	2006	$12 per hour	"Terminated due to lack of transportation."
Ranger Air Conditioning	2004–2005	$8.50 per hour	"Better employment opportunity."

Again, Tradition Auto employed Mr. Smith as a mechanic at the time of his April 14, 2018, motor vehicle accident. He informed me he worked 40 hours per week and was paid $600 per week. Mr. Smith noted that he performed his job in a repair shop with five bays and that his job responsibilities included vehicle maintenance work. He also described oil and brake changes, engine repairs, and installing nitrous oxide systems.

Mr. Smith apprised me his mechanic job required him to perform the full range of body movements, contort his body, and engage in bimanual tasks throughout his work-day. He reported he handled objects weighing from 110 to 115 pounds, such as a manual transmission.

After his April 2018 accident, Mr. Smith said, "I went back to work about four to five days later. They told me I was a liability." He indicated he eventually attempted a one-day return to work with Tradition and had an exacerbation of lower back problems, and his employer terminated him. Mr. Smith discussed employment he subsequently assumed as a mechanic before undergoing two lumbar spine operations—on July 27, 2018, and January 16, 2019.

Mr. Smith advised me he secured his current employment as a mechanic with Scott's Automotive & Golf Car Repair, Inc., in October 2020. He conveyed he works 40 hours per week and earns $800 per week. Informing me his job responsibilities and associated physical demands are comparable to those he performed with Tradition at the time of his 2018 accident, Mr. Smith said: "I have to do what I have to do. If I can't do my job, how can I provide for my family?"

When Mr. Smith described how performing his job exacerbates his lower back symptoms, I inquired about accommodations extended to him. He replied that his employer knows "everything" about his lower back symptoms and suggested Scott's has been support-ive. "Not like Tire Kingdom," Mr. Smith said about his employer before Scott's.

Mr. Smith expressed concern about his ability to persist with his job as a mechanic. He noted Dr. Dunlap, who most recently operated on his lower back, "said in the next few years I should think about a career change." Mr. Smith assessed light-duty work remains within his capacity and would be more compatible with his presenting problems. "I'm not much of a people person," he stated when I asked about alternate employment including work as a service writer. He assessed employment as a parts clerk remains within his capacity. "That's what my wife does, and she earns $13 per hour," Mr. Smith said.

Concerning his preaccident career plans, Mr. Smith apprised me they included advancing his career development as a mechanic. "I want to stay in the same field. I want to own my own business," he added.

Records Reviewed

Records from the following sources were reviewed with this evaluation:

- Florida traffic crash report
- Complaint
- Answers to interrogatories, January 20 and June 18, 2020
- Access Urgent Care
- Anesthesia MD Services, Inc., billing only
- Arnold Dental, includes billing
- Back Rehabilitation Wellness Clinic, includes billing
- Beaches MRI, includes billing
- Booker, Inc., includes billing
- Clearwater Surgical Center, includes billing
- Craig & Associates Anesthesia Services, billing only
- Frost Surgical Assist, LLC, billing only
- Good Expressions, includes billing
- Headache & Pain Center of Fort Lauderdale, includes billing
- Helix, billing only
- SMF Medical, LLC, billing only
- Stuart Imaging Associates, billing only
- Stuart Medical Center, includes billing
- Stuart Surgical Center, includes billing
- Fort Lauderdale County Fire Rescue, billing only
- Donald D. Dunlap, MD, Orthopedic and Spinal Surgery
- Sheridan Emergency Physician Services, Inc., billing only
- Sierra Surgical, billing only
- Mary Jones, MD
- Donald J. Daniels, MD
- Edward Clark, MD
- David Johnston, MD
- Sarah Madison, DC
- Donald D. Dunlap, MD
- Keith Adkins, DMD
- Don Anderson, MD
- Hal M. Tobias, MD
- David George, DC
- Sarah C. Hensley, MD
- W-2 wage and tax statements, 2014–2017 and 2019
- Individual income tax returns
- PDA Fort Pierce Property Damage Appraisers, report
- Bodily injury photos
- Property damage photos

Assessment Measures

The following assessment measures were used in this evaluation:

- Clinical interview
- Multidimensional Aptitude Battery-II
- Beck Depression Inventory-II
- Self-Directed Search Form R
- Minnesota Multiphasic Personality Inventory

Background Information

The following background information was obtained from records and my clinical interview:

FULL NAME:	David Smith, Jr.
DATE OF BIRTH:	June 1, 1988
ONSET OF DISABLING PROBLEMS:	April 14, 2018, motor vehicle accident
RACE:	Caucasian
DOMINANT HAND:	Right
HEIGHT:	5 feet 11½ inches
CURRENT WEIGHT:	195 pounds
PREACCIDENT WEIGHT:	210 pounds
MARITAL STATUS:	Married, Kristiana Dos Santos, born December 26, 1989
CHILDREN:	Dean Smith, 4
RESIDENCE:	Jensen Beach, Florida
PRESENTING PROBLEMS:	Dental injuries to three top/front teeth
	Occasional headaches, decreased
	Ongoing left ear tinnitus
	Intermittent neck "stiffness," prominent in morning and evening
	Ongoing lower back pain with left lower extremity radiculopathy
	Difficulty sleeping
	Anxiety
	Depression
	Trouble with sexual activity
	Short-term memory loss

PROCEDURES SINCE ACCIDENT:	Laminotomy with microdiscectomy at L5-S1, left, David Johnston, MD, July 27, 2018
	Injection in the right and left SI joint, Donald D. Dunlap, MD, January 16, 2019
	Endoscopically assisted sacroiliac joint fusion, Donald D. Dunlap, MD, January 16, 2019
	#19: A full thickness flap with distobuccal release. Peripheral osteoplasty under irrigation. Tooth was elevated and removed, Keith Adkins, DM, March 13, 2020
TREATMENT SINCE ACCIDENT:	Physical therapy
	Psychotherapy/counseling
	Chiropractic treatment
	Dental
	Pain management with injections
PRESENT TREATMENT:	None
TREATING DOCTORS:	None, "I can't afford it."
MEDICATIONS/ SUPPLEMENTS:	Over-the-counter Aleve, pain, three to four times per week
	Prime Male supplement, "for energy, testosterone, stamina"
	Melatonin, sleep
	Over-the-counter Excedrin, headaches
EDUCATION:	Completed ninth grade
	Passed GED exam, age 18
	Indian River Community College, botany/chemistry, three to four months, age 19
	Automotive Service Excellence certificate, air conditioning
	Employer-sponsored classes while employed with Advantage Ford in automotive repair—brakes, suspension, air conditioning, engine diagnostics, and electrical repair
EMPLOYER AT TIME OF ACCIDENT:	Tradition Auto Service
JOB TITLE AT TIME OF ACCIDENT:	Mechanic
RATE OF PAY AT TIME OF ACCIDENT:	$600 per week
PRESENT WORK STATUS:	Mechanic, Scott's Automotive & Golf Car Repair, Inc., $800 per week

Clinical Interview

Introduction

David Smith, Jr., presented as a bearded Caucasian male who had light-brown hair and blue eyes. He appeared his stated age of 32. Mr. Smith reported he does not wear corrective lenses and said, "I don't have problems with my eyesight." He repositioned more frequently while seated as my clinical interview progressed. His top/front-teeth dental injuries were quite evident.

I inquired about his gait, and Mr. Smith said, "I favor my right side more than my left, especially when my back's hurting me [more]." He did not use adaptive aids during my clinical interview.

Mr. Smith indicated he is right-hand dominant, 5 feet 11½ inches tall, and weighs 195 pounds. He advised me he weighed 210 pounds at the time of his April 14, 2018, motor vehicle accident. He conveyed that his body strength has diminished, postaccident, and that he has become apprehensive about performing physical tasks in which he risks sustaining additional injury. "My muscles, my arms [have atrophied]," Mr. Smith said.

On December 13, 2019, Mr. Smith informed me, he and Kristiana Dos Santos married, although he added, "We've been together for almost seven [years]." He noted this has been his only marriage. Mr. Smith apprised me that his wife was born December 26, 1989, and that Caliber Collision in Stuart, Florida, employs her as a parts coordinator/manager. He reported he has one child—a four-year-old son. Mr. Smith told me his spouse continues to have postaccident difficulties with anxiety when riding in a vehicle.

Mr. Smith indicated he lives with his wife and son in a 32-foot travel trailer he owns in a mobile home park. He estimated he has lived in his home for five years. Before his 2018 accident, Mr. Smith advised me, he and Ms. Dos Santos had planned to rent an apartment and then purchase a house; however, postaccident financial difficulties and his loss of employment income caused him to abort those plans. "Every day, we struggle [financially]," he said.

I inquired about near-term plans to relocate, and Mr. Smith responded negatively. "I just can't afford it," he stated. He denied modifying his home for disabilities. When asked about accessibility within it, Mr. Smith discussed difficulties accessing areas below his waist. Further, he conveyed that descending the three steps necessary to exit his home exacerbates his lower back pain. Regarding pets, he has a dog and a cat.

Physical Condition and Medical Information

Mr. Smith denied having any medical problems or restrictions near the time before his April 14, 2018, motor vehicle accident. He described physically demanding tasks he performed, such as assisting friends with heavy truck repair work, "with no issues."

As for his preaccident surgeries, Mr. Smith cited only wisdom teeth extractions at age 19 or 20. During elementary school, he informed me, he injured his right-hand third digit. Mr. Smith noted it was cast, "and I had to wear [my arm in] a sling." He apprised me he fully recovered. "I was on Ritalin when I was a kid [for] ADD and ADHD," he said, recalling he last took medication for the conditions during the sixth grade.

Approximately six months before his April 2018 accident, Mr. Smith reported, he experienced chest pain and presented at Martin Memorial South Hospital. I inquired about diagnoses, and he replied, "I may have pulled a chest muscle." He denied having subsequent chest pain. No prior motor vehicle accidents were identified.

Concerning unrelated postaccident problems, Mr. Smith told me he lacerated his left-hand fourth digit in spring 2019. He indicated his finger was sutured and that he regained full functioning in it.

Mr. Smith underwent a laminotomy with microdiscectomy at L5/S1 on July 27, 2018, and a sacroiliac joint fusion on January 16, 2019. He recounted his diagnosis of a concussion, which, he relayed, Dr. Daniels rendered. Mr. Smith was not aware of any other current diagnosis.

The primary problem Mr. Smith relates to his 2018 accident is "my [lower] back, my physical well-being." He went on to cite his tinnitus, disfigurement due to his dental injuries, functional limitations, and numerous unwelcome lifestyle changes.

Mr. Smith advised me his lower back is his most symptomatic body part. He described his pain as follows: "Sometimes it's pins and needles. Sometimes it's stiffness and a muscle spasm feeling. When it's really bad, I have to do almost a crabwalk—hunch over a few minutes until it [exacerbating pain] goes away." Mr. Smith conveyed this occurs three or four times per week, "sometimes more depending on my exertion at work, the way I sleep."

Describing his lower back pain distribution, Mr. Smith informed me it concentrates in the center of his lower back. Occasionally, he noted, extended sitting and certain movements cause his pain to radiate into his left lower extremity. He apprised me that twisting movements, lifting, bending his waist, and bearing weight for extended periods also exacerbate his lower back symptoms.

Mr. Smith described problems with tinnitus in his left ear and said, "It sounds like a cricket in my ear." He reported the sound "gets louder" when he exerts himself.

Three or four times per week, Mr. Smith assessed, he has a headache that typically lasts from one to two hours. He told me his head pain concentrates in the frontal area, and he said about the sensation he feels, "Kind of like heat and throbbing." Mr. Smith indicated he takes over-the-counter Excedrin to relieve his headaches. When asked about headache triggers, he said, "The only thing I can think of is exertion or stress."

Mr. Smith disclosed feeling self-conscious about his dental injuries. "I don't smile, and, the way I talk, I try to lean down so people can't see my teeth, and I try to keep my lips over my teeth," he stated.

Using a 0-to-10 scale, Mr. Smith rated his pain intensities as follows:

- Lower back—around an 8
- Neck "when it gets stiff"—5
- Pain caused by tinnitus—3

Mr. Smith advised me he is not currently treating with any doctors, and he said, "I can't afford it." He conveyed he last treated with Dr. Daniels approximately one year before my exam. I inquired about his last office visit with Dr. Dunlap, and Mr. Smith estimated it was four months ago. No future medical appointments were identified.

Please see the Review of Medical Records, Operations/Procedures section of this report for details about Mr. Smith's postaccident operations and procedures. Regarding future surgery, we discussed Dr. Johnston's June 20, 2018, office note that documents the surgeon's consideration of a maximal discectomy with arthrodesis from C5 to C7. Mr. Smith also informed me Dr. Dunlap discussed additional future lumbar surgery with him.

As for treatment and therapy since his 2018 accident, Mr. Smith cited physical therapy, psychotherapy/counseling, chiropractic treatment, pain management including injections, and dental treatment. He noted Dr. Dunlap recommended additional injections after his January 2019 operation; however, he apprised me he has not had a subsequent injection. No current treatment or therapy was identified. Although Mr. Smith denied using adaptive aids, he reported he occasionally applies heat to his lower back, which he told me helps to reduce his pain.

Mr. Smith indicated he takes the following over-the-counter medications and supplements: Aleve, Excedrin, Prime Male supplement, and melatonin. He denied taking the aforementioned medications/supplements before his 2018 accident, and no current medication side effects were identified.

Discussing his aversion to taking medication, Mr. Smith explained, "I drink a little more alcohol than I should to ease the pain." While working with Tire Kingdom, he recollected, he drank 18 beers per night. "Now where I'm working, it's less physically demanding. I drink four to six [beers per night] now," Mr. Smith said. Before his 2018 accident, he advised me, he restricted his alcohol consumption to weekends and some social events.

Concerning physical capacities, Mr. Smith conveyed he can safely lift and carry 30 pounds, although he informed me Dr. Dunlap advised a 25-pound lifting limit. Mr. Smith noted lifting exacerbates his lower back pain, "and I get tension in my neck."

Mr. Smith denied being limited in any cervical spine movements; however, he apprised me crepitation accompanies turning his head to either side. He also reported that, occasionally, when extending his neck, "I get a little lightheaded." He denied having problems with using either hand or arm. Mr. Smith told me his left lower extremity feels weak "when I get that tingling sensation [from my lower back radiculopathy]."

During my clinical interview, Mr. Smith demonstrated he can touch each finger to his thumb on either hand, make a fist with either hand, and extend his arms horizontally and overhead without problems. He indicated his fine motor functioning is intact in both hands.

Regarding physical, everyday activities, Mr. Smith cited no problems with walking or standing for short durations. He complained that bending his waist, squatting, and ascending stairs exacerbate his lower back pain. He also advised me that "sudden jolts" caused by jarring aggravate his lower back symptoms.

Generally, Mr. Smith conveyed, he can sit 60 minutes, stand from four to five minutes, and walk from 25 to 30 minutes before overexerting himself or needing to rest. He informed me he operates an automatic transmission pickup truck with standard equipment, daily.

Mr. Smith identified the following additional physical problems:

- Balance
- Hearing—Along with his tinnitus, he assessed his left ear hearing has diminished.
- Dental health—I reviewed with Mr. Smith a dental record from March 15, 2017. He noted he last saw a dentist in March 2020, "when they took my molar out."
- Exposure to cold temperatures—exacerbates his lower back pain

Mr. Smith denied having postaccident falls, although he recalled an occurrence before Dr. Dunlap's surgery "when my legs went numb, and I hit the ground." He denied having problems with smell, taste, breathing, or bowel/bladder.

When asked about physician-advised restrictions, Mr. Smith recounted Dr. Dunlap's 25-pound lifting limit. He apprised me the surgeon also recommended he restrict his work participation to 40 hours per week "because I have a very physically demanding job."

As for the status of his physical condition, Mr. Smith told me he is "staying the same." He went on to cite improvements in his lower back since Dr. Dunlap's January 2019 operation.

Mr. Smith said about his emotional status, "[It is] in between getting worse and staying the same." He went on to reference his financial difficulties and compromised functional capacities that limit activities in which he can engage with his son. "He's getting older, and he wants to do more things with me," Mr. Smith stated.

Activities of Daily Living

Mr. Smith denied having difficulty sleeping before his April 14, 2018, motor vehicle accident. Currently, he reported, his sleep is interrupted due to pain and positional discomfort three times per night. Mr. Smith went on to indicate that tinnitus also interferes with his sleep. He expressed his desire to purchase a Sleep Number bed to help remedy his postaccident sleep problems.

Usually, Mr. Smith advised me, he goes to sleep between 8:00 and 9:00 p.m. and awakens at 5:45 a.m. He denied napping. Occasionally, Mr. Smith conveyed, he takes melatonin, 5 mg, as a sleep aid.

I inquired about problems with nightmares, and Mr. Smith responded affirmatively. "Those have subsided a little bit. Over the last couple of months, I haven't been having them as much," he stated. He described recurrent themes of hearing his son screaming and assorted types of motor vehicle accidents.

Mr. Smith informed me he is independent in grooming and self-care. He cited bathing, however, noting he has difficulty washing areas below his waist.

Concerning household chores, Mr. Smith apprised me he can prepare meals, launder clothes, and make a bed. He reported cleaning surfaces below his waist exacerbates his lower back pain. Mr. Smith denied employing a housekeeper.

When asked about leisure activities he enjoyed before his April 2018 accident, Mr. Smith cited riding a four-wheeler, hunting, fishing, and "I used to run through the woods with dogs chasing hogs." He told me he has been unable to use his shotgun since his accident, and he added, "Just holding it hurts."

Mr. Smith indicated he has not been fishing in approximately five months because the jarring from a boat worsens his lower back pain. Regarding current leisure pursuits, he advised me he enjoys operating radio-controlled cars. "That's really the only thing I can do with my son that doesn't put strain on my back," Mr. Smith said. He also conveyed he shoots a 9 mm pistol. "It's easier for me to use. I just got that about three months ago. I'm trying to change the way I do hobbies," he elaborated.

As for his average day, Mr. Smith said, "It takes me a good half hour after I get up before I can start getting ready for work. I have to move around [before I begin preparing for my workday]. It takes me a little bit to get moving in the morning." He informed me his place of employment is a 25-minute drive from his home. Mr. Smith noted he works Monday through Friday, from 8:00 a.m. to 4:00 or 5:00 p.m. "I get there around 7 a.m.," he added.

At the end of his workday, Mr. Smith apprised me, he returns home. He said about his evening activities, "Just mainly being at home, sitting outside in a chair, letting our son play outside." He also discussed light housework he performs.

Mental Health

Mr. Smith did not recall when he was diagnosed with attention-deficit disorder or attention-deficit/hyperactivity disorder. He denied having a family history of mental illness. Mr. Smith reported he has not undergone a neuropsychological evaluation since his April 14, 2018, motor vehicle accident.

We reviewed Dr. Daniels's records, and Mr. Smith informed me he participated in psychotherapy, postaccident, with Ms. Brown—most recently from nine to 12 months before my exam. No subsequent mental health treatment was identified.

Citing changes in his body and the effect on his self-esteem, Mr. Smith stated, "Since the accident, I feel like I've become half the man I used to be. I don't feel like a man anymore. I feel like a porcelain doll." He went on to discuss his reduced ability to participate in activities with his son as he desires.

Mr. Smith became quite sullen, discussing problems with increased depression during the Christmas holiday season. "We can't afford to buy toys [for Christmas gifts] for our son. Last Christmas, we had to give him donated toys. Some of them were broken," he said.

Concerning his overall psychological status, Mr. Smith noted his disability adjustment continues to be problematic. He expressed his belief he currently needs mental health treatment.

The primary mental health concerns Mr. Smith identified related to anxiety, his physical health, depression, loss of employment income, and sexual activity. When asked about his depression, he cited his age of 32, injuries he has sustained, and concerns about degenerative changes and future impairment as he ages. Although Mr. Smith disclosed a prior occurrence of suicidal ideation, he does not feel he is currently at risk of self-harm.

Mr. Smith characterized his marital relationship as "strong." Because of his injuries, he apprised me, his wife has assumed a disproportionate amount of housekeeping and childcare chores.

Regarding sexual activity, Mr. Smith explained that, during periods of lower back symptom exacerbation, he is unable to attain an erection. He also described how his lower back symptoms interfere with positions he can assume during sexual intimacy, which, he relayed, has become less pleasurable, postaccident.

Before his 2018 accident, Mr. Smith reported, he and Ms. Dos Santos had intimate relations every one or two days. Now, he told me, their rate is "one or two times every week or every other week at most. Sometimes it won't happen for a week or longer because I am in [too much] pain."

Mr. Smith was pleasant and likable, and he projected a somewhat depressed and anxious affect. His memory and concentration were fair. Although he spoke clearly and coherently, his speech was occasionally pressured. Mr. Smith evidenced some minor difficulties with word retrieval. He did not exhibit a thought disorder or confabulation.

Education and Special Training

Mr. Smith described difficulties he had in school before placement in remedial education. He indicated he repeated the fifth grade and said, "That was around the time I stopped taking my Ritalin, and I wasn't paying attention in school." I inquired whether he was ever diagnosed with a learning disability, and Mr. Smith responded negatively. He advised me he left school at age 17 during the tenth grade. Before passing the GED exam at age 18, he conveyed, he participated in remedial education.

At age 19, Mr. Smith informed me, he attended Indian River Community College, where he studied botany and chemistry from three to four months. Additionally, he noted Automotive Service Excellence (ASE) certified him in air conditioning. Mr. Smith also apprised me he had employer-sponsored training related to automotive repair—brakes, suspension, air conditioning, engine diagnostics, and electrical repair—while employed with Advantage Ford. No other formal education or training was identified.

Apart from ASE certification, Mr. Smith cited no other work-related credentials. No second language skills were identified. He described on-the-job training in vehicle repair and maintenance, installing/maintaining irrigation systems including replacing well pumps and sprinkler heads, and general repair of household electrical systems, plumbing, and air conditioning.

Mr. Smith reported he does not have access to a computer and is not familiar with Microsoft software. "I'm not very computer literate," he stated, although he told me he can access the Internet and correspond by email.

Through training and work experience, Mr. Smith indicated, he developed the following skills:

- Using hand, power, pneumatic, and hydraulic tools
- Reading schematic drawings
- Repairing/maintaining vehicles including air-conditioning problems and rebuilding engines, suspension systems, and drive lines
- MIG and stick welding
- Electrical repair
- Detecting and repairing irrigation system problems

Mr. Smith suggested he is mechanically adept. He denied having estimating or supervisory experience.

I inquired whether he has considered retraining, and Mr. Smith responded affirmatively. He cited interest in "the ability to run my own business, like my own [auto] repair shop." Mr. Smith recounted concern about his work life as a mechanic because of his injuries.

Career Development

The following work history was obtained from records and my clinical interview:

Job Title	Name of Organization	Dates
Mechanic	Scott's Automotive & Golf Car Repair, Inc.	10/2020–present
Mechanic	Tire Kingdom	5/2020–10/2020
Mechanic	Limitless Auto Service	10/2019–5/2020
Mechanic	Auto Performance Center	8/2019–10/2019
Mechanic	Tradition Auto	eight months
Mechanic	Roosevelt Bridge Tire & Auto, Inc.	two years, 2016–2017
RV Technician	JDM Acquisition Company, LLC	2015–2017
General Service Technician/Mechanic	Advantage Ford of Stuart	2013 to 2015
General Maintenance/ Mechanic	Treasure Coast Toyota	five months, 2014
General Service Technician	Tire Kingdom	two years
Housekeeper	Mother	approx. one year
Mechanic	Auto Air & More	eight months, 2010
Mechanic	Cartenders of Stuart	five months, 2009
Service Technician	Treasure Coast Irrigation	2006–2008
Gas Line Installer	Enterprise Plumbing Services	2006
Helper	Ranger Air Conditioning	2004–2005

Since securing his current mechanic job with Scott's Automotive & Golf Car Repair, Mr. Smith advised me, he has not had work absences. I inquired whether he believes he is meeting his employer's performance expectations, and he replied, "Yes and no." Mr. Smith assessed he would be more productive if not for his lower back injury. "Right now, I'm at 65 percent of my potential," he said, assessing the decrease in his productivity.

Mr. Smith conveyed he has not searched for another job since securing his current employment with Scott's, and he cited no plan to begin a job search. As for current sources of income, he noted his and his wife's employment earnings.

Copies of a W-2 wage and tax statement indicate JDM Acquisition Company, LLC, paid Mr. Smith the following wages:

Year	Wages, Tips, Other Compensation
2015	$13,059
2016	$33,979
2017*	Amount illegible

*A copy of a W-2 wage and tax statement notes JD Acquisition Company paid Mr. Smith earnings in 2017; however, the figure is not legible.

A copy of a W-2 wage and tax statement indicates Roosevelt Bridge Tire & Auto, Inc., paid Mr. Smith the following wages:

Year	Wages, Tips, Other Compensation
2017	$15,354

A copy of a W-2 wage and tax statement notes TBC Retail Group paid Mr. Smith the following wages:

Year	Wages, Tips, Other Compensation
2019	$3,140

Mr. Smith filed an individual income tax return in 2019 and reported the following income:

Year	Wages, Tips, Other Compensation
2019	$3,140

Review of Medical Records

Results of Diagnostic Testing

04/14/18   *Nicholas Gutierrez, MD*

CT Head and Facial Bones W/O Contrast

Impression:

> No acute intracranial hemorrhage, mass effect or midline shift.

05/17/18   *Andrew S. Gallant, MD*

MRI Imaging of the Cervical Spine Without Contrast

Impression:

> 1. C4-5, C5-7 and C6-7d disc bulges.
>
> 2. Straightening of the cervical lordosis, which may be due to muscle spasm.

MRI Imaging of the Lumbar Spine Without Contrast

Impression:

> 1. L5-S1 focal central disc protrusion/herniation without significant stenosis.
>
> 2. L3-4 and L4-5 disc bulges.

10/08/18   *Donald D. Dunlap, MD*

MRI Lumbar Spine Dated 5/17/2018

Impression:

> L5 S1: Mild desiccation. Disc space height is well preserved. There is a central disc herniation. There appears to be a mass effect most particularly on the exhilarate of the left S1 nerve root. This appears to cause some degree of compression.
>
> L4-5: Mild desiccation. Disc space height is well preserved.
>
> L3-4: Significant desiccation. Disc space is narrowed. There is disc bulging. Anteriorly, there is an annular tear and a disc herniation.
>
> L-3: The disc space height and hydration are normal. There is no significant disc herniation noted. No significant foraminal stenosis is present. There is no neural compression.
>
> L1-2: The disc space height and hydration are normal. There is no significant disc herniation noted. No significant foraminal stenosis is present. There is no neural compression.

10/25/18   Donald J. Daniels, MD

EMG and Nerve Conduction Study

Impression:

> Normal electrodiagnostic study. There is no electrodiagnostic evidence of peripheral neuropathy or radiculopathy.

10/26/18   Unknown

ECG

Impression:

> Sinus rhythm.

> Left atrial abnormality.

10/29/18   Andrew T. Walker, MD

MRI Imaging of the Lumbar Spine Without Contrast

Impression:

> 1. L5-S1 postoperative change, new from 5/17/18. A recurrent left paracentral disc herniation is present, which results in left lateral recess and left neural foraminal stenosis, in combination with postoperative epidural fibrosis and a new left facet joint synovial cyst. The central canal and right neural foramen remain within normal limits.

12/30/18   Frank Fayz, MD

Chest

Impression:

> No acute process.

06/29/20   Andrew T. Walker, MD

MRI of the Lumbar Spine Without and With Contrast

Impression:

> 1. L5-S1 postoperative change with resection of the recurrent left paracentral disc herniation and left facet joint synovial cyst in comparison to 10/29/18. No recurrent/residual central canal or rate neural foraminal stenosis is present. The left lateral recess and left neural foramen remain narrowed secondary to residual degenerative and postoperative change.

> 2. Mild lumbar scoliosis, convex left, progressed from 10/29/18.

> 3. Incidental note is made of bilateral sacroiliac joint postsurgical change, new from the prior exam.

Operations/Procedures

06/22/18   **David Johnston, MD**

Procedure:

1. Cervical epidurogram.

2. Cervical epidural steroid injections using corticosteroid agent, C6-7.

3. Lumbar epidurogram.

4. Lumbar transforaminal epidural steroid injections using corticosteroid agent and local anesthetic, L5-S1, bilateral.

07/27/18   **David Johnston, MD**

Procedures:

Laminotomy with microdiscectomy at L5-S1, left.

10/31/18   **Donald D. Dunlap, MD**

Procedure:

The solution was placed on the needle and injected in the right and left SI joint.

01/16/19   **Donald D. Dunlap, MD**

Procedure:

Endoscopically assisted sacroiliac joint fusion.

03/13/20   **Keith Adkins, DMD**

Procedure:

#19: A full thickness flap with distobuccal release. Peripheral osteoplasty under irrigation. Tooth was elevated and removed.

Assessments

04/14/18   **Don Anderson, MD/Stuart Medical Center**

Comments:

Hgt: 180 cm. Wgt: 92.99 kg.

History of Present Illness:

29 y/o male patient presents to the ED with an MVA that began 15 minutes ago. Contextually, the pt states he was at a complete stop when he was struck from behind by another vehicle causing him to strike another vehicle in front of him. Pt was not restrained and airbags did

not deploy. The patient notes associated LOC after hitting the steering wheel. He complains of an epistaxis localized to both nares and swelling to the upper lip.

Transported from scene of accident by ambulance on a stretcher but not immobilized. History of local pain affecting the face. Has a soft tissue injury/contusion to the face; complains of soft tissue swelling affecting the face; has an acute injury to the mouth. Presents with a moderate nosebleed, which started prior to coming. The bleeding is stable.

Assessment:

Epistaxis.

Motor vehicle accident.

Fracture of maxilla.

Kevin Lewis, DMD

History of Present Illness:

X-ray findings: decay chronic moderate bone loss from periodontal disease.

Patient presents with pain from fractured roots associated with accident. Large swelling #8, 9 for maxillary fracture. New tx plan organized.

04/18/18   Hal M. Tobias, MD

History of Present Illness:

Since the accident, the patient reports pain 100% of the day. The patient reports his overall condition and complaints have deteriorated daily regarding functionality at work and home. Patient presents today with current complaints of cervical pain, thoracic pain. The pain is described as dull, aching, sharp, constant, deep. Duties in duress include caring for family, dressing, getting in or out of car, performing household chores, performing personal care, rising out of a chair.

Assessment:

Cervicalgia.

Sprain of ligament of cervical spine region.

Cervical paraspinal muscle spasm.

Acute strain of neck muscle, initial encounter.

Plan:

Consult Dr. Madison and/or Dr. George for chiropractic evaluation and treatment.

Recommended possible trigger point injections as needed.

04/20/18   *Sarah Madison, DC*

Plan:

Chiropractic care was recommended high frequency of 2-3x per week for 4 weeks.

05/11/18   *Hal M. Tobias, MD*

History of Present Illness:

He describes the cervical pain as sharp, shooting pain that results in dizziness and migraines occurring multiple times a day. In regards to lumbar pain he is having bilateral radiculopathy that is worse when standing for prolonged periods of time. He discontinued the use of cyclobenzaprine saying he "doesn't like the way it makes him feel." He is also complaining of "tunnel vision" since the accident.

Plan:

Proceed with chiropractic care and recommendations.

Patient instructed to use cryotherapy and NSAIDs as needed.

Ordered cervical and lumbar MRI.

Neuro consult with Dr. Tobias; eval and treat dizziness/visual changes.

06/01/18   *Briannon Bebble, PA/Back in Action Wellness Center*

Work Status:

Return to work with the following restrictions: as tolerated.

Lifting none > 10 pounds.

Carrying none > 10 pounds.

Pushing: no repetitive.

Pulling: no repetitive.

Standing: no prolonged period.

May take breaks as needed for back pain.

Hal M. Tobias, MD

Assessment:

1. Lumbar disc herniation.

2. Cervicalgia.

3. Sprain and ligament of cervical spine region.

4. Cervical spine paraspinal muscle spasm.

5. Low back pain.

6. Muscle spasm of back.

06/05/18   Hal M. Tobias, MD

History of Present Illness:

He describes numbness and burning in the legs every morning with sharp stabbing pain in the low back. This pain is beginning to affect his work. He tells us that his legs "fall out from under him" at times resulting in significant spasm.

Assessment:

1. Lumbago of lumbar region with sciatica.

2. Cervical radiculopathy.

3. Sprain of ligament of cervical spine region.

4. Cervicalgia.

5. Cervical paraspinal muscle spasm.

6. Strain of neck muscle, subsequent encounter.

7. Dizziness.

8. Low back pain.

9. Muscle spasm of back.

06/20/18   David Johnston, MD

History of Present Illness:

Right hand dominant male.

Social History:

The patient admits to smoking a half pack a day for six years. The patient is single with one child. The patient is presently working.

Assessment:

1. Cervical disc disruption at C4 to C7.

2. Bilateral cervical reticular component.

3. Lumbar disc disruption at L5-S1.

4. Bilateral lumbar radicular component.

Plan:

I have recommended the patient to undergo C6-7 cervical facet injection along with bilateral L5-S lumbar transforaminal epidural steroid injection to help alleviate neurologic components of the upper and lower extremities. Most definitive treatment options include maximal discectomy with arthrodesis from C5 to C7 for the cervical spine along with bilateral microdiscectomy and laminotomy at L5-S1. The patient would like to consider this option and get back with us. I did provide prescription for diclofenac 75 mg to take twice a day.

07/18/18 **David Johnston, MD**

Assessment:

    1. Cervical disc disruption at C4 to C7.

    2. Bilateral cervical reticular component.

    3. Lumbar disc disruption at L5-S1.

    4. Left lumbar radicular component.

Plan:

    Most definitively, my opinion is that he should undergo a left micro discectomy and laminotomy at L5-S1.

08/22/18 **David Johnston, MD**

History of Present Illness:

    The patient states that he has returned to work and that his job as an auto mechanic is physically demanding. He states that he has had difficulty following postoperative restrictions and he is here today to discuss activity limitations as well as other recommendations.

Plan:

    The patient does admit to being a smoker and also having problems in the past with wound healing. I have also given the patient a prescription for an anti-inflammatory and a muscle relaxer to be taken as needed for inflammation, pain and muscle spasms. The patient also has been given a note to refrain from his duties as a mechanic for the next month to give his lumbar spine time to heal due to numerous physically demanding requirements of his job.

09/17/18 **David Johnston, MD**

Plan:

    He has been given a referral to see a neurologist in reference to the tinnitus that he continues to have in his left ear.

10/04/18 **Donald J. Daniels, MD**

History of Present Illness:

    He had fracture of the maxillary area and he lost some teeth. He has headaches that start with left ear tinnitus and then go to the frontal area. He feels that he has trouble concentrating and that he has loss of speech at times.

Assessment:

    1. Closed head injury, possible concussion with postconcussion syndrome.

    2. Facial fracture and dental injury.

3. Posttraumatic headaches.

4. Left-sided tinnitus, question of ear injury.

5. Neck and back pain.

6. Numbness in feet, possible radiculopathy versus other cause.

Plan:

He will have an EEG and he will follow up. We will consider neuropsychological testing if he is still having cognitive issues. We will consider diffusion tensor MRI of the brain. He can try acupuncture for the headaches or Excedrin Migraine.

10/08/18   *Donald D. Dunlap, MD*

History of Present Illness:

He was working as a mechanic but was placed on restrictions with no more than 20 pounds of lifting. This was incompatible with his job and he was released.

Assessment:

Sprain of ligaments of cervical spine, sequela.

Other cervical disc displacement, unspecified cervical region.

Intervertebral disc disorders with radiculopathy, lumbar region.

Sprain of ligaments of the lumbar spine, sequela.

Sacroiliitis, not elsewhere classified.

Plan:

This patient may benefit from a lumbar fusion. The cost of lumbar fusion is approximately $75,000 to $85,000 with approximately $25,000 for each additional level. If the procedure requires hospitalization for medical reasons, the cost may be $25,000 more. This does not include lost wages or necessary home care.

I discussed sacroiliac injection with the patient.

We will proceed with SI injection.

11/19/18   *Donald D. Dunlap, MD*

Plan:

The patient is a candidate for infusion of the sacroiliac joint(s). This involves localizing the pain with a series of injections followed by a minimally invasive approach to fusing the SI joints using bone dowels. These are placed across the SI joints to lock the joints in place, providing stability and eventually effusion.

This procedure is done under general anesthetic and requires a significant amount of coverage. The cost of the procedure is approximately $30,000–$40,000 for a one-sided procedure and $50,000–$60,000 for a two-sided procedure. This does not include lost time from work or the cost of rehabilitation.

11/26/18   *Donald J. Daniels, MD*

Assessment:

Insomnia.

Plan:

He is having trouble sleeping with nightmares about the accident and anxiety while driving. He should get counseling regarding these issues. Poor sleep may be contributing to memory issues. He still needs to see ENT re: tinnitus.

02/28/19   *Donald J. Daniels, MD*

History of Present Illness:

Does not have much trouble concentrating but he feels somewhat depressed and his libido is poor.

Assessment:

Neck pain, improved.

Low back pain improved after surgery.

Depression.

Plan:

Try Lexapro for mood. Get a general checkup w PCP re libido if issue persists.

03/25/19   *Donald D. Dunlap, MD*

Work Status:

Light duty 15–20#. Avoid repetitive bending, twisting and lifting more than 15–20#. He should avoid lifting anything below the knees. I expect that at the three-month point postop he will be returned to unrestricted duty.

07/13/20   *Donald D. Dunlap, MD*

Assessment/Plan:

He has significant low back tenderness over the scar in the incision from the laminectomy site. I believe it may have been irritated in the injury and subsequent SI fusion. I believe a field injection with long acting level and steroid may be beneficial. Whether it will last is another issue. It will be helpful in finding a source of pain potentially preventing failed back surgery.

We discussed discectomy at L3-4. That would be next.

Preinjury Assessments

03/15/17   Kevin Lewis, DDS

History of Present Illness:

Pain from number #6 to #11. Could not bite down on front teeth to take x-rays in a lot of pain.

Results of Testing

The Multidimensional Aptitude Battery-II (MAB-II) was used to assess Mr. Smith's intellectual skills and abilities. Scores from this instrument are presented relative to a normative sample.

The MAB-II Verbal, Performance, and Full Scale scores are converted to deviation IQ scores that are based upon an average score of 100 with a standard deviation of 15. The scores express where an individual's score falls in relation to the average score. Additionally, the MAB-II subscales are converted to T-scores that are based upon an average score of 50 with a standard deviation of ten. For example, a score of 60 on the MAB-II would indicate a performance that is one standard deviation above average relative to the individual's peer group, and a score of 40 would indicate a performance that is one standard deviation below average relative to the individual's peer group.

Overall, Mr. Smith scored as follows on the MAB-II:

Verbal IQ	91
Performance IQ	84
Full Scale IQ	87

Mr. Smith's performance placed him in the low average range of mental functioning. His individual scores on the MAB-II subscales follow.

Information	41
Comprehension	48
Arithmetic	40
Similarities	47
Vocabulary	41
Digit Symbol	50
Picture Completion	44
Spatial	30
Picture Arrangement	37
Object Assembly	40

On the Beck Depression Inventory-II, Mr. Smith generated a total score of 44, which corresponds to the severe range of depression.

Results of personality testing on the MMPI-2 were valid. Mr. Smith's results indicate he is experiencing a high degree of stress and several psychological difficulties. Likely, he feels overwhelmed by anxiety, tension, and depression. Health concerns were prominent in Mr. Smith's profile. Additionally, he likely has been reclusive, tending to view the world as a highly negative place. He also seems lacking in basic social skills, and he appears to have difficulty with concentrating and making decisions.

On the Self-Directed Search Form R, Mr. Smith scored highest on the Realistic occupational theme. This theme is most often associated with hands-on, mechanically oriented occupations. Mr. Smith rated his mechanical ability and manual skills as very high. He also assessed his math ability is above average. He did not identify any occupations he has recently considered pursuing. Among the occupations from the Self-Directed Search Form R that correspond with Mr. Smith's test results are teacher, industrial arts; diesel mechanic; electronic home entertainment equipment installer and repairer; fish farmer; plumber; repairer, welding equipment; watch repairer; bricklayer; prosthetics technician; drafter, detail; sound technician; tailor; gunsmith; and inspector, tester, sorter, sampler, and weigher.

Summary and Impressions

I.   Describing scholastic difficulties and problems with learning, Mr. Smith reported he left school during the tenth grade and passed the GED exam at age 18. He described work as a mechanic (DOT #638-281-014) he performed during the approximately 12-year period before his April 14, 2018, motor vehicle accident. Mr. Smith reported Tradition Auto employed him as a mechanic at the time of his accident. Based on my understanding of his job responsibilities, performing maintenance and repair work on automobiles, Mr. Smith engaged in semiskilled/skilled tasks requiring medium/heavy exertion. He apprised me of a short-lived return-to-work effort four days after he became injured, and he conveyed his work exacerbated his lower back problems. He noted his employer terminated him due to his inability to perform the full scope of his job responsibilities. Mr. Smith relayed medical treatment—including two lumbar spine surgeries—and physician restrictions interfered with his work participation. He secured his current employment as a mechanic with Scott's Automotive & Golf Car Repair, Inc., in October 2020. Mr. Smith's job responsibilities and associated physical demands are comparable to those he performed with Tradition at the time of his 2018 accident. He described how performing his job exacerbates his lower back symptoms, and he expressed concern about his ability to persist as a mechanic. The surgeon who most recently operated on his lower back encouraged him to consider an occupational change soon. Mr. Smith reckoned light-duty employment remains within his capacity and would be more compatible with his presenting problems. The fear he disclosed about a diminished work life expectancy as a mechanic, from a vocational rehabilitation perspective, is valid. Mr. Smith assessed his injuries significantly suppress his work productivity. He has not sought alternate employment since he secured his current job with Scott's. Mr. Smith impressed me as motivated to pursue vocational rehabilitation. He is in the establishment phase of his career development.

II. Mr. Smith reported he had no medical problems or restrictions near the time before his April 14, 2018, motor vehicle accident. I am unaware of evidence that refutes his representation.

III. More than two years have elapsed since Mr. Smith's April 14, 2018, motor vehicle accident. Objective evidence provides support for his presenting problems. Again, he underwent operations on his lumbar spine on July 27, 2018, and January 16, 2019. Mr. Smith apprised me his lower back is his most symptomatic body part. Records also document a head injury he experienced, and he presented ongoing cognitive difficulties. Additionally, Mr. Smith noted he is self-conscious about his dental injuries. Consistent with my clinical impression, he scored in the severe range of depression on testing administered during my exam. Mr. Smith described several unwelcome lifestyle changes he has encountered secondary to his injuries and associated disabling problems. From a functional perspective, he estimated he can safely handle 30 pounds, although he noted his surgeon advised a 25-pound lifting limit. He does not complain of restricted range of motion in his neck; however, Mr. Smith cited problems with crepitation. Of note, an office note Dr. Johnston composed indicates a two-level cervical fusion had been considered. Mr. Smith indicated his fine motor functioning is intact in both hands. He estimated he can sit 60 minutes, stand from four to five minutes, and walk from 25 to 30 minutes before overexerting himself or needing to rest. My analysis has led me to conclude that the full scope of Mr. Smith's job exceeds the limits of his capacities, and I recommend he transition to employment more compatible with his residual functional capacities. I appreciate the conundrum confronting Mr. Smith: financial need is driving his work behavior, namely, persisting in an occupation that is incompatible with his injuries due to his responsibility to financially provide for his young family.

IV. On a positive note, Mr. Smith is a younger individual (age 32) with low-average intellect (Full Scale IQ = 87). He scored in the average range on a measure of ability to quickly learn, retain, and apply new information. Although Mr. Smith has experienced scholastic and learning difficulties as a youth, my analysis has led me to conclude he has the capacity for some types of retraining; an applied retraining program would best suit him. Mr. Smith has attained Automotive Service Excellence certification in air conditioning, and he has work experience, employer-sponsored training, and skills as previously described.

V. To preserve Mr. Smith's residual earning capacity, I recommend that he initiate an occupational change, restricting his future work participation to occupations that involve sedentary and light exertion tasks. Ideally, he will initiate this transition within the next few years. To facilitate Mr. Smith's transition, I recommend a budget for vocational guidance services to include assistance with career decision-making and planning, retraining costs, and job placement. My specific recommendation will be under separate cover in a life care plan I am preparing. At this time, I recommend Mr. Smith consider precision handwork occupations such as dental appliance technician, orthotics technician, or sound technician. A period of 24 to 30 months for retraining and workplace reentry is reasonable to anticipate. At the end of this period, Mr. Smith would likely be able to generate compensation commensurate with his preinjury capacity.

VI. Again, I am preparing a life care plan for Mr. Smith. This document will specify rehabilitation interventions he is reasonably anticipated to require because of injuries and associated disabling problems he acquired in April 2018. My work to this end will involve consulting with his physicians.

Date _____

_____

Michael Shahnasarian, PhD
Certified Life Care Planner #258
Certified Rehabilitation Counselor #3701
Certified Vocational Evaluator #58360
International Psychometric Evaluator Certification #985
Licensed Psychologist PY5644
Fellow, American Psychological Association
Fellow, International Academy of Life Care Planners
Fellow, National Career Development Association

PART III

Construction of Opinions on Life Care Plans

Expanding on the foundational work Part II details—including records review, examination protocols, and clinical assessments—Part III first focuses on constructing opinions essential to sound life care planning, emphasizing life care planner roles and methodological considerations. Ensuing chapters address the development of noncatastrophic life care plans (Chapter 7), catastrophic life care plans (Chapter 8), international life care plans (Chapter 9), and life care plans when healthcare professionals dispute causation (Chapter 10).

CHAPTER 6

Foundations of Life Care Plan Damages Assessments

Chapter 1 discusses the purposes of life care plans, manner in which they are developed, and type of information they include, as well as standards of practice governing life care plan practice. This chapter focuses on the rudiments of constructing a life care plan.

Life Care Planner Roles

A life care planner's assignment sometimes expands in accord with a lawyer's litigation strategy. For example, an evaluator may initially be asked to critique a life care plan and, if problems with it are detected, proceed with researching cost aberrations and/or developing a competing life care plan. A description of the discrete roles life care planners assume follows.

Life Care Plan Consultant

Defense counsel are more likely than plaintiff's counsel to retain life care planners solely as consultants, without requesting that they prepare a life care plan. This gives lawyers the benefit of obtaining experts' knowledge and guidance while avoiding the risks associated with disclosing them to opposing counsel. The risks include validating parts of a life care plan plaintiff's expert prepared, exposure to potentially damaging cross-examination, and setting a "floor" for life care plan damages (please refer to the discussion in Chapter 1).

   Of course, conversely, a major risk defense counsel assumes in using a life care planner as a consultant only is that the opposition and triers of fact will not have the benefit of testimony and an alternate life care plan to consider. As a consultant, the life care planner will be invisible to all but the retaining lawyer, and beneficial expert work product a consulting expert might produce—documentary and/or testimonial—will not enter into evidence.

Life Care Plan Cost Comparison Deriver

When lawyers perceive asserted costs in an opposing life care plan are amiss, they frequently retain a life care planner to perform a cost analysis. Appendix H is a sample cost analysis report comparing plaintiff's expert's costs to values the defense consulting expert would ascribe for the same recommendations. This work is then typically relayed to a forensic economist or accountant who performs a valuation analysis featuring differentials between the life care planners' assessments.

Defense lawyers often find these analyses instructive in refining their strategies. The outcomes can help them determine how life care planners can best facilitate their objectives.

In Appendix H, note the caveats the life care planner includes in the cost analysis introductory comments. Namely, the information is presented solely for comparison purposes, and the reader should not presume that the consulting life care planner consents with the opposing life care planner's recommendations or protocols. Adjustments to these, likely having monetary implications, would be made if the lawyer were to choose to expand the scope of the consulting expert's retention to include developing a life care plan.

Life Care Planner

When retained to prepare a life care plan, an evaluator engages in the full scope of activities required to comprehensively illuminate these damages' monetary value. Of course, evaluators know their work will be carefully scrutinized and challenged—another reason they must adhere to practice standards and be prepared to ardently defend it. The remainder of this chapter addresses issues pertaining to a life care planner's work.

Contextual Considerations

When a life care planner is asked to prepare a life care plan, the end results of the planner's efforts include developing a document(s) that describes an evaluee's rehabilitation needs acquired via issues in dispute and outlines interventions intended to remedy them. Some life care planners compose a narrative report with information inclusive of a summary of an evaluee's medical records and findings from a life care plan examination, along with a separate report identifying specific future care recommendations with associated costs. Others combine the reports.

Beyond an evaluee's presenting problems and basic demographic information, a life care plan that complies with practice standards identifies its contributors, recommended rehabilitation interventions with specified protocols to address presenting problems, and costs of interventions, along with the costs' sources. An evaluee's life expectancy is necessary to compute the future value of life care plan expenses. In some cases, this can be extracted from generally accepted sources that incorporate an evaluee's demographics, such as the Social Security Administration Life Expectancy Calculator (n.d.). In other cases, especially when a reduction in life expectancy is anticipated, life expectancy specialists typically provide this estimate. Many cases involve acquired catastrophic disabling problems—persistent vegetative state, quadriplegia, or sequelae from severe cerebrovascular accidents, to name a few—that can cause an evaluee a shortened life expectancy and have significant implications for computing a life care plan's value.

After an evaluator establishes a life care plan's essential data points, qualified economists and/or forensic accountants compute the plan's monetary value. These calculations involve, among other things, analyses of historical cost increases of the plan's rehabilitation interventions, projections of future cost values incorporating historic growth rates and life expectancy, and application of discount rates to arrive at reductions of future costs to present value. Needless to say, these statistical analyses—well beyond the scope of this book—often become complex. The point in alluding to them here is to provide context when considering the interrelationship between disciplines involved in preparing a life care plan and to introduce an awareness of how life care plan data is processed to arrive at a value presented to those who ultimately opine and determine this important damage element.

Categorizing Life Care Plan Interventions

The needs categories included in a life care plan correspond to an evaluee's injuries and associated disabling problems. A below-elbow amputee, for example, will have needs far different than a paraplegic. The categories of needs most often appearing in life care plans include:

- Evaluations
- Therapeutic needs
- Diagnostic tests
- Wheelchair needs
- Orthotics/prosthetics
- Aids for independent living
- Drug and supply needs
- Home/facility care
- Transportation needs
- Personal fitness
- Architectural renovations
- Travel expenses/accommodations
- Hospitalizations/surgeries
- Potential complications
- Vocational/educational needs

Regarding the last category in the previous list, in cases in which life care plans emanate from those not qualified to independently render opinions on vocational/educational needs—such as nurses and physician life care planners—the life care planner will need to obtain relevant input from qualified sources. These sources include vocational experts, human resources professionals, school psychologists, teachers, tutors, and others competent to specify reasonable interventions to facilitate vocational rehabilitation.

In addition to identifying rehabilitation interventions and their costs, life care plans specify treatment protocols and their timing. Some interventions, such as an operation, may be projected to occur only once. Others, such as imaging studies, may be projected to recur on a schedule, while interventions such as follow-up office visits with a pain management specialist may be ongoing.

Appendix I is a sample life care plan prepared for a woman who, at age 57, underwent a total hip replacement and, later that day, experienced a fall incident that caused her to acquire new injuries and disabling problems. An evaluator performed an examination (complete with a clinical interview and standardized testing), consulted with treating physicians, researched and sourced information associated with rehabilitation interventions, and developed the life care plan. It aims to identify acquired needs the fall incident presumably caused, distinct from any preexisting or unrelated treatment needs.

While reviewing the life care plan, note the type of information it contains, including names and dates of consultations with medical specialists, sources of cost information and cost ranges, evaluee demographic information and presenting problems, and treatment recommendations categorically organized with the duration and frequencies of interventions. This presentation serves several purposes including facilitating the efforts of a forensic economist or accountant to compute the life care plan's monetary value and complying with standards of professional practice and Daubert rule requirements (discussed in Chapter 11).

Methodological Considerations

Although the standards of practice delineated in Chapter 1 state general methods that bind life care planners, the retention source and court, to a degree, also govern the methods life care planners employ. For example, life care planners retained by defense counsel can consult only with defense-retained experts, although life care planners retained by plaintiffs' counsel have access to both plaintiff-retained experts and the plaintiff's treating healthcare providers (more information on consultations with life care plan contributors is provided later in this chapter). Additionally, retention sources may request that life care planners address narrowly focused areas of need and/or make certain assumptions in preparing their work.

A defense-retained expert who attempts to consult with a plaintiff's treating healthcare providers would be looked at askance, to say the least, and risks being disqualified, sanctioned, or otherwise disciplined. Florida enacted a statute—Fla. Stat 456.057(8) (Fla., 1996)—that prohibits defendants from conducting informal interviews with plaintiff's treating doctors. It is highly improbable that a plaintiff lawyer would grant permission for a defense-retained expert to initiate these consultations, although under adversarial cross-examination, lawyers sometimes imply a defense-retained expert relied only on opinions of other biased defense-retained experts. When confronted with this misleading innuendo, experts should state the limits of their consultation sources and document a request made to the opposing lawyer to consult with their client's healthcare providers; these requests invariably go ignored or are outwardly rejected but nonetheless are necessary to create an accurate record.

The following discussion describes protocols life care planners implement to identify current and future care needs an evaluee is reasonably expected to require due to injuries and associated disabling problems in question. Requests for life care plans sometimes emerge before a complaint is filed and facilitate settlement before litigation ensues.

Life Care Planner Assessment Protocols

The process involved in preparing a life care plan is analogous to the process involved in performing a vocational rehabilitation evaluation, detailed in Chapter 3. Evaluations undertaken to develop life care plans sometimes include procedures beyond those undertaken when evaluating work capacity—such as conducting a home assessment to determine an evaluee's accessibility issues and conferring with caregivers to gain insight into an evaluee's needs for specialized assistance with activities of daily living.

Obviously, the contents of life care plans vary widely due to multiple factors, not the least of which include an assessment of an evaluee's preexisting and unrelated injuries/disabling problems, the nature of an acquired disabling problem(s), evaluee-specific characteristics, health care providers' treatment plans, and the region in which an evaluee resides and likely will pursue treatment. Even two evaluees with a similar disabling problem such as paralysis would not be expected to have identical life care plans. Likewise, the costs for the same services can vary from one life care plan to another: the availability of rehabilitation services and costs for treatment are likely far different in Sopchoppy, Florida, than they are in Los Angeles, California, for example. Additionally, healthcare providers who provide input into a life care plan's contents often have varying approaches that govern their prescriptions for treatment, which affects life care plan costs.

Simply put, there is no "one-size-fits-all" life care plan to which one can refer when evaluating the needs of an evaluee with a specific disability, such as an above-knee amputation, spinal cord injury, or traumatic brain injury. Some needs, of course, are ubiquitous across disability types (e.g., all evaluees with quadriplegia will require mobility aids and other durable medical equipment); however, all life care plans are evaluee-specific, determined by case-specific factors.

While the contents of life care plans can be expected to vary for the reasons just presented, evaluators must remain consistent in the methods they apply to perform their work, employing standards of practice, regardless of the retention source. Despite the individualistic nature of life care plans, evaluators should presume opposing counsel will obtain and scrutinize life care plans they have prepared in prior cases with similar disabling problems, aiming to expose inconsistencies that imply bias that undermines the evaluator's credibility.

Generally, life care plans fall into two categories: noncatastrophic and catastrophic. Chapter 7 features the former and Chapter 8 features the latter. The following discussion elaborates on life care plan development procedures that go beyond the evaluation procedures described in Chapter 3.

Records Review

An evaluator's perspective while conducting a records review differs depending on whether vocational capacities or life care plan needs are being evaluated; of course, there are instances when both are being evaluated concurrently. For example, while reviewing academic records of a young person with scholastic achievement difficulties, an evaluator focusing on vocational implications may extract from these records evidence that foretells the likelihood of an evaluee succeeding in various occupations. On the other hand, an evaluator discerning future care needs, while reviewing the same records, is apt to focus on how acquired disabling problems may compound the preexisting scholastic difficulties, potentially necessitating remedial interventions such as tutorial assistance and job placement services—interventions to consider in a life care plan.

In cases in which plaintiffs' counsel retain life care planners, their reviews of evaluees' healthcare provider depositions that include testimony addressing anticipated future treatment needs can supplement information derived during subsequent consultations with these treating professionals (described later in this chapter). Again, when retained by defense counsel, evaluators are prohibited from communicating directly with an evaluee's healthcare providers; likewise, they cannot communicate with damages expert witnesses retained by plaintiff's counsel. They can, however, appropriate in their life care plans these sources' treatment protocols as specified during their testimonies.

Plaintiff lawyers sometimes commission "day-in-the-life" video recordings that demonstrate evaluees' capacities and special needs. Among other things, evaluators can learn from viewing them an evaluee's functional limitations, assistance required, accessibility problems, and specialized treatment and durable equipment needs. These videos typically feature an evaluee engaged in activities of daily living—such as bathing, dressing, and other self-care tasks and venturing out of the home—and provide perspective on interventions necessary to include in a life care plan.

Other records beyond those discussed in Chapter 3 of potential interest to a life care planner include medical bills. These records document an evaluee's preinjury and postinjury consumption of rehabilitation services with associated costs, providing a benchmark to forecast future rates. They might also help establish postinjury baseline data and provide information necessary to compare/contrast postinjury costs incurred to future costs anticipated for rehabilitation interventions.

A review of an evaluee's therapy records provides insight into factors that range from progress made toward postinjury rehabilitation goals to motivation and compliance. When evaluees have documented high rates of "no show" for therapy sessions and a life care plan includes future protocols for such treatment of which evaluees have not previously taken advantage, evaluators should anticipate this evidence will be juxtaposed. Further inquiry into reasons for the apparent noncompliance and consideration of treatment alternatives may be in order.

In some cases, life care planners' review of medical bills and subsequent research lead them to conclude evaluees have been overbilled for services rendered. Such suspicions and the need for corresponding investigations sometimes also lead to retentions of life care planners (please refer to "Life Care Plan Cost Comparison Deriver" earlier in this chapter).

Life Care Planning Examination

Lawyers, insurance adjusters, economists, and other experts involved in evaluating the outcome of a life care planning examination initiated for litigation purposes—namely, the life care plan itself—should ensure its contents solely address rehabilitation needs reasonably associated with issues in dispute. Although needs related to an exacerbation of preexisting comorbidities requiring intervention(s) beyond ordinary requirements can legitimately be included in a life care plan, needs for unrelated comorbidities cannot be claimed.

Similar to exams initiated to assess vocational capacities, exams undertaken to assess life care plan needs generally involve a clinical interview and, depending on case-specific facts, testing. The examination's objectives include identifying and valuing rehabilitation needs associated solely with the mechanism of injury from which the evaluee's claim emanates.

Clinical Interview

The subject matter of clinical interviews for evaluating life care plan needs are, again, like those in vocational rehabilitation examinations in terms of format, content, and evaluator involvement (please refer to Chapter 3). The major difference between the two is that vocational rehabilitation clinical interviews focus on work and earning capacity, whereas life care plan clinical interviews focus on present and future care needs.

Depending on an evaluee's age and level of disability, clinical interviews for developing a life care plan sometimes expand to include others. Parents and/or guardians of pediatric evaluees might need to be present, as might caregivers of pediatric and adult evaluees who require more than nominal assistance with activities of daily living and/or experience cognitive difficulties that restrict their ability to fully and knowledgeably respond to questions life care planners pose.

Caregivers can provide specific information about evaluees' special care needs ranging from self-care to specialized interventions severely impaired evaluees sometimes require—such as suctioning, tube feedings, wound care, catheterizing, and assistance with bowel programs. This information is useful in discerning the amount of care and level of skilled care an evaluee requires.

A visit to an evaluee's home can be helpful, enabling an evaluator to tour the premises and observe firsthand accessibility barriers and/or threats to safety that may confront an evaluee. Photos taken during home visits sometimes facilitate an evaluator's efforts to document and communicate the need for home modifications included in a life care plan. Figure 6.1, for example, shows a plastic chair placed in a traditional bathtub located in an elderly wheelchair user's bathroom. A life care planner included this photo in her report to support her opinion that home modifications—including enlarging the bathroom and installing both a roll-in shower stall and a roll-in sink basin that could accommodate a wheelchair underneath—would facilitate the evaluee's accessibility, safety, and independence.

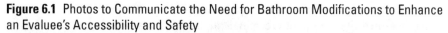

Figure 6.1 Photos to Communicate the Need for Bathroom Modifications to Enhance an Evaluee's Accessibility and Safety

Life care planners sometimes conduct their exams in hospitals, inpatient rehabilitation centers, and skilled care facilities. Under these conditions, in addition to a clinical interview, their exam protocols include a review of the evaluee's chart and consultations with staff providing the evaluee ongoing care. Among the relevant records in a chart are medications prescribed, physician orders, and therapist and nurse progress notes. Examinations in institutional settings tend to occur when evaluees are in the acute phase of their postinjury recovery or have sustained severe injuries that require regular nursing care and treatment beyond what can be adequately provided in most home environments.

During the clinical interview, when retained by plaintiff's counsel, life care planners should obtain signed authorization from the evaluee or the evaluee's guardian for the evaluator to consult with the evaluee's healthcare providers after the exam (more information on this topic follows). A sample authorization form appears as Appendix J.

Standardized Test Administration

Testing accompanying life care plan exams tends be less extensive than testing administered in vocational rehabilitation examinations. Personality tests and some screening measures of intellect are the most common measures administered. Unlike standardized testing in vocational rehabilitation examinations, occupational interest inventories and extensive aptitude testing are typically not performed in exams undertaken solely to assess life care plan needs.

The testing component of a life care plan exam can aid in determining whether interventions such as psychological counseling, case management, tutoring, and/or cognitive rehabilitation may be in order. Of course, the life care planner must possess the proper credentialing necessary to secure, administer, and interpret any tests used.

During recent years, a growing number of physicians—most often physiatrists and neurologists—have obtained life care plan credentials and have transitioned their practices to include this specialty. Their examinations sometimes include a physical exam with associated diagnostic tests.

Postexamination Life Care Plan Development

A life care planning examination provides evaluators an opportunity to gather information necessary to advance the process of preparing an evaluee-specific life care plan, including preparing for consultations with those qualified to address specialized interventions. After an exam, evaluators synthesize evidence assembled and include in their in-progress life care plans recommendations within their scope of expertise. Their postexamination work also includes developing areas of inquiry for their upcoming consultations with life care plan contributors.

Life Care Plan Contributors

As Chapter 1 noted, a life care plan typically requires multidisciplinary collaboration, and standards of practice require evaluators to seek collaboration when possible to secure input and recommendations beyond their expertise (IARP, 2015). Shahnasarian (2017) and Shahnasarian and Hilby (2020) elaborated on details essential to eliciting rehabilitation recommendations during forensic life care plan consultations, including reducing barriers to securing contributor cooperation, initiating preemptive measures to facilitate quality contributor input, and conducting the consultation.

Qualifying Contributors

As gatekeepers of a life care plan's contents, and ultimately the document's publishers and defenders, life care planners rely on specialists from multiple disciplines to specify rehabilitation interventions they adopt. Before eliciting any recommendations, life care planners should vet potential contributors by obtaining affirmative responses to the following two questions:

- Does the potential contributor possess current knowledge of the evaluee's presenting problems, history, and recent diagnostic studies and treatment?
- Does the potential contributor possess the expertise necessary to identify and prescribe appropriate rehabilitation interventions?

Contributors qualify to provide input to a life care plan via their knowledge of an examinee through treatment and/or records review, research, and/or expertise gained from professional experience. Presuming potential contributors satisfy the qualification criteria, life care planners can proceed with their consultations. Alternately, options include referring the evaluee to another specialist who is better positioned to provide life care plan recommendations, excluding the potential contributor, and recommending the contributor conduct an update exam of an evaluee and/or review updated/additional medical records to ensure questions about current and future rehabilitation interventions can be adequately addressed.

Life care planners can sometimes appropriate from recommendations specialists' records. For example, a specialist might have detailed an evaluee's anticipated treatment protocol in a report or during a deposition, and an evaluator can incorporate this information in a life care plan. In some cases, documentary and testimonial evidence spawns further questions an evaluator can pose during a consultation, generating supplemental recommendations and refinements to treatment protocols.

Generally, interactive consultations that enable a life care planner to provide a contributor supplemental case information and ask specific questions are preferable to relying solely on documentary and/or testimonial evidence. The interaction tends to encourage contributors to expound on recommendations initially provided and reflect more expansively on an evaluee's prognosis and needs for rehabilitation interventions.

Consultations with Contributors

For various reasons, potential contributors may resist consulting with a life care planner. Some, weary of adversarial proceedings, become inhibited when they learn a consultation involves a matter in litigation. Preoccupied with their practice responsibilities, they view a life care plan consultation as a low priority, reckon their participation could cause a need for them to hire legal counsel and incur associated costs, and suspect their involvement increases the likelihood of being deposed and/or summoned to provide trial testimony—events that cause a loss of practice income and expose them to potentially unwelcome and harassing challenges of their diagnoses, treatment, and billing.

In medical malpractice cases, potential life care plan contributors risk potentially accusing a community member—directly or indirectly—of inappropriate practice, exposing them to disfavor among their peers. Of course, beyond these factors, many contributors require compensation before they consent to a consultation.

There are several options available to life care planners who encounter difficulties scheduling consultations with potential contributors, including:

- Make inferences from available information—Some health care providers outline treatment plans in their records, and evaluators can sometimes extrapolate from them interventions to include in a life care plan.
- Enlist evaluee assistance—A request from a health care provider's patient (i.e., the evaluee) may encourage a potential contributor to cooperate.
- Enlist surrogates—Although some physicians, for example, may truly have scheduling restrictions, their colleagues—including other physicians with whom they practice, residents, and nurse practitioners—may be more accessible and, in some cases, have greater knowledge of an evaluee.
- Enlist the retaining lawyer's assistance—When resistance to a life care planning consultation emanates from a health care expert witness retained by the same lawyer who retained the evaluator, a prompting for cooperation from the lawyer sometimes remedies the problem.
- Make referrals to alternate contributors—An evaluator referral of an evaluee to another specialist, bypassing the noncooperative potential contributor, can expedite obtaining the necessary life care plan information.
- Provide lawyers deposition questions—Evaluators sometimes prepare for their retaining lawyer deposition questions akin to those they would pose to elicit life care plan recommendations from an elusive contributor.

Some contributors decline to engage in an interactive consultation but consent to respond to written questions a life care planner prepares. Figure 6.2 includes sample questions prepared for an orthopedic surgeon.

Figure 6.2 Sample Written Questions to Elicit Life Care Plan Recommendations, courtesy of RehabPro (from Shahnasarian, M. (2017). Eliciting rehabilitation recommendations during forensic life care plan consultations. *Journal of Life Care Planning, 15*, 13–19)

Re: JJJ

DOB: 10/25/87

Questions for Dr. N for future care needs of Ms. J

What current and future diagnostic evaluations (e.g., CT scan, X-rays, MRIs) do you recommend for Ms. J because of injuries she sustained in her February 17, 2015, motor vehicle accident? Please specify schedules of any recurrent and serial diagnostic evaluations now and over the remainder of Ms. J's life.

_____

_____

_____

_____

What current and future treatment do you recommend for Ms. J (e.g., PT, OT, exercise program) because of injuries she sustained in her February 17, 2015, motor vehicle accident? Please specify treatment protocols including the frequency and duration of each protocol, both now and in the future.

_____

_____

_____

_____

How frequently do you believe Ms. J will require follow-up visits with you or another orthopedic surgeon because of injuries she sustained in her February 17, 2015, motor vehicle accident? Please consider present and future protocols.

_____

_____

_____

_____

Do you believe that Ms. J would benefit from consultations and/or treatment with other specialists (e.g., pain management, neuropsychologist, orthopedic surgeon) because of injuries she sustained in her February 17, 2015, motor vehicle accident? Please specify specialists, along with frequency of office visits.

_____

_____

_____

_____

Do you believe that Ms. J will most likely require ongoing prescriptions of medications because of injuries she sustained in her February 17, 2015, motor vehicle accident? Please delineate present and future prescriptions including name of medication, reason for prescription, dosage, and duration.

_____

_____

_____

_____

Are injections anticipated for Ms. J because of injuries she sustained in her February 17, 2015, motor vehicle accident? If so, please specify the type, number, and locale, along with an anticipated administration schedule—both now and in the future. Please also specify whether any injections will need to be administered in a specialized facility.

_____

_____

_____

_____

Do you have any recommendations for current and/or future durable medical equipment for Ms. J because of injuries she sustained in her February 17, 2015, motor vehicle accident? Please consider current and future needs over Ms. J's lifespan, indicating when the need for different types of durable medical equipment is anticipated.

_____

_____

_____

_____

What, if any, future surgeries will be required for Ms. J because of injuries she sustained in her February 17, 2015, motor vehicle accident? Please specify the procedure(s), time frame, and postoperative care protocols.

_____

_____

_____

_____

Will Ms. J require physical therapy or other specified treatment after each projected surgery, if any, because of injuries she sustained in her February 17, 2015, motor vehicle accident? Please specify treatment protocols.

_____

_____

_____

_____

Are there any other rehabilitation recommendations that you have for Ms. J as you consider her future course of medical treatment because of injuries she sustained in her February 17, 2015, motor vehicle accident? Please specify treatment protocols including when interventions are anticipated.

_____

_____

_____

_____

Structuring Consultations

To optimize their consultations, life care planners should consider contributors' frames of reference; these include their practice specialties and perspectives on treatment. For example, surgeons who discharge patients after rendering postoperative care tend to have short-term views on evaluees' needs, focusing on their acute treatment period and typically being less attuned to long-term needs after their discharge. Additionally, many contributors require prompting to consider longer-term evaluee needs due to a progression of pathologies.

Life care planners have a limited window of opportunity to elicit quality input during consultations. Preparation and focus facilitate their efforts. Figure 6.3 presents recommended life care planner activities before, during, and after consultations (Shahnasarian & Hilby, 2020).

After preparing for and scheduling a consultation, life care planners typically review with contributors dates of their treatment and/or evaluations and current assessments of an evaluee's presenting problems. The discourse then evolves to an inquiry of proposed rehabilitation interventions—both near-term and long-term. This discussion is most often accomplished by reviewing an evaluee's presenting problems independently and cumulatively, identifying appropriate mitigation interventions. For example, a middle-aged, insulin-dependent evaluee with bilateral lower extremity amputations and colostomy bag acquired rehabilitation needs associated with each of these problems that, taken together, gave rise to additional needs, such as attendant care and mental health treatment.

Along with specific rehabilitation interventions associated with the categories detailed earlier in this chapter (i.e., evaluations, therapeutic needs, diagnostic tests, etc.), life care planners elicit contributors' treatment protocols and schedules; some interventions may occur once, while others may recur. For example, for a young person who sustained a moderate traumatic brain injury, a neuropsychologist may recommend serial update neuropsychological evaluations at intervals of one to two years for four years and then once every ten to 15 years over the remainder of the evaluee's life, along with a current one-time, three-month prescription of cognitive rehabilitation.

Questions an evaluator poses should be pertinent to the contributor's specialty. When an evaluator is consulting with a hand surgeon, for example, inquiry about an evaluee's unrelated needs secondary to a seizure disorder will likely call into question the evaluator's knowledge of rehabilitation specialties and competence. At the end of a consultation, the contributor should review the recommendations and treatment protocols specified.

Figure 6.3 Recommended Life Care Planner Activities before, during, and after Consultations

Contributor Consultations...

Before	During	After
• Request and schedule appointment • Provide authorization forms, when requested, in advance • Prepare in advance • Have knowledge of treatment recommendations already documented	• Structure the consultation • Aim for a synergystic exchange • Make inquiries pertinent to the contributor • Avoid the need for a repeat consult	• Provide the life care plan to contributor • Invite consent/dissent • Make changes and update as necessary • Secure documentation of review and consent

Documenting Consultations

Life care planners should carefully document their consultations for reasons that include complying with practice standards; permitting others interested in issues at hand, including opposing experts, the opportunity to verify their work; and preempting/responding to Daubert challenges (discussed in Chapter 11). Documentation of contributor consultations generally includes topics discussed and, of course, specific recommendations a contributor offered.

Most evaluators distribute their completed life care plans to the contributors; their communication also includes a request to respond, noting their review of the life care plan and expressing agreement or disagreement with it. In the event of the latter, contributors are encouraged to elaborate on changes they propose. Appendix K is a sample contributor verification form developed for this purpose. It becomes part of an evaluee's records and serves as evidence of the origins of recommendations obtained and contributors' assent. Further, when contributors are later questioned during a deposition and/or trial and testify they do not recall having participated in a life care plan consultation, which might have occurred long before their testimony, the document provides a record of the event.

Additionally, distribution of a completed life care plan to its contributors with an invitation for final review and opportunity to make revisions promotes the development of a consistent, cohesive document, devoid of duplicate recommendations. It also can promote enhanced coordination of services among an evaluee's healthcare providers.

Sourcing Life Care Plan Costs

Costs associated with interventions incorporated in a life care plan should represent reasonable, fair-market values specific to the locale in which an evaluee resides and/or expects to pursue treatment. Further, the sources of costs should be identified so as to allow others to verify them.

When sourcing costs of rehabilitation interventions, life care planners usually avoid sources that include negotiated rates for rehabilitation interventions—for instance, by insurance carriers and large corporations. They also tend to omit benefits extended by the Social Security Administration, Medicare/Medicaid, the Department of Veterans Affairs, and other collateral sources such as disability-oriented nonprofit organizations. Mention of these sources and the resources they potentially offer an evaluee, however, is sometimes noteworthy when evaluees have had access to them but have not pursued them.

Evaluators generally seek more than one source when presenting values for life care plan interventions; this helps to ensure a value cited represents a reasonable cost charged in a community and is not over- or understated. Exceptions to this occur, such as when an evaluee has established a relationship with a surgeon who has performed multiple operations on him or her and anticipates undergoing additional ones with the same provider. Large ranges in costs quoted for an intervention can signal values represented are amiss.

Frequently used life care planner sources for costing recommendations include:

- Costs evaluees have historically incurred for proposed rehabilitation interventions
- Inquiry of costs for services with healthcare providers' billing offices
- Vendor catalogs (e.g., wheelchairs, orthotics, durable medical equipment)
- Quotes for specific services (e.g., home modifications by a contractor, prosthetic needs specified by a prosthetist, costs for an operation and postoperative care specified by a surgeon)
- Billing codes healthcare providers use for reimbursement

- Websites specifying costs of rehabilitation interventions (e.g., therapy centers, pharmacies, skilled care facilities)
- Published fee-for-service surveys by nonprofit healthcare organizations such as the FAIR Health database (n.d.), American Hospital Directory (n.d.), and the American Society of Anesthesiologists *Relative Value Guide* (2020)

Berens (2019) presented a review of life care planning research. Additional information on life care planning and case management appears in Weed and Berens (2019), and Crowley and Huber (2021) addressed numerous life care plan management issues.

The high stakes accompanying most life care plans invariably result in interested parties' due diligence to ensure treatment protocols and their costs are necessary, reasonable, and derived in sync with practice standards. Life care planners should presume that their work will be carefully scrutinized and that those who investigate it will seek to compare it with prior, similar efforts they have undertaken to detect inconsistencies that could discredit them.

CHAPTER 7

The Noncatastrophic Life Care Plan

Generally, life care plans fall into one of two categories: noncatastrophic or catastrophic. As the terms connote, candidates for noncatastrophic life care plans have lower levels of impairment than candidates for catastrophic life care plans. Correspondingly, the latter group's life care plans tend to be more rehabilitation intensive, complex, and costly. Figure 7.1 presents key differences between noncatastrophic and catastrophic life care plans.

Chapter 6 discussed processes associated with developing a life care plan, including reviewing pertinent records, conducting examinations, consulting with contributors, sourcing costs for rehabilitation interventions, and assembling and refining the plan. This chapter focuses on nuances related to the development of noncatastrophic life care plans. Chapter 8 addresses issues specific to catastrophic life care plans, and Chapter 9 discusses international life care plans.

Figure 7.1 Differentiating Features of Noncatastrophic and Catastrophic Life Care Plans

Evaluee Capacities	Life Care Plan Type	
	Noncatastrophic	Catastrophic
Rehabilitation Gain Capacity	Possible/Likely	Nominal Capacity/No Capacity
Work Capacity	Not Impaired/May Be Some-what Impaired	No Capacity
Ability to Perform Activities of Daily Living	Not Impaired/May Be Some-what Impaired	Nominal Capacity/No Capacity
Need for Attendant Care	No Need/Nominal Need	Need for Full or Near-Full Care
Capacity for Independent Living	Full Capacity/Near Full Capacity	Nominal Capacity/No Capacity
Life Expectancy	Usually Not Diminished	Usually Diminished

Chapter 10 discusses situations in which extraneous issues—such as the progression of an evaluee's preinjury pathologies and/or an evaluee's new, unrelated postinjury trauma—require life care planners to carefully parse recommendations, isolating them to issues in dispute. As an example, visits to healthcare professionals and costs of medications prescribed for an evaluee's preexisting hypertension, diabetes, and anxiety would not be included in a life care plan an injury in question necessitated—unless the new injury exacerbated preexisting problems, such as causing a need for increased medication dosages. In this case, the life care planner would include as damages only the incremental costs associated with the need for the higher dosages.

Noncatastrophic Life Care Plan Considerations

Much of the discussion that follows pertains more often to noncatastrophic life care plans than to catastrophic life care plans. Of course, many concepts relate to both.

Classifying a life care plan as noncatastrophic rather than catastrophic is not intended to discount or diminish the significance of injuries or their damages values; the distinction is for purposes of perspective and application of a framework for evaluating damages and costs. In keeping with standards of practice, a fundamental premise of *The Valuation of Monetary Damages in Injury Cases: A Damages Expert's Perspective* is that all injuries and their sequelae must be dignified by comprehensive and objective evaluation.

Indeed, all permanent injuries—whether they portend noncatastrophic or catastrophic life care plans—are significant. While injuries and associated disabling problems addressed in a noncatastrophic life care plan generally require less rehabilitation intervention, they nonetheless can involve multisystem disabling problems and hold implications for evaluees' functioning in important life domains including psychological, social, medical, vocational, and avocational.

Life care plans prepared in cases outside of litigation differ from those prepared for litigation purposes. Specifically, the former incorporate all evaluee rehabilitation needs—regardless of etiologies underlying them. Unless otherwise prefaced, the contents of life care plans prepared for litigation specify rehabilitation interventions attributable solely to events in question.

Conceptual Considerations

Paradoxically, in some ways, preparing a noncatastrophic life care plan is more complex than preparing a catastrophic life care plan, even though a noncatastrophic plan usually has relatively less aggressive rehabilitation interventions and a constricted scope of treatment and specialist involvement. The reasons for this paradox are subtle and manifold.

Consider essential and basic life activities. There usually is no question that a catastrophically disabled evaluee either cannot perform or is quite limited in performing such activities as housework, yard maintenance, and securing and sustaining employment, while a noncatastrophically disabled evaluee may possess full or somewhat limited capacities to engage in these activities.

Forensic experts can often impute a full monetary value with scant analysis to assess losses in the former situation, reckoning the catastrophic impairments preclude any participation in the noted activities. The latter situation, however, requires evaluations of (1) degrees of retained capacity and, in some cases, the introduction of interventions and their associated costs to supplement fractional diminished capacities, and (2) potential future impairment in performing the activities, along with needs for supplemental services and their costs. These additional levels of analysis and clinical interpretation and underlying assumptions invite parties adverse to the evaluator to second guess and aggressively challenge the foundations of opinions rendered.

Evaluees with noncatastrophic disabling problems generally display fewer if any visible restrictions than those with catastrophic disabling problems. Catastrophically injured evaluees are often nonambulatory, relying on wheelchairs, prosthetics, and other devices and sometimes using oxygen and/or other breathing equipment, leg bags, and various medical devices that visibly signal their impaired status. This type of essential medical equipment use is far less prevalent in noncatastrophic cases and, coupled with the nonexistence of visible impairments, can foster a perception that an evaluee has few if any disabling problems. This perception can complicate an evaluator's task of justifying life care plan interventions.

Further, the comparative lack of disabling problems visible to those valuing injury claims—sometimes supplemented with surveillance of an evaluee engaging in customary activities of daily living without apparent problems—can further complicate explaining the necessity of rehabilitation interventions in noncatastrophic cases. For example, defense counsel may present surveillance of a noncatastrophically disabled evaluee driving, grocery shopping, performing yard work, and participating in moderate exercise to bolster arguments the evaluee is unscathed and requires nominal if any rehabilitation intervention. Plaintiff lawyers' counterarguments to dispel assertions that their clients do not need remediation equate to the notion that disability does not mean inability. Astute evaluators finesse the limits of these bounds, applying the science of their profession, to determine bona fide interventions to include in their life care plans.

Most laypeople have difficulty discerning impairments through routine interactions with people with noncatastrophic disabling problems. They are not qualified to identify clinical symptoms emanating from maladies such as mild traumatic brain injury, posttraumatic stress disorder and other emotional difficulties, hypersomnolence, and assorted musculoskeletal injuries. The adage "You can't judge a book by its cover" is apropos, and an evaluator's task often transmutes to providing insight to those evaluating damages on implications of evaluee problems that may not be evident but nonetheless require rehabilitation intervention.

A well-developed life care plan assessment facilitates insight and understanding into pending and future care needs that those evaluating damages may lack and, by extension, may overvalue or undervalue. Elucidating underlying needs for rehabilitation interventions can also promote insight into pain and suffering an injury has caused and will cause, which apply to assessing a case's nonmonetary value.

Figure 7.2 presents excerpts from a rehabilitation report an evaluator prepared after examining the widow of a decedent who also left two young sons. The evaluator's work included developing noncatastrophic life care plans for the three surviving family members without physical injuries but nonetheless in need of intense rehabilitation intervention. By illuminating complex factors underlying recommendations for rehabilitation interventions, the evaluator also discerns and describes the effects of nonvisible, complex factors relevant to valuing pain and suffering damages. In this case, beyond mental health treatment, the evaluator included in a life care plan interventions such as the services of a case manager, tutor, and life skills coach and private school placement.

Figure 7.2 Example of an Evaluator Illuminating Nonvisible, Complex Factors Underlying Recommendations Included in a Noncatastrophic Life Care Plan

---

Summary and Impressions

Born in Guatemala, where she attended school in a rural area through the sixth grade, Ms. Natella has no further education. She does not speak English and, in addition to issues related to her husband's 2019 death, continues to experience cultural assimilation difficulties.

At age 41, Ms. Natella became a widow and single parent of two boys—one with special needs and one with significant mental health problems that have thus far necessitated three inpatient psychiatric hospitalizations. Among other things, she lost her spouse, his financial support, and the partnership their union provided. In her husband's absence, Ms. Natella has persisted in facing the challenges that beset her in grieving his loss, persevering in her life, and tending to her children's complex, intensive needs to the best of her ability. Indeed, the Natella family dynamics are quite complicated and, based on evidence available, largely attributable to Mr. Natella's death. Ms. Natella is now 43 years old. She appears overwhelmed by the many challenges that continue to confront her.

Currently, Ms. Natella informed me, she experiences the following problems related to her husband's untimely death:

- Ongoing mood-related problems and grief for her husband
- Difficulty managing behavioral problems exhibited by 15-year-old son Carlos
- Stress related to consoling 12-year-old son Francesco
- Stress associated with raising two sons as a single mother: "The load is heavy."
- Financial challenges due to loss of husband's employment income
- Loss of assistance with housekeeping and other chores
- Loss of fatherly guidance provided to her sons
- Loss of husband's companionship
- Unwelcome lifestyle changes contributing to depression

Testing administered during my exam was consistent with my clinical impression that Ms. Natella is experiencing severe depression. I support her ongoing participation in mental health treatment. She will require considerable assistance to manage her situation as best as possible, given the unfortunate factors at hand.

I am preparing a life care plan for Ms. Natella. Additionally, I am preparing individual rehabilitation evaluation reports for Carlos and Francesco, along with individual life care plans for them.

Evaluators also consider an evaluee's residual rehabilitation capacities including unrealized abilities to enhance functioning and, by extension, the potential for ripple effects throughout a life care plan. As an example, in one case, an incomplete quadriplegic prescribed intensive occupational therapy gained the capacity to self-catheterize, independently perform a bowel program, self-administer medication, and engage in other previously untenable manual tasks. This development diminished the skilled care necessary to include in the life care plan, with an associated reduction in costs. Holistic, concurrent analyses of an evaluee's capacity to realize gains and implications for rehabilitation interventions can have a major effect on a life care plan's implementation and value.

Comparing and contrasting historical rates of an evaluee's consumption of rehabilitation interventions with those a life care plan proposes can prove instructive, especially if a significant amount of time has elapsed since the plan's preparation. Reasons for large differentials require investigation. More discussion on this matter is in the following section on updating life care plans.

Updating Life Care Plans

As Figure 7.1 indicates, evaluees with catastrophic disabling problems typically have nominal or no capacity to realize rehabilitation gains, whereas those with noncatastrophic disabling problems likely have retained or somewhat possess this capacity. This differentiating feature has implications for updating life care plans.

Although both noncatastrophic and catastrophic life care plans may require updating—for a myriad of reasons, related and unrelated to pending litigation—noncatastrophic evaluees' conditions are generally more fluid, and their life care plans more often require updating than do catastrophic life care plans. This is especially true in pediatric cases, where unrealized developmental gains/setbacks and rehabilitation interventions unknown at a life care plan's inception subsequently emerge.

Of course, unforeseen injury-related complications, new technologies and medical breakthroughs, and changes in an evaluee's personal situation—such as a relocation to a new region, vicissitudes associated with adapting to disability, and variances in support and financial resources—can also cause a need to modify a life care plan. Additionally, evaluees sometimes transition to the care of new/additional healthcare providers who may recommend treatment plans differing from those previously prescribed.

Costs for rehabilitation interventions fluctuate like all economic commodities including labor and material. Generally, technologically based interventions—such as MRIs and other diagnostic modalities, prosthetics, and medications that become generic—decrease in cost over time, while the converse is true for service-related interventions such as therapies, skilled care, and invasive procedures.

Timing is another variable in determining whether a life care plan merits updating. Especially before testifying, life care planners aspire to convey accurate, contemporary information on the value of proposed rehabilitation interventions. Most life care planners update their work—at a minimum, cost estimates—when more than a year has elapsed since their last effort. An update examination and review of updated records and/or updated consultations with life care plan contributors (please refer to Chapter 6) may also be in order.

In addition to revising costs, current treatment protocols, and evaluee-specific information, updated life care plans address details that include expunging outdated information and incorporating new information. For example, if an evaluee underwent a surgery anticipated in an earlier life care plan, the intervention would be deleted in a subsequent edition, and the claim for this damage would transition from the category of a future life care plan damage to a past medical cost. Or, if an evaluee failed a course of projected interventional pain management treatment outlined in an initial life care plan and more aggressive interventions have since been prescribed, an updated life care plan would also reflect this change; likewise, incurred and projected costs would be allocated to appropriate categories.

Changes in claimed life care plan damages—especially increased monetary amounts—are subject to intense scrutiny. Lawyers invariably compare iterations of protocols specified in life care plan editions, along with cost variances (including costs projected in prior life care plans compared to costs billed, along with offsets), seeking explanations for changes. Their efforts include gathering and creating evidence that could impeach experts' methodology and credibility, potentially leading to a Daubert challenge (discussed in Chapter 11). Reasons for life care plan changes should be considered in this context.

Compliance with standards of practice and methods described in Chapter 6 can avert unfounded challenges to a properly constructed life care plan update. Support from the following bolsters life care planners' defense of reasons for changes:

- Updated medical bills and records
- References to changed evaluee conditions necessitating life care plan recommendations
- Updated evaluee examination
- Updated contributor consultations, including revisions to previously specified treatment plans
- Record of consumption of rehabilitation interventions

In some cases, the need for new life care plan interventions arises from initially unforeseen problems. This occurred in a case in which a maritime worker sustained major amputations to his dominant hand and fingers. A prosthesis provided little gain in his residual manual abilities, and to compensate for his functional deficits, he began using his teeth to assist with tasks he would ordinarily perform with his dominant hand and fingers. Over time, this caused him to acquire dental injuries and, by extension, the need for rehabilitation interventions not initially identified.

Those scrutinizing later life care plan editions will also focus on interventions previously represented as reasonably probable in terms of need and later altered, including omissions and changes in treatment protocols. For example, an update of a life care plan that does not include ongoing administration of pain management injections included in an earlier edition is likely to spawn questions about reasons for the change, along with underlying theories that the evaluee is improving and that former projections of rehabilitation needs were and continue to be inflated.

Further, when significant periods have elapsed between life care plan editions and evaluees have not undergone one or more interventions included in a prior edition(s), life care planners will again be expected to explain reasons for the differentials between what plans projected and what actually occurred. Queries on this subject often have undertones including less than subtle accusations that interventions initially proposed were superfluous; they might also imply that evaluees were noncompliant with recommendations tendered. Such allegations threaten to erode the credibility of all associated with the recommendation—including the contributor who proposed the intervention, the evaluee who did not undergo the intervention as prescribed, the life care planner who represented the intervention as a reasonably probable need, and counsel representing the evaluee who argued for monetary compensation to fund interventions not implemented.

In defense of the types of issues just cited, life care planners may explore the merits of rationales that include evaluees' lacking the financial resources to pursue interventions recommended. Another plausible explanation relates to evaluees' sophistication or lack thereof, along with logistical support necessary to implement a life care plan's variegated interventions. An evaluator applied this latter defense in a case involving an evaluee who sustained mild traumatic brain injury. The evaluee's initial life care plan included cognitive rehabilitation, a brain MRI, and an updated neuropsychological evaluation—none of which the evaluee had undergone during the interval between the initial life care plan and its update more than one year later. In the updated life care plan, the evaluator maintained these recommendations and added one for a case manager, presenting the rationale that this additional intervention was necessary to facilitate the modestly educated, socioeconomically disadvantaged, impaired evaluee's ability to obtain needed treatment.

Life care planners should also consider collateral sources for rehabilitation available to evaluees at no cost that they have not pursued. While from a legal perspective introducing into evidence the associated monetary value of any potential offset may call for a legal conclusion and may be inadmissible, the significance from a life care planning perspective is that an evaluee might have had unencumbered resources available to mitigate alleged disabling problems that went unused. For example, a military veteran alleging hearing loss caused by an industrial accident may be able to obtain hearing aids at no cost from the Department of Veterans Affairs. The nonuse of this resource could call into question the severity of the evaluee's hearing impairment along with efforts to mitigate claimed damages.

Quality Assurance

As a life care plan approaches fruition, the mechanics of its development ultimately culminate in a conceptual assessment of its efficacy. The sections that follow address quality control checks to facilitate this objective.

Accurate Documentation of Contributor Recommendations

Evaluators committed to developing well-constructed life care plans employ procedures to ensure their work accurately reflects treatment protocols contributors intend. This relates, of course, to interventions communicated during consultations as well as to those extrapolated from records.

A statement of a life care planner's understanding and summary of a contributor's recommendations at the end of a consultation facilitates effective communication, especially when interventions are technical, complex, and interdependent. For example, such a statement might clarify that a future surgical recommendation may be contingent on outcomes realized from initial interventions hierarchically implemented, along the lines of medication trials combined with conservative treatment and interventional pain management.

Other practices that facilitate accurate recording and communication of contributor recommendations include conducting multiple, detailed levels of review that compare records, notes, and life care plan contents. Additionally, as discussed in Chapter 6, the distribution of a completed life care plan to contributors with whom the evaluator has consulted with requests to review it and respond, noting agreement/revisions, helps to further ensure accuracy (please refer to the sample verification form referenced in Chapter 6 and included as Appendix K). When contributors amend their recommendations, evaluators should revise their life care plans accordingly.

Evaluators most often extrapolate recommendations from records—including office progress notes, reports, responses to written life care plan questions, and deposition testimony—

when they cannot consult with contributors. These extrapolations sometimes include tacit contributor attributions to a life care plan that evaluators adopt when they are on the opposite side of the case from the contributor. In these circumstances, evaluators apply caution not to selectively adopt and/or under- or overextrapolate recommendations.

Unless needs are presumed as perpetual—such as in cases in which prescriptions of prosthetics, orthotics, and various types of durable medical equipment will likely continue into the foreseeable future or indefinitely—evaluators avoid adopting interventions from dated records. Again, evaluators should tentatively approach recommendations made a long time from when they construct a life care plan.

Discerning Cost and Related Irregularities

Once an evaluator assembles cost information, often from more than one source for each intervention, due diligence requires another level of review: assessing variances in cost estimates among sources for the same or similar services. For instance, when significant differences arise in pricing for the same surgery, reasons for the variance beg answering. Sometimes, reasons include varying assumptions made in offering an estimate, such as the duration of an inpatient hospitalization after an operation or the type of instrumentation procedures will require. Further, one estimate could include the fees and costs associated with postoperative care while another estimate could include operative costs only.

Sometimes an outlier cost is unjustifiably inflated. Why? Some practitioners quote especially high fees to discourage consideration of their services. An evaluator encountered this situation when an evaluee's neurologist quoted an exorbitant fee—$2,000 for 15 minutes—to participate in a life care planning consultation. The prospective contributor informed his patient, the evaluee, that his aversion to being involved in litigation motivated him to demand the lofty fee, intended to fend off attempts to enlist him in a pending matter. In this instance, the lawyer who retained the evaluator did not approve the consultation fee and, instead, took the neurologist's deposition, posing questions the evaluator prepared. Interestingly, under subpoena for the deposition as a fact witness, the neurologist received no compensation for his time.

Additionally, it is not uncommon for healthcare professionals who extend services with payment terms specified in a letter of protection—an agreement to defer collections in whole or in part until funds emerge via settlement or jury verdict—to quote costs for their services higher than prevailing community rates. These practitioners do not always recover the full values they bill, especially in cases in which their retaining party realizes an outcome less remunerative than anticipated; hence, their practice is to set fees above prevailing market values, allowing them to offset occasions when they cannot recover the full fee.

The most expensive items a life care plan contains typically draw the most scrutiny from those evaluating damages claims. Quite often, these include ongoing attendant and skilled care costs. Defense counsel's tactic in challenging them frequently implies the intervention is unnecessary, overstated, or overvalued, while plaintiff's counsel most often infer an opposing evaluator has understated and/or undervalued levels of care. This latter charge often occurs in disputes over the skill level required to provide various nursing services.

Generally, invasive nursing services—such as administering IVs, suctioning, and catheterizing—require higher levels of skilled care intervention than noninvasive nursing services such as transferring and assisting with activities of daily living. State nurse practice acts identify competencies qualifying providers to perform various nursing services, and it is important that evaluators appropriately match the disabilities in need of assistance with a care provider qualified to provide the services. A mismatch can lead to significantly under- or overstating damages.

In the following deposition excerpt, an evaluator provides a rationale to a cynical opposing lawyer for attendant care and housekeeping services a life care plan specified. Briefly, the case involved a 60-year-old evaluee who sustained musculoskeletal injuries because of a fall incident two years before undergoing a life care plan assessment. The testimony describes why the evaluee requires the identified level of care, delineates examples of needed attendant care, and explains the need to increase services over time.

Q   If you had to give me a brief summary of your—of what you believe are Ms. Viola's main issues, what would you say?

A   On page 5, under Presenting Problems, there is a summary of her main issues.

Q   Okay. So she has severely impaired mobility?

A   Yes.

Q   Ongoing left lower extremity pain, most intense in the knee, ongoing left hip pain, intermittent low back pain due to altered gait, tends to onset when bearing weight, and intermittent right ankle/heel pain due to altered gait, tends to onset when bearing weight, and depression due to unwelcome postincident lifestyle changes and functional decline?

A   Correct.

Q   And Ms. Viola described her left knee as the most symptomatic body part?

A   Yes.

Q   And she's also having right ankle and heel symptoms related to altered body mechanics?

A   Correct.

Q   And what types of adaptive devices is she using?

A   When I saw her—and you'll see the picture in the appendix of my report—she was wearing a soft left knee brace, and she was using a HurryCane. She also informed me she has a hard, long left-leg brace she uses. She has a shower chair, wheeled walker, and hot/cold packs, and she described a device that helps her to put on her socks.
      She previously had used a TENS unit. I think she still has it, but she said it wasn't effective. So, she doesn't use it on a regular basis.

Q   Okay. And she's on the baclofen, the diclofenac, and the Icy Hot for her pain?

A   Yes. She was when I examined her.

Q   And you noted that Ms. Viola can safely lift and carry less than ten pounds?

A   Yes.

Q   And she's not having any issues of fine motor functioning in her hands, correct?

A   Her fine motor functioning is intact, and she did well on a test of hand/eye coordination I administered to her.

Q   And she noted that she can walk slowly for 15 to 20 minutes?

A   Yes.

Q   And she can stand for less than ten minutes?

A   Yes.

Q   And she can sit from 30 to 40 minutes?

A   Correct.

Q   Page 10, you note additional problems identified by Ms. Viola. You already testi-fied that her balance problems relate to the incident. Are her complaints of fatigue related to the incident?

A   I understand them to be.

Q   And why is that?

A   Well, if you read what it says next to fatigue, it says, "She told me she tires easily and said 'I'm overly tired, but I can't sleep.'"
       And then on the next page, I elaborated about her sleep difficulties, namely interrupted sleep every one to two hours, because of pain and positional discomfort.

Q   Okay. And on Page 13 you've recommended a personal care attendant for Ms. Viola. Why does she need a personal care attendant?

A   Well, she doesn't require a skilled care attendant. Skilled would be like a CNA or an LPN or an RN. She does not require that level of care, but she clearly requires some assistance with everyday activities and tasks because of her acquired dis-abling problems and her functional limitations.
       Ms. Viola doesn't require an attendant 24 hours a day, but two to four hours a day of this service for the next ten years would be reasonable. And then increas-ing that level to four to six hours per day after ten years for the remainder of her lifetime, in my opinion, is also reasonable. Given the limitations she has, given the diminution in her ability to perform many activities of daily living, many of which her husband has assumed on her behalf or that go undone, in my opinion I've pro-posed a conservative and reasonable schedule.

Q   So, you're recommending currently—so from Year 1 to 10, when this care plan begins, two to four hours per day for a personal care attendant, right?

A   Yes.

Q   Even though we noted before that Ms. Viola is able to perform most of her activi-ties of daily living?

A   No. That's not true. She's able to do most of her self-care activities. That was the discussion.

Q   Well, she's also able to perform—she's also able to prepare her meals. Her husband does the laundry.
       So, what is this person going to do for two to four hours per day?

A   Okay. I think that's not quite accurate, the way you paraphrased it. She's able to prepare simple meals, is what's stated in my report. She used to enjoy cooking, and now she doesn't prepare complex meals. But, can she microwave something in the oven? Yes. Can she make a sandwich? Yes. Can she make a bowl of cereal? Yes. She can prepare simple meals, but not complex meals.

Weight bearing and mobility is very difficult for her. Basic chores like grocery shopping challenge her. Driving is difficult for her. She opts not to drive whenever she can. It's very cumbersome for her to wear her leg brace when she's in a vehicle.

Her husband does most of the driving. He performs the household errands. Buying her medications, transporting her to and from medical appointments, basic housework, these are all things that are either at or beyond the limit of Ms. Viola's capacity. So, these are the kinds of things I understand her husband is doing on her behalf, and there's a value to the services he provides. Some chores go undone.

And that's one of the reasons that she has a very impoverished quality of life and one of the reasons she's very depressed.

Q   Okay. So, tell me what this person is going to do for two to four hours per day for Ms. Viola.

A   I just mentioned some of the tasks.

Q   So, drive her around, grocery shopping?

A   Assistance with transportation, assistance with grocery shopping and household errands, including her medications, transportation to and from medical appointments, as needed, providing assistance with heavy housekeeping chores.

The life care plan I prepared does include a housekeeper, but you'll see it's every one to two weeks. It's not every week, until later on, when she's older.

Q   Okay. And then from Year 11 through the end of her life, you increase the attendant care to four to six hours per day. Why is that?

A   Because I believe she's—let's see. Yes. She's 60 years old now—60 and a half. Her physicians anticipate that as she gets older she will experience degenerative problems secondary to her injuries, and her functional capacities will continue to diminish. The interaction between her disabling problems and degenerative issues, along with the natural aging process, are reasons she will require more care. So, I increased the schedule just a little bit, about an hour a day, when she nears age 70.

Q   So, once we have the personal care attendant, we're assuming her husband isn't doing anything at home?

A   I'm not saying he's not going to do anything at home. Ms. Viola's husband is older than she is, and he was employed the last I knew. Ms. Viola requires the assistance and services Mr. Viola provides; of course, there's a value associated with the services.

Q   Okay. And then you have the housekeeper, because Mr. Viola isn't cleaning the house as good as Ms. Viola would like?

A   There would be no need for a housekeeper, period, if Ms. Viola wasn't disabled. She is disabled, and her husband has assumed housekeeping chores that she otherwise would have performed, or the chores go undone. And, in my opinion, it's very reasonable to employ a housekeeper every two weeks to supplement the housework Mr. Viola is able to do.

Ensuring Internal Consistency

Besides ensuring consistency between external inputs to a life care plan and the document's contents—namely, contributors' recommendations, cost estimates, and interventions appropriate for an evaluee's needs—quality control also involves an assessment to safeguard its internal consistency. This includes ensuring the document suffices in meeting the constellation of disabling problems an evaluee has acquired and does not have recommendations that conflict or are duplicative. A life care plan should also offer pragmatic recommendations.

An evaluator appeared to violate several of the previously noted tenets in a life care plan prepared for a 47-year-old man who acquired nonoperative neck and back symptoms after a vehicular accident. The plan included ostensibly superfluous conservative treatment recommendations—specifically, recurrent physical therapy protocols, a fitness center membership with personal training services three times per week, and the purchase of home exercise equipment. His credibility waned when deposed, he chose not to concede the duplicative nature of his proposed interventions, and he rejected the prospect of purchasing a Peloton exercise machine through which the examinee could participate in streamed home exercise guidance and consolidate the proposed treatments.

Sample Noncatastrophic Life Care Plan with Narrative from a Report of a Vocational Rehabilitation Evaluation

The remainder of this chapter includes sample analyses—namely, for sake of context, the Summary and Impressions section from an evaluator's vocational rehabilitation evaluation report, followed by the evaluator's life care plan—pertaining to a 60-year-old man who pursued earning capacity and future care needs damages claims related to a motor vehicle accident. While the evaluator deemed the evaluee a candidate for vocational rehabilitation, he determined the accident caused the evaluee a loss of earning capacity.

Since the evaluee's sole treating doctor declined to consult with the evaluator on future treatment needs, the evaluator appropriated recommendations from records to construct the life care plan. Further, collaborating with the evaluee's lawyer, the evaluator developed questions used to depose the treating doctor; the questions were crafted to elicit recommendations also incorporated in the plan. The evaluator supplemented this collateral source information with her recommendations.

Summary and Impressions from Report of Vocational Rehabilitation Evaluation

I.   Born in Australia, Mr. Granson emigrated from there to Canada, where he completed high school in 1978, a four-year pipefitting apprenticeship in 1982, and a bachelor's degree in business in 1985. He became a U.S. citizen approximately 25 years ago, and, during approximately the last ten years, he has been involved in sourcing, buying, and reselling consumer electronic products. At the time of his August 3, 2018, motor vehicle accident, Mr. Granson reported, he was a 20 percent partner in Rocket Electronics in Louisville. Based on my understanding of his job responsibilities as a part owner/buyer/sales representative with Rocket, he performed semiskilled tasks requiring light/medium exertion. In May 2020, Mr. Granson testified that, after his 2018 accident, he had a period of work absence from five to six weeks. He provided information to me consistent with his May 2020 deposition about the demise of Rocket in February 2020, which he related to the pre-COVID economic downturn and not to his 2018 accident. Medical records identify operations Mr. Granson underwent on his cervical spine on April 4, 2019, and lumbar spine on August 6, 2019, and he described how his injuries and functional limitations impaired his work capacity. Mr. Granson noted that, when he returned to work after his accident, he performed more sedentary tasks. The only employment he noted holding since February 2020 was a job as a general warehouse associate with United Distribution Center from August through November 2020. Mr. Granson described unskilled/semiskilled, medium/heavy work he performed. He conveyed his United Distribution job responsibilities proved incompatible with his injuries, prompting his resignation. Mr. Granson has since engaged in work-related activities inclusive of facilitating a former customer's sourcing of footwear, selling clothing at a flea market on Sundays, and selling woodwork he and his significant other restore. Mr. Granson assessed he remains capable of sedentary and light exertion work, and he described a plan to establish a retail business in his locale, similar to the Rocket model he previously helped to develop. Mr. Granson apprised me his preaccident career plans were to continue developing Rocket, and he noted his current plans are similar. He reckoned his accident-related injuries restrict the scope of tasks he remains capable of performing. "There's a physical element. I would have to hire people to help me handle merchandise, unload trucks," Mr. Granson explained. He also cited additional future treatment anticipated for him along with the progression of his injuries, while describing anticipated adverse effects on his future career development. Mr. Granson estimated his presenting problems diminish his job performance "by probably 50 percent of my capacity." He is 60 years old and in the decline phase of his career development. He impressed me as an industrious and entrepreneurial person, motivated to pursue vocational rehabilitation.

II. Discussing his medical history before his August 3, 2018, motor vehicle accident, Mr. Granson recollected a motor vehicle accident circa 2014. Imaging from August 2014 notes abnormalities in his lumbar spine, including a herniated L4-5 disc. He subsequently presented lower back pain complaints and, in February 2016, was deemed a candidate for a lumbar epidural steroid injection. Mr. Granson apprised me his symptoms subsequently abated, and he chose not to pursue the intervention. Further, he reported he fully recovered from his lower back injury and had been asymptomatic for several years before his 2018 accident. Mr. Granson responded negatively when asked about injury to his neck before August 2018. I am unaware of documentation that refutes his representations.

III. Postaccident medical records provide objective support for Mr. Granson's presenting problems. More than two years have elapsed since his accident, and he remains symptomatic as noted. As indicated earlier, he underwent surgeries on his cervical spine in April 2019 and on his lumbar spine in August 2019. The most recent records I reviewed from Dr. Tindall include her notes from March 2020; these notes document a progression of Mr. Granson's neck and back pain symptoms. Her September 22, 2020, note includes a recommendation for an anterior lumbar interbody fusion at L4-5 and L5-S1. Mr. Granson told me his headaches and stiffness he feels in his neck are his primary problems. He also complained of lower back stiffness. Mr. Granson conveyed his neck and lower back are his most symptomatic body parts. He described how lifting aggravates his neck and back symptoms, and he noted essentially all cervical spine movements are problematic. Mr. Granson conveyed bending his waist and kneeling exacerbate his lower back symptoms. My analysis has led me to conclude his accident-related injuries are incompatible with his preaccident employment with Rocket and his postaccident employment with United Distribution. Mr. Granson is a surgical candidate, and I recommend he temper his work participation. At this time, from a vocational rehabilitation perspective, I recommend he limit his work activities to those that are sedentary/light exertion.

IV. On a positive note, Mr. Granson demonstrated superior intelligence (Full Scale IQ = 120) on a measure of intellect administered during my exam. He scored particularly well on measures of attention to detail, visual analysis, and mental organization and planning. From a functional perspective, Mr. Granson assessed he can safely lift and carry from 40 to 50 pounds. He denied having problems with the functioning in any of his extremities. His fine motor functioning is intact. Generally, Mr. Granson estimated, he can sit from 30 to 45 minutes with repositioning, stand up to two to three hours, and walk up to 60 minutes before overexerting himself or needing to rest. He assessed he is psychologically well adjusted. I found Mr. Granson interpersonally skilled, pleasant, and likeable. Along with his work motivation, education, training, work experience, and transferable skills, these factors are facilitative to his vocational rehabilitation.

V. My analysis has led me to conclude Mr. Granson is a candidate for vocational rehabilitation; however, he has acquired several vocational handicaps that merit considering. Again, he is in the latter phase of his career development, and his functional capacities have diminished. Further treatment, including operative treatment, has been prescribed. The universe of work opportunities previously available to him has become constricted, and he may require accommodations and/or replacement labor to enable him to accomplish work tasks previously within his capacity. Mr. Granson's options for retraining are limited due to his age and injuries. Based on information available at this time, within a reasonable degree of vocational rehabilitation probability, Mr. Granson has acquired injuries and associated disabling problems from his 2018 motor vehicle accident that have caused him a reduction in earning capacity in the range of 10 to 20 percent over the remainder of his work life. This is a conservative estimate. Mr. Granson is at risk of a truncated work life, and, depending on the outcome of his future treatment, he may experience periods of work absence and symptom exacerbation that further erode his residual earning capacity. I plan to continue to monitor his progress and amend my assessment accordingly.

VI. Injuries and associated disabling problems Mr. Granson acquired because of his August 3, 2018, motor vehicle accident require ongoing rehabilitation intervention. I am developing a life care plan for him.

Sample: Noncatastrophic Life Care Plan

Prepared for
Marcos Granson
Michael Shahnasarian, PhD
February 17, 2021

Table of Contents

Contributors to Life Care Plan

Contributor	Specialty	Consultation Date	Telephone
Dr. Michael Shahnasarian	Rehabilitation Psychologist	12/22/2020	(813) 555-xxxx
Dr. Lisa Tindall	Neurosurgeon	02/02/21 Deposition 09/22/20 Report	(800) 555-xxxx

All opinions presented herein are within a reasonable degree of life care planning certainty.

Year 1 in the duration section of this life care plan begins on the date this life care plan is published.

FAIR Health is a national independent not-for-profit organization whose mission is to bring transparency, integrity, reliability and accessibility to healthcare costs and insurance information for all stakeholders. FAIR Health maintains the nation's largest database of privately billed healthcare claims from 493 distinct geographic regions nationwide, and offers medical/surgical, anesthesia, inpatient facility, outpatient facility, and ambulatory surgery center charge benchmarks. The database is continually updated and currently includes over 32 billion billed procedures nationwide. FAIR Health's FH® Charge Benchmarks, which are widely used by the life care planning community, are based directly on the distribution of actual, non-discounted fees for each service in a specific geographic area and time-period, and do not reflect any adjustments for any contractual or in-network agreements.

The FAIR Health data base is endorsed by the International Association of Rehabilitation Professionals (IARP).

Anesthesia costs are derived from the American Society of Anesthesiologists (ASA) 2021 Relative Value Guide and 2021 Crosswalk; A Guide for Surgery/Anesthesia CPT Codes.

Diagnostic costs such as X-rays, MRI's, and CT scans are obtained solely from the 2021 FAIR Health data base because costs cited by diagnostic centers are based on insurance reimbursement, thereby undervaluing the true cost.

Medication costs in this life care plan are pharmacy cash prices.

BACKGROUND INFORMATION

NAME:	Marcos Granson
DATE OF BIRTH:	September 4, 1960
ONSET OF DISABLING PROBLEM:	August 3, 2018, motor vehicle accident
RACE:	Caucasian
DOMINANT HAND:	Right
HEIGHT:	5 feet 7 inches
CURRENT WEIGHT: PREACCIDENT WEIGHT: MARITAL STATUS:	167 pounds 167 pounds Single/divorced Significant other, Lee Remick, age 58
NAMES AND AGES OF CHILDREN:	Nina, daughter, 34 Sam, son, 28
RESIDENCE:	Largo, Florida
PRESENTING PROBLEMS:	"Bouts of severe, throbbing headaches" "Stabbing, pulling pressure behind the eye" Intermittent neck pain radiating bilaterally into shoulders Ongoing lower back pain radiating bilaterally into lower extremities, worse on right side Tingling sensation in right thigh

EVALUATIONS

Item	Duration	Frequency	Estimated Cost	Recommended By
PHYSIATRIST EVALUATION	Year 1–2*	One Time	$334–$420 Per Evaluation	Dr. Shahnasarian

*Note: Per Dr. Shahnasarian, additional recommendations will follow.

Per Laura Smith, practice administrator at Rehab Group, office of Dr. Paul Davis, 813-555-xxxx (Tampa, FL): Physiatrist evaluation, $420 using CPT Code 99204.

Physiatrist evaluation, CPT Code 99204 (office or other outpatient visit for the evaluation of a new patient requires these 3 key components: a comprehensive history; a comprehensive examination; and medical decision making of moderate complexity. Counseling and/or coordination of care with other physicians, other qualified health care professionals, or agencies are provided consistent with the nature of the problem(s) and the patient's and/or family's needs. Usually the presenting problem(s) are of moderate to high severity. Typically, 45 minutes are spent face-to-face with the patient and/or family), $334 to $415 per evaluation according to the FAIR Health database, www.flonline.fairhealth.org/ FH Benchmarks/ Medical.

Item	Duration	Frequency	Estimated Cost	Recommended By
PAIN MANAGEMENT EVALUATION	Year 1	One Time	$334–$445 Per Evaluation	Dr. Tindall

Per Dr. Tindall's February 2, 2021, deposition pg. 25, "If he continues to have pain, then pain medicine would be another option." Additional recommendations will follow.

Per Carrie Miller, billing specialists at Suncoast Spine, office of Dr. Darin Stevens, 813-555-xxxx (Clearwater, FL): Pain management evaluation, $445 using CPT Code 99204.

Pain management evaluation, CPT Code 99204 (office or other outpatient visit for the evaluation of a new patient requires these 3 key components: a comprehensive history; a comprehensive examination; and medical decision making of moderate complexity. Counseling and/or coordination of care with other physicians, other qualified health care professionals, or agencies are provided consistent with the nature of the problem(s) and the patient's and/or family's needs. Usually the presenting problem(s) are of moderate to high severity. Typically, 45 minutes are spent face-to-face with the patient and/or family), $334 to $415 per evaluation according to the FAIR Health database, www.flonline.fairhealth.org/ FH Benchmarks/ Medical.

Item	Duration	Frequency	Estimated Cost	Recommended By
UPDATE LIFE CARE PLAN	Year 1–Life	To Be Determined	To Be Determined	Dr. Shahnasarian

Per Dr. Shahnasarian, update life care plan, to be determined.

THERAPEUTIC NEEDS

Item	Duration	Frequency	Estimated Cost	Recommended By
BIOFEEDBACK TRAINING	Year 1–2*	8–12 Sessions Total	$124–$195 per Session	Dr. Shahnasarian

*Note: Per Dr. Shahnasarian, reassess potential to benefit from further training at the end of this period. The goal of biofeedback is to teach the individual to take control of physiological functions such as heart rate, respiratory rate, and muscle tension. In a typical training session, a person is affixed to electrical sensors that provide information about those functions. Over time, the person can learn to pace breathing or relax muscles to produce a desired change in physiology.

Per Britany Smith, neurotherapist at Behavioral Care, office of Dr. William Miller, 813-555-xxxx (Tampa, FL): Biofeedback, $195 per session using CPT Code 90901.

Biofeedback training, CPT Code 90901 (biofeedback training by any modality), $124–$160 per session according to the FAIR Health database, www.flonline.fairhealth.org/FHBenchmarks/Medical.

Item	Duration	Frequency	Estimated Cost	Recommended By
PSYCHOLOGICAL COUNSELING	Year 1–2*	5–10 Sessions Total	$140–$180 per Session	Dr. Shahnasarian

*Note: Per Dr. Shahnasarian, reassess potential to benefit from additional treatment at the end of this period

Per Martha Smith, office administrator at the office of Dr. Gerard Miller, 727-555-xxxx (Largo, FL): Psychological counseling, $180 per 60-minute session using CPT Code 90837.

Psychological counseling, CPT Code 90837 (psychotherapy, 60 minutes with patient), $140 to $175 per visit according to the FAIR Health database, www.flonline.fairhealth.org/FHBenchmarks/Medical.

Item	Duration	Frequency	Estimated Cost	Recommended By
MEDIAL BRANCH BLOCK LUMBAR	Year 1–2*	1–2 Times	$8,486 Each Time	Dr. Tindall

Per Dr. Tindall's February 2, 2021, deposition pg. 24, "They [medial branch blocks in the future for low back or neck] could be helpful."

*Note: Reassess potential to benefit from additional treatment at the end of this period.

Per billing dated December 12, 2018, from Spine Doctors, office of Dr. Tindall, medial branch block lumbar, $8,486.

Item	Duration	Frequency	Estimated Cost	Recommended By
MEDIAL BRANCH BLOCK CERVICAL	Year 2–4*	1–2 Times	$8,468 Each Time	Dr. Tindall

Per Dr. Tindall's February 2, 2021, deposition pg. 24, "They [medial branch blocks in the future for low back or neck] could be helpful."

*Note: Reassess potential to benefit from additional treatment at the end of this period.

Per billing dated November 14, 2018, from Spine Doctors, office of Dr. Tindall, medial branch block cervical, $8,486.

Item	Duration	Frequency	Estimated Cost	Recommended By
PHYSICAL THERAPY FOLLOWING SURGERIES	Year 1–4	3 Sessions per Week for 2–3 Months per Protocol per Surgery	$100–$150 per Session	Dr. Tindall

Per Dr. Tindall's February 2, 2021, deposition pgs. 23 and 24, "Generally when someone has fusion, there is a need for follow-up MRIs, follow-up therapy. Physical therapy can be very helpful [after lumbar surgery]."

Per Leah Smith, patient care coordinator at XYZZ, 727-555-xxxx (Largo, FL): Physical therapy, $100 per 30-minute session.

Physical therapy (therapeutic procedure, one or more areas, each 15 minutes; therapeutic exercises to develop strength and endurance, range of motion, and flexibility), $65 to $75; totaling $130 to $150 per session according to the FAIR Health database, www.flonline.fairhealth.org/FHBenchmarks/Medical.

DIAGNOSTIC TESTS

Item	Duration	Frequency	Estimated Cost	Recommended By
X-RAY LUMBAR SPINE	Year 1–2	One Time	$160–$275	Dr. Tindall

Per Dr. Tindall's February 2, 2021, deposition pgs. 22 and 23, "And we evaluate with X-rays to make sure that we can visualize good bony fusion."

X-ray of lumbar spine, CPT Code 72100 (radiologic examination, spine, lumbosacral; two to three views), $160 to $275 each time according to the FAIR Health database, www.flonline.fairhealth.org/FHBenchmarks/Medical.

Item	Duration	Frequency	Estimated Cost	Recommended By
X-RAY CHEST	Year 2–4	One Time	$75–$83	Dr. Tindall

Per Dr. Tindall's February 2, 2021, deposition, pg. 22, "He would be sent for medical clearance and have EKG and chest X-ray and blood work and an evaluation by a medical-clearing doctor."

X-ray chest, CPT Code 71046 (radiologic examination, chest, two views), $75 to $83 each time according to the FAIR Health database, www.flonline.fairhealth.org/FHBenchmarks/Medical.

Item	Duration	Frequency	Estimated Cost	Recommended By
MRI LUMBAR SPINE	Year 2–4	One Time	$1,396–$2,400	
	Year 3–5 to Life	One Time	Each Time	Dr. Tindall

Per Dr. Tindall's February 2, 2021, deposition pgs. 22 and 24, "So I'd want to make sure that I had up-to-date MRIs [prior to surgeries]. Generally when somebody has had a fusion, there is a need for follow-up MRIs, follow-up therapy."

MRI lumbar spine, CPT Code 72148 (magnetic resonance, imaging, spinal canal and contents, lumbar; without contrast material), $1,396 to $2,400 each time according to the FAIR Health database, www.flonline.fairhealth.org/FHBenchmarks/Medical.

Item	Duration	Frequency	Estimated Cost	Recommended By
ELECTROCARDIOGRAM (EKG)	Year 2–4	One Time	$80–$90	Dr. Tindall

Per Dr. Tindall's February 2, 2021, deposition, pg. 22, "He would be sent for medical clearance and have EKG and chest X-ray and blood work and an evaluation by a medical-clearing doctor."

Electrocardiogram (EKG), CPT Code 93010 (electrocardiogram, routine EKG with at least 12 leads; with interpretation and report), $80 to $90 each time according to the FAIR Health database, www.flonline.fairhealth.org/FHBenchmarks/Medical.

Item	Duration	Frequency	Estimated Cost	Recommended By
BLOOD ANALYSIS	Year 2–4	One Time	$78–$154.94	Dr. Tindall

Per Dr. Tindall's February 2, 2021, deposition, pg. 22, "He would be sent for medical clearance and have EKG and chest X-ray and blood work and an evaluation by a medical-clearing doctor."

Per Florida price line for Quest Labs, 800-555-xxxx, CBC, test code 6399, $45.50; CMP, test code 10231, $88.07, and venipuncture, test code 36415, $21.37; totaling $154.94 each time.

Blood analysis, including complete blood count (CBC), CPT Code 85025 (automated CBC and automated differential WBC count), $29 to $30 each time; complete metabolic panel (CMP), CPT Code 80053 (comprehensive metabolic panel), $39 to $55; and venipuncture, CPT Code 36415 (collection of venous blood by venipuncture), $10 to $15, totaling $78 to $100 according to the FAIR Health database, www.flonline.fairhealth.org/FHBenchmarks/Medical.

ORTHOTICS

Item	Duration	Frequency	Estimated Cost	Recommended By
LUMBAR BRACE	Year 1–2	One Time	$64.99–$159	Dr. Tindall

Per Dr. Tindall's February 2, 2021, deposition pgs. 22 and 24, "He'll need a brace during his recuperation time. After the surgery, he would wear a brace for six to 12 weeks. More often it's 12 weeks."

Per Better Braces, www.betterbraces.com: DonJoy Hard Lumbar Back Brace, $76.99; Bell-Horn Stabilizing Lumbar Back Brace, $76.99; DonJoy Performance Reel Adjusted Back Brace, $149.99.

Per Braceability, www.braceability.com: LSO Spinal Stenosis Lumbar Brace, $159; Adjustable Spine Brace for Lower Back, $74.99; Mac Plus Lumbar Spine Brace, $64.99.

Item	Duration	Frequency	Estimated Cost	Recommended By
CERVICAL COLLAR	Year 2–4	One Time	$14.99–$15.22	Dr. Tindall

Per Dr. Tindall's February 2, 2021, deposition pgs. 22 and 24, "He'll need a brace during his recuperation time. After the surgery, he would wear a brace for six to 12 weeks. More often it's 12 weeks."

Per Walgreens, www.walgreens.com: Rigid Cervical Collar, $14.99.

Per Walmart, www.walmart.com: Rigid Cervical Collar, $15.22.

AIDS FOR INDEPENDENT LIVING

Item	Duration	Frequency	Estimated Cost	Recommended By
MISCELLANEOUS ADAPTIVE AIDS/PATIENT EDUCATION	Year 1–Life	Annually	$300–$400 per Year	Dr. Shahnasarian

Per Dr. Shahnasarian, miscellaneous adaptive aids/patient education, $300 to $400. Examples include grab rails; handheld showerhead; shower chair; hot/cold packs; heating pad; and massage devices.

DRUG AND SUPPLY NEEDS

Item	Duration	Frequency	Estimated Cost	Recommended By
CYCLOBENZAPRINE (FLEXERIL) 10 MG	Year 1–Life	3 Tablets per Day	$15.75–$49.99 per 90 Tablets	Dr. Tindall

Per Dr. Shahnasarian's December 22, 2020, evaluation, Mr. Granson indicated he is prescribed cyclobenzaprine 10 mg, three tablets per day.

Per Dr. Tindall's February 2, 2021, deposition pg. 24, "I would say medications as needed; sometimes muscle relaxers, sometimes nonsteroidal anti-inflammatories."

Per pharmacies listed below, Flexeril is the brand medication for cyclobenzaprine. Per Walgreens, Flexeril 10 mg, $200.89; per CVSA, $197.99 per 90 tablets.

Per GoodRX/Walgreens and GoodRX/CVS, Flexeril is no longer available.

Per Summer Smith, pharmacy technician at Walgreens Pharmacy, 727-555-xxxx (Largo, FL): Cyclobenzaprine 10 mg, $48.99 per 90 tablets.

Per Lindsay Miller, pharmacist at CVS Pharmacy, 727-555-xxxx (Largo, FL): Cyclobenzaprine 10 mg, $49.99 per 90 tablets.

Per GoodRX/Walgreens: Cyclobenzaprine 10 mg, $27.96 per 90 tablets.

Per GoodRX/CVS: Cyclobenzaprine 10 mg, $15.75 per 90 tablets.

Item	Duration	Frequency	Estimated Cost	Recommended By
IBUPROFEN (MOTRIN) 800 MG	Year 1–Life	3 Tablets per Day	$18.56–$32.99 per 90 Tablets	Dr. Tindall

Per Dr. Shahnasarian's December 22, 2020, evaluation, Mr. Granson indicated he is prescribed ibuprofen 800 mg, three tablets per day.

Per Dr. Tindall's February 2, 2021, deposition pg. 24, "I would say medications as needed; sometimes muscle relaxers, sometimes nonsteroidal anti-inflammatories."

Per pharmacies listed below, Motrin is the brand medication for ibuprofen. Per Walgreens, Motrin 800 mg, $52.99; per CVS, they no longer carry Motrin.

Per GoodRX/Walgreens and GoodRX/CVS, Motrin is no longer available.

Per Summer Smith, pharmacy technician at Walgreens Pharmacy, 727-555-xxxx (Largo, FL): Ibuprofen 800 mg, $32.89 per 90 tablets.

Per Lindsay Miller, pharmacist at CVS Pharmacy, 727-555-xxxx (Largo, FL): Ibuprofen 800 mg, $32.99 per 90 tablets.

Per GoodRX/Walgreens: Ibuprofen 800 mg, $22.94 per 90 tablets.

Per GoodRX/CVS: Ibuprofen 800 mg, $18.56 per 90 tablets.

HOME/FACILITY CARE

Item	Duration	Frequency	Estimated Cost	Recommended By
HOME HEALTH AIDE FOLLOWING FUTURE SURGERIES	Year 1–Life	4 Hours per Day; 7–10 Days Each Time	$22–$27 per Hour	Dr. Shahnasarian

Per Laura Smith, director of sales at Home Care Help, 727-555-xxxx (Largo, FL): Personal care attendant, $27 per hour.

Per Amanda Miller, client service manager at Ocean Home Health, 727-555-xxxx (Clearwater, FL): Home health aide, $25 per hour.

Per Lisa Stevens, intake coordinator at In-Home Health Care–Largo, 727-555-xxxx (Largo, FL): Home health aide, $22 to $25 per hour.

HOSPITALIZATIONS/SURGERIES

Item	Duration	Frequency	Estimated Cost	Recommended By
ANTERIOR LUMBAR INTERBODY FUSION L4-L5–L5-S1	Year 1–2	One Time	$126,370	Dr. Tindall

Per Dr. Tindall's September 22, 2020, report, "My recommendation at this point for his lumbar spine is anterior lumbar interbody fusion at L4-L5 and L5-S1."

Per Dr. Tindall's February 2, 2021, deposition pgs. 16, 17, and 21, "And I recommended a larger surgery for his lower back at the L4-L5 and the L5-S1 levels. It's called an anterior lumbar interbody fusion. It's a fairly large surgery. It's something I wouldn't want to put him through at an elderly age. So I would say sooner rather than later."

Unable to obtain costs from Dr. Tindall's office. Per Tara Smith, billing manager at Broken Spine, office of Dr. Urban, physician fee for anterior lumbar interbody fusion is $28,270 using CPT Codes 22558, 22858, 22840, 20930, and 20936. This is an outpatient procedure performed at Northern Surgery Center. This includes an estimated cost of hardware.

> Physician fee: $28,270

> Facility fee: $92,000

Per Karri Smith, administrator at Northern Surgery Center, 813-555-xxxx (Tampa, FL), $92,000 for outpatient facility fee for CPT Codes 22558, 22858, 20930, and 20936.

> Anesthesia fee: $6,100

$6,100 for procedure codes 22558, 022858, 22840 (20930 and 20936 are not primary codes) with procedure time of 45 minutes according to the American Society of Anesthesiologists (ASA) *2021 Relative Value Guide* and *2021 Crosswalk; A Guide for Surgery/Anesthesia CPT Codes*.

Item	Duration	Frequency	Estimated Cost	Recommended By
CERVICAL DISC REPLACEMENT C5-C6	Year 2–4	One Time	$72,620 Total	Dr. Tindall

Per Dr. Tindall's February 2, 2021, deposition pg. 23, "He may need to have a disc replacement at the C5-C6 level. We did not treat that level, and he does have a herniation there, if he continues to have pain."

Dr. Tindall performed a cervical disc replacement on C3-C4 and C4-C5 on April 4, 2019. Per billing from Spine Group dated April 4, 2019, physician fee for cervical disc replacement for one level, $8,100. Per billing from Central Surgery Center dated April 4, 2019, cervical disc replacement for one level, $64,520; totaling $72,620. This includes disk replacement hardware.

POSSIBLE HOSPITALIZATIONS/SURGERIES

Item	Duration	Frequency	Estimated Cost	Recommended By
POSSIBLE ADJACENT LUMBAR FUSION	To Be Determined	To Be Determined	$103,356	Dr. Tindall

Per Dr. Tindall's February 2, 2021, deposition, "And sometimes people develop adjacent segment disease, which might require another surgery down the road."

Unable to obtain costs from Dr. Tindall's office. Per Tara Smith, billing manager at Broken Spine, office of Dr. Urban, physician fee for lumbar fusion surgery is $27,000 using CPT Codes 22612, 22614, 20930, and 20936. This is an outpatient procedure performed under general anesthesia at Northern Surgery Center. This includes an estimated cost of hardware.

    Physician fee: $27,500

    Facility fee: $70,000

Per Kari Johnson, administrator at Northern Surgery Center, 813-555-xxxx (Tampa, FL), outpatient facility fee for lumbar fusion using CPT Codes 22612, 22614, 20930, and 20936.

    Anesthesia fee: $5,856

$5,856 for general anesthesia using CPT Codes 22612 and 22614 (20930 and 20936 are not primary codes) with a procedure time of 45 minutes according to the American Society of Anesthesiologists (ASA) *2021 Relative Value Guide* and *2021 Crosswalk; A Guide for Surgery/Anesthesia CPT Codes.*

Item	Duration	Frequency	Estimated Cost	Recommended By
POSSIBLE ADJACENT CERVICAL FUSION	To Be Determined	To Be Determined	$104,756	Dr. Tindall

Per Dr. Tindall's February 2, 2021, deposition, "And sometimes people develop adjacent segment disease, which might require another surgery down the road." Mr. Granson underwent cervical fusion on April 4, 2019.

Unable to obtain costs from Dr. Tindall's office. Per Tara Smith, billing manager at Broken Spine, office of Dr. Urban, physician fee for lumbar fusion surgery is $27,900 using CPT Codes 22533, 22534, 20930, and 20936. This is an outpatient procedure performed under general anesthesia at Northern Surgery Center. This includes an estimated cost of hardware.

    Physician fee: $27,900

    Facility fee: $71,000

Per Alysia Ortega, billing office manager at Northern Surgery Center, 813-555-xxxx (Tampa, FL), outpatient facility fee for lumbar fusion using CPT Codes 22533, 22534, 20930, and 20936: $71,000.

    Anesthesia fee: $5,856

$5,856 for general anesthesia using CPT Codes 22533 and 22534 (20930 and 20936 are not primary codes) and a procedure time of 45 minutes according to the American Society of Anesthesiologists (ASA) *2021 Relative Value Guide* and *2021 Crosswalk; A Guide for Surgery/Anesthesia CPT Codes.*

CHAPTER 8

The Catastrophic Life Care Plan

Catastrophic disability designation is reserved for cases of a person losing the capacity to perform essential life functions—perhaps foremost, the ability to live and function independently. These disabling conditions arise from the likes of severe spinal cord injuries, multiple body part amputations, and severe, traumatic brain injury. Severe psychological trauma can also lead to catastrophic disabling problems. Quite often, people with catastrophic disabilities suffer from multisystem impairments.

Beyond lacking capacity to live independently, those with catastrophic disabling problems often require some level(s) of skilled care to subsist and have one or more risk factors that threaten to reduce their life expectancies. From a life care planning perspective, the major and typically most costly implications of these conditions pertain to residential placement and the types of care required to optimize residual capacities, ensure a living environment as safe as possible, and promote opportunities for enhanced quality of life.

Candidates for noncatastrophic and catastrophic life care plans tend to have several common categories of rehabilitation need—like diagnostic tests, therapies, medications, and specialist follow-up. A primary differentiating feature between these groups, as Figure 7.1 delineates, relates to capacity to live independently with variable levels of specialized care and the implications these interventions portend.

Earlier chapters of *The Valuation of Monetary Damages in Injury Cases: A Damages Expert's Perspective* addressed issues common to life care plans in general, with Chapter 7 more specifically addressing noncatastrophic life care plans. This chapter focuses on bedrock factors differentiating noncatastrophic and catastrophic life care plans: namely, residential placement and caregiver requirements. It also presents a discussion of psychological considerations beyond those addressed via life care plan recommendations—those common to all disabled people, manifest in varying degrees, and often a large component of nonmonetary damages. A sample report of a catastrophic life care plan completes this chapter.

Residential Placement and General Catastrophic Life Care Plan Considerations

Since evaluees with catastrophic life care plan needs typically cannot live autonomously, their residential options tend to be twofold: home-based placement with considerable support or institutional placement. In some cases, a hybrid of these offers a third option. As examples, intervals of home placement during stable periods and institutional placement during periods of intensive rehabilitation interventions, or placement in a congregate living facility, offer other options.

Catastrophically disabled evaluees tend to experience primary multisystem disabling problems along with secondary risk factors contributing to their reduced life expectancies. For example, a ventilator-dependent quadriplegic is at risk of comorbidities stemming from respiratory, cardiac, and vascular problems that, independently and cumulatively, pose complications that more likely than not will shorten his or her life. The progression of disabling problems and related pathologies requires evaluators to consider in the life care planning process more intensive interventions—such as hospitalizations and increased skilled care needs—near the end of an evaluee's life expectancy.

When evaluators propose in a life care plan an evaluee's residential options and associated care needs, several variables merit consideration, including:

- **The environment best suited for an evaluee's disabling problems.** Evaluee safety, potential to realize functional gains, and quality of life issues are always paramount considerations when evaluating suitable placements. In some cases, home placement—regardless of efforts to accommodate an evaluee via architectural modifications, staffing, and procuring needed medical equipment—lacks the comprehensive resources and continuity of care a skilled nursing facility offers.
- **Quality of care available and suitability of care for an evaluee's needs.** Some evaluees, especially during periods of symptom exacerbation and instability, require multidisciplinary rehabilitation intervention. Placement recommendations should ensure the availability of comprehensive, competent care in sync with an evaluee's needs.
- **The welfare and desires of the evaluee, family, and others close to the evaluee.** Family members and others close to the evaluee sometimes shun the notion of institutional placement for a myriad of reasons that include strong emotional bonds, sense of duty, remorse, guilt, and stereotypical perceptions of a "nursing home" and like facilities. These emotions and attitudes require perspective including an objective focus on selecting the optimal placement for an evaluee and addressing the practicality and reality of caring for a catastrophically disabled person in a home environment (discussed in more detail in the next section).

The intensity of evaluees' rehabilitation needs and the stability of their conditions often take precedence over other relevant factors when evaluating placement options—especially when conditions require complex treatment and/or pose life-threatening consequences. For example, a nonambulatory evaluee with sepsis and history of progressive worsening of decubiti with current stage 4 ulcers, along with other comorbidities, would likely be better served in a skilled care facility staffed with wound care specialists and equipped with appropriate durable medical equipment than in a private home with more modest resources.

In some cases, evaluators offer home and institutional placement options aiming to afford quality, professionally considered information and opinions so that those entrusted with assessing and evaluating life care plan details can arrive at informed valuation decisions. The life care plan at this chapter's end provides an example.

Competent evaluators attempt to place in proper context information necessary to impute fair and reasonable values to this bedrock component of a life care plan. Of course, the choice of residential placement is ultimately a private decision—one at which evaluees typically arrive with input from family members, those close to them, and healthcare professionals—based on the evaluee's available resources. A discussion on the advantages and disadvantages of home-based and institutional placement follows.

Home-Based Placement

Some catastrophically disabled evaluees have periods when they can function safely and productively while unattended; others require 24/7 care. Staffing considerations include establishing requirements for caregiver coverage and determining the types and levels of care an evaluee requires. Evaluators arrive at these decisions in conjunction with evaluating safeguards necessary to protect an evaluee and opportunities to promote a de minimis restrictive environment and the fullest degree possible of independent functioning.

Individual differences and evaluee-specific circumstances govern staffing decisions. A young, high-functioning quadriparetic evaluee living in an adapted residence and capable of self-catheterizing and independently taking medication, for example, may require two to three hours of attendant care in the morning to assist with self-care and other tasks, two to three hours of similar services when retiring to bed, and a nurse every other day to assist with a bowel program and to provide general condition surveillance. A person with a similar level of disability but with other circumstances that affect functioning—such as significant difficulties with disability adjustment and complications including recurrent urinary tract infections and other comorbidities—may require a more intensive staffing protocol. Additionally, a catastrophically disabled person's needs for in-home assistance quite often wax and wane over time. Simply put, there is no template or formula to which an evaluator can refer to discern an evaluee's needs; case-specific factors undergird each assessment.

In addition to reviewing medical records, examining an evaluee, and consulting with other healthcare professionals, evaluators can use interviews of caregivers to provide insight into evaluee staffing needs. These interviews focus on tasks an evaluee can accomplish, those that require varying levels of assistance, safety assessments (including capacity to be left unattended and/or monitored semiremotely), and other input that could benefit the comprehensive development of an evaluee's life care plan.

The care that family members and others close to the evaluee provide, whether compensated or uncompensated, has a monetary value. Beyond that source of care, evaluees have two other viable sources from which they can procure care services: an agency that provides caregivers to perform required services or private-duty employment of service providers. Again, a hybrid of these sources offers another option.

Like many variables associated with life care planning, the bivariate service source options available to evaluees present advantages and disadvantages, as noted next. In either case, a major consideration in employing in-home care services relates to host home privacy issues: staffing is accomplished by shifts of staff cycling in and out of the home or live-in service providers. Many hosts dislike activity and people entering and exiting their homes at all hours of the day, causing disruptions ranging from noises they create to smells from food they prepare to consume while on duty.

Typically, home-based placement is more expensive than institutional placement. Further, some home environments are unfavorable options for reasons that range from a lack of family members and friends able to commit to housing a catastrophically disabled person to logistical issues including space and balancing other family/friend commitments.

Contracted Agency Services

The advantages of procuring caregivers through an agency include the contractual obligation that, in exchange for a fee, provides for labor and associated agreed-upon services necessary to care for a catastrophically disabled person. Employing services through an agency subsumes administrative details part and parcel of this agreement—such as managing service providers, processing payroll, tending to employee benefits and required insurances, and providing replacement labor when a contracted employee becomes ill, is injured on the job, or is otherwise unable to provide caregiver services. The contract absolves the evaluee and others involved from procuring, providing, and maintaining the services—at least in theory—and the many personnel matters associated with staffing.

Of course, in real life, circumstances arise that adversely affect continuity of service. Contracted service providers sometimes arrive at their scheduled shifts late or become ill on short notice, prohibiting the contracted agency from securing a replacement in a timely manner. Further, service providers leave their jobs for a myriad of reasons. Securing a suitable replacement who can establish a simpatico relationship with a catastrophically disabled patient often can be lengthy and/or challenging.

Typically, during periods of interrupted service, the consumer of caregiver services assumes responsibility for providing services to the catastrophically disabled person, or the services go undone. Occasions also arise when the personalities of service providers and evaluee and/or host do not mesh or when the quality of services provided is less than satisfactory. When procuring services through an agency, the consumer has less control in staffing and case management decisions than when privately employing these services.

Private-Duty Employment of Contracted Services

Consumers who opt to privately procure caregiver services for catastrophically disabled people confront staffing issues akin to those possible when contracting services through agencies. Further, since private-duty employment requires consumers to become employers, they assume responsibility for the full scope of personnel administration issues. This includes recruiting and selecting qualified service providers, staffing and securing replacements as needed, intervening in situations that involve job performance, and managing the numerous administrative and cost issues employers incur—insurances, employee benefits, and lawyer and accounting fees and costs, to name a few.

The advantages private-duty employment of caregiver services offer include greater control in medical case management decisions and sole decision-making on personnel matters— both of which require more consumer time and personal investment; some would assert these are not advantages but burdens. These factors, along with the added administrative costs associated with this care model, often negate any cost savings compared to in-home, all-inclusive agency contract services. Control of hiring/retaining caregiver staff can somewhat mitigate the privacy issues hosts encounter—another consideration in selecting a best-suited alternative.

Types of Daily Care Services Provided

Generally, the home-based care services evaluees require fall into three categories: attendant care, skilled care, and administrative services. Examples of services from these areas follow.

Attendant Care

Basic attendant care services require no or nominal medical intervention; however, those providing the service, at a minimum, should be trained in CPR and basic first aid. They should also understand needs specific to the catastrophically disabled person to whom they are providing services, with knowledge of appropriate action to take during periods of instability. Examples of attendant care services include:

- Housekeeping, preparing meals, laundering clothes, assisting with dressing and other self-care activities
- Assisting with transfers and repositioning
- Transportation services
- Companionship
- Grocery shopping and performing personal errands
- Property maintenance
- General oversight

Skilled Care Services

State laws specify minimum requirements necessary to provide skilled care services. Of course, complex cases call for more than the minimum, along with committed and conscientious professionals adept at intervening as situations require. Skilled care services include:

- Assisting with passive range of motion, stretching, and exercising
- Medication administration including IVs
- Providing nutrition via feeding tubes
- Suctioning and respiratory care
- Catheterizing
- Wound care
- Ostomy care
- Assisting with bowel programs
- Overseeing and assisting with administering medications
- Nail care

Administrative Services

Those providing catastrophically disabled people administrative services often interact with them infrequently, and providing hands-on caregiver services is not generally within their scope of responsibilities. Nonetheless, administrative services, like attendant and skilled care services, are essential to these people's well-being. Administrative services include:

- Case management
- Scheduling and coordinating routine medical appointments
- Medical record keeping
- Processing information necessary to ensure treatment and payment of medical expenses
- Guardianship/medical decision-making/tending to competency issues
- Managing finances

Institutional Placement

Family and friends of people who become catastrophically disabled may look askance at institutional placement due to stereotypes—smells of human waste, neglected residents, and uncaring staff, to name a few—associated with this alternative. The stigma and imagery of a "nursing home" cause some to dismiss housing loved ones there.

While often well-intentioned and sometimes grounded in emotions that include guilt, sense of obligation, and belief that placement outside a home will result in inferior care, a decision to house in a private residence a catastrophically disabled person with intensive, round-the-clock skilled care service requirements can overwhelm and emotionally drain all involved. Further, this option can compromise the catastrophically disabled person and those dear to her or him.

In a case involving a minimally conscious adolescent girl requiring a feeding tube and other life support equipment, her parents eventually opted to transition her from their home to a skilled care facility. The reasons that led to their decision included unanticipated absences of contracted caregivers, requiring the family to upend their plans and assume the intensive caregiver responsibilities necessary to care for their daughter; a sense of diminished privacy due to caregivers sometimes unknown to them entering/exiting their home throughout the day; and arranging transportation for multiple emergency trips to hospitals during periods of instability.

Family dynamics can also influence a residential placement decision. Elaborating on the prior example, the girl's parents' decision-making incorporated an assessment of the family's best interests, including their determination that the situation was unfair to their other two children. Specifically, the parents expended an inordinate amount of time and energy tending to their catastrophically disabled daughter, leaving far less time for her siblings, and the home environment became more hospital-like and sterile, contributing to the able-bodied children's discomfort with it and feeling uneasy, for example, inviting friends to their home. Taking all into account, the girl's parents discerned an institutional placement best served their daughter's and family's interests.

For similar reasons, it is not uncommon for a catastrophically disabled person to transition from a home-based residential placement to an institutional setting. Institutional placement provides advantages over home-based placement that include comprehensive service provision, resources typically superior to those that can be constructed in a home environment, better likelihood of continuity of services, and greater accountability to regulatory bodies, which promotes service quality. This option also has disadvantages.

Regulatory agencies overseeing skilled care facilities establish standards and monitor a myriad of factors intended to evaluate and enforce the provision of proper care and quality control. These include minimum requirements for, among other things, skilled care staffing ratios, on-site specialty staff, cleanliness, resident safety, documentation of medical care, case management, and nutrition. Depending on the resident population and facility, they may offer on-site transportation services to healthcare venues, access to therapy resources, and social programming. Skilled care facilities offer continuity and a breadth of services difficult to replicate in a home environment, typically at a lower cost, and relieve the disabled person's family and friends of the administrative requirements and costs associated with private-duty employment of in-home contracted care.

Of course, despite regulation, institutional care varies in quality. Like all facets of decision-making undergirding the care of catastrophically disabled people, soliciting professional input and employing due diligence to evaluate viable options—which sometimes involves crafting one option from an amalgamation of them—help those entrusted with selecting a skilled care facility to execute their responsibilities diligently.

Beyond potential quality of care issues, the disadvantages of institutionally placing a catastrophically disabled person include family and/or friends' diminished convenience and access, since loved ones are not in the home. Institutional placement also affords less input into and control of a disabled person's maintenance and rehabilitation. This includes staffing decisions, control of daily care and activities, and need to adapt to a more structured, regimented lifestyle than in a home environment with dedicated staff.

Astute evaluators and those involved in residential placement decisions for catastrophically disabled people appreciate the most expensive residential option—or, for that matter, other costly rehabilitation interventions—does not promise better care or offer a superior placement/rehabilitation outcome. When retained by defense counsel and presenting a life care plan with an institutional placement option, evaluators typically encounter plaintiff counsel's cross-examination laden with innuendo that self-serving intentions to minimize economic damages motivate their presentation; namely, beholden to a defense lawyer and insensitive to the plaintiff's welfare, they seek only to diminish damage values. By extension, this argument insinuates the less expensive institutional placement option yields inferior care, detrimental to the plaintiff.

The circumstances just cited call for evaluators to provide professional assessments of available options and their advantages and disadvantages, acknowledging that placement decisions are personal—ultimately, ones catastrophically disabled people, if competent, and/or others entrusted with the authority will make.

Many considerations underlie the selection and presentation of residential placement options. No right or wrong decision exists, and incisive evaluator analyses of and counsel about the variegated, complex variables specific to a case at hand facilitate prudent decision-making.

Psychological Considerations

Individual differences largely govern psychological adjustment to disability. A person who acquired what many would perceive as a relatively minor disabling problem(s) may cope far less well than one meeting criteria for catastrophic disabling problems. Generally, however, those with catastrophic disabling problems experience greater difficulties in their disability adjustment than those with noncatastrophic disabilities.

Life care planners—especially those with training in mental health—assess all aspects of disability intervention needs including those beyond medically based interventions and are particularly well suited to discern the complex, internecine psychological manifestations of disability. The implications of this assessment pertain to both monetary and nonmonetary damages assessments.

Monetary Aspects of Psychologically Based Damages

The most common mental health concerns and problems people with acquired disabilities present relate to anxiety, depression, anger, concern about progressive degeneration of their functionality, and unwelcome lifestyle changes. Financial concerns and, in some cases, difficulties managing interpersonal relations and suicidal ideation may trigger and exacerbate their symptom presentation.

A wide range of behavioral manifestations sometimes accompanies these underlying concerns and problems—not limited to the likes of diminished frustration tolerance, reclusive tendencies, anhedonia, substance abuse, and aggression. Those with catastrophic disabilities exhibit a higher prevalence of these symptoms than do those with noncatastrophic disabilities.

Like all rehabilitation interventions, case-specific factors undergird prescriptions to mitigate mental health–related damages. An individual with mild cognitive dysfunction secondary to head trauma, for example, may require a protocol of neuropsychological surveillance coupled with psychological counseling and prescriptions of psychotropic medications. A person with a similar injury and symptoms but different personality profile and personal circumstances, on the other hand, may better respond to an alternate protocol.

Simply put, like all rehabilitation assessments and prescriptions of appropriate interventions, there is no universal remedy for the unique ways in which people who acquire disabling problems respond to their new, unanticipated, and unwanted life circumstances. Again, qualified evaluators do not apply one-size-fits-all, cookie-cutter solutions in their life care plans; rather, they employ standards of practice to evaluate case-specific factors leading to their discernment of appropriate rehabilitation interventions.

Unlike nonmonetary aspects of psychological sequelae accompanying disability, evaluators can quantify the economic value of mental health interventions aimed to mitigate alleged mental anguish damages. These interventions, administered on a fee-for-services basis, include:

- Follow-up by mental health professional (e.g., psychologist, psychiatrist, mental health counselor, social worker, family counselor, life skills coach)
- Psychological counseling
- Family counseling
- Group counseling
- Prescription(s) of psychotropic medication
- Diagnostic testing (e.g., psychological assessments, neuropsychological assessments)
- Biofeedback
- Transcranial magnetic stimulation
- Electroconvulsive treatment
- Inpatient mental health rehabilitation

Similar to medically based disabling problems, interventions to address psychological sequelae accompanying the onset of a disabling condition(s) do not always fully resolve presenting problems—especially when cases involve catastrophic disabilities. This brings up the question of nonmonetary damages, which, again, life care planners with expertise in mental health are particularly well positioned to assess and explain to those valuing damages.

Nonmonetary Aspects of Psychologically Based Damages

An evaluator's presentation of a life care plan provides a means to describe how acquired disabling problems have affected and will affect a disabled person. The progression of physically disabling problems and associated psychological fallout often coexist, operating reciprocally.

For example, a degenerative condition affecting a nonambulatory, brain-damaged person that furthers mobility restrictions and causes a concomitant need for increased skilled care services, increased loss of independence, and other unwelcome changes can trigger psychological reactions ranging from self-harm ideation to delusional thinking. Skilled evaluators with clinical expertise and insight necessary to evaluate and articulate these intangible factors provide context facilitative to appreciating and valuing pain and suffering damages.

Evaluators can illuminate others about an evaluee's hard-to-quantify intangible pain and suffering damages by providing qualitative descriptions of a disabling condition's psychological manifestations. Quite often, these include diminished self-esteem secondary to loss of independence and need to rely on others, as well as embarrassment over diminished functioning and changes in appearance, which can contribute to self-consciousness, negative self-image, and self-isolative tendencies.

Other common psychological reactions accompanying the transition from an able-bodied person to a person with disabilities arise from an inability or limited ability to pursue activities due to functional deficits. Examples include inability to engage in desired vocational and avocational pursuits, impaired ability to interact with family and friends, and problems caused by sexual dysfunction. Needless to say, the loss of these capacities extends to other psychologically rooted artifacts of disability adjustment, such as undesirable changes in roles and diminished ability to contribute to a household, which also can have deleterious mental health consequences.

Sample Catastrophic Life Care Plan

This chapter concludes with a sample catastrophic life care plan. Briefly, the evaluee acquired multisystem disabling problems resulting from a moped versus motor vehicle accident, rendering him nonambulatory, unable to communicate verbally, and unable to live independently.

The life care plan includes two options: option A posits continued residence in a skilled care facility, and option B posits home placement with the evaluee's son. The options differentiate how treatments would be administered, and Option B elaborates on details associated with home-based placement, such as skilled care staffing, home modifications, and durable medical equipment needs. Of course, the majority of the evaluee's requirements are common to both options, including routine evaluations, diagnostic testing, orthotics, and pharmacy needs.

Sample:
Catastrophic Life Care Plan

Prepared for
Robert Pendel
Michael Shahnasarian, PhD
February 8, 2019

Table of Contents

CONTRIBUTORS TO LIFE CARE PLAN

The following individuals provided recommendations for this life care plan:

Contributor	Specialty	Consultation Date	Telephone
Dr. Michael Shahnasarian	Rehabilitation Psychologist	01/26/21	(555) 555-xxxx
Dr. Mahesh Jensen	Internal Medicine Physician	01/31/21	(718) 618-0401

Note: Raymond Pendel, son and legal guardian of Robert Pendel, has been traveling from Florida to New Jersey to visit his father. This life care plan does not incorporate the costs associated with these visits. Raymond Pendel desires that his father rejoin the family in Florida, living with them as he had before his February 8, 2020, moped vs. motor vehicle accident.

All opinions presented herein are within a reasonable degree of life care planning certainty.

Year 1 in the duration section of this life care plan begins on the date this life care plan is published.

The *National Fee Analyzer* is published by FAIR Health, a nonprofit agency developed to ensure transparency in medical costs. The National Fee Analyzer provides physician practices with three percentiles (50th, 75th, and 90th) of charge data; only the 50th and 75th percentiles are incorporated into this life care plan. This resource provides physician practices with national charge date for fee scheduled evaluation and competitive analysis for contracting purposes. Compiled from a database of 650 million charge records arranged by CPT Codes, the *National Fee Analyzer* has no insurance company paid amounts incorporated into its product.

The *American Hospital Directory* is an online resource that compiles annual average cost data from hospitals nationwide.

Anesthesia costs are derived from the American Society of Anesthesiologists (ASA) *2019 Relative Value Guide* and *2019 Crosswalk; A Guide for Surgery/Anesthesia CPT Codes*.

Medication costs in this life care plan are pharmacy cash prices.esia costs are derived from the American Society of Anesthesiologists (ASA) 2021 Relative Value Guide and 2021 Crosswalk; A Guide for Surgery/Anesthesia CPT Codes.

Diagnostic costs such as X-rays, MRI's, and CT scans are obtained solely from the 2021 FAIR Health data base because costs cited by diagnostic centers are based on insurance reimbursement, thereby undervaluing the true cost.

Medication costs in this life care plan are pharmacy cash prices.

BACKGROUND INFORMATION

NAME:	Robert Pendel
DATE OF BIRTH:	July 30, 1963
ONSET OF DISABLING PROBLEM:	February 8, 2020, moped vs. motor vehicle accident
RACE:	Asian/Indian
DOMINANT HAND:	Left
HEIGHT:	5 feet 4 inches
CURRENT WEIGHT: PREACCIDENT WEIGHT: MARITAL STATUS:	177.4 pounds Unknown Single/Widowed
NAMES AND AGES OF CHILDREN:	Three adults (Raymond Pendel—guardian, son, and youngest child)
RESIDENCE:	Preaccident: Central Florida Currently: Kingston Multicare Center, Bronx, New Jersey
PRESENTING PROBLEMS:	Severe cognitive dysfunction Right side hemiparesis Unable to communicate verbally Totally dependent in all activities of daily living Feeding tube dependent Bowel and bladder incontinent Nonambulatory

RESIDENTIAL OPTIONS

Item	Duration	Frequency	Estimated Cost	Recommended By
OPTION A: SKILLED NURSING FACILITY— BRADENTON, FLORIDA	Year 1–2 to Life	24 Hours per Day; 365 Days per Year	$540–$650 per Day	Dr. Shahnasarian Dr. Jensen

Per Sandra Haines, business office assistant at New Life Living, 555-751-0557 (Bradenton, FL): Skilled nursing facility, $570 for a private room and $540 for a semiprivate. This includes room and board and skilled care.

Per Denay Mack, admissions liaison at Bradenton Oaks Center, 555-977-4214 (Bradenton, FL): Skilled nursing facility, $250 per day for room and board and $300 to $400 for skilled care depending on the patient's needs; totaling $550 to $650 per day.

Item	Duration	Frequency	Estimated Cost	Recommended By
OPTION B: HOME PLACEMENT WITH RAYMOND PENDEL	Year 1–2 to Life	24 Hours per Day; 365 Days per Year	*	Dr. Shahnasarian Dr. Jensen

*See option B in life care plan for these costs.

EVALUATIONS

Item	Duration	Frequency	Estimated Cost	Recommended By
NEUROPSYCHOLOGICAL EVALUATION	Year 1–2*	One Time	$5,197–$7,800	Dr. Shahnasarian

*Note: Per Dr. Shahnasarian, additional recommendations will follow.

Per Shelly Arnold, medical assistant to Dr. Richard Huff, (555) 977-2924 (Bradenton, FL): Neuropsychological evaluation, $7,800. This includes a full day of testing and a full day of interpretation and report preparation (16 to 18 hours) using CPT Codes 96136 and 96137.

Per 2019 National Fee Analyzer, neuropsychological evaluation, CPT Code 96136 (psychological or neuropsychological test administration and scoring by a physician or other qualified health care professional, two or more tests, any method; first 30 minutes), $175 to $226; and CPT Code 96137 (psychological or neuropsychological test administration and scoring by a physician or other qualified health care professional, two or more tests, any method; each additional 30 minutes), $162 to $210 (16 to 18 hours); totaling $5,197 to $7,576 per evaluation.

Item	Duration	Frequency	Estimated Cost	Recommended By
GASTROENTEROLOGIST EVALUATION	Year 1–Life	1 Time per Year	$270–$395 per Evaluation	Dr. Jensen

Per Susan Santana, medical assistant to Dr. Leopoldo Gray, 555-673-8545 (Bradenton, FL): Gastroenterologist evaluation, $270 using CPT Code 99204.

Per 2019 National Fee Analyzer, gastroenterologist evaluation, CPT Code 99204 (office or other outpatient visit for the evaluation of a new patient requires these three key components: a comprehensive history; a comprehensive exam; and medical decision-making of moderate complexity. Usually the presenting problem(s) are of moderate to high severity. Typically, 45 minutes are spent face to face with the patient and/or family), $313 to $395 per evaluation.

Item	Duration	Frequency	Estimated Cost	Recommended By
NUTRITIONIST EVALUATION	Year 1–Life	1 Time per Year	$185–$350 per Evaluation	Dr. Jensen

Per Jennifer Bowyer, RD LD/N, Director at The Medical Nutrition Center, 555-850-7592 (Bradenton, FL): Nutritionist evaluation, $350 for a 2½ hour consultation and assessment using CPT Code 99404.

Per 2019 National Fee Analyzer, nutritionist evaluation, CPT Code 99404 (preventative medicine counseling and/or risk factor reductions intervention(s) provided to an individual; approximately 60 minutes), $185 to $200 per evaluation.

Item	Duration	Frequency	Estimated Cost	Recommended By
INTERNAL MEDICINE EVALUATION	Year 1–Life	1 Time per Year	$205–$275 per Evaluation	Dr. Jensen

Per Helen Battles, client care coordinator at Bradenton Internal Medicine, office of Dr. Todd Webster, 555-252-2770 (Bradenton, FL): Internal medicine evaluation, $275 per evaluation using CPT Code 99203.

Per 2019 National Fee Analyzer, internal medicine evaluation, CPT Code 99203 (office or other outpatient visit for the evaluation and management of a new patient, which requires these three components: a detailed history; a detailed exam; and medical decision-making of low complexity. Usually the presenting problem(s) are of moderate severity. Typically 30 minutes are spent face to face with the patient), $205 to $260 per evaluation.

EVALUATIONS

Item	Duration	Frequency	Estimated Cost	Recommended By
NEUROLOGIST EVALUATION	Year 1–Life	1 Time per Year	$205–$275 per Evaluation	Dr. Jensen

Per Ellen Barrios, medical assistant to Dr. Arthur Peters, 555-879-7940 (Bradenton, FL): Neurologist evaluation, $275 per evaluation using CPT Code 99203.

Per 2019 National Fee Analyzer, neurologist evaluation, CPT Code 99203 (office or other outpatient visit for the evaluation and management of a new patient, which requires these three components: a detailed history; a detailed exam; and medical decision-making of low complexity. Usually the presenting problem(s) are of moderate severity. Typically 30 minutes are spent face to face with the patient), $205 to $260 per evaluation.

Item	Duration	Frequency	Estimated Cost	Recommended By
UROLOGIST EVALUATION	Year 1–Life	1 Time per Year	$205–$260 per Evaluation	Dr. Jensen

Per Lori Carter, receptionist at Bradenton Urology, office of Dr. Lenard, 727-596-9652 (Bradenton, FL): Urologist evaluation, $250 per evaluation using CPT Code 99203.

Per 2019 National Fee Analyzer, urologist evaluation, CPT Code 99203 (office or other outpatient visit for the evaluation and management of a new patient, which requires these three components: a detailed history; a detailed exam; and medical decision-making of low complexity. Usually the presenting problem(s) are of moderate severity. Typically 30 minutes are spent face to face with the patient), $205 to $260 per evaluation.

Item	Duration	Frequency	Estimated Cost	Recommended By
PHYSIATRIST EVALUATION	Year 1–Life*	1 Time per Year	$313–$420 per Evaluation	Dr. Jensen Dr. Shahnasarian

*Note: Per Dr. Shahnasarian, physiatrist evaluation, year 1 to 2. Additional recommendations will follow.

Per Lisa Porter, practice administrator at Rehabilitation and Electrodiagnostics, office of Dr. Thompson, 555-228-7696 (Bradenton, FL): Physiatrist evaluation, $420 using CPT Code 99204.

Per 2019 National Fee Analyzer, physiatrist evaluation, CPT Code 99204 (office or other outpatient visit for the evaluation of a new patient requires these three key components: a comprehensive history; a comprehensive exam; and medical decision-making of moderate complexity. Usually the presenting problem(s) are of moderate to high severity. Typically, 45 minutes are spent face to face with the patient and/or family), $313 to $395 per evaluation.

Item	Duration	Frequency	Estimated Cost	Recommended By
ORTHOPEDIST EVALUATION	Year 1–Life	Every 2–3 Years	$205–$260 per Evaluation	Dr. Jensen

Per Crystal Anderson, billing specialist at Florida Orthopaedic Institute, office of Dr. Aaron West, 555-978-9700 (Bradenton, FL): Orthopedist evaluation, $260 each visit using CPT Code 99203.

Per 2019 National Fee Analyzer, orthopedist evaluation, CPT Code 99203 (office or other outpatient visit for the evaluation and management of a new patient, which requires these three components: a detailed history; a detailed exam; and medical decision-making of low complexity. Usually the presenting problem(s) are of moderate severity. Typically 30 minutes are spent face to face with the patient), $205 to $260 per evaluation.

EVALUATIONS

Item	Duration	Frequency	Estimated Cost	Recommended By
PODIATRIST EVALUATION	To Be Determined	To Be Determined	$137–$175 per Visit	Dr. Jensen

Per Amy Parker, client care coordinator at Advanced Podiatry, office of Dr. Brett Brandon, 555-971-4678 (Bradenton, FL): Podiatrist evaluation, $175 per evaluation using CPT Code 99202.

Per 2019 National Fee Analyzer, podiatrist evaluation, CPT Code 99202 (office or other outpatient visit for the evaluation of a new patient requires these three key components: an expanded problem-focused history; an expanded problem-focused exam; and straightforward medical decision-making. Usually the presenting problem(s) are of low to moderate severity. Typically 20 minutes are spent face to face with the patient and/or family), $137 to $175.

Item	Duration	Frequency	Estimated Cost	Recommended By
OPTION A: PHYSICAL THERAPY EVALUATION IN FACILITY	Year 1–Life	Every 3–5 Years	$100–$192 per Evaluation	Dr. Jensen

Per Sandra Haines, business office assistant at New Life Bradenton, 555-751-0557 (Bradenton, FL): Physical therapy evaluation, $100 per evaluation using CPT Code 97162.

Per 2019 National Fee Analyzer, physical therapy evaluation, CPT 97162 (physical therapy evaluation: high complexity, requiring these components: history of present problem with three or more personal factors and/or comorbidities that impact the plan of care; an exam of body systems using standardized tests and measures addressing a total of four or more elements from any of the following: body structures and functions, activity limitations, and/or participation restrictions; a clinical presentation with unstable and unpredictable characteristics; and clinical decision-making of high complexity using standardized patient assessment instrument and/or measurable assessment of functional outcome. Typically 30 minutes are spent face to face with the patient and/or family), $150 to $192 per evaluation.

Item	Duration	Frequency	Estimated Cost	Recommended By
OPTION B: IN-HOME PHYSICAL THERAPY EVALUATION	Year 1–Life	Every 3–5 Years	$150–$192 per Evaluation	Dr. Jensen

Per Lisa Glidden, clinical supervisor at Grant Health, 555-814-4025 (Bradenton, FL): In-home physical therapy evaluation, $160 per evaluation using CPT Code 97162.

Per 2019 National Fee Analyzer, physical therapy evaluation, CPT 97162 (physical therapy evaluation: high complexity, requiring these components: history of present problem with three or more personal factors and/or comorbidities that impact the plan of care; an exam of body systems using standardized tests and measures addressing a total of four or more elements from any of the following: body structures and functions, activity limitations, and/or participation restrictions; a clinical presentation with unstable and unpredictable characteristics; and clinical decision-making of high complexity using standardized patient assessment instrument and/or measurable assessment of functional outcome. Typically 30 minutes are spent face to face with the patient and/or family), $150 to $192 per evaluation.

EVALUATIONS

Item	Duration	Frequency	Estimated Cost	Recommended By
OPTION A: OCCUPATIONAL THERAPY EVALUATION IN FACILITY	Year 1–Life	Every 3–5 Years	$100–$210 per Evaluation	Dr. Jensen

Per Sandra Haines, business office assistant at New Life Bradenton, 555-751-0557 (Bradenton, FL): Occupational therapy evaluation, $100 per evaluation using CPT Code 97165.

Per 2019 National Fee Analyzer, occupational therapy evaluation, CPT Code 97165 (occupational therapy evaluation: moderate complexity, requiring these components: occupational profile and medical and therapy history, which includes a brief history including review of medical and/or therapy records relating to the presenting problem; and assessment(s) that identifies one to three performance deficits that result in activity limitations and/or participation restrictions; and clinical decision-making of low complexity, which includes an analysis of occupational profile, analysis of data for problem-focused assessment(s), and consideration of limited number of treatment options. Typically 30 minutes are spent face to face with the patient and/or family), $168 to $210 per evaluation.

Item	Duration	Frequency	Estimated Cost	Recommended By
OPTION B: IN-HOME OCCUPATIONAL THERAPY EVALUATION	Year 1–Life	Every 3–5 Years	$160–$210 per Evaluation	Dr. Jensen

Per Lisa Glidden, clinical supervisor at Grant Health, 555-814-4025 (Bradenton, FL): In-home occupational therapy evaluation, $160 per evaluation using CPT Code 97165.

Per 2019 National Fee Analyzer, occupational therapy evaluation, CPT Code 97165 (occupational therapy evaluation: moderate complexity, requiring these components: occupational profile and medical and therapy history, which includes a brief history including review of medical and/or therapy records relating to the presenting problem; and assessment(s) that identifies one to three performance deficits that result in activity limitations and/or participation restrictions; and clinical decision-making of low complexity, which includes an analysis of occupational profile, analysis of data for problem-focused assessment(s), and consideration of limited number of treatment options. Typically 30 minutes are spent face to face with the patient and/or family), $168 to $210 per evaluation.

Item	Duration	Frequency	Estimated Cost	Recommended By
UPDATE LIFE CARE PLAN	Year 10–15	One Time	$10,000 Total	Dr. Shahnasarian Dr. Jensen

Per Dr. Jensen, update life care plan, year 10 to life, one time.

Per Dr. Shahnasarian, update life care plan, year 10 to 15, one time, $10,000 total.

THERAPEUTIC NEEDS

Item	Duration	Frequency	Estimated Cost	Recommended By
GASTROENTEROLOGIST FOLLOW-UP	Year 1–Life	2 Visits per Year	$131–$167 per Visit	Dr. Jensen Dr. Shahnasarian

Per Susan Santana, medical assistant to Dr. Leopoldo Gray, 555-673-8545 (Bradenton, FL): Gastroenterologist follow-up, $150 per visit using CPT Code 99213.

Per 2019 National Fee Analyzer, gastroenterologist follow-up visit, CPT Code 99213 (office visit for the evaluation and management of an established patient, which requires at least two of these three components: an expanded problem-focused history; an expanded problem-focused exam; and medical decision-making of low to moderate complexity. Typically 15 minutes are spent face to face with the patient), $131 to $167 per visit.

Item	Duration	Frequency	Estimated Cost	Recommended By
INTERNAL MEDICINE FOLLOW-UP	Year 1–Life	2 Visits per Year	$145–$167 per Visit	Dr. Jensen

Per Helen Battles, client care coordinator at Bradenton Internal Medicine, office of Larry Underwood, 555-252-2770 (Bradenton, FL): Internal medicine follow-up, $145 per visit using CPT Code 99213.

Per 2019 National Fee Analyzer, internal medicine follow-up, CPT Code 99213 (office or other outpatient visit for the evaluation and management of an established patient, which requires at least two of these three components: an expanded problem-focused history; an expanded problem-focused exam; and medical decision-making of low to moderate complexity. Typically 15 minutes are spent face to face with the patient and/or family), $131 to $167 per visit.

Item	Duration	Frequency	Estimated Cost	Recommended By
NEUROLOGIST FOLLOW-UP	Year 1–Life	1–2 Visits per Year	$131–$205 per Visit	Dr. Jensen

Per Ellen Barrios, medical assistant to Dr. Arthur Peters, 555-879-7940 (Bradenton, FL): Neurologist follow-up, $205 per visit using CPT Code 99213.

Per 2019 National Fee Analyzer, neurologist follow-up, CPT Code 99213 (office or other outpatient visit for the evaluation and management of an established patient, which requires at least two of these three components: an expanded problem-focused history; an expanded problem-focused exam; and medical decision-making of low to moderate complexity. Typically 15 minutes are spent face to face with the patient and/or family), $131 to $167 per visit.

Item	Duration	Frequency	Estimated Cost	Recommended By
UROLOGIST FOLLOW-UP	Year 1–Life	1–2 Visits per Year	$131–$167 per Visit	Dr. Jensen

Per Lori Carter, receptionist at Bradenton Urology, office of Dr. Lenard, 727-596-9652 (Bradenton, FL): Urologist follow-up, $145 per visit using CPT Code 99213.

Per 2019 National Fee Analyzer, urologist follow-up, CPT Code 99213 (office or other outpatient visit for the evaluation and management of an established patient, which requires at least two of these three components: an expanded problem-focused history; an expanded problem-focused exam; and medical decision-making of low to moderate complexity. Typically, 15 minutes are spent face to face with the patient and/or family), $131 to $167 per visit.

THERAPEUTIC NEEDS

Item	Duration	Frequency	Estimated Cost	Recommended By
PHYSIATRIST FOLLOW-UP	Year 1–Life	2 Visits per Year	$195–$270 per Visit	Dr. Jensen

Per Lisa Porter, practice administrator at Rehabilitation and Electrodiagnostics, office of Dr. Thompson, 555-865-4777 (Bradenton, FL): Physiatrist follow-up, $270 using CPT Code 99214.

Per 2019 National Fee Analyzer, physiatrist follow-up, CPT Code 99214 (office visit for the evaluation and management of an established patient, which requires at least two of these three components: a detailed history; a detailed exam; and medical decision-making of moderate complexity. Typically 25 minutes are spent face to face with the patient), $195 to $240 per visit.

Item	Duration	Frequency	Estimated Cost	Recommended By
PODIATRIST FOLLOW-UP	Year 1–Life	6 Visits per Year	$84–$109 per Visit	Dr. Jensen

Per Amy Parker, client care coordinator at Advanced Podiatry, office of Dr. Brett Brandon, 555-971-4678 (Bradenton, FL): Podiatrist follow-up, $95 per visit using CPT Code 99212.

Per 2019 National Fee Analyzer, podiatrist follow-up visit, CPT Code 99212 (office visit for the evaluation and management of an established patient, which requires at least two of these three components: a problem-focused history; a problem-focused exam; and medical decision-making of low to moderate complexity. Typically 10 minutes are spent face to face with the patient), $84 to $109 per visit.

Item	Duration	Frequency	Estimated Cost	Recommended By
OPTION A: PHYSICAL THERAPY IN FACILITY	Year 1–Life	8–12 Sessions Every 3–5 Years	$70–$150 per 30-Minute Session	Dr. Jensen

Per Sandra Haines, business office assistant at New Life Bradenton, 555-751-0557 (Bradenton, FL): Physical therapy $70 per 30-minute session using CPT Code 99110.

Per 2019 National Fee Analyzer, physical therapy, CPT Code 99110 (therapeutic procedure, one or more areas, each 15 minutes; therapeutic exercises to develop strength and endurance, range of motion, and flexibility), $56 to $75; $112 to $150 per 30-minute session.

Item	Duration	Frequency	Estimated Cost	Recommended By
OPTION B: IN-HOME PHYSICAL THERAPY	Year 1–Life	8–12 Sessions Every 3–5 Years	$112–$160 per Session	Dr. Jensen

Per Lisa Glidden, clinical supervisor at Grant Health, 555-814-4025 (Bradenton, FL): In-home physical therapy, $160 per 30-minute session using CPT Code 99110.

Per 2019 National Fee Analyzer, physical therapy, CPT Code 99110 (therapeutic procedure, one or more areas, each 15 minutes; therapeutic exercises to develop strength and endurance, range of motion, and flexibility), $56 to $75; $112 to $150 per 30-minute session.

THERAPEUTIC NEEDS

Item	Duration	Frequency	Estimated Cost	Recommended By
OPTION A: OCCUPATIONAL THERAPY IN FACILITY	Year 1–Life	8–12 Sessions Every 3–5 Years	$70–$150 per Session	Dr. Jensen

Per Sandra Haines, business office assistant at New Life Bradenton, 555-751-0557 (Bradenton, FL): Occupational therapy, $70 per 30-minute session using CPT Code 99110.

Per 2019 National Fee Analyzer, occupational therapy, CPT Code 99110 (therapeutic procedure, one or more areas, each 15 minutes; therapeutic exercises to develop strength and endurance, range of motion, and flexibility), $56 to $75; $112 to $150 per 30-minute session.

Item	Duration	Frequency	Estimated Cost	Recommended By
OPTION B: IN-HOME OCCUPATIONAL THERAPY	Year 1–Life	8–12 Sessions Every 3–5 Years	$112–$160 per Session	Dr. Jensen

Per Lisa Glidden, clinical supervisor at Grant Health, 555-814-4025 (Bradenton, FL): Occupational therapy, $160 per 30-minute session using CPT Code 99110.

Per 2019 National Fee Analyzer, occupational therapy, CPT Code 99110 (therapeutic procedure, one or more areas, each 15 minutes; therapeutic exercises to develop strength and endurance, range of motion, and flexibility), $56 to $75; $112 to $150 per 30-minute session.

DIAGNOSTIC TESTS

Item	Duration	Frequency	Estimated Cost	Recommended By
X-RAY CHEST	Year 1–Life	Every 3–5 Years	$92–$110 Each Time	Dr. Jensen

Per 2019 National Fee Analyzer, X-ray chest, CPT Code 71046 (radiologic exam, chest, two views), $92–$110 each time.

Item	Duration	Frequency	Estimated Cost	Recommended By
CT SCAN BRAIN/HEAD	Year 1–Life	Every 3–5 Years	$576–$714 Each Time	Dr. Jensen

Per 2019 National Fee Analyzer, CT scan brain/head, CPT Code 70450 (computed tomography, head or brain; without contrast material), $576 to $714 each time.

Item	Duration	Frequency	Estimated Cost	Recommended By
BLOOD ANALYSIS	Year 1–Life	2 Times per Year	$88–$107 Each Time	Dr. Jensen

Note: Per Dr. Jensen, including CMP. Most recently performed January 28, 2019.

Per 2019 National Fee Analyzer, complete blood count (CBC), CPT Code 85025 (automated CBC and automated differential WBC count), $35 to $42 each time; complete metabolic panel (CMP), CPT Code 80053 (comprehensive metabolic panel), $53 to $65; totaling $88 to $107 each time.

Item	Duration	Frequency	Estimated Cost	Recommended By
RENAL ULTRASOUND	To Be Determined	To Be Determined	$325–$422 Each Time	Dr. Jensen

Per 2019 National Fee Analyzer, renal ultrasound, CPT code 76770 (ultrasound, retroperitoneal, real time with image documentation, complete), $325 to $422 each time.

Item	Duration	Frequency	Estimated Cost	Recommended By
DEXA SCAN	Year 1–Life	Every 3–5 Years	$529–$801 Each Time	Dr. Jensen

Per 2019 National Fee Analyzer, dexa scan, CPT code 77078 (computed tomography, bone mineral density study, AXIAL skeleton (hips, pelvis, spine)), $529 to $801 each time.

Item	Duration	Frequency	Estimated Cost	Recommended By
URINALYSIS WITH CULTURE	Year 1–Life	1–2 Times per Year	$89–$109 Each Time	Dr. Jensen

Per 2019 National Fee Analyzer, urinalysis with culture, CPT Code 87086 (culture, bacterial; quantitative colony count, urine), $58 to $61; and CPT Code 81001 (urinalysis, by dip stick or tablet reagent for bilirubin, glucose, hemoglobin, ketones, leukocytes, nitrite, pH, protein, specific gravity, urobilinogen, any number of the constituents; automated, with microscopy), $31 to $48, totaling $89 to $109 each time.

Item	Duration	Frequency	Estimated Cost	Recommended By
EEG (ELECTRO-ENCEPHALOGRAM)	To Be Determined	To Be Determined	$650–$850 Each Time	Dr. Jensen

Per 2019 National Fee Analyzer, electroencephalogram (EEG), CPT Code 95816 (electroencephalogram (EEG); including recording awake and drowsy), $650 to $850 each time.

WHEELCHAIR NEEDS

Item	Duration	Frequency	Estimated Cost	Recommended By
MANUAL CUSTOM TILT-IN-SPACE WHEELCHAIR	Year 1–2 to Life	Replace Every 7–10 Years	$2,119–$2,690 Each	Dr. Jensen Dr. Shahnasarian

Per Spinlife, www.spinlife.com: Lightweight Tilt-in-Space VIP Manual Wheelchair, $1,619 each; MVP-502 Ergonomic Manual Wheelchair, $1,699 each.

Per 1800 Wheelchair, www.1800wheelchair.com: Karman Tilt-in-Space and Recliner Wheelchair, $1,990 each; Karman Tilt-in-Space Wheelchair, $1,619 each.

Additional accessories/options, $500–$700.

Item	Duration	Frequency	Estimated Cost	Recommended By
MANUAL WHEELCHAIR—PORTABLE	Year 1–2 to Life	Replace Every 7–10 Years	$669–$1,019 Each	Dr. Jensen

Per SpinLife, www.spinlife.com: Invacare 2000 XT Custom Wheelchair, $425 each; Harmon Lightweight S-Ergo Wheelchair, $569 each.

Per 1-800 Wheelchair, www.1800wheelchair.com: Featherweight Custom Wheelchair, $499 each; Karman S115 Ergonomic Wheelchair, $569 each; Karman LT980 Ultralight Wheelchair, $369 each.

Add-ons and options, $300 to $450.

Item	Duration	Frequency	Estimated Cost	Recommended By
MANUAL WHEELCHAIR MAINTENANCE (2)	Year 1–2 to Life	Annually	$145 per Year per Wheelchair	Dr. Jensen Dr. Shahnasarian

Per Alison Webster, manager at A-Ability Medical Equipment, Inc., 555-620-4475 (Bradenton, FL): The estimated annual maintenance fee for a manual wheelchair is $145 for cleaning and lubrication. Replacement parts are additional cost. No maintenance necessary in year of purchase.

Item	Duration	Frequency	Estimated Cost	Recommended By
OPTION B: SHOWER COMMODE WHEELCHAIR	Year 1–2 to Life	Replace Every 7–10 Years	$1,611 Each	Dr. Jensen Dr. Shahnasarian

Note: Per Dr. Shahnasarian, shower table.

Per SpinLife, www.spinlife.com: Roll-in-Buddy with Tilt Shower/Commode Wheelchair, $1,611 each.

Per 1-800 Wheelchair, www.1800wheelchair.com: Roll-In Buddy with Tilt Shower/Commode Wheelchair, $1,611 each.

WHEELCHAIR NEEDS

Item	Duration	Frequency	Estimated Cost	Recommended By
OPTION B: WHEELCHAIR RAMP—PORTABLE	Year 1–2 to Life	Replace Every 7–10 Years	$250–$525 Each	Dr. Jensen

Per 1-800 Wheelchair, www.1800wheelchair.com: Portable wheelchair ramp—Portable Multifold Bariatric Ramp, $525 each; EZ Access Graphite Single-Fold Suitcase Ramp, $485 each.

Per Emed Ramps, www.emedramps.com: Portable wheelchair ramp—Prairie View PVI Multi-Fold Wheelchair Ramp, $380 each; Prairie View PVI Single-Fold Wheelchair Ramp, $250 each.

Item	Duration	Frequency	Estimated Cost	Recommended By
WHEELCHAIR SEATING EVALUATION	Year 1–Life	Every 3–5 Years	No Charge	Dr. Jensen Dr. Shahnasarian

Included in the cost of the wheelchair.

Item	Duration	Frequency	Estimated Cost	Recommended By
ROHO CUSHION (2)	Year 1–Life	Replace Every 2–4 Years	$220–$374 Each	Dr. Jensen

Per Southwest Medical Supply, www.southwestmedical.com: Roho Cushion—Roho MiniMax, $280 each; Roho Harmony, $220 each; and Roho Enhancer Cushion, $374 each.

Per Allegro Medical Supply, www.allegromedical.com: Roho Cushions—Roho High Profile Cushion, $357 each; The Galaxy Roho Cushion, $339; and Roho Hybrid Elite, $369 each.

ORTHOTICS

Item	Duration	Frequency	Estimated Cost	Recommended By
HAND SPLINT RIGHT	Year 1–Life	Replace Every 2–3 Years	$17.99–$29.99 Each	Dr. Jensen Dr. Shahnasarian

Note: Per Dr. Jensen, orthotics/braces.

Per Better Braces, www.betterbraces.com: Aircast A2 Wrist Brace, $19.99 each; Procare Universal Wrist Splint, $17.99 each; DonJoy Wrist and Thumb Splint, $29.99 each.

Item	Duration	Frequency	Estimated Cost	Recommended By
MULTIPODUS BOOTS BILATERAL	Year 1–Life	Replace Every 2–3 Years	$292–$322 per Pair	Dr. Jensen

Note: Per Dr. Jensen, orthotics/braces.

Per Vitality Medical, www.vitalitymedical.com: Posey Deluxe Podus Boot, $161 each; $322 per pair.

Per Rehab Mart, www.rehabmart.com: Posey Deluxe Podus Boot, $146 each; $292 per pair.

Item	Duration	Frequency	Estimated Cost	Recommended By
SOFT HAND RESTING SPLINT RIGHT	Year 1–Life	Replace Every 2–3 Years	$26.99–$29.99 Each	Dr. Shahnasarian Dr. Jensen

Note: Per Dr. Jensen, orthotics/braces.

Per The Brace Shop, www.braceshop.com: DonJoy Soft Wrist Brace, $26.99 each; DonJoy Universal Neoprene Wrist Splint, $29.99 each; DonJoy Soft Thumb/Wrist Splint, $29.99 each.

AIDS FOR INDEPENDENT LIVING

Item	Duration	Frequency	Estimated Cost	Recommended By
OPTION B: ELECTRIC HOSPITAL BED	Year 1–2 to Life	Replace Every 7–10 Years	$799–$949 Each	Dr. Jensen Dr. Shahnasarian

Per SpinLife, www.spinlife.com: Electric Hospital Bed—Invacare DLX Hospital Bed with side rail, $949 each; Basic Full Electric Hospital Bed with side rail, $799 each; Medlite Full Electric Bed with side rail, $800 each.

Per Express Hospital Beds, www.expresshospitalbeds.com: Electric Hospital Bed—Invacare Full Electric Hospital Bed with side rail, $865 each; Invacare Hi-Lo Hospital Bed with side rail, $935 each.

Item	Duration	Frequency	Estimated Cost	Recommended By
AIR LOSS/AIR FLOW MATTRESS	Year 1–Life	Replace Every 7–10 Years	$1,004–$3,198 Each	Dr. Jensen

Per Rehab Mart, www.rehabmart.com: Air Mattress—BioClinic APL Pressure Reliever Mattress System, $1,126 each; Prius Salute DX Mattress System, $1,004 each; Hybrid Select Low Air Loss Mattress System, $3,198 each.

Per Med Mart, www.medmart.com: Air Mattress—Med Aire Plus Low Air Loss Mattress System, $1,328 each; Future Air True Low Air Loss Mattress System, $2,225 each; Micro Aire 55 Alternating Pressure Mattress System, $1,250 each.

Item	Duration	Frequency	Estimated Cost	Recommended By
OPTION B: HOSPITAL BED TRAY TABLE	Year 1–2 to Life	Replace Every 7–10 Years	$65–$119 Each	Dr. Jensen

Per 1-800 Wheelchair, www.1800wheelchair.com: Hospital tray table—Adjustable Height Overbed Non-Tilt Table, $74 each; Tilt Top Overbed Table, $79 each; Deluxe Tilt-Top Overbed Table, $92 each.

Per Vitality Medical, www.vitalitymedical.com: Hospital tray table—Independence Bed Table, $119 each; Wheelchair and Overbed Adjustable Table by Carex, $107 each; Invacare Bedside Tilt Top Table, $65 each.

Item	Duration	Frequency	Estimated Cost	Recommended By
OPTION B: ELECTRIC HOYER LIFT	Year 1–2 to Life	Replace Every 7–10 Years	$2,299–$4,985 Each	Dr. Jensen Dr. Shahnasarian

Per 1-800 Wheelchair, www.1800wheelchair.com: Invacare Reliant Plus 450 Power Patient Lift with Low Base, $2,699 each; Invacare Reliant 450 Patient Lift, $2,299 each.

Per SpinLife, www.spinlife.com: Hoy Advance E Patient Lift, $2,400; Hoy Presence Patient Lift, $4,985 each.

Item	Duration	Frequency	Estimated Cost	Recommended By
OPTION B: SLING REPLACEMENT	Year 1–2 to Life	Replace Every 2–3 Years	$240–$350 Each	Dr. Jensen Dr. Shahnasarian

Per PHC Online, www.phc-online.com: Advance QuickFit Deluxe Sling, $240 each; Long Seat Standard Ply Sling, $289 each; Transport/Standing Sling, $350 each.

Per SpinLife, www.spinlife.com: Professional QuickFit Deluxe Sling, $273 each; QuickFit Mesh Sling, $271; Professional 6-Point Sling, $299.60.

AIDS FOR INDEPENDENT LIVING

Item	Duration	Frequency	Estimated Cost	Recommended By
OPTION B: SUPINE STANDER	Year 1–2 to Life	Replace Every 7–10 Years	$6,225 Each	Dr. Jensen

Per Nancy Claudette, medical sales representative at Live Well Medical, 877-748-3935, www.livewellmedical.com: EasyStand Evolv Medium Standing Frame, $6,225 each. Per Claudette, this is the proper size stander for Mr. Pendel and includes options recommended for someone with Mr. Pendel's presenting problems.

OPTION B: GERI CHAIR	Year 1–2 to Life	Replace Every 7–10 Years	$1,101–$2,539 Each	Dr. Jensen Dr. Shahnasarian

Per SpinLife, www.spinlife.com: Flextilt Tilt-in-Space Clinical Recliner, $2,539 each.

Per 1-800 Wheelchair, www.1800wheelchair.com: Winco Clinical Recliner, $1,101 each; Winco Elite Clinical Recliner, $1,700 each; Winco Drop Arm Clinical Recliner, $1,676 each.

OPTION B: IV POLE	Year 1–2 to Life	Replace Every 7–10 Years	$32.03–$49.31 Each	Dr. Jensen

Per Vitality Medical Supply, www.vitalitymedical.com: IV Pole—Drive Medical IV Pole with Removable Top, $44.75 each; Drive Medical IV Pole with Weights, $32.03 each.

Per Allegro Medical Supply, www.allegromedical.com: IV Pole—DMI I.V. Pole with Top, $49.31 each; Economy IV Pole with Removable Top, $43.61 each.

OPTION B: BLOOD PRESSURE MONITOR AND CUFF	Year 1–2 to Life	Replace Every 5 Years	$28.12–$80.14 Each	Dr. Jensen

Per Vitality Medical, www.vitalitymedical.com: LifeSource Automatic Blood Pressure Monitor, $54.12; Medline Elite Automatic Digital Blood Pressure Monitor, $28.12 each.

Per Allegro Medical, www.allegro.com: Mark of Fitness Blood Pressure Cuff, $80.14 each; Mark of Fitness Auto Inflate Blood Pressure Cuff, $70.72 each.

MISCELLANEOUS ADAPTIVE AIDS/PATIENT EDUCATION	Year 1–Life	Annually	$500–$1,200 per Year	Dr. Shahnasarian Dr. Jensen

Per Dr. Shahnasarian, miscellaneous adaptive aids/patient education, $1,200 per year.

Per Dr. Jensen, miscellaneous adaptive aids, $500 to $1,000 per year.

DRUG AND SUPPLY NEEDS

Item	Duration	Frequency	Estimated Cost	Recommended By
CARVEDILOL 6.25 MG	Year 1–Life	2 Tablets via G-Tube per Day	$43.59–$47.99 per 60 Tablets	Dr. Jensen

Per physician's orders from Kingston Multicare Center dated October 14, 2018, Mr. Pendel is given carvedilol 6.25 mg, two tablets per day via G-tube.

Note: Per Dr. Jensen, maintain medications.

Per Mark Vance, pharmacy technician at Walgreens Pharmacy, 555-932-2264 (Bradenton, FL): Carvedilol 6.25 mg, $47.99 per 60 tablets.

Per Karina Rivera, pharmacy technician at CVS Pharmacy, 555-968-1457 (Bradenton, FL): Carvedilol 6.25 mg, $43.59 per 60 tablets.

Item	Duration	Frequency	Estimated Cost	Recommended By
DESMOPRESSIN 0.1 MG	Year 1–Life	2 Tablets via G-Tube per Day	$105.99–$146.99 per 30 Tablets	Dr. Jensen

Per physician's orders from Kingston Multicare Center dated October 14, 2018, Mr. Pendel is given desmopressin 0.1 mg via G-tube two times per day.

Note: Per Dr. Jensen, maintain medications.

Per Mark Vance, pharmacy technician at Walgreens Pharmacy, 555-932-2264 (Bradenton, FL): Desmopressin 0.1 mg, $146.99 per 30 tablets.

Per Karina Rivera, pharmacy technician at CVS Pharmacy, 555-968-1457 (Bradenton, FL): Desmopressin 0.1 mg, $105.99 per 30 tablets.

Item	Duration	Frequency	Estimated Cost	Recommended By
LISINOPRIL 10 MG	Year 1–Life	1 Tablet via G-Tube per Day	$12.49–$15.39 per 30 Tablets	Dr. Jensen

Per physician's orders from Kingston Multicare Center dated October 14, 2018, Mr. Pendel is given lisinopril 10 mg via G-tube daily.

Note: Per Dr. Jensen, maintain medications.

Per Mark Vance, pharmacy technician at Walgreens Pharmacy, 555-932-2264 (Bradenton, FL): Lisinopril 10 mg, $15.39 per 30 tablets.

Per Karina Rivera, pharmacy technician at CVS Pharmacy, 555-968-1457 (Bradenton, FL): Lisinopril 10 mg, $12.49 per 30 tablets.

Item	Duration	Frequency	Estimated Cost	Recommended By
ACETAMINOPHEN 160 MG/5 ML ORAL ELIXIR	Year 1–Life	20 ml via G-Tube per Day	$253.99–$314.99 per 600 ml	Dr. Jensen

Per physician's orders from Kingston Multicare Center dated October 14, 2018, Mr. Pendel is given acetaminophen 160 mg/5 ml oral elixir 20 ml via G-tube daily.

Note: Per Dr. Jensen, maintain medications.

Per Mark Vance, pharmacy technician at Walgreens Pharmacy, 555-932-2264 (Bradenton, FL): Acetaminophen 160 mg/5 ml, $253.99 per 600 ml.

Per Karina Rivera, pharmacy technician at CVS Pharmacy, 555-968-1457 (Bradenton, FL): Acetaminophen 160 mg/5 ml, $314.99 per 600 ml.

DRUG AND SUPPLY NEEDS

Item	Duration	Frequency	Estimated Cost	Recommended By
ZANTAC 150 MG	Year 1–Life	1 Tablet via G-Tube per Day	$18.99–$19.99 per 60 Tablets	Dr. Jensen

Per physician's orders from Kingston Multicare Center dated October 14, 2018, Mr. Pendel is given Zantac 150 mg via G-tube daily.

Note: Per Dr. Jensen, maintain medications.

Per Walgreens Pharmacy, www.walgreens.com: Zantac 150 mg, $18.99 per 60 tablets.

Per CVS Pharmacy, www.cvs.com: Zantac 150 mg, $19.99 per 60 tablets.

Item	Duration	Frequency	Estimated Cost	Recommended By
VITAMIN C 500 MG	Year 1–Life	1 Tablet via G-Tube per Day	$22.99–$24.49 per 150 Tablets	Dr. Jensen

Per physician's orders from Kingston Multicare Center dated October 14, 2018, Mr. Pendel is given Vitamin C 500 mg via G-tube daily.

Note: Per Dr. Jensen, maintain medications.

Per Walgreens Pharmacy, www.walgreens.com: Vitamin C 500 mg, $22.99 per 150 tablets.

Per CVS Pharmacy, www.cvs.com: Vitamin C 500 mg, $24.49 per 150 tablets.

Item	Duration	Frequency	Estimated Cost	Recommended By
GASTROSTOMY TUBE AND SUPPLIES	Year 1–Life	Monthly	$197.57–$229.51 Every 4–6 Months	Dr. Jensen Dr. Shahnasarian

Per Vitality Medical, www.vitalitymedical.com:

   MIC-KEY Tube Low Profile Gastrostomy Feeding Tube Kit, size 18 French, 3.7 cm, $143 each

   MIC-KEY Tube SECUR LOK Extension Feeding Sets, 12-inch Bolus with catheter tip, box of 5, $54.57 each

Totaling $197.57 every 4–6 months.

Per Allegro Medical Supply, www.allegromedical.com:

   MIC-KEY Tube Low Profile Gastrostomy Feeding Tube Kit, size 18 French, 3.7 cm, $159.53 each

   MIC-KEY Tube SECUR LOK Extension Feeding Sets, 12-inch Bolus with catheter tip, box of 5, $69.98 each

Totaling $229.51 every 4–6 months.

Item	Duration	Frequency	Estimated Cost	Recommended By
FEEDING PUMP	Year 1–Life	Replace Every 3–5 Years	$599–$1,264.73 Each	Dr. Shahnasarian

Per Vitality Medical, www.vitalitymedical.com: Feeding pump—Kangaroo Joey Enteral Feeding Pump, $599 each; EnteraLite Infinity Enteral Feeding Pump, $1,027.46 each.

Per Allegro Medical Supply, www.allegromedical.com: Feeding pump—Kangaroo Joey ePump, $649.93 each; EnteraLite Enteral Feeding Pump, $1,264.73 each.

DRUG AND SUPPLY NEEDS

Item	Duration	Frequency	Estimated Cost	Recommended By
FEEDING PUMP SUPPLIES	Year 1–Life	2–3 Sets per Week	$2.75–$5.67 Each	Dr. Shahnasarian

Per Vitality Medical, www.vitalitymedical.com: Feeding pump supplies—Kangaroo ePump Enteral Feeding Set Overinfusion extension, $2.75 each; Kangaroo Max Plus Extension Set, $3.40 each.

Per Allegro Medical Supply, www.allegromedical.com: Feeding pump supplies—Kangaroo 924 Enteral Feeding Pump Set, $5.46 each; Kangaroo Joey 1000 ml Feed Set with Screw Spike, $5.67 each.

Item	Duration	Frequency	Estimated Cost	Recommended By
ADULT BRIEFS	Year 1–Life	4–6 per Day	$32–$53.55 per Case of 96	Dr. Jensen

Per Vitality Medical, www.vitalitymedical.com: Adult briefs—Wings Ultra Quilted Adult Briefs, $37.35 per case of 96; Simplicity Extra Adult Briefs, $32.77 per case of 96; Passport Premium Adult Briefs, $50.33 per case of 96.

Per Allegro Medical, www.allegromedical.com: Adult briefs—First Quality Full Mat Adult Briefs, $53.55 per case of 96; Prevail Breezers Adult Briefs, $47.73 per case of 96; McKesson Adult Briefs, $32 per case of 96.

Item	Duration	Frequency	Estimated Cost	Recommended By
INCONTINENCE SUPPLIES	Year 1–Life	Monthly	$45.74 per Month	Dr. Jensen

Per Vitality Medical, www.vitalitymedical.com: The monthly estimated cost for incontinent and bowel program supplies is $45.74 per month. Specifications are as follows:

  Disposable under pads (chux), $39.69 per pack of 100 ($0.40 each/2 chux per day), $24 per month

  Latex gloves, $7.59 per box of 100 (2 boxes per month), $15.18 per month

  Purell Hand Sanitizer, 12 ounces, $6.56 per month

Item	Duration	Frequency	Estimated Cost	Recommended By
JEVITY	Year 1–Life	1500 ml Each Night	$51.95–$75.69 per Case of 8 IV Containers, 1000 ml	Dr. Jensen

Per physician's orders from Kingston Multicare Center dated October 14, 2018, Mr. Pendel is given 1500 ml each night (80 ml per hour/continuous nocturnal).

Per Vitality Medical, www.vitalitymedical.com: Jevity 1000 ml Ready to Hang Container, $75.69 per case of 8 IV containers, 1000 ml.

Per CWI Medical, www.cwimedical.com: Jevity 1000 ml Ready to Hang Container, $51.95 per case of 8 IV containers, 1000 ml.

HOME/FACILITY CARE

Item	Duration	Frequency	Estimated Cost	Recommended By
OPTION A: LPN ONSITE SUPPLEMENTAL VISITS	Year 1–Life	10 to 14 Hours per Week	$33.95–$43 per Hour	Dr. Jensen

Per Cindy Diaz, director at Totally Private Homecare, 555-405-3376 (Bradenton, FL): LPN, $43 per hour.

Per Katelyn Rivera, intake director at Utopia Home Health, 555-639-1915 (Bradenton, FL): LPN, $33.95 per hour on weekdays and $34.95 per hour on weekends.

Item	Duration	Frequency	Estimated Cost	Recommended By
OPTION B: LPN HOME CARE	Year 1–2 to Life	Two 12-Hour Shifts per Day	$33.95–$43 per Hour	Dr. Jensen

Per Cindy Diaz, director at Totally Private Homecare, 555-405-3376 (Bradenton, FL): LPN, $43 per hour.

Per Katelyn Rivera, intake director at Utopia Home Health, 555-639-1915 (Bradenton, FL): LPN, $33.95 per hour on weekdays and $34.95 per hour on weekends.

Item	Duration	Frequency	Estimated Cost	Recommended By
OPTION B: EXTRA EXPENSES FOR LPN HOME CARE	Year 1–2 to Life	Two 12-Hour Shifts	To Be Determined	Dr. Shahnasarian

Per Dr. Shahnasarian, to be determined by an economist.

Item	Duration	Frequency	Estimated Cost	Recommended By
OPTION B: HOME HEALTH AIDE/ATTENDANT CARE	Year 1–2 to Life	4–6 Hours per Day	$16–$24.95 per Hour	Dr. Jensen Dr. Shahnasarian

Per Cindy Diaz, director at Totally Private Homecare, 555-405-3376 (Bradenton, FL): Home health aide/personal care attendant, $16 per hour.

Per Katelyn Rivera, intake director at Utopia Home Health, 555-639-1915 (Bradenton, FL): Home health aide/personal care attendant, $23.95 per hour on weekdays and $24.95 per hour on weekends.

Item	Duration	Frequency	Estimated Cost	Recommended By
OPTION B: RN CARE/HOME VISIT	Year 1–2 to Life	1–2 Visits per Month	$85–$95 per Visit	Dr. Jensen

Per Cindy Diaz, director at Totally Private Homecare, 555-405-3376 (Bradenton, FL): RN care home visit, $85 per visit.

Per Katelyn Rivera, intake director at Utopia Home Health, 555-639-1915 (Bradenton, FL): RN care home visit, $95 per visit.

Item	Duration	Frequency	Estimated Cost	Recommended By
OPTION B: CASE MANAGER	Year 1–2 Year 3 to Life	40–60 Hours Total, 2 Hours per Month	$110 per Hour	Dr. Shahnasarian Dr. Jensen

Note: Per Dr. Jensen, case manager, 1–2 hours per month.

Per Care Management Service Professionals, LLC, Debra Cox, MA, CMC, 555-615-1110 (Bradenton, FL): Case management services including travel time, $110 per hour.

HOME/FACILITY CARE

Item	Duration	Frequency	Estimated Cost	Recommended By
OPTION B: HOUSEKEEPER	Year 1–2 to Life	1 Visit Every 2 Weeks	$122–$157 per Visit	Dr. Shahnasarian Dr. Jensen

Per Brian Conner, owner at Molly Maids, 555-284-3700 (Bradenton, FL): Housekeeping services, one visit every two weeks, $122 per visit.

Per Hope Oliver, office assistant at Merry Maids, 555-559-0209 (Bradenton, FL): Housecleaning services, one visit every two weeks, $157 per visit.

Item	Duration	Frequency	Estimated Cost	Recommended By
ACCOUNTING SERVICES	Year 1–Life	2–4 Hours per Month	$50–$60 per Hour	Dr. Shahnasarian Dr. Jensen

Per Accounting Management Services, 555-907-8656 (Wesley Chapel, FL): Accounting and bookkeeping services, $50 to $60 per hour. Service area includes Bradenton, Clearwater, and St. Petersburg.

Item	Duration	Frequency	Estimated Cost	Recommended By
GUARDIANSHIP	Year 1–Life	2–3 Hours per Month	$85 per Hour	Dr. Shahnasarian Dr. Jensen

Per Care Management Service Professionals, LLC, Debra Cox, MA, CMC, 555-615-1110 (Bradenton, FL): Guardian services, $85 per hour.

TRANSPORTATION NEEDS

Item	Duration	Frequency	Estimated Cost	Recommended By
AIR AND GROUND MEDICAL TRANSPORTATION SERVICES	Year 1–2	One Time	$17,550 Total	Dr. Shahnasarian Dr. Jensen

Note: Per Dr. Shahnasarian, to transport Mr. Pendel from New Jersey to Bradenton. To be accompanied by skilled nursing staff.

Per Janice Moy, flight coordinator at Air Trek Air Ambulance Service, a one-way flight from Bronx, New Jersey, to Bradenton, Florida, would be a total of $17,550. This includes the ground transport from Kingston to Teterboro Airport ($700), the flight with skilled nursing staff ($16,300), and the ground transport from Bradenton Airport to Mr. Pendel's home ($550).

Item	Duration	Frequency	Estimated Cost	Recommended By
OPTION B: ADAPTED VAN	Year 1–2 to Life	Replace Every 7–10 Years	$55,020– $65,775 Each	Dr. Shahnasarian Dr. Jensen

Per William Roy, sales manager at Mobil Transportation Systems, 555-246-9116 (Bradenton, FL): Certified preowned vehicles available include a 2017 Dodge Caravan SXT, with side entry, $55,020, and a 2018 Chrysler Pacifica Touring L, with side entry, $65,775. All vehicles were converted by BraunAbility.

Item	Duration	Frequency	Estimated Cost	Recommended By
OPTION B: ADAPTED VAN MAINTENANCE	Year 1–2 to Life	Annually	$500–$700 per Year	Dr. Shahnasarian Dr. Jensen

Per William Roy, sales manager at Mobil Transportation Systems, 555-246-9116 (Bradenton, FL): Adapted van maintenance, approximately $500 to $700 per year, except in year of purchase.

Item	Duration	Frequency	Estimated Cost	Recommended By
OPTION B: DISABLED PERSON PARKING PERMIT	Year 1–2 to Life	Every 4 Years	No Charge	Dr. Shahnasarian Dr. Jensen

Per the State of Florida, Department of Highway Safety and Motor Vehicles, www.flhsmv.gov/dmv/disabled_pkg: Chapter 320.0848, Florida Statutes, allows for the issuance of permanent Disabled Parking Permits. There is no charge for a four-year disabled person parking permit. The fee for a temporary disabled person parking permit is $15, including tax collector fees. Form HSMV 83039 must be completed and signed by the certifying authority within the last 12 months that establishes your eligibility for a disabled parking permit. Proof of the disability must be indicated on Form HSMV 83039, certifying authority's Statement of Certification section.

Item	Duration	Frequency	Estimated Cost	Recommended By
OPTION A: MEDICAL TRANSPORT SERVICES	Year 1–Life	3–5 Trips per Year	$100–$185 per Trip	Dr. Shahnasarian Dr. Jensen

Per Sandra Haines, business office assistant at New Life Living, 555-751-0557 (Bradenton, FL): Medical transportation to and from doctor's visits, $100 to $150 per trip depending on distance.

Per Denay Mack, admissions liaison at Bradenton Oaks Center, 555-977-4214 (Bradenton, FL): Medical transportation to and from doctor's visits, $145 to $185 per trip depending on distance.

PERSONAL FITNESS

Item	Duration	Frequency	Estimated Cost	Recommended By
OPTION B: HI-LOW THERAPY MAT TABLE	Year 1–2 to Life	Replace Every 7–10 Years	$2,560.75–$4,158.15 Each	Dr. Jensen

Per Tiger Medical, www.tigermedical.com: Clinton Industries, Hi-Lo Mat Electric Therapy Table, $4,158.15 each.

Per Alimed Medical, www.alimed.com: Bailey Hi-Low Manual Therapy Table, $2,560.75 each.

ARCHITECTURAL RENOVATIONS

Item	Duration	Frequency	Estimated Cost	Recommended By
OPTION B: HOME ENVIRONMENTAL ANALYSIS	Year 1–2	One Time	$789 Total	Dr. Shahnasarian Dr. Jensen

Note: Per Dr. Shahnasarian, additional recommendations will follow.

Per Joseph Brian, project manager estimator at Paul Jones Construction, Inc., www.sierraconstruction.com or 800-409-5897, the cost of a home assessment for accessibility and modifications is $789 for the Bradenton Bay area. This includes assessment and estimate.

Item	Duration	Frequency	Estimated Cost	Recommended By
OPTION B: ARCHITECTURAL MODIFICATIONS	Year 1–2	One Time	$50,000–$100,000 Total	Dr. Jensen Dr. Shahnasarian

Per Dr. Jensen, a budget of $50,000 to $100,000 for home modifications is anticipated.

HOSPITALIZATIONS/SURGERIES

Item	Duration	Frequency	Estimated Cost	Recommended By
HOSPITAL EMERGENCY ROOM VISITS	Year 1–Life	5–8 Visits Total	$1,687 Each Time	Dr. Jensen

Emergency room visits at St. Joseph's Hospital (Bradenton, FL): $1,687 each time according to the 2019 American Hospital Directory, https://www.ahd.com/.

Item	Duration	Frequency	Estimated Cost	Recommended By
HOSPITALIZATION DAYS	Year 1–Life	3–5 Stays Total; 3–5 Days Each Stay	$8,849 per Day	Dr. Jensen

Hospitalization days at St. Joseph's Hospital (Bradenton, FL): $8,849 per day according to the 2019 American Hospital Directory, https://www.ahd.com/.

HOSPITALIZATIONS/SURGERIES

Item	Duration	Frequency	Estimated Cost	Recommended By
UPPER EXTREMITY CONTRACTURE RELEASE BILATERAL	To Be Determined	To Be Determined	$23,745–$26,113	Dr. Jensen

The estimated cost for bilateral contracture release of upper extremities ranges from $23,745 to $26,113. This is an overnight inpatient stay at the hospital with general anesthesia.

Specifications are as follows:

Physician's fee: $6,160 to $8,528.

CPT Code 24357 (tenotomy, elbow, lateral or medial; percutaneous), $1,316 to $2,000 (x 2), $2,632 to $4,000; and CPT Code 25109 (excision of tendon, forearm, and/or wrist, flexor or extensor, each), $1,764 to $2,391 (x 2), $3,528–$4,782 according to 2019 National Fee Analyzer.

Hospital/Facility fee: $16,365.

$16,365 per one-day inpatient stay at St. Joseph's Hospital (Bradenton, FL) according to the 2019 American Hospital Directory, https://www.ahd.com/.

Anesthesia: $1,220.

$1,220 for general anesthesia using CPT Codes 24357 and 25109 according to the American Society of Anesthesiologists (ASA) *2019 Relative Value Guide* and *2019 Crosswalk; A Guide for Surgery/Anesthesia CPT Codes.*

Item	Duration	Frequency	Estimated Cost	Recommended By
LOWER EXTREMITY CONTRACTURE RELEASE BILATERAL	To Be Determined	To Be Determined	$25,617–$28,421	Dr. Jensen

The estimated cost for bilateral contracture release of lower extremities ranges from $25,617 to $28,421. This is an overnight inpatient stay at the hospital with general anesthesia.

Specifications are as follows:

Physician's fee: $6,568 to $9,372.

CPT Code 27606 (tenotomy, percutaneous Achilles tendon, general anesthesia), $1,037 to $1,470 (x 2), $2,074 to $2,940; and CPT Code 27307 (tenotomy, percutaneous, adductor or hamstring; multiple tendons), $2,247 to $3,216 (x2), $4,494 to $6,432 according to 2019 National Fee Analyzer.

Hospital/Facility fee: $16,365.

$16,365 per one-day inpatient stay at St. Joseph's Hospital (Bradenton, FL) according to the 2019 American Hospital Directory, https://www.ahd.com/.

Anesthesia: $2,684.

$2,684 for general anesthesia using CPT Codes 27606 and 27307 according to the American Society of Anesthesiologists (ASA) *2019 Relative Value Guide* and *2019 Crosswalk; A Guide for Surgery/Anesthesia CPT Codes.*

POTENTIAL COMPLICATIONS

Per Dr. Shahnasarian:
At risk of injuries during transfers
At risk of skin breakdown problems

CHAPTER 9

The International Life Care Plan

Evaluators occasionally receive requests for life care plans intended to be used abroad. The reasons for these requests vary.

Foreign visitors sometimes become disabled in this country and plan to return to their homeland to continue their rehabilitation when sufficiently recovered. An injured person's immigration status can also prompt a request for a life care plan outside the United States. Those who become injured while in a country illegally, for example, may face deportation and a need to obtain rehabilitation services elsewhere, triggering a request for an international life care plan. Other reasons underlying requests for nondomestic life care plans include injured people's desires to undergo treatment in a place they perceive offers a higher level of quality or other advantages such as proximity to family and friends.

When lawyers surmise facts support a reasonable scenario of an individual temporarily relocating, emigrating, or for any other reason pursuing medical services abroad, they may request a life care plan specific to the locale in question. Advocacy objectives often underlie their motivations: plaintiff lawyers seek to maximize their clients' opportunities to recover disputed damages, while defense lawyers aim to mitigate disputed damages values. A plaintiff lawyer pursued this strategy while commissioning a Germany-based life care plan for a U.S. citizen that proposed scenarios in which the plaintiff would undergo expensive orthopedic procedures not yet approved by the U.S. Food & Drug Administration.

Of course, the value of a life care plan in a given place cannot be overlooked as a reason lawyers commission life care plans for varying places. A case involving a 30-year-old citizen of the United Kingdom who alleged to have acquired mild cognitive impairments and back injuries while on vacation in California five years earlier provides a good example. As a U.K. citizen, the plaintiff had full access at no charge to numerous treatment modalities under the National Health Service in the United Kingdom, including recurrent neuropsychological evaluations and orthopedic surgeon, neurosurgeon, and psychiatrist office visits; psychological counseling; and Botox treatment. Nevertheless, the plaintiff had not pursued any of these interventions for more than three years. A plaintiff-retained evaluator, however, prepared a California-based life care plan with these interventions fully costed in U.S. dollars, along with airfare and other travel expenses to transport and house the plaintiff. Of note, there was no evidence to support a premise the plaintiff planned to relocate to the United States or to pursue treatment there.

This chapter addresses issues pertaining to preparing an international life care plan. It concludes with a sample international life care plan featuring rehabilitation interventions intended for implementation in Guatemala.

Development of an International Life Care Plan

Many factors well beyond the scope of this discussion merit consideration when preparing an international life care plan, including differing customs and accepted healthcare practices in Eastern and Western societies, assessments of resources and quality of care available in developed and less-developed countries, and availability of some form(s) of universal health care services in another country. Regardless of a life care plan's intended place of implementation, the profession's standards of practice remain a touchstone for evaluators preparing international life care plans and those evaluating their viability.

Stereotypes about the quality of foreign healthcare services abound and also influence the preparation and presentation of international life care plans. These stereotypes include perceptions that, in comparison to developed Western countries, healthcare quality elsewhere is inferior. Whether true, partially true, or false, these notions cause most to dismiss or discount a life care plan prepared for an evaluee in locales they deem subpar.

Depending on their objectives, lawyers tend to exploit stereotypes to advance their arguments, promoting a life care plan option—domestic versus international—that best serves their interests. For example, consider a case in which a defense-retained life care planner develops a viable international life care plan less expensive than a plaintiff-retained expert's domestic option. The defense lawyer is apt to praise the international plan's merits, while opposing counsel denounces it as detrimental to the plaintiff's welfare with an ill-disguised cost-cutting motive.

Despite regulation, just as the quality of healthcare in the United States varies, the same holds true abroad. Further, in some cases, an international destination may lack the resources necessary to adequately care for a disabled person—especially one who has multisystem, catastrophic disabilities.

Competent evaluators anticipate the added scrutiny international life care plans typically undergo and, accordingly, employ due diligence to ensure their work complies with practice standards and offers interventions an evaluee requires. To this end, they earnestly research and evaluate options before proposing them. When they detect deficiencies in rehabilitation care and/or resources, they propose alternatives to eliminate or mitigate them as best as possible.

An evaluator encountered challenges in preparing a comprehensive life care plan for a Tunisian national who became quadriplegic and ventilator dependent after an industrial accident in Los Angeles. The evaluee subsequently returned to his North African home—located in a midsized resort city, an approximately two-hour drive from Tunis, the country's capital and center for rehabilitation interventions.

The complexity of his disabled status and full scope of care he required, the evaluator determined after researching and inspecting treatment options near him, exceeded the resources available both in his hometown and in his country's capital. Hence, the evaluee's life care plan included semiannual, inpatient admissions for evaluations and treatment at facilities in Rome and Paris to which the evaluee was to be transported by air ambulance. Such improvisations enabled the evaluator to prepare a life care plan that enlisted resources the evaluee required but were more challenging to secure in his locale.

Site Visits

An evaluee's advance scouting visit of a site(s) where an international life care plan is being contemplated can inform all who have a stake in it. The event—including interviewing prospective rehabilitation providers and touring rehabilitation facilities to determine capability to implement required evaluee services—provides an opportunity to professionally evaluate the veracity of any stereotypes about a place's quality of rehabilitation services. By extension, intelligence evaluators gather and analyses they formulate can educate others who evaluate a life care plan's viability, dispelling when appropriate inaccurate perceptions and negative attributions.

An evaluator experienced in preparing life care plans in several Caribbean and Latin American countries, for example, became aware through on-site assessments of often wide ranges in quality between public and private rehabilitation sources. His experiences led him to conclude, generally, while public facilities offer services at no or nominal cost, they often fall short in meeting standards he deemed acceptable on important quality metrics—such as excessive service provision wait times, dated and limited therapy equipment, and inadequate ratios of skilled care workers to patients.

On the other hand, he determined privately rendered services in these countries, available via cash payment at costs affordable only to the most affluent citizens, albeit typically less than those in the United States, generally compare favorably to those in Western countries. Conveying this firsthand knowledge, supplemented with supportive data from authoritative sources, helped him to dispel unwarranted negative attributions and gain third-party acceptance of prudent life care plan recommendations.

Conferring with prospective evaluee treatment providers and inspecting treatment facilities in advance also enable evaluators to personalize life care plans in situations where resources and customs are atypical of those in domestic plans. Interactive, on-site consultations better position evaluators to qualify/disqualify rehabilitation intervention sources. As in the Tunisian example earlier, identifying gaps in continuity and quality of required treatment facilitates making necessary life care plan adjustments and employing mitigation strategies. Needless to say, when presenting an international life care plan to those with little familiarity with and perhaps inherent stereotypes about a locale in question, evaluators gain credibility when they adeptly communicate their knowledge and experience about pending questions and apply professional due diligence to vet their recommendations in places unknown to those relying on their judgment. Following are before, during, and after considerations related to an international life care plan site visit.

Preparing for the Site Visit

The bedrock preparation for an international site visit involves determining the scope of rehabilitation services an evaluee requires. Only then can a life care planner research, identify, and begin to assess the viability of prospective interventions in a foreign place. This information can be gathered by a review of medical records, evaluee examination, and, when appropriate, consultations with an evaluee's treating healthcare providers and other contributors qualified to identify evaluee-specific treatment protocols.

Optimizing valuable time spent at an international site while evaluating its potential to address an evaluee's rehabilitation needs requires efficient preparation and planning. Much research can be done in advance via the Internet, telephone inquiries with prospective treatment providers and facilities, and queries of public sources such as diplomatic consulates.

Quite often, interpreters are needed to conduct oral communications with places abroad, and differences in local customs and time zones can also complicate the information-gathering process.

The main work associated with the preparation phase is ascertaining treatment sources appropriate for the rehabilitation tasks at hand and scheduling appointments to visit them. This involves coordinating appointments to meet with prospective healthcare providers (e.g., surgeons, specialist physicians, mental health professionals, therapists) and to tour facilities (e.g., hospitals, skilled care facilities, therapy centers, clinics). In some countries, healthcare professionals in private facilities require payment for their time.

The logistics involved in planning travel to international destinations also typically include arranging air and ground travel, reservations at hotels, and sometimes meeting facilities. Once at the destination, evaluators often require the services of interpreters and drivers; most hotels can provide referrals for these services. Those participating in site visits should allow adequate time to conduct appointments and to travel to places between them—another planning detail best tended to before the sojourn. In some countries, security issues pose yet another consideration.

Finally, advance knowledge of cultural attitudes and practices in an international destination, including attitudes about people with disabilities, can facilitate the on-site information-gathering process. Shahnasarian (2010) addressed cross-cultural differences in views on life care planning in North America, South America, and Europe.

Compliance, sensitivity, and deference to local traditions and customs help to build goodwill important to earning trust and cooperation with an evaluator's objectives, which in turn can determine a planned visit's success. An evaluation may fail to occur if a country's visitation requirements go unmet.

As an example, a life care planner preparing for an exam and site visit in Saudi Arabia learned securing a visa necessary to enter the country was contingent on, among other things, a formal, written invitation from the evaluee. Complying with this requirement complicated and elongated the many associated trip-scheduling details, and the evaluator's inability to secure this invitation led to an aborted site visit—despite an order from a U.S. federal court judge sanctioning it. Quite likely, the failure to extend the requisite invitation related, at least in part, to the evaluator being retained by counsel opposing the Saudi plaintiff/evaluee. In this vein, gender-related norms and institutions specific to a region can also have important implications for an on-site visit, ranging from accepted dress to access to desired rehabilitation sources.

Expanding on this line of thinking, from macrolevel to microlevel cultural-sensitivity details, the need for a visiting evaluator to communicate knowledge of and respect for indigenous norms cannot be overemphasized. The South Korean consulate in Washington, D.C., enlightened an evaluator on an important custom, easy for a Westernized person to overlook, when making a visit to an evaluee's home in Seoul: doff your shoes before entering the dwelling.

Conducting Site Visits

Like all activities associated with damages assessments, competent evaluators carefully document important site visit findings. The absence of this documentation exposes them to potential impeachment and disqualification of their findings and opinions for reasons that could range from noncompliance with professional standards of practice to Daubert challenges.

Lawyers opposing an evaluator routinely attack the lack of support or evidence connecting an evaluator's assessments with underlying factual bases. In cases involving international matters, when those directly and indirectly evaluating damages claims and evaluators' assessments likely have less familiarity with and knowledge of underlying information than with domestic claims—not to mention conscious/unconscious stereotypes about a locale—evaluators who lack adequate documentation to support their findings become more vulnerable to the inevitable question opposing lawyers pose: "If it was important, you would have documented it, correct?"

Documentation helps to obviate or blunt these challenges and innuendo that evaluators have faulty memory and/or are fabricating evidence to appease a referral source. Documentary evidence, as noted throughout this book, derives from sources beyond testimonial evidence, such as evaluator notes, photos, and print and digital records, as well as audio and video recordings.

Subject matter of an international site visit requiring documentation includes key information derived from consultations conducted and places visited, such as the following:

- Names, titles, and responsibilities of those participating in consultations
- Names and descriptions of places visited
- Topics discussed, including those specific to an evaluee
- Expertise and resources necessary to address an evaluee's rehabilitation needs
- Fees and payment options for rehabilitation services
- Impressions about places visited (e.g., cleanliness, organization, continuity of services)

Available print literature and other supplemental descriptive information published by places visited provide additional sources of evidence. Photos life care planners take can also add to their documentation gathering and narration—via a report, deposition, and/or trial testimony—to communicate important concepts and negate stereotypes those who evaluate damages claims may hold.

Figure 9.1 presents two photos a life care planner from the United States took while in Guatemala, assessing the viability of a life care plan for a Guatemalan evaluee injured in the United States. The images show a patient's room and a therapy center in a private rehabilitation facility, conjuring images of like places people from Western cultures envision in their locales. Capturing and displaying such images supplement and reinforce an evaluator's appraisal that a prospective rehabilitation placement meets the standards an evaluee requires.

Figure 9.1 Photos of rehabilitation facilities a life care planner took during a site visit to Guatemala City, Guatemala: a patient room in an inpatient rehabilitation facility and a therapy room.

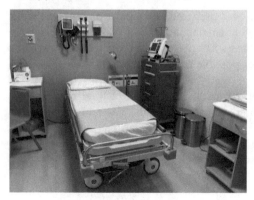 

Appendix L includes notes summarizing a life care planner's consultations and visits to rehabilitation facilities while in Guatemala; these notes appeared in the evaluator's rehabilitation evaluation report. Before the site visit, the evaluator prepared, with input from domestic contributors, a life care plan intended for the United States, in the locale where the evaluee had been residing. As the notes in Appendix L indicate, the document became an important focal point during the international consultations.

Follow-Up to the Site Visit

Life care planners have two main responsibilities after an international site visit: (1) to ensure, within a reasonable degree of rehabilitation probability, interventions proposed abroad can meet the standards an evaluee requires and (2) to execute details necessary to complete an international life care plan. Accomplishing the former objective sometimes requires additional consultation(s) with contributors—especially in cases when a site visit detected deficiencies in capacity to fully meet an evaluee's needs. When these situations arise, the focus shifts to assessing potential remedial interventions to close gaps.

Like domestic life care plans, all contributors to an international life care plan should have an opportunity to review and comment on it. Clinical correlation between domestic and international life care plans developed for the same evaluee serves to ensure consistency of proposed treatment; lawyers opposing evaluators will certainly challenge the lack thereof.

Obtaining costs for proposed interventions abroad, typically one of the last details necessary to bring a life care plan to fruition, may be more challenging than for domestic plans: customary sources on which evaluators rely in the United States differ from available sources abroad. This may require additional research to verify costs quoted for proposed treatment are fair market value. This follow-up can usually be accomplished via email and/or telephone, sometimes with translator assistance.

Forensic economists and/or forensic accountants apply their expertise to perform the final valuation of international life care plans. Beyond the processes implemented to accomplish this task with a domestic life care plan, this work includes converting currency, applying life expectancy of the international destination, and computing total values of life care plan expenditures based on country-specific economic information (e.g., inflation factors, historic cost increases of interventions specified, discount rates). Because of the many nuances associated with international life care plans, evaluators commonly provide context and clarification to those computing monetary values of life care plan damages.

Sample International Life Care Plan Report

A sample international life care plan follows. It was prepared in conjunction with the work described in Figure 9.1 and Appendix L for a Guatemalan citizen injured in a work-related incident that occurred in Arizona. Almost all costs are presented in Guatemalan currency (quetzals), except when an intervention was not possible to source there (in these few cases, costs appear in U.S. dollars).

Briefly, the evaluee sustained burns on approximately 50 percent of total body surface area while operating a bulldozer that encountered an underground gas tank. Beyond the evaluee's wound problems, his presenting problems included limitations with essentially all cervical spine movements and use of either arm/hand. Of note, surveillance showed him engaging in activities far beyond what he represented were within his capacity.

Guatemalan Life Care Plan

Prepared for
Miguel Sanchez
Michael Shahnasarian, PhD
February 4, 2020

Table of Contents

CONTRIBUTORS TO LIFE CARE PLAN

The following individuals provided recommendations for this life care plan:

Contributor	Specialty	Consultation Date	Telephone
Dr. Michael Shahnasarian	Rehabilitation Psychologist	07/14/19	(813) 555-xxxx
Dr. Christopher Delhouse	Physiatrist	08/25/19	(210) 555-xxxx
Mauricio Romero	Licensed Mental Health Counselor	08/22/19 08/01/19 01/05/19 Report	

As of January 1, 2020, 1.00 U.S. dollar = 7.55 quetzal (Q); all currency in this life care plan is presented in quetzals (Q), except in a few cases when an intervention was not possible to source in Guatemala and costs therefore appear in U.S. dollars.

BACKGROUND INFORMATION

NAME:	Miguel Sanchez
DATE OF BIRTH:	July 31, 1989
ONSET OF DISABLING PROBLEM:	February 5, 2018, work-related gas explosion incident
RACE:	Hispanic
DOMINANT HAND:	Right
HEIGHT:	5 feet 7 inches
CURRENT WEIGHT:	Approximately 150 pounds
PREINCIDENT WEIGHT:	147 pounds
MARITAL STATUS:	Single/Never married
RESIDENCE:	Scottsdale, Arizona
PRESENTING PROBLEMS:	Vision difficulties Impaired speech and trouble with vocal projection Burn injuries throughout body, mostly upper part of body and left leg Pain, numbness, and itching sensations in burned body parts and skin donor sites Lung and stomach problems Occasional difficulty voiding bowels Intermittent periods of poor appetite Occasional difficulty sleeping, including "lots of nightmares" Sexual dysfunctional trouble including erectile dysfunction Depression "A lot of" headaches

EVALUATIONS

Item	Duration	Frequency	Estimated Cost	Recommended By
PSYCHIATRIST EVALUATION	Year 1*	One Time	630Q–800Q	Dr. Delhouse Dr. Shahnasarian

*Note: Per Dr. Delhouse, additional recommendations will follow.

Per Dr. Neri Ortiz, psychiatrist, 502-5865-7865 (Guatemala City, Guatemala): Psychiatrist evaluation, 630Q per evaluation.

Per Dr. Javier Blanco, psychiatrist, 502-5558-1910 (Guatemala City, Guatemala): Psychiatrist evaluation, 700Q per evaluation.

Per Janet, administrator at the office of Dr. Luis Pedro Torre Biarte, 502-2337-2179 (Guatemala City, Guatemala): Psychiatrist evaluation, 800Q per evaluation.

Item	Duration	Frequency	Estimated Cost	Recommended By
ENT/OTOLARYNGOLOGIST EVALUATION	Year 1	One Time	300Q	Dr. Delhouse

Per Caudia, assistant to Dr. Alejandro Bailey, 502-2366-6533 (Guatemala City, Guatemala): ENT/Otolaryngologist evaluation, 300Q per evaluation.

Per Sara Toc, secretary to Dr. Carlos Mateo, 502-2332-4165 (Guatemala City, Guatemala): ENT/Otolaryngologist evaluation, 300Q per evaluation.

Item	Duration	Frequency	Estimated Cost	Recommended By
OPTOMETRIST EVALUATION	Year 1–Life	1 Visit per Year	300Q per Evaluation	Dr. Delhouse

Per Sonia, receptionist at Clinica y Optica Sixtino, 502-2269-7200 (Guatemala City, Guatemala): Optometrist evaluation, 300Q per evaluation.

Per Hilda Lopez, receptionist at Optica Tornoe, 502-2334-5831 (Guatemala City, Guatemala): Optometrist evaluation, 300Q per evaluation.

Item	Duration	Frequency	Estimated Cost	Recommended By
PULMONOLOGIST EVALUATION	Year 1–4 Year 5–Life	1 Visit per Year Every 4 Years	300Q–425Q per Evaluation	Dr. Delhouse

Per Diana Soc, secretary to Dr. Juan Manuel Rodriguez, 502-2324-0404 (Guatemala City, Guatemala): Pulmonologist evaluation, 420Q per evaluation.

Per Ingrid Orosco, secretary to Dr. Gustavo Adolfo Anleu Alonso, 502-2385-7589 (Guatemala City, Guatemala): Pulmonologist evaluation, 325Q per evaluation.

Per Priscilla Monroy, secretary to Dr. Juan Pablo Moralejo, 502-2361-2044 (Guatemala City, Guatemala): Pulmonologist evaluation, 425Q per evaluation.

Per Wendy, secretary to Dr. Marco Binicio Flores, 502-3221-4798 (Guatemala City, Guatemala): Pulmonologist evaluation, 300Q per evaluation.

EVALUATIONS

Item	Duration	Frequency	Estimated Cost	Recommended By
PSYCHOLOGICAL EVALUATION	Year 1–Life	Every 3 Years	600Q per Evaluation	Dr. Delhouse

Per Dr. Javier Blanco, psychiatrist, 502-5558-1910 (Guatemala City, Guatemala), he has a psychologist at his clinic. Psychological evaluation, 600Q per evaluation.

Per Sara Sin Fuentes, secretary to Dr. Sonia Melville, 502-2385-7738 (Guatemala City, Guatemala): Psychological evaluation, 600Q per evaluation.

PHYSICAL THERAPY EVALUATION	Year 1–Life	Every 4 Years	200Q–300Q per Evaluation	Dr. Delhouse

Per Dr. Tito Rodriguez, physiatrist, 502-5708-9237 (Guatemala City, Guatemala): Physical therapy evaluation, 200Q per evaluation.

Per Carlos Lopez, physical therapist, 502-4218-1994 (Guatemala City, Guatemala): Physical therapy evaluation, 200Q per evaluation.

Per Sergio Amado, physical therapist, 502-5709-2048 (Guatemala City, Guatemala): Physical therapy evaluation, 200Q per evaluation.

Per Lily Piril, secretary at Clinica Marta Pinera, 502-2360-9457 (Guatemala City, Guatemala): Physical therapy evaluation, 300Q per evaluation.

OCCUPATIONAL THERAPY EVALUATION	Year 1–Life	Every 4 Years	200Q per Evaluation	Dr. Delhouse

Per Dr. Tito Rodriguez, physiatrist, 502-5708-9237 (Guatemala City, Guatemala): Occupational therapy evaluation, 200Q per evaluation.

Per Sergio Amado, physical therapist, 502-5709-2048 (Guatemala City, Guatemala): Occupational therapy evaluation, 200Q per evaluation.

Per Lily Piril, secretary at Clinica Marta Pinera, 502-2360-9457 (Guatemala City, Guatemala): Occupational therapy evaluation, 200Q per evaluation.

POSTSURGICAL OCCUPATIONAL THERAPY EVALUATION*	Year 1–Life	2 Times Total	200Q per Evaluation	Dr. Delhouse

*Note: Per Dr. Delhouse, to include fitting of pressure garments, supplies, activities of daily living instruction, self-care, orthotic fitting, and training.

Per Dr. Tito Rodriguez, physiatrist, 502-5708-9237 (Guatemala City, Guatemala): Occupational therapy evaluation, 200Q per evaluation.

Per Sergio Amado, physical therapist, 502-5709-2048 (Guatemala City, Guatemala): Occupational therapy evaluation, 200Q per evaluation.

Per Lily Piril, secretary at Clinica Marta Pinera, 502-2360-9457 (Guatemala City, Guatemala): Occupational therapy evaluation, 200Q per evaluation.

THERAPEUTIC NEEDS

Item	Duration	Frequency	Estimated Cost	Recommended By
PLASTIC SURGEON FOLLOW-UP	Year 1–2 Year 3–Life	1–2 Visits per Year Every 5 Years	200Q–400Q per Visit	Dr. Delhouse

Per Johana Seqen, secretary to Dr. Carlos Garcia Salas, 305-2334-6153 (Guatemala City, Guatemala): Plastic surgeon follow-up, 400Q per visit.

Per Marilyn Perez, secretary to Dr. Pedro Jerez, 502-2361-0132 (Guatemala City, Guatemala): Plastic surgeon follow-up, 200Q per visit.

Per Wendy Archila, secretary to Dr. Eduardo Olmstead, 502-2362-7384 (Guatemala City, Guatemala): Plastic surgeon follow-up, 350Q per visit.

Item	Duration	Frequency	Estimated Cost	Recommended By
ORTHOPEDIST FOLLOW-UP	To Be Determined	To Be Determined	300Q–350Q per Visit	Dr. Delhouse

Per Marta Perez, secretary to Dr. Raul Amenaba, 502-2331-9111 (Guatemala City, Guatemala): Orthopedist follow-up, 300Q per visit.

Per Tatiana Ruiz, secretary to Dr. Eduardo Silva, 502-2362-2322 (Guatemala City, Guatemala): Orthopedist follow-up, 350Q per visit.

Item	Duration	Frequency	Estimated Cost	Recommended By
PHYSIATRIST FOLLOW-UP	Year 1–5 Year 6–Life	1 Visit Every 2–3 Months 2 Visits per Year	150Q per Visit	Dr. Delhouse

Per Dr. Tito Rodriguez, psychiatrist, 502-5708-9237 (Guatemala City, Guatemala): Physiatrist follow-up, 150Q per visit.

Per Yaniri Castillo, therapist at Clinic Rehab, 502-2269-7145 (Guatemala City, Guatemala): Physiatrist follow-up, 150Q per visit.

Item	Duration	Frequency	Estimated Cost	Recommended By
INTERNAL MEDICINE FOLLOW-UP	Year 1–Life	1 Extra Visit per Year	300Q–448Q per Visit	Dr. Delhouse

Per Caterine Caniz, secretary to Dr. Ernesto Ponce De Boya, 502-2337-3575 (Guatemala City, Guatemala): Internal medicine follow-up, 300Q per visit.

Per Ester Gomez, assistant to Dr. Carino Giron, 502-2362-8681 (Guatemala City, Guatemala): Internal medicine follow-up, 350Q per visit.

Per Edith Morales, secretary to Dr. Boris Castillo, 502-2334-5932 (Guatemala City, Guatemala): Internal medicine follow-up, 448Q per visit.

THERAPEUTIC NEEDS

Item	Duration	Frequency	Estimated Cost	Recommended By
PSYCHOLOGICAL COUNSELING	Year 1–2 Year 3–Life	12 Sessions per Year 13 Protocols of 6 Sessions per Protocol	350Q–400Q per Session	Dr. Delhouse Dr. Shahnasarian Mr. Romero

Per Mr. Romero's January 5, 2016, report, he recommends individual counseling to promote adaptive coping skills, one session per month for the next 24 months. Thereafter, through life stressors, life events, and milestones. Each event would require at least six sessions every several weeks at a cost of $125 per session.

Per Sara Sin Fuentes, secretary for Dr. Sonia Melville, 502-2385-7738 (Guatemala City, Guatemala): Psychological counseling, 350Q per session.

Per Dr. Javier Blanco, psychiatrist, 502-5558-1910 (Guatemala City, Guatemala), he has a psychologist at his clinic. Psychological counseling, 400Q per session.

Item	Duration	Frequency	Estimated Cost	Recommended By
PHYSICAL THERAPY FOLLOWING SURGERIES	Year 1–Life	2 Protocols Total; Each Protocol 2–3 Sessions per Week for 4 Months	100Q–300Q per Session	Dr. Delhouse

Per Dr. Tito Rodriguez, physiatrist, 502-5708-9237 (Guatemala City, Guatemala): Physical therapy, 100Q per session.

Per Carlos Lopez, physical therapist, 502-4218-1994 (Guatemala City, Guatemala): Physical therapy, 200Q per session.

Per Sergio Amado, physical therapist, 502-5709-2048 (Guatemala City, Guatemala): Physical therapy, 225Q per session.

Per Lily Piril, secretary at Clinica Marta Pinera, 502-2360-9457 (Guatemala City, Guatemala): Physical therapy, 300Q per session.

Item	Duration	Frequency	Estimated Cost	Recommended By
PHYSICAL THERAPY*	Year 1–Life	10 Sessions Every 4 Years	100Q–300Q per Session	Dr. Delhouse

*Note: Per Dr. Delhouse, for maintenance.

Per Dr. Tito Rodriguez, physiatrist, 502-5708-9237 (Guatemala City, Guatemala): Physical therapy, 100Q per session.

Per Carlos Lopez, physical therapist, 502-4218-1994 (Guatemala City, Guatemala): Physical therapy, 200Q per session.

Per Sergio Amado, physical therapist, 502-5709-2048 (Guatemala City, Guatemala): Physical therapy, 225Q per session.

Per Lily Piril, secretary at Clinica Marta Pinera, 502-2360-9457 (Guatemala City, Guatemala): Physical therapy, 300Q per session.

Item	Duration	Frequency	Estimated Cost	Recommended By
OCCUPATIONAL THERAPY*	Year 1–Life	10 Sessions Every 4 Years	100Q–300Q per Session	Dr. Delhouse

*Note: Per Dr. Delhouse, for maintenance.

Per Dr. Tito Rodriguez, physiatrist, 502-5708-9237 (Guatemala City, Guatemala): Occupational therapy, 100Q per session.

Per Sergio Amado, physical therapist, 502-5709-2048 (Guatemala City, Guatemala): Occupational therapy, 225Q per session.

Per Lily Piril, secretary at Clinica Marta Pinera, 502-2360-9457 (Guatemala City, Guatemala): Occupational therapy, 300Q per session.

DIAGNOSTIC TESTS

Item	Duration	Frequency	Estimated Cost	Recommended By
X-RAY ELBOWS— BILATERAL	Year 1–10	1 Time per Year	300Q–424Q Each Time	Dr. Delhouse

Per Andrea or Suzy, secretaries at the Hospital Herrera Llerandi, 502-2384-5959 (Guatemala City, Guatemala): X-ray elbows, 424Q (212Q each).

Per Mildred Mendez, X-ray technician at Hospital Universidad Esperanza, 502-2415-9000 ext. 1308 (Guatemala City, Guatemala): X-ray elbows, 300Q for both; 200Q for one.

Item	Duration	Frequency	Estimated Cost	Recommended By
X-RAY SHOULDERS— BILATERAL	Year 1–10	1 Time per Year	300Q–798Q Each Time	Dr. Delhouse

Per Andrea or Suzy, secretaries at the Hospital Herrera Llerandi, 502-2384-5959 (Guatemala City, Guatemala): X-ray shoulders, 798Q (399Q each).

Per Mildred Mendez, X-ray technician at Hospital Universidad Esperanza, 502-2415-9000 ext. 1308 (Guatemala City, Guatemala): X-ray shoulders, 300Q for both; 200Q for one.

Item	Duration	Frequency	Estimated Cost	Recommended By
X-RAY CHEST	Year 1–Life	1 Time per Year	265Q–300Q Each	Dr. Delhouse

Per Andrea or Suzy, secretaries at the Hospital Herrera Llerandi, 502-2384-5959 (Guatemala City, Guatemala): X-ray chest, 265Q each.

Per Mildred Mendez, X-ray technician at Hospital Universidad Esperanza, 502-2415-9000 ext. 1308 (Guatemala City, Guatemala): X-ray chest, 300Q each.

Item	Duration	Frequency	Estimated Cost	Recommended By
BLOOD ANALYSIS	Year 1–Life	1 Time per Year	255Q–739Q	Dr. Delhouse

Note: Per Dr. Delhouse, CBC and CMP.

Per Andrea Mora, laboratory technician at Laboratorio Viral, 502-2277-0600 (Guatemala City, Guatemala): Blood analysis, 739Q. This includes a CBC and a series of tests to measure kidney and liver function and sugar, electrolyte, fluid, and protein levels in the blood. They do not have a test called CMP (Complete Metabolic Panel).

Per Ivon Estrada, receptionist at Laboratorio Clinico MED & K, 502-2438-8013 (Guatemala City, Guatemala): Blood analysis, 255Q. This includes 40Q for the CBC and 215Q for the CMP.

Item	Duration	Frequency	Estimated Cost	Recommended By
EKG (ELECTROCARDIOGRAM) TRACING (PRESURGERY)	Year 1–Life	2 Times Total	211Q–235Q Each Time	Dr. Delhouse

Per Andrea and Suzy, secretaries at Hospital Herrera Llerandi, 502-2384-5959 (Guatemala City, Guatemala): EKG (electrocardiogram) tracing, 235Q each time.

Per Mildred Mendez, X-ray technician at Hospital Universidad Esperanza, 502-2415-9000 ext. 1308 (Guatemala City, Guatemala): EKG (electrocardiogram) tracing, 211Q each time.

DIAGNOSTIC TESTS

Item	Duration	Frequency	Estimated Cost	Recommended By
PULMONARY FUNCTION TEST	Year 1–Life	1 Time per Year	200Q–2,400Q	Dr. Delhouse

Per Priscilla Monroy, secretary to Dr. Juan Pablo Moralejo, 502-2361-2044 (Guatemala City, Guatemala): Pulmonary function test, 200Q for simple test and 2,400Q for extensive test each time.

AIDS FOR INDEPENDENT LIVING

Item	Duration	Frequency	Estimated Cost	Recommended By
CUSTOMIZED PRESSURE LIP AND NECK COMPRESSION CONFORMERS	Year 1–Life	1–2 Times	155.53Q–211.40Q Each $20.60–$28 Each	Dr. Delhouse

Per Medico International, www.medicointernational.com: T118 Two Strap Neck & Facial Support, $24.50 each; T-124 Two Strap Neck and Facial Support, $24.50 each; T850C-4B High Compression Soft Stretch Wrap for Face and Neck, $20.60 each.

Per Make Me Heal, www.makemeheal.com: Chin Strap Facial Surgery Compression Garment, $28 each; Face & Neck Support Compression Garment, $26.95 each; Facial Compression Garment with Full Neck Support, $21.95 each.

Item	Duration	Frequency	Estimated Cost	Recommended By
MISCELLANEOUS ADAPTIVE AIDS/PATIENT EDUCATION	Year 1–Life	Annually	7,550Q per Year $1,000 per Year	Dr. Delhouse

Per Dr. Delhouse, miscellaneous adaptive aids/patient education, year 1 to life, $1,000 per year.

Item	Duration	Frequency	Estimated Cost	Recommended By
HANDHELD SHOWER NOZZLE	Year 1–Life	Replace Every 5–7 Years	188.75Q–619.10Q Each $25–$82 Each	Dr. Shahnasarian

Per Patterson Medical Products, Inc., www.pattersonmedical.com: Deluxe handheld shower spray, $56 each; Moen pause control handheld shower, $68 each; Full spray handheld shower, $82 each.

Per Southwest Medical, www.southwestmedical.com: Handheld shower head spray with diverter valve, $25 each; Handheld shower spray massager, $27 each.

Item	Duration	Frequency	Estimated Cost	Recommended By
PORTABLE GRAB RAILS	Year 1–Life	Replace Every 5–7 Years	1,162.70Q–1,766.70Q Each $154–$234 Each	Dr. Shahnasarian

Per Patterson Medical Products, Inc., www.pattersonmedical.com: The cost of grab bars depends on the size and material. ADA-approved grab bars, chrome or white, straight, 12" to 32", heavy-duty, $27 to $42 each. Installation of two rails by a local contractor, approximately $100 to $150. Estimated total cost, $154 to $234 for a pair of grab rails.

DRUG AND SUPPLY NEEDS

Item	Duration	Frequency	Estimated Cost	Recommended By
LOTEMAX OPHTHALMIC GEL 0.5%	Year 1–Life	4 Times per Day	92.10Q per 5 ml Tube	Dr. Delhouse

Per Judith Lopez, telephone operator at Farmacia Batres Calling Center, 502-2200-1010 (Guatemala City, Guatemala): Lotemax ophthalmic gel 0.5%; sold as Lotesoft 0.5%, 92.10Q per 5 ml tube.

TRAMADOL 50 MG	Year 1–Life	2–4 Tablets per Day	429Q– 689.70Q per 120 Tablets	Dr. Delhouse

Per Sandy Aldana, assistant at Farmacia Cruz Verde Colon, 502-7942-1250 (Guatemala City, Guatemala): Tramadol 50 mg, 429Q per 120 tablets. Only sold in box of 10 tablets at a cost of 35.75Q.

Per Judith Lopez, telephone operator at Farmacia Batres Calling Center, 502-2200-1010 (Guatemala City, Guatemala): Tramadol 50 mg, 689.70Q. Sold in 50 mg tablets in a box of 20 tablets at a cost of 114.95Q.

ZOLPIDEM 10 MG	Year 1–Life	1 Tablet at Bedtime	187.20Q– 291.10Q per 30 Tablets	Dr. Delhouse

Per Sandy Aldana, assistant at Farmacia Cruz Verde Colon, 502-7942-1250 (Guatemala City, Guatemala): Zolpidem 10 mg, 187.20Q per 30 tablets. Only sold in box of 10 at a cost of 62.40Q.

Per Judith Lopez, telephone operator at Farmacia Batres Calling Center, 502-2200-1010 (Guatemala City, Guatemala): Zolpidem 10 mg, 291.10Q. Sold as Nocpidem 10 mg.

VENTOLIN HFA 90 MCG INHALER	Year 1–Life	2 Puffs per Day	99.84Q– 99.85Q per 200 Puffs	Dr. Delhouse

Per Sandy Aldana, assistant at Farmacia Cruz Verde Colon, 502-7942-1250 (Guatemala City, Guatemala): Ventolin HFA 90 mcg, 99.85Q per 200 puffs.

Per Judith Lopez, telephone operator at Farmacia Batres Calling Center, 502-2200-1010 (Guatemala City, Guatemala): Ventolin HFA 90 mcg, 99.84Q per 200 puffs.

ADVAIR DISKUS 250 MCG	Year 1–Life	2 Puffs per Day	260.25Q– 388.82Q per 60 Puffs	Dr. Delhouse

Per Sandy Aldana, assistant at Farmacia Cruz Verde Colon, 502-7942-1250 (Guatemala City, Guatemala): Advair diskus 250 mcg, 260.25Q per 60 puffs. Sold under the name of Flixotide.

Per Judith Lopez, telephone operator at Farmacia Batres Calling Center, 502-2200-1010 (Guatemala City, Guatemala): Advair diskus 250 mcg, 388.82Q per 60 puffs. Sold under the name of Flixotide.

DRUG AND SUPPLY NEEDS

Item	Duration	Frequency	Estimated Cost	Recommended By
CELECOXIB (CELEBREX) 200 MG	Year 1–Life	1 Capsule per Day	240.96Q–273Q per 30 Capsules	Dr. Delhouse

Per Sandy Aldana, assistant at Farmacia Cruz Verde Colon, 502-7942-1250 (Guatemala City, Guatemala): Celecoxib (Celebrex) 200 mg, 273Q per 30 capsules. Only sold in box of 10 capsules at a cost of 91Q.

Per Judith Lopez, telephone operator at Farmacia Batres Calling Center, 502-2200-1010 (Guatemala City, Guatemala): Celecoxib (Celebrex) 200 mg, 240.96Q per 30 capsules. Sold under the name of Valdyne.

Item	Duration	Frequency	Estimated Cost	Recommended By
FAMOTIDINE (PEPCID AC) 10 MG	Year 1–Life	2 Tablets per Day	170.40Q–333.60Q per 30 Tablets	Dr. Delhouse

Per Sandy Aldana, assistant at Farmacia Cruz Verde Colon, 502-7942-1250 (Guatemala City, Guatemala): Famotidine 10 mg, 333.60Q per 30 tablets. Only sold in boxes of 10 tablets at a cost of 55.60Q.

Per Judith Lopez, telephone operator at Farmacia Batres Calling Center, 502-2200-1010 (Guatemala City, Guatemala): Famotidine 10 mg, 170.40Q per 30 tablets. Only sold in blister packs of 10 tablets at a cost of 28.40Q.

Item	Duration	Frequency	Estimated Cost	Recommended By
DUCOSATE SODIUM 100 MG	Year 1–Life	2 Tablets per Day	287.555Q per 60 Tablets	Dr. Delhouse

Per Judith Lopez, telephone operator at Farmacia Batres Calling Center, 502-2200-1010 (Guatemala City, Guatemala): Ducosate sodium 100 mg (sold as SENAX, 50 mg, box of 20 tablets), 95.85Q per 20 tablets; 287.55Q per 60 tablets.

Item	Duration	Frequency	Estimated Cost	Recommended By
BENEPROTEIN ORAL POWDER	Year 1–Life	7 Grams per Day 2 Times per Day	225Q per 275 Grams	Dr. Delhouse

Per Judith Lopez, telephone operator at Farmacia Batres Calling Center, 502-2200-1010 (Guatemala City, Guatemala): Beneprotein Oral Powder, 225Q. Sold under the name of Proteinex and comes in bags of 275 grams (9.70 ounces).

HOME/FACILITY CARE

Item	Duration	Frequency	Estimated Cost	Recommended By
ATTENDANT CARE	Year 1–Life	2–4 Hours per Week	100Q–150Q per 4 Hours	Dr. Delhouse

Per Ingrid De Santiago, nurse, 502-5972-8165 (Guatemala City, Guatemala): Attendant care, 100Q for 4 hours with a 4-hour minimum.

Per Abel Lopez, nurse, 502-4677-3032 (Guatemala City, Guatemala): Attendant care, 150Q for 4 hours with a 4-hour minimum.

TRANSPORTATION NEEDS

Item	Duration	Frequency	Estimated Cost	Recommended By
PROVIAL (AAA AUTO CLUB)	Year 1–Life	As Needed	No Charge	Dr. Delhouse

Per Directorate General Protection and Road Safety, PROVIAL is a roadside assistance force and provides patrols for most of the major highways in the country. PROVIAL can be contacted by calling 502-2419-2121. Their vehicles are equipped with basic tools and first aid supplies, and their services are free.

Item	Duration	Frequency	Estimated Cost	Recommended By
TRANSPORTATION AND LODGING STIPEND	Year 1–Life	As Needed	37,750Q–56,625Q $5,000–$7,500	Dr. Shahnasarian

Per Dr. Shahnasarian, Mr. Sanchez will be required to travel from Malacatancito Huehuetenango to Guatemala City for procedures and therapy recommended in this life care plan. Accordingly, a $5,000–$7,500 stipend would be appropriate for travel and lodging.

Per Wikipedia Travel, https://wikitravel.org/en/Guatemala_City, there are two bus companies that travel to Malacatancito Huehuetenango: Los Halcones and Linea Dorada.

Per Michelle, receptionist at Los Halcones Bus Service, 502-7963-3000 (Guatemala City, Guatemala): Their bus service travels from Guatemala City to Malacatancito Huehuetenango at a cost of 75Q to 85Q each way, 150Q to 170Q round trip. These are large buses with air conditioning and bathrooms.

Per David Castillo, sales representative at Linea Dorada, 502-7768-1566 (Guatemala City, Guatemala): Their bus service travels from Guatemala City to Malacatancito at a cost of 115Q one way or 200Q round trip.

PERSONAL FITNESS

Item	Duration	Frequency	Estimated Cost	Recommended By
FITNESS CENTER MEMBERSHIP	Year 1–Life	Monthly	200Q per Month	Dr. Delhouse

Per Flavio Lopez, receptionist at Ruinas Gym, 502-7932-5555 (Huehuetenango, Guatemala): Fitness center membership, 200Q per month.

EDUCATIONAL NEEDS

Item	Duration	Frequency	Estimated Cost	Recommended By
VOCATIONAL GUIDANCE SERVICES	Year 1–2	One Time	2,800Q	Dr. Shahnasarian

Per Sara Sin Fuentes, secretary to psychologist Dr. Sonia Melville, 502-2385-7738 (Guatemala City, Guatemala): Vocational guidance services, 350Q each session, 2,800Q for a total of 8 sessions. Each session is one hour with a formal report at the conclusion.

HOSPITALIZATIONS/SURGERIES

Item	Duration	Frequency	Estimated Cost	Recommended By
BILATERAL CONTRACTURE RELEASE–HANDS	Year 1–Life	One Time	43,646.55Q	Dr. Delhouse

Per Dr. Ernest Cofino, plastic surgeon, 502-5083-8962 (Guatemala City, Guatemala): Bilateral contracture release—hands, $5,781. This includes physician fee, assistant surgeon fee, anesthesiologist, and hospital cost. Dr. Cofino preferred to give his estimates in U.S. dollars.

Item	Duration	Frequency	Estimated Cost	Recommended By
CONTRACTURE RELEASE— FACE, NECK/LIP (2)	Year 1–Life	One Time	32,374.40Q	Dr. Delhouse

Note: Per Dr. Delhouse, this will be two separate procedures.

Per Dr. Ernest Cofino, plastic surgeon, 502-5083-8962 (Guatemala City, Guatemala): Contracture release—face, neck/lip, $4,288. This includes initial assessment, physician fee, assistant surgeon fee, anesthesiologist, and hospital cost. Dr. Cofino preferred to give his estimates in U.S. dollars.

CHAPTER 10

The Life Care Plan When Causation Is Disputed

Many times, typically when retained by defense counsel, life care planners encounter situations in which contributors with whom they consult develop opinions about the cause of injury and an evaluee's future care that vastly differ from what treating healthcare providers and/or plaintiff experts reckon. Another complicating factor for life care planners in these situations arises when evaluees have, in fact, undergone considerable treatment beyond what consulting experts deemed necessary beyond a specified period.

A common fact pattern illustrating this scenario arises in motor vehicle accidents in which a defense expert(s) opines as follows: a plaintiff experienced musculoskeletal strain/sprain injuries that, with little or no rehabilitation, would have fully resolved after a specified acute period (e.g., 30 to 90 days) after the trauma; no permanent trauma-related injury occurred; and, accordingly, no future treatment needs have developed. They may also opine no aggravation of any preexisting condition(s) occurred. Opposing expert opinions and case facts, however, may radically differ from this assessment and include a record of extensive postaccident interventional pain management treatment a plaintiff underwent before submitting to one or more surgeries. Further, the opposing opinions quite often forecast significant future treatment needs.

The challenges confronting defense-retained life care planners not independently qualified to reconcile the differing opinions include how to rebut the opposing plan. If they wholly adopt the defense medical expert position, then logic follows that no life care plan is merited. This decision risks exposing the defense to significant unchallenged damages if the trier of fact reaches a disposition counter to the defense medical experts' assessments.

For example, presume a jury reaches a verdict that an auto accident both exacerbated a plaintiff's preexisting injuries and caused new ones that necessitated considerable treatment and, more likely than not, extensive future treatment will occur. Without an alternate life care plan to reference, the jury's sole point of reference for valuing claimed rehabilitation intervention damages derives from the plaintiff expert's life care plan, which may be inflated and/or overstated, in whole or in part.

Additionally, from a credibility perspective, not to propose a single rehabilitation intervention for a person who has undergone extensive treatment—regardless of the relationship between the treatment and events in dispute—may be interpreted as insensitive and disingenuous, especially if plaintiff's counsel prevails on causation arguments. Again, the absence of alternate life care plan recommendations leaves no defense to claimed damages and only the plaintiff expert's life care plan as a reference point to value them.

A defense-retained expert, in line with her physician contributor's assessment of no permanent accident-related injuries, prepared no life care plan in a case that involved a middle-aged food service worker who underwent a three-level lumbar fusion and reported residual symptoms including lower back pain and lower extremity radicular symptoms. The expert encountered cross-examination questions that included "Is it true that you have not a single treatment recommendation, not even an over-the-counter pain reliever, for my client?" and "How many patients have you had who, having undergone a multilevel spine operation and continue to experience ongoing symptoms, never encounter a bump in the road that causes some need for medical intervention such as, at the least, a doctor office visit, X-ray, medication prescription, short-term protocol of therapy, or specialist referral?"

Obviously, few experts welcome this line of questioning, especially when underlying facts support an organic basis for a plaintiff's symptom presentation and treatment rendered has been in response to those symptoms. Life care planners' lack of contingency plans to thwart aggressive questioning aimed to neutralize, negate, and/or disenfranchise them can greatly undermine their credibility as impartial arbiters, present to facilitate sage insight to critical issues being adjudicated.

The reasons for disparate expert viewpoints, as noted throughout *The Valuation of Monetary Damages in Injury Cases: A Damages Expert's Perspective,* may emanate from factors that include earnest differences of opinion between professionals, lack of key information about interceding events that might have caused/contributed to an evaluee's presenting problems, and/or advocacy positions those assessing damages assume. Regardless, competent life care planners take action, as much as possible, to preempt and address challenges to their assessments.

Although liability matters typically are beyond a life care planner's purview, disagreements on mechanisms causing an evaluee's presenting problems have ramifications for preparing a life care plan. When healthcare professionals and experts on whom evaluators rely disagree on what caused a person's claimed injuries and associated disabling problems, the life care planner essentially has two options from which to choose in presenting future damages:

- Option 1: Adopt in full one of the polarized positions (i.e., an issue in dispute did or did not cause a person to acquire disabling problems in question), offering no alternative to remedy disputed life care plan damages under scenarios that deny a causal relationship between an event in question and alleged injuries associated with it. Plaintiff-retained experts more often adopt the former position, while defense-retained experts more often adopt the latter position.
- Option 2: Interpolate disputed causation positions, offering damages scenarios that provide those evaluating damages claims with options from which to select should they rule in or rule out an event in question caused the need for future rehabilitation intervention. Defense-retained experts more often pursue this presentation, while plaintiff-retained experts tend not to dignify a scenario in which claimed damages did not result from issues in dispute.

The following discussions expand on life care planners' damages assessments under these options, with accompanying analyses from plaintiff and defense expert perspectives. This chapter concludes with a sample report of an interpolated life care plan presentation.

Regardless of their retention source, competent, ethical life care planners seek to remain above the fray of adversarial efforts aimed at impeaching their credibility. The interpolated life care plan, offering pertinent caveats, can facilitate this objective.

Option 1: Adopt a Position

Plaintiff Perspective

Life care plan experts who unequivocally assume an issue in dispute (e.g., motor vehicle accident, trip-and-fall incident, assault) aggravated an evaluee's preexisting conditions and/or caused new disabling problems adopt a view that spawns an in-kind life care plan: all injuries evaluated and determined reasonably likely to require rehabilitation interventions stem from the disputed issue. These life care plans do not take into account potential alternate causes for injuries and associated interventions to remediate them; they tacitly attribute all life care plan damages to the liability issues at hand.

This approach maximizes damages computations—a central goal, of course, of plaintiff lawyers arguing damages their clients ostensibly merit. It also introduces risks defense counsel may exploit and, depending on a case's underlying facts, may use to undermine their objectives. These risks include the likes of portraying a life care plan as overextrapolating claimed damages by ignoring/minimizing alternate, plausible causes of an evaluee's presenting problems.

An evaluee with a preincident history of medical problems akin to those being associated with an event in question, for example, invariably attracts defense lawyers' attention and invites insinuations their opposing counsel is misattributing and/or comingling unwarranted damages with those in dispute. Their strategies often assert a plaintiff's claimed damages derive from preexisting pathologies and their natural progression, unaffected by disputed issues; hence, damages plaintiff's counsel seek lack merit—wholly or in large part.

Defense Perspective

In contrast to the plaintiff perspective discussed earlier, the underlying defense perspective presumes the converse: any verifiable injuries and needs for rehabilitation interventions stem from something other than the disputed issue(s). In sum, an issue(s) in dispute caused no permanent injury and no life care plan needs.

Presuming this position leaves one or more of the following explanations for an evaluee's ongoing symptom presentation:

- Whatever injuries an evaluee might have acquired would have fully resolved within an acute recovery period. Any treatment rendered thereafter was either unnecessary (such as a surgery that in itself invites complications and new conditions/treatment needs) or for reasons unrelated to issues in dispute.
- A preexisting and/or unrelated injury and/or unknown reason(s) (e.g., unrelated disease or injury not yet identified; event and/or disabling problems an evaluee failed to disclose) is the root cause(s) of an evaluee's presenting problems. The progression of preexisting pathologies and/or other causes coupled with the natural aging process may account for symptoms an evaluee manifests.
- Either consciously or unconsciously, an evaluee has assumed symptoms that lack substantiation via objective measures.
- An evaluee is exaggerating and/or malingering symptoms for secondary gain, which a favorable outcome to a dispute may offer.

Adopting one or more of these positions typically transmutes to a decision not to publish a life care plan, asserting a plaintiff deserves no future care damages award for issues in dispute. This perspective optimizes the defense's objectives of negating damages a life care plan offers but injects risks that, like the plaintiff perspective, require careful evaluation.

Presenting a sole life care plan to value damages—namely, one a plaintiff-retained expert prepared—to triers of fact exposes defense counsel to multiple risks. Foremost among these is a liability decision adverse to the defense position, fully exposing them to the possibility that plaintiff experts' damages values will be adopted for lack of a differing professional perspective. In this scenario, a plaintiff life care plan's costs, reasonableness of treatment protocols, and needs for interventions—all of which contribute to potentially large monetary damages and influence nonmonetary damage awards—become evidence without a response from a qualified defense-retained life care planner.

Defense lawyers often debate whether to prepare a competing life care plan when a plaintiff has undergone considerable treatment, such as one or more operations and extensive pain management treatment, and they argue the interventions were unnecessary and/or unrelated to liability issues. These cases also often include evidence supplied by the plaintiff's healthcare providers and expert witnesses that prognosticates ongoing rehabilitation treatment. The risks of forgoing a life care plan in these situations can increase significantly when triers of fact reach conclusions on liability counter to the defense position: attempting to advance the premise that a plaintiff will require little or no future rehabilitation treatment contrary to fact patterns and other evidence is counterintuitive and makes the defense vulnerable to losing credibility via perceptions of disingenuous representations.

Decisions to forgo a life care plan sometimes emanate from defense lawyers' preference not to set a "floor," or minimum damage value, from which opposing counsel can build to increase their claim. Most often they tend to aggressively adopt this position when they have strong confidence of prevailing on liability issues and/or when they presume plaintiffs seek unsupportable, inflated damages claims they can defeat with rational argument.

Option 2: Interpolate a Position

Plaintiff Perspective

While liability issues typically exceed the ken of life care planners and their retentions focus on defining liability-related damages, in compliance with standards of practice, they cull damages related to issues in dispute and do not incorporate in their assessments unrelated damages. Consider a case in which a life care planner evaluated lower extremity orthopedic injuries a previously nonambulatory, elderly person sustained in a fall incident. Costs of mobility devices used before the incident would not be added to claimed incident-related damages unless the new injuries had implications related to these devices' specifications and/ or caused the need for new equipment.

The matter of discerning disputed related and unrelated damages is far less clear cut, however, when treating professionals and experts relied on by plaintiff-retained life care planners disagree with the causation opinions of defense expert witnesses. For example, plaintiff's counsel may take the position in a case that all injuries and damages in question emanate from a motor vehicle accident; conversely, defense counsel may take the position that any damages sought have little or no relationship to the accident in question.

When such disagreements emerge, plaintiff lawyers most often request that their retained life care plan expert prepare a sole life care plan; namely, one in concert with the liability positions of treating doctors and other plaintiff-retained experts. When the scope of planners' retentions expands to preparing life care plans responding to differing causation scenarios, they develop an interpolated life care plan, employing a process along the lines described later.

Defense Perspective

While an interpolated life care plan can offer a floor for damages (discussed earlier), defense lawyers commission it to afford a measure of insurance and second level of defense if their liability defense falters. Specifically, it helps offset the risk posed by the following circumstance: What if the trier of fact accepts the plaintiff's position on liability and the only damages assessment from which they have an informed basis to render a disposition is the one the plaintiff's expert provided?

Careful analyses of a plaintiff's preexisting problems and manifestations of new problems alleged to have begun after an issue in dispute underlie the development of an interpolated life care plan. Consultations with life care plan contributors then address interventions attributable to preexisting conditions and those alleged to be newly acquired and/or aggravated. Interpolated life care plans heavily footnote what is and what is not being attributed to an alleged causal event.

Case Study

This case study serves to illustrate the analytical process a life care planner implemented while preparing an interpolated life care plan. Briefly, the plaintiff had a long history of performing heavy labor before experiencing an industrial accident in which liability went uncontested; however, claimed damages associated with the accident were heavily disputed.

Excerpts from the life care planner's rehabilitation report, including information from preaccident and postaccident records, appear next. A qualifying statement included in the life care plan preceding the presentation of damages is also presented. It clearly disassociates the presentation of damages from the industrial accident, noting the treatment recommendations pertain to a progression of preexisting pathologies. Of note, the value of damages was far less than what the opposing life care planner proposed without qualification of antecedent causal events.

Summary of Preaccident Medical Records

Disabling problems Mr. Wells has experienced before and after his September 2, 2019, motor vehicle accident are quite significant from a rehabilitation perspective. Medical records document that he has had several multisystem, permanent injuries with rehabilitation implications. These injuries, independently and in toto, must be considered when evaluating Mr. Wells's claim of vocational and other damages he attributes to his September 2019 accident. To begin, in 2006, he lacerated three left/dominant hand fingers, which were reattached. In 2012, he underwent a C6-7 cervical decompression and fusion and left rotator cuff surgery. Mr. Wells underwent a left knee arthroscopy in 2016. Regarding injury to his left eye, he described a gunshot injury in 1996 that caused him total loss of vision; he has subsequently been diagnosed with glaucoma.

Longstanding problems with lower back pain are also well documented in Mr. Wells's preaccident medical records. The first complaints of preaccident lower back pain of which I am aware are documented in Dr. Milhouse's office notes from 2008. Dr. Milhouse continued to treat Mr. Wells through the time of his September 2019 accident, and his records document ongoing lower back pain complaints Mr. Wells presented. In July 2016, Dr. Benton read Mr. Wells's lumbar MRI scan and detected several abnormalities that led to a series of lumbar epidural steroid injections. Several other physicians—including Dr. Amos, Dr. Incher, and Dr. Ultz—documented significant complaints of lumbar pain Mr. Wells presented. In an April 9, 2019, office record, Dr. David diagnosed chronic pain syndrome and stated, "Patient states that he has had three epidural injections, but [they] weren't successful." A physical therapy note from April 25, 2019, indicates Mr. Wells was a candidate for back surgery. On July 26, 2019, Dr. Self recommended fluoroscopically guided diagnostic right sacroiliac joint injection, and the pain management specialist's records document narcotic medication he prescribed Mr. Wells. Additionally, Mr. Wells was prescribed Lyrica for neuropathic pain. Records indicate he was undergoing active pain management treatment at the time of his September 2019 accident. In fact, he had a prescheduled appointment with Dr. Self the day of his accident. Mr. Wells underwent a sacroiliac injection in August 2019. Also noteworthy in terms of his preaccident medical history are diagnoses of diabetes in 2006 or 2007 and a history of hypertension. Apparently, Mr. Wells has had longstanding preaccident problems with depression for which he had been prescribed psychotropic medications, and he continues to take antidepressants. A particularly concerning postaccident unrelated medical problem Mr. Wells informed me about has been significant weight loss: he reported an approximately 80-pound weight loss during the past four months. Mr. Wells conveyed multiple specialists have yet to diagnose or treat his rapid recent weight loss. He also cited the recent onset of alarming breathing problems associated with his weight loss. In this regard, Mr. Wells described days when "I can't breathe at all," and he told me his wife on multiple occasions has been concerned to the point that she has considered a hospital admission. According to Mr. Wells, his weight loss, breathing, and gastrointestinal issues are "continuing to get worse." Regardless of any injuries Mr. Wells might have acquired because of the September 2, 2019, motor vehicle accident, his medical history unrelated to his accident merits consideration in light of his claimed accident-related damages. Regardless of any injuries or disabling problems his accident might have caused, his unrelated medical problems would likely have adversely affected his career development and caused him to require rehabilitation intervention. It should be noted that imaging of Mr. Wells's lumbar spine the day of his 2019 accident detected advanced degenerative changes. I defer to a qualified medical professional for an opinion about the progression of Mr. Wells's preaccident and unrelated postaccident pathologies in the absence of his September 2, 2019, accident.

Summary of Postaccident Medical Records

Records documenting Mr. Wells's postaccident medical treatment include references to complaints and treatment similar to his preaccident treatment. After his September 2, 2019, industrial accident, Mr. Wells underwent surgeries on his lumber spine in June 2019 and August 2020. After his initial surgery, he pursued treatment with Dr. Rich, who documented in an office note dated January 2, 2021, "Patient states he wants to wait for SI joint injection to be scheduled until lawsuit is finished." Dr. Sweeper reported his opinions after a compulsory medical evaluation on July 3, 2021. Referencing Mr. Wells's significant preaccident medical history, his review of postaccident records, and his examination, Dr. Sweeper determined Mr. Wells had no objective findings attributable to his 2019 accident. Obviously, if Dr. Sweeper's assessment is correct, Mr. Wells's September 2, 2019, motor vehicle accident has not affected his earning capacity. The primary problem Mr. Wells relayed to me with respect to his accident was ongoing lower back pain, which he said is "pretty much localized." From a functional perspective, he assessed he can safely lift and carry 30 pounds. Again, Mr. Wells emphasized several times he employs proper body mechanics. He denied being limited in any cervical spine movement, and he did not present limitations with using either lower extremity. Mr. Wells conveyed his fine motor functioning is intact, despite his preaccident left finger injuries. He denied having problems with squatting. Regarding his ability to walk, Mr. Wells said: "I really don't have a problem. I walk all day in my job." Likewise, he denied having limitations in the duration he can stand comfortably. Mr. Wells estimated he can generally sit comfortably—from 45 to 60 consecutive minutes—by displacing his weight. I am unaware of any specific physician-advised restriction that may be documented. Dr. Sweeper testified in November 2021 that, because of Mr. Wells's preexisting problems, he would limit him to lifting 30 to 40 pounds. Dr. Sweeper qualified his assessment of Mr. Wells's functional capacities by stating, "My feeling on this is the condition for which he had surgery was not caused by the accident, so even though he may need restrictions now, it's because of the degenerative condition [for] which he ultimately had surgery, not caused by the accident." My analysis had led me to conclude Mr. Wells remains capable of performing light/medium exertion tasks. His current job responsibilities, as he described them, appear within his capacity, and I am unaware of a reason Mr. Wells would not be able to continue to perform his job, as he has demonstrated he has been capable to do. I am continuing to evaluate claims for future treatment Mr. Wells is pursuing in conjunction with his September 2, 2019, industrial accident.

Qualifying Statement for Case Study Life Care Plan

Based on his review of preaccident and postaccident records, examination of the plaintiff, and consultation with the defense-retained orthopedic surgeon, the life care planner included the following note:

> In both his July 3, 2021, report and November 10, 2021, deposition testimony, Dr. Sweeper opined that Mr. Wells's September 2, 2019, industrial accident did not cause a need for future rehabilitation intervention. Dr. Sweeper determined Mr. Wells did not acquire any permanent injury from his September 2019 accident, and he acquired no additional treatment needs that can reasonably be attributed to it. Further, the orthopedic surgeon concluded Mr. Wells's ongoing symptoms and need for treatment are manifestations of his preexisting pathologies. The recommendations presented herein are for sake of reference, unrelated to Mr. Wells's September 2, 2019, industrial accident, and are associated with his preaccident and unrelated postaccident needs.

Sample Report of an Interpolated Life Care Plan

A 63-year-old man pursued a product liability claim for future care damages he associated with a fall from a chair. His preincident medical records included imaging that detected multilevel degenerative changes in his cervical spine and lumbar spine. The plaintiff underwent a three-level cervical fusion with instrumentation nine months before the incident, and a postoperative record three months before the incident documented his surgeon's assessment that he experienced an incomplete fusion and that "his continued smoking is a likely cause of the nonunion and some decreased sagittal balance." Other preincident comorbidities included hypertension, high cholesterol, diabetes, obesity, and sleep apnea.

Two months after the incident, the plaintiff underwent a multilevel cervical fusion. Postoperative records document several complaints he continued to present, including ones associated with his urological functioning.

The sample interpolated life care plan presents two perspectives: (1) the chair event in question caused no permanent injury and, by extension, no needs for future treatment (please refer to the multiple footnotes on the Contributor page); and (2) if the trier of fact determines the evaluee's presenting problems in whole or in part emanate from the event, the life care plan incorporates reasonable interventions with their associated costs. Of course, the trier of fact also has options that include adopting the opposing life care plan, which presumes all future life care plan damages arose from the event, and configuring a hybrid option from the various opinions set forth.

Sample:
Interpolated Life Care Plan

Prepared for
John Emerson
Michael Shahnasarian, PhD
May 29, 2021

Table of Contents

CONTRIBUTORS TO LIFE CARE PLAN

The following individuals provided recommendations for this life care plan:

Contributor	Specialty	Consultation Date	Telephone
Dr. Michael Shahnasarian	Rehabilitation Psychologist	Report from Records	
Dr. Anthony Rogers	Orthopedic Surgeon	05/26/21 05/15/21 03/02/21 Report	(619) 695-1217
Dr. Jack Gilliam	Neurologist	05/22/21 Report 05/18/21	(858) 436-9793

CONTRIBUTORS TO LIFE CARE PLAN

The following individuals provided recommendations for this life care plan:

Contributor	Specialty	Consultation Date	Telephone
Dr. Ralph Dickens	Urologist	05/13/21	(619) 302-6260

Note: Per Dr. Rogers' March 2, 2021, report:

> Within a reasonable degree of medical certainty, I believe that the claimant's condition is preexisting with degenerative disease. The fact that it is preexisting and degenerative is well documented throughout his medical history prior to the incident. As far as the claimant's incident is concerned, no further medical treatment is necessary. The claimant does not require future treatment as it relates to his incident of June 30, 2019. I do not believe the treatment rendered, including surgical management of the cervical spine, was related to his June 30, 2019, incident. Mr. Emerson has a permanent impairment rating of 0% for his cervical spine, as it relates to the June 30, 2019, incident, according to the *American Medical Association Guide to the Evaluation of Permanent Impairment*, Sixth Edition.

Note: Dr. Anthony Rogers determined that Mr. Emerson's June 30, 2019, incident did not cause any aggravation or new injury to his preincident cervical spine and lumbar spine pathologies. By extension, the incident did not cause Mr. Emerson to acquire any new rehabilitation intervention needs beyond those he would have required due to the progression of his preexisting comorbidities.

Note: Per Dr. Gilliam's May 22, 2021, report:

> The incident in question did not cause or accelerate any underlying progressive spinal degenerative disorder that was radiographically documented back in 2014 and followed with serial radiographs, which have all shown longitudinal progression. Patient's clinical symptomatology is entirely related to this progressive spondylitic degenerative disorder, complicated by cigarette smoking and multiple metabolic comorbidities—all predating and unrelated to the chair incident in question.

> He has suffered no neurologic impairment attributable to the incident in question, nor does he require any further medical care or treatment related to that incident. The conclusions expressed herein are within a reasonable degree of medical certainty based upon the information thus far provided as well as today's examination.

Note: Dr. Gilliam determined Mr. Emerson's June 30, 2019, chair incident neither aggravated his preexisting pathologies nor caused him to acquire new permanent injury. Further, he assessed Mr. Emerson's presenting problems are a progression of his preexisting pathologies and other issues unrelated to his incident, including diabetes, obesity, and smoking habit, along with his longstanding spine problems.

Note: Per Dr. Gilliam, Mr. Emerson is not a surgical candidate due to his multiple uncontrolled comorbidities. Mr. Emerson experienced a natural progression of degenerative disease affecting his cervical spine, complicated by metabolic processes and nicotine addiction.

Note: Dr. Dickens determined Mr. Emerson's June 30, 2019, incident did not cause him to acquire any treatment needs from a urological perspective.

Note: Drs. Dickens, Gilliam, and Rogers have no life care plan recommendations for Mr. Emerson that they relate to his June 30, 2019, chair incident. Likewise, Dr. Shahnasarian has no recommendations to this end. The recommendations contained herein are intended to address Mr. Emerson's symptoms that he attributes to his incident.

Opinions presented herein are within a reasonable degree of life care planning certainty.

Year 1 in the duration section of this life care plan begins on the date this life care plan is published.

The National Fee Analyzer is published by FAIR Health, a nonprofit agency developed to ensure transparency in medical costs. The National Fee Analyzer provides physician practices with three percentiles (50th, 75th, and 90th) of charge data; only the 50th and 75th percentiles are incorporated into this life care plan. This resource provides physician practices with national charge data for fee scheduled evaluation and competitive analysis for contracting purposes. Compiled from a database of 650 million charge records arranged by CPT Codes, the National Fee Analyzer has no insurance-company-paid amounts incorporated into its product.

Diagnostic costs such as X-rays, MRIs, and CT scans are obtained solely from the 2021 National Fee Analyzer because costs cited by diagnostic centers are based on insurance reimbursement, thereby undervaluing the true cost.

Medication costs in this life care plan are pharmacy cash prices.

BACKGROUND INFORMATION

NAME:	John Emerson
DATE OF BIRTH:	September 27, 1957
ONSET OF DISABLING PROBLEM:	June 30, 2019, fall incident
RACE:	Caucasian
CURRENT WEIGHT:	Approximately 300 to 315 pounds
MARITAL STATUS:	Married, Thelma Ann Emerson
CHILDREN:	Four adult daughters
RESIDENCE:	San Diego, California
PRESENTING PROBLEMS:	Cervical spine nerve damage Balance difficulty Inability to walk long distances Feet numbness Erectile dysfunction Neck pain Loss of independence

THERAPEUTIC NEEDS

Item	Duration	Frequency	Estimated Cost	Recommended By
ORTHOPEDIC SURGEON FOLLOW-UP	Year 1–5*	1 Visit per Year	$139–$176 per Visit	Dr. Gilliam Dr. Rogers

*Note: Per Dr. Gilliam, reassess need to continue this intervention at the end of year five.

Note: Per Dr. Rogers, to monitor plate implanted in cervical spine.

Per Nancy Protsman, patient care coordinator at Orthopedic and Sports Medicine, office of Dr. Randy Benchman, 858-947-7690 (San Diego, CA): Orthopedic surgeon follow-up, $165 using CPT Code 99213.

Per 2021 National Fee Analyzer, orthopedic surgeon follow-up, CPT Code 99213 (office or other outpatient visit for the evaluation and management of an established patient, which requires at least two of these three components: an expanded problem-focused history; an expanded problem-focused examination; and medical decision-making of low complexity. Counseling and/or coordination of care with other physicians, other qualified health care professionals, or agencies are provided consistent with the nature of the problem(s) and the patient's and/or family's needs. Usually the presenting problems(s) are of low to moderate severity. Typically, 15 minutes are spent face to face with the patient and/or family), $139 to $176 per visit.

Item	Duration	Frequency	Estimated Cost	Recommended By
PHYSICAL THERAPY	Year 1–5	2 Protocols per Year; 12 Sessions per Protocol	$100–$158 per Session	Dr. Gilliam Dr. Rogers

Per Ann Nunez, office manager at Performance Physical Therapy, 619-230-3288 (San Diego, CA): Physical therapy, $100 per 30-minute session using CPT Code 97110.

Per 2021 National Fee Analyzer, physical therapy, CPT Code 97110 (therapeutic procedure, one or more areas, each 15 minutes; therapeutic exercises to develop strength and endurance, range of motion, and flexibility), $60 to $79; $120 to $158 per 30-minute session.

DIAGNOSTIC TESTS

Item	Duration	Frequency	Estimated Cost	Recommended By
X-RAY CERVICAL SPINE (2 VIEWS)	Year 1–5*	1 Time per Year	$100–$129 Each Time	Dr. Rogers Dr. Gilliam

*Note: Per Dr. Gilliam, reassess need to continue with this intervention at the end of year five.

Per 2021 National Fee Analyzer, X-ray cervical spine, CPT Code 72040 (radiologic examination, spine, cervical; two views), $100 to $129 each time.

Item	Duration	Frequency	Estimated Cost	Recommended By
MRI CERVICAL SPINE	Year 1–5*	One Time	$1,300–$1,700 Each Time	Dr. Gilliam

*Note: Per Dr. Gilliam, reassess need to continue with this intervention at the end of year five.

Per 2021 National Fee Analyzer, MRI cervical spine, CPT Code 72141 (magnetic resonance, imaging, spinal canal and contents, cervical; without contrast material), $1,300 to $1,700 each time.

WHEELCHAIR NEEDS

Item	Duration	Frequency	Estimated Cost	Recommended By
MANUAL WHEELCHAIR	Year 1–Life	Replace Every 7–10 Years	$875–$1,599 Each	Dr. Gilliam

Per Spin Life, www.spinlife.com: Breezy 600 Custom Wheelchair, $575 each; Quickie LX Custom Wheelchair, $945 each; Quickie LXI Custom Wheelchair, $999 each.

Per 1-800 Wheelchair, www.1800wheelchair.com: Karman Ergo Flight Custom Wheelchair, $689 each; Karman Flex Fully Adjustable Wheelchair, $1,099 each.

Additional $300 to $500 for added accessories and options.

Item	Duration	Frequency	Estimated Cost	Recommended By
MANUAL WHEELCHAIR MAINTENANCE	Year 1–Life	Annually	$69.95 per Year	Dr. Gilliam

Per Ela Faux, customer service at Medical Mobility (MedMo), 858-213-4760 (San Diego, CA): Manual wheelchair maintenance, $69.95 each time, except in years of new purchase.

Item	Duration	Frequency	Estimated Cost	Recommended By
ROHO CUSHION	Year 1–Life	Replace Every 3–5 Years	$220–$369 Each	Dr. Gilliam

Per Southwest Medical Supply, www.southwestmedical.com: Roho Cushion—Roho MiniMax, $280 each; Roho Harmony, $220 each.

Per Allegro Medical Supply, www.allegromedical.com: Roho High Profile Cushion, $357 each; Roho Hybrid Elite, $369 each.

AIDS FOR INDEPENDENT LIVING

Item	Duration	Frequency	Estimated Cost	Recommended By
SHOWER CHAIR	Year 1–Life	Replace Every 5–7 Years	$24.99–$54.99 Each	Dr. Gilliam

Per Walgreens Pharmacy, www.walgreens.com: Nova Bath Seat with Arms and Back, $54.99 each; Nova Bath Seat with Detachable Back, $39.99 each; AquaSense Adjustable Bath and Shower Chair, $24.99 each.

Per CVS Pharmacy, www.cvs.com: Drive Medical Bathroom Safety Shower Chair, $54.99 each; AquaSense Bath and Shower Chair with Backrest, $44.99 each; Juvo Comfort Series Shower Stool, $44.99 each.

Item	Duration	Frequency	Estimated Cost	Recommended By
GRAB RAIL (2)	Year 1–Life	Replace Every 3–5 Years	$139.96–$223.96 Total	Dr. Gilliam

Per Home Depot, www.homedepot.com: Delta Lyndall Decorative Assist Bar, $29.98 each; Delta Traditional Curved Grab Bar, $19.98 each; Delta Greenwich Decorative Assist Grab Bar, $24.98 each.

Per Lowes, www.lowes.com: Moen Home Care Grab Bar, $29.98 each; Moen Stainless Steel Assist Grab Bar, $36.98 each. Installation of two rails by a local contractor, approximately $100 to $150.

DRUG AND SUPPLY NEEDS

Item	Duration	Frequency	Estimated Cost	Recommended By
ADVIL	Year 1–Life	As Needed	$16.99–$17.99 per 160 Capsules	Dr. Gilliam

Per Walgreens Pharmacy, www.walgreens.com: Advil 200 mg, $17.99 per 160 capsules.

Per CVS Pharmacy, www.cvs.com: Advil 200 mg, $16.99 per 160 capsules.

HOME/FACILITY CARE

Item	Duration	Frequency	Estimated Cost	Recommended By
PERSONAL CARE ATTENDANT	Year 3–4 to Life	7 Hours per Week	$16–$20 per Hour	Dr. Gilliam

Per Sam Culpepper, administrator at AAA Home Healthcare, 619-831-5417 (San Diego, CA): Personal care attendant, $20 per hour.

Per Lance Tindale, intake coordinator at Full Life Home Health, 858-170-5918 (San Diego, CA): Personal care attendant, $16 per hour.

PART IV

Special Considerations

Part IV concludes *The Valuation of Monetary Damages in Injury Cases* with a focus on the denouement of damages experts' work: providing opinions to enlighten triers of fact on technical matters in dispute. To provide opinion testimony, expert witnesses must anticipate and survive Daubert challenges that aim to strike or limit the presentation of their opinions—the subject of Chapter 11. The final chapter, "Presentation of Damages Assessments," describes how expert witnesses navigate the numerous adversarial challenges they encounter throughout their involvement in a case—from counsel's initial disclosure of them as expert witnesses through their trial testimony.

CHAPTER 11

Daubert Motions

This chapter explains the purpose of Daubert motions and presents both formal criteria and case law applied to evaluate their merits. Methods to defend a Daubert motion and to establish bases for pursuing one are also discussed.

Admissibility of Evidence

Daubert motions emanate from the *Daubert v. Merrell Dow Pharmaceuticals, Inc.* (1993) case and a predecessor case, *Frye v. United States* (1923), which established bounds for admitting expert testimony into evidence. Under *Daubert* and Federal Rule of Evidence 702 (Committee on the Judiciary, 2010b), the court serves as the gatekeeper to the admission of scientific, technical, or other specialized evidence.

Expert witnesses interject new evidence in disputes—namely, via methods they apply and opinions they ultimately develop—beyond documentary and testimonial evidence that otherwise evolves and becomes discovered during litigation. This expert-generated evidence can seriously undermine a party's interests, motivating intense efforts to quash it. Daubert motions provide a means to this end, adding another important variable in the analysis and strategy associated with prosecuting a case.

The Daubert guidelines to determining whether an expert's methodology is valid consist of five factors:

1. Whether the theory or technique in question can be and has been tested
2. Whether it has been subjected to peer review
3. Its known or potential error rate
4. The existence and maintenance of standards controlling its operation
5. Whether it has attracted widespread acceptance within a relevant scientific community

Daubert challenges aim to exclude expert evidence on the basis of it not being admissible under Rule 702 of the Federal Rules of Civil Procedure (Committee on the Judiciary, 2010a, 2010b). The rule states:

> If scientific, technical or other specialized knowledge will assist the trier of fact to understand the evidence or to determine a fact in issue, a witness qualified as an expert by knowledge, skill, experience, training, or education, may testify thereto in the form of an opinion or otherwise, if:

1. The expert's scientific, technical, or other specialized knowledge will help the trier of fact to understand the evidence or to determine a fact in issue;
2. The testimony is based on sufficient facts or data;
3. The testimony is the product of reliable principle and methods; and
4. The expert has applied the principles and methods reliably to the facts of the case.

Lawyers assert a range of reasons justifying why a court should grant a Daubert motion to exclude or otherwise limit expert testimony adverse to them. The most common include contentions that an expert lacks the qualifications necessary to tender said opinions, opinions are not tied to facts, methodologies employed are not reliable, sources relied upon are not reliable, and/or unreliable opinions were adopted when performing analyses.

While empowering the courts on admissibility matters, the landmark *Daubert* ruling notes, "Vigorous cross-examination, presentation of contrary evidence, and careful instruction on the burden of proof are traditional and appropriate means of attacking" expert testimony. The court in *Allison v. McGhan Medical Corp.* elaborated on this responsibility, concluding the gatekeeper role "is not intended to supplant the adversary system or the role of the jury."

Examples of Relevant Case Law Rulings

A number of court rulings have addressed the sacrosanct nature of expert evidence. Under Florida law, for instance, *Pascual v. Dozier* and *Keller Industries v. Volk* underscored a party's due process right to call a witness. This right has been further defined in cases involving expert witness testimony by noting the exclusion of this testimony must be carefully considered and sparingly done (e.g., *Pascual v. Dozier*; *Rojas v. Rodriguez*). Further, rulings including *Aguila-Rojas v. City Management Group Corp.* and *Davis v. Pfund* determined the exclusion of expert testimony is a drastic remedy that should be invoked only in the most compelling of circumstances.

Further, the *Pasqual v. Dozier* ruling stated, "A trial court should exercise caution when the witness sought to be excluded is a party's only witness or one of the party's most important witnesses because if the witness is stricken, that party will be left unable to present evidence to support his or her theory of the case." In this vein, appellate courts found error in excluding testimony essential to defense counsel (*Keller Industries v. Volk*) and in excluding a physician's testimony essential to a party's case (*LoBue v. Travelers Insurance Co.*) and determined reversible error to exclude testimony of the defense's medical expert witness concerning the etiology of a plaintiff's medical condition (*Santos Wrestling Enterprise, Inc. v. Perez*).

Other relevant rulings emanate from *H.K. Corp. v. Estate of Miller*, "The sufficiency of facts required to form an opinion must normally be decided by the expert himself and any deficiency relates to the weight rather than the admissibility of expert's opinion," and *Lombard v. Executive Elevator Service, Inc.*, which determined a trial court's concern about an expert should relate only to the weight of the testimony and not its admissibility. A decision in *Orpe v. Carnival Corp.* suggested any deficiency in an expert's testimony is a subject for impeachment or reduction in the weight of the testimony, rather than an issue of admissibility. Similarly, in *Robinson v. Hunter*, the court ruled the reasonableness of an expert's reliance on supporting facts is likewise tested on cross-examination.

Appendix M features an order denying a Daubert motion to exclude or otherwise limit the testimony of a defense expert in a medical malpractice case. Briefly, the issue related to the admissibility of evidence contained in a life care plan pertaining to residential options for a plaintiff in a persistent vegetative state who had been living in a skilled care facility during the past three years. Plaintiff's expert, a medical doctor, prepared a life care plan with a sole residential option: placement in a private home with round-the-clock nursing services and all associated interventions accompanying this placement. The defense expert, a nonmedical doctor and a certified life care planner, prepared a life care plan with two residential options: private home placement comparable to what the plaintiff's expert proposed and ongoing placement in a skilled care facility.

The crux of the plaintiff's challenge related to its assertion that a nonmedical doctor was not qualified to enter into evidence the skilled care facility placement option. In denying the motion, the court cites an analytical decision-making process that references relevant legal precedent, the court's role as a gatekeeper of admissible evidence rather than the ultimate arbiter on the matter, an assessment of the expert's qualifications and methods applied to arrive at reasonably probable opinions, and the plaintiff's opportunity to challenge at trial the weight ascribed to the expert's opinions.

Meeting a Daubert Challenge

It goes without saying that, regardless of its merits, a ruling and possibly a future misinterpretation of it (intentional or unintentional) faulting an expert's methods and/or opinions can damage both a case at hand and an expert's career beyond the pending case. Indeed, a ruling to exclude or otherwise limit expert witness testimony can have long-lasting implications, and stakeholders should aggressively address these challenges. Ease of access to information about an expert's history and opposing counsel's motivation to dispel/eliminate expert testimony—especially in high-stakes litigation—all but ensures any ruling insinuating an expert witness misstep will be magnified.

Central to meeting a Daubert challenge is to preemptively seek to dispel problems that might arise. These measures begin with retaining quality experts who employ mainstream methodologies, adhere to the bounds of their expertise, carefully document their work, and competently present their findings. When met with a Daubert challenge, counsel defending it should aggressively address every question subsumed in it. This often includes discussing methodologies competing with those an expert employed and presenting a rationale for methods selected and applied. Choosing not to dignify and counter a contention can prove fatal to the admissibility of an expert's testimony.

An attorney defending a Daubert challenge should also become familiar with the expert's specialization and testimony to anticipate the points the Daubert challenger will make. Along these lines, the defending attorney should prepare counterpoints to neutralize anticipated attacking arguments. According to Rahman (2020), when making their points, lawyers should remain mindful that judges are quite conscious of judicial efficiency and adhering to precedent.

Not all Daubert hearings include comprehensive oration by counsel and witnesses, and rulings often derive from judicial review. Accordingly, documentary responses and supporting evidence should be comprehensive; supplemental, relevant evidence that supports an expert's position can also facilitate a Daubert challenge's defense.

Appendix E, an affidavit a vocational expert prepared at the request of another vocational expert undergoing a Daubert challenge, provides an example of this latter evidence. In it, the affiant represents he reviewed the work of the challenged expert and deduced the expert employed proper methods and complied with generally accepted practice standards. Appendix N illustrates how an expert can provide supplemental information to help elucidate the bases for opinions being challenged. In this case, plaintiff's counsel challenged an expert's qualifications, bases for formulating opinions, and appropriate application of methodologies to derive opinions. The court ruled not to exclude the expert's testimony, several times citing supplemental information the expert provided while rationalizing the disposition.

Facilitating Daubert Challenge Efforts

In addition to assisting in the defense of a Daubert challenge, expert witnesses can facilitate lawyers' efforts to craft a Daubert challenge of an opposing expert. Their knowledge of standards of practice, appropriate applications of methodologies, and proper and improper inferences drawn from analyses can prove invaluable in determining grounds for a motion and providing fodder to impeach an opposing expert.

The following example critique derives from a case in which counsel pursuing a Daubert challenge retained a life care planner as a consulting expert to review and critique an opposing expert's assessment. The consulting expert found the proposed life care plan deficient on multiple levels. Defense counsel referenced the noted deficiencies to depose the plaintiff's life care planner, eliciting on the record admissions consistent with what the consulting expert cited. The opposing expert's combined documentary and testimonial evidence provided grist for an ensuing Daubert motion.

Example of Critique of Opposing Expert's Analysis, Contributing to Grounds for Daubert Challenge

Briefly, a plaintiff's damages claim stemming from a 2018 vehicular accident included a life care plan valued in excess of $4.5 million. The plaintiff, Mr. Melkov, testified his highest level of education was the ninth grade, and he noted he worked with labor unions in Illinois and Michigan as a painter. After a 2007 motor vehicle accident that caused him neck, back, and hand injuries, he conveyed, he ceased working in 2008 and had since been receiving disability benefits from the Social Security Administration. According to his testimony, Mr. Melkov stopped receiving treatment for his 2007 injuries approximately two years later; this testimony was inconsistent with his Facebook postings and medical records that indicated he had been participating in pain management treatment, with symptoms reportedly worsening, through November 2018, when his pain management physician, Dr. Dinkle, discharged him for multiple noncompliance reasons. Mr. Melkov had a history of antisocial behavior, including criminal activity and drug abuse—both prescribed and nonprescribed medications.

Excerpts from a report prepared by defense counsel's consulting expert follow. The critique focuses on, among other things, the opposing expert's failure to consider in his analysis the plaintiff's preaccident history and the expert's violations of life care planning standards of practice.

I.   Dr. Pelton, a life care planner retained by counsel representing Mr. Melkov, apparently did not review any records predating Mr. Melkov's June 1, 2018, motor vehicle accident. All the records he identified postdate the accident, and he apparently relied on the history Mr. Melkov presented to him. Likewise, it does not appear Dr. Pelton consulted with any of Mr. Melkov's treating doctors, and the recommendations that appear in his life care plan emanate from him. It is unusual that a life care planner retained by plaintiff's counsel would not consult with plaintiff's treating doctors; arguably, this violates Standard 7 of the Standards of Practice published by the International Association of Life Care Planners, which conveys that the life care planner seeks collaboration when possible. In view of Mr. Melkov's very significant preaccident medical history, drug abuse problems, and failure to comply with his preaccident pain management physician's protocols, Dr. Pelton's failure to incorporate this information is significant from a life care planning perspective.

II. The preaccident medical history Mr. Melkov presented to Dr. Pelton is inconsistent with preaccident medical records on many accounts. For example, Dr. Pelton notes in his March 17, 2021, report that Mr. Melkov's neck and back issues from his 2007 accident resolved, and he had no limitations. Obviously, this information is inconsistent with records from Dr. Dinkle, which indicate Mr. Melkov's complaints were worsening—despite aggressive interventional pain management treatment including injections, conservative treatment, and prescriptions of narcotic medications. Of note, as indicated earlier, Mr. Melkov had also been receiving disability benefits from the Social Security Administration for more than a decade before his June 2018 accident; presuming the history he relayed to Dr. Pelton was accurate, Mr. Melkov had been defrauding the Social Security Administration before his 2018 accident.

III. Another fallacy associated with Dr. Pelton's failure to review Mr. Melkov's preaccident medical records—reliance on Mr. Melkov for an accurate preaccident medical history and apparent failure to consult with Mr. Melkov's treating doctors—is a failure to consider a progression of his preaccident pathologies in the absence of his 2018 accident. Again, Mr. Melkov represented to Dr. Dinkle that his symptoms were worsening, despite the pain management treatment being rendered. In fact, Dr. Dinkle's October 16, 2017, office note indicates Mr. Melkov requested a motor scooter because of preexisting mobility problems.

IV. There are numerous indications that, beyond the noncompliance Dr. Dinkle documented, Mr. Melkov has been noncompliant with other rehabilitation treatment and recommendations. For example, there is considerable documentation of Mr. Melkov's preaccident noncompliance with chiropractic treatment and physical therapy. Dr. Jefferson noted in his November 5, 2020, report: "The patient smokes a pack [of cigarettes] per day and has for 40 years. This can affect wound healing and chronic pain." Of further note, during his August 2020 deposition, Mr. Melkov testified he has not pursued injections postaccident because he did not find them helpful. Despite Mr. Melkov's history and testimony, however, Dr. Pelton included in his life care plan aggressive protocols of treatment including modalities of which Mr. Melkov chose not to avail himself and ones that he avowed did not benefit him. Along these lines, Dr. Pelton included in his life care plan a recommendation for lifelong narcotic medication (oxycodone) for Mr. Melkov; Dr. Dinkle's November 16, 2017, note discharging Mr. Melkov from his practice specifically indicates he was noncompliant in his use of this medication. Dr. Pelton's significant oversight and inclusion of a rehabilitation intervention specifically contraindicated by a treating doctor potentially conflict with the Hippocratic Oath all physicians take: Do no harm.

V.   Another failure of Dr. Pelton's life care plan relates to his costs. He does not identify the source of his costs, making it impossible for another expert to verify the information he cites. Similarly, Dr. Pelton does not list the healthcare professional who made the recommendations he deems necessary, leaving one to surmise all the recommendations emanate from him. This calls into question Dr. Pelton's compliance with several life care planning standards of practice, including:

- Standard 1a The life care planner remains within the scope of practice for his or her profession as determined by state, provincial, or national credentialing bodies.

- Standard 2a The life care planner consults with others and obtains education when the life care planner must address healthcare needs that are new or unfamiliar.

- Standard 3c The life care planner obtains information from medical records, evaluee/family (when available or appropriate), relevant treating or consulting healthcare professionals and others.

- Standard 4b The life care planner researches appropriate options and charges for recommendations, using sources that are reasonably available to the evaluee.

- Standard 4e The life care planner uses classification systems to correlate care recommendations and charges when these systems are available or helpful at providing clarity.

- Standard 4f The life care planner uses and relies upon relevant research that should be readily available for review and reflected within the life care plan.

- Standard 6c The life care planner develops recommendations for content of the life care plan cost projections for each evaluee and a method for validating inclusion or exclusion of content.

- Standard 6d The life care planner makes recommendations that are within the life care planner's own professional scope of practice; seeks recommendations from other qualified professionals and/or relevant sources for inclusion of care items and services outside the life care planner's scope of practice.

- Standard 7c The life care planner shares relevant information to aid in formulating recommendations and opinions.

- Standard 8b The life care planner provides relevant information about the life care planning process to involved parties to elicit cooperative participation.

VI. Dr. Pelton's life care plan lacks internal consistency. For example, he recommends implantation of a spinal cord stimulator in year 1 while continuing aggressive interventional pain management treatment including prescriptions of narcotic medication, radiofrequency ablations, and epidural injections; all these recommendations, along with surgical intervention recommended at an undefined time, are proposed to continue indefinitely. The prescription of these interventions is out of sync with traditional medical models that terminate ineffective treatment modalities or maintain them if effective, recommending more aggressive interventions only if/when needed.

VII. Obviously, Dr. Jefferson, a neurosurgeon who performed a compulsory medical evaluation of Mr. Melkov, determined Mr. Melkov acquired no additional treatment needs from his June 2018 accident. Unlike Dr. Pelton, Dr. Jefferson has knowledge of Mr. Melkov's extensive medical history, both before and after his September 2018 accident.

VIII. I am comparing costs for treatment Dr. Pelton specified in his 2021 report with costs I believe reasonable. The most recent information I have about Mr. Melkov's whereabouts is that he resides in St. Petersburg, Florida; accordingly, costs I present will be specific to the Tampa Bay area.

_____   Date _____

Michael Shahnasarian, PhD
Certified Life Care Planner #258
Certified Rehabilitation Counselor #3701
Certified Vocational Evaluator #58360
International Psychometric Evaluator Certification #985
Licensed Psychologist PY5644
Fellow, American Psychological Association
Fellow, International Academy of Life Care Planners
Fellow, National Career Development Association

CHAPTER 12

Presentation of Damages Assessments

Damages experts' work culminates in the presentation of their assessments, and astute experts consider the scrutiny their work will undergo throughout the process of gathering necessary evidence, applying evaluation methods, developing and preparing new evidence, and presenting opinions. Their assessments evolve in the context of adversarial proceedings, adding to the due diligence and vigilance they must employ to attain their objective: to apply the science of their profession and withstand adversarial litigation challenges that threaten to alter, dilute, or otherwise denigrate opinions they aim to present to those involved in the judicial process, including triers of fact.

Every aspect of an expert's analysis will be scrutinized and challenged—beyond methods applied, opinions developed, and defenses of opposing counsel's assertions of errors made and/or remiss evaluation components. Regardless of a challenge's merits, competent experts attempt to preempt problems in their analyses, prepare defenses of their opinions, and make reasonable concessions when appropriate.

This last chapter of *The Valuation of Monetary Damages in Injury Cases: A Damages Expert's Perspective* aims to integrate core concepts presented throughout this book—beginning with the fundamentals of expert witness damages assessments and the construction of opinions in claims of loss of earning capacity and in developing life care plans—associated with experts' presentations of damages assessments. Expert evidence quite often far exceeds what an expert envisioned when retained.

Types of Expert Evidence

Experts' reports subsume evidence that they will be held accountable to defend during a deposition or cross-examination at trial. While reports memorialize the culmination of experts' work in a case at hand and disclose opinions generated, the evidence they present and defend goes far beyond them.

Figure 12.1 summarizes expert evidence routinely scrutinized by opposing counsel. Their objectives include discovering evidence they can use to impeach an expert by casting him or her as unqualified, financially beholden to a retention source, biased, unethical, uninformed,

Figure 12.1 Opposing Counsel Analyses of Expert Evidence

Type of Expert Evidence	Potential Opposing Counsel Objectives in Attempting to Undermine Expert Evidence
Curriculum Vitae	Portray the witness as unqualified.
	Imply the witness is not a practitioner but rather a professional expert witness.
	Imply the witness has not remained current with professional practices.
Interrogatory Responses	Expose potential bias (e.g., tendencies to be retained more frequently by plaintiff or defense counsel).
	Insinuate the witness is beholden to the retaining source because of amounts of fees paid.
Recordings of Examinations	Compare with expert report(s) in an attempt to detect inconsistencies.
Reports	Uncover pertinent evidence an expert has not considered.
	Discover/imply errors, omissions, and deficiencies are present.
Deposition Testimony	Test the expert's mettle when challenged.
	Elicit testimony favorable to opposing counsel's case theories.
	Dispel opinions not favorable to opposing counsel's case theories.
	Fully discover opinions/evidence planned for trial, with an aim of filtering/questioning counterproductive evidence.
Trial Testimony	Impeach adverse expert opinions by attacking any and all vulnerable areas including qualifications, inconsistencies, methodology, and bias.
	Appropriate favorable evidence.
Billing Records	Gather evidence to assert the expert is beholden to the retaining source, driven by greed, and therefore not trustworthy.
	Shock triers of fact by the high fees billed, alienating them from the expert.
History of Retentions with the Retention Source	The expert and retaining lawyer have a covert relationship that makes them untrustworthy, and the expert is financially beholder to the retaining lawyer.
Prior Testimony/Reports from Other Cases; Professional Publications	Discover prior opinions inconsistent with those rendered in an instant case, thereby portraying the expert as not trustworthy.

and/or flawed in methods applied to derive opinions—all leading to innuendo and/or outright assertion that an expert is not trustworthy and, by extension, opinions should be stricken, limited in scope, or otherwise discounted and/or ignored.

Counsel opposing an expert routinely appropriates expert-generated evidence favorable to their case. For example, it is not uncommon for plaintiff lawyers, when supported by facts and evidence to their advantage, to adopt in their arguments treatment protocols an opposing expert has specified in a life care plan, along with any other expert-generated evidence that can further their damages arguments.

A discussion of expert-generated evidence subject to opposing counsel scrutiny follows. Expert anticipation of opposing counsel challenges and responses, also discussed, is essential to preserving the integrity of opinions rendered, the expert's raison d'etre.

Curriculum Vitae

An expert's curriculum vitae (CV)—an expert-prepared document that describes an expert's education, qualifications, and experience—is a very important point of reference to determine whether an expert is legally qualified to render expert opinions. It is usually a retaining lawyer's first consideration in selecting an expert, and it remains evidence to be evaluated throughout succeeding litigation events, including Daubert hearings and voir dire questioning at trial, that permit a lawyer to examine and challenge an expert's qualifications to provide opinions before testimony on substantive matters commences.

Beyond suggesting an expert lacks the qualifications necessary to provide testimony on pending issues in dispute, opposing counsel's objectives in examining a witness's CV can also include finding support for implications that an expert has not remained current on trends involved in the pending dispute and/or is less qualified than opposing counsel's expert. This latter implication connotes the trier of fact should apportion less weight to testimony of a less-accomplished expert.

Vocational experts alert to attacks on their qualifications refrain from straying outside their areas of expertise when developing and presenting opinions. They also remain diligent in their professional development and comply fully with standards of practice. These habits limit the grist opposing lawyers can garner to support attacks of them on the bases of lack of qualifications and/or faulty methods employed to formulate opinions.

Interrogatory Responses

Boecher v. Allstate Co., 731 So. 2d 993 (Fla. 1999), led to a precedent-setting ruling on the types of expert evidence that opposing counsel can request, including:

- The identity of each matter in which the expert has been retained, performed services, rendered an opinion, conducted an examination, or provided testimony for any legal action at the retention source's request during the preceding three years. This includes the identification of case numbers, names of the courts, the county and state of filing, the date of filing, the insurance claim number, the defendant's name, and the plaintiff(s)' name.
- For each matter just listed, the amount in dollars paid directly or indirectly to the expert, specifying who made the payments and when they were made.
- The identity of all cases in which the expert has provided expert witness testimony during the preceding three years, either in a deposition or a court appearance, and as to each whether he or she was testifying as a treating physician or consulting expert, whether the plaintiff or the defendant requested the testimony, and all fees the expert charged for the work that led to that testimony.

- The total amount of money the retention source or anyone acting on its behalf paid the expert during the past three years.
- Regarding a pending case, records provided to the expert.
- The percentage of work the expert performed at the requests of plaintiff and defendant lawyers during the preceding three years.
- The number of hours devoted annually to being an expert witness during each of the preceding three years.
- The percentage of hours devoted to work as an expert witness during each of the preceding three years.
- The percentage of income the expert earned from serving as an expert witness during each of the preceding three years.
- Total amounts paid in the instant litigation, including the dates and amounts of each payment, the work performed corresponding to each payment, and any balance due on outstanding fees.
- The expert's fee schedule.

Most of the interrogatory questions just listed aim to uncover financial evidence that could be used to imply an expert is biased, monetarily beholden to a retention source—essentially, a "hired gun." The requirement to maintain details sufficient to provide information about an expert's testimonies during the past three years avails to opposing lawyers ready access to potentially volumes of information they could cull to discover occurrences of an expert historically providing opinions and/or testimony inconsistent with those offered in an instant case. Again, this exercise aims to discredit experts, asserting testimony cannot be trusted.

Competent, ethical experts adhere to generally accepted methodologies and render opinions objectively and consistently. They appreciate the scrutiny and due diligence opposing counsel will exercise on their clients' behalf and apply the science of their profession, resolute in defending their opinions, to resist baseless accusations. When confronted with accusations of discordant past testimony, they earnestly delve into reasons for the alleged differences and, as appropriate to the situation, provide context necessary to explain reasons for any divergent opinions historically rendered. This perspective helps to neutralize opposing counsel's attack on an expert, explaining how divergent fact patterns necessitate the derivation of different analyses and opinions.

Recordings of Exams

When experts are retained by defense counsel, expert examinations may be recorded by a court reporter and/or videographer, thus generating another source of expert evidence. Common reasons plaintiff counsel chooses to generate this evidence include ensuring an expert accurately recorded and reported examination events; use of the recording, in whole or in part, in a mock trial; monitoring and evaluating potential problems to be addressed (e.g., a plaintiff's manner that jurors may find offensive); and assessing the expert's presentation and potential impact of testimony on triers of fact.

Of course, there are other reasons lawyers record expert examinations. A creative use of this evidence occurred in a case in which a quadriplegic plaintiff was undergoing a life care plan examination in his home and his four-year-old daughter crawled into his hospital bed and snuggled with his inert body. This poignant, unscripted moment captured visceral nonmonetary damages evidence more powerful than testimonial and documentary evidence. This video evidence facilitated plaintiff counsel's closing arguments on pain and suffering damages.

Recordings of exams are generally considered plaintiff counsel's work product and are rarely used at trial. Intended use of a recorded expert examination at trial requires advance disclosure and, in this event, becomes available to defense counsel.

Reports

Arguably, reports are the most salient evidence experts create. The fountainhead from which their testimony emanates, reports disclose expert opinions that presage evidence that may in whole or in part survive to bear witness to triers of fact and forewarn opposing parties of essential information that may threaten to disprove their cases.

Chapter 3 addressed the preparation of reports of vocational rehabilitation evaluations, and Chapter 6, similarly, presented details necessary to assemble a life care plan. Opposing lawyers' evaluation of evidence these reports communicate will be multifactorial. Often this evaluation is contingent on input from the lawyers' counterpart experts, who will propose incisive, technical questions intended to despoil their counterparts' assessments and testimony. All experts should anticipate this inquiry beyond the cross-examination opposing counsel would independently pose.

An expert's report serves as a touchstone to provide testimony—both during a deposition and at trial and possibly during a Daubert hearing. It should incorporate all opinions an expert can reasonably foresee presenting to a trier of fact; otherwise, opposing counsel may move to strike portions of testimony offering new opinions, insulated from fair scrutiny that is mandated by rules of evidence.

Shahnasarian (2012, 2015) elaborated on plaintiff and defense lawyers' perspectives in evaluating and challenging experts' damages assessments. Babitsky, Mangraviti, and Melhorn (2004) detailed recommended expert witness considerations when writing and defending reports.

Discussion on Expert Proffers

Excerpts from a vocational expert's report of a vocational rehabilitation evaluation, featured in the next section, provide insight on how the expert documented the bases for his conclusions and eventual opinions after a pretrial hearing, during trial before jurors, and during a proffer at trial in the absence of jurors. The court ruled in a pretrial hearing that the defense expert was prohibited from testifying at trial about the plaintiff's preinjury drug history and preinjury and postinjury criminal history, reasoning that the prejudicial effects of this testimony would undermine the probative value as it pertained to issues in dispute.

Following direct and redirect examination at trial, the expert responded during a proffer, in the absence of the jury, to questions the court ruled could not be presented in open court to elicit testimony deemed inadmissible. Testimony elicited through the proffer preserved for defense counsel the reasons it deemed excluded testimony relevant to its case.

If counsel believes a verdict is egregiously unjust due to a trier of fact's inability to consider relevant testimony elicited via a proffer, such testimony can, with the expert's report, provide compelling evidence of an appeal's merits. Regardless of whether experts anticipate their opinions and/or supporting evidence will be admissible, they must analyze and cite in their reports every scintilla of evidence relevant to referral questions, noting the relevance in addressing issues in dispute. For reference, in the noted case, defense counsel realized a favorable verdict and did not pursue an appeal of the jury's verdict.

Briefly, the plaintiff was 19 years old and working as a stevedore when he experienced an injury, which defense counsel asserted he caused. He subsequently underwent multiple orthopedic operations and complained of ongoing symptoms through the time of his trial.

Although the plaintiff did not resume his preinjury stevedore job, he secured other employment before he founded a business offering residential rules compliance services.

In sync with the Earning Capacity Assessment Theory detailed in Chapter 2, the expert's analysis integrates key case facts (including the plaintiff's negligence in two work-related injuries, criminal history, and record of illicit drug use) with evidence generated during the expert's evaluation (including a clinical interview, test results, and factors both limiting and facilitative to vocational rehabilitation) to arrive at earning capacity opinions. The expert also places in perspective the plaintiff's guilty plea of selling prescribed narcotic medication, postinjury, with its relevance to injury-related life care planning damages the plaintiff claimed.

Sample Excerpt from Expert Report

Summary and Impressions

I. Mr. Strawe reported he completed high school in 2008 and attended one semester of college at Gulf Coast State College. Longshoreman Peninsular, Inc., hired him on February 6, 2009, and his service with the organization continued through the time of his March 21, 2016, industrial accident. Employment records indicate Mr. Strawe had an earlier industrial accident in August 2013, associated with his negligence while operating a forklift. An investigation conducted in conjunction with his 2016 accident determined he was not wearing required protective equipment, which "was the cause of this accident." At the time of his March 21, 2016, accident, Longshoreman employed Mr. Strawe as a stevedore (DOT #922.687-090). Based on my understanding of his job responsibilities, he performed unskilled/semiskilled, heavy/very heavy exertion tasks. He earned $17 per hour. Internal Revenue Service wage and income transcripts indicate Mr. Strawe's wages were $44,654 in 2014 and $37,410 in 2015. Mr. Strawe did not return to work with Longshoreman after his March 21, 2016, accident. His postaccident employment included jobs as a forklift operator with M&M Stores and a helper/laborer with A&B Roofing before he founded Pyramid Portfolio in February 2020. Mr. Strawe has since pursued self-employment as a compliance officer, contracted by Community Management Associates. He assessed his former stevedore job exceeds his capacity. Based on my understanding of his work as a compliance officer, Mr. Strawe performs unskilled/semiskilled tasks that require light exertion. He described a seasonal component to his compliance officer work, noting his service is in greatest demand between the months of May and September. At the time of my clinical interview (June 7, 2021), Mr. Strawe told me he had work extended to him seven days per week, 12 hours per day. Due to his long work hours and demand for his business's services, Mr. Strawe reported, he hired an employee the week before my exam. His contracted compliance officer services yield compensation of $22 per hour, and he pays his employee $20 per hour. He advised me his contracted work does not offer employee benefits. Mr. Strawe indicated his current job responsibilities as a compliance officer are within his capacity, and he expressed his belief that sedentary work and "anything light duty" remain within his capacity. The career plans Mr. Strawe presented included earning a business degree and "expanding my company to get other properties." He had been working up to 84 hours per week until recently, when he hired his first employee. Since he began Pyramid Portfolio, Mr. Strawe conveyed, he has not pursued alternate employment, and he denied planning to do so. He is in the exploration/establishment phase of his career development.

II. Mr. Strawe's medical history before his March 21, 2016, work-related accident is significant from a vocational rehabilitation perspective. At age 14 or 15, he underwent a right meniscus repair operation; he said his knee "completely healed" afterward. Records document longstanding weight management challenges Mr. Strawe has had. Additionally, he was diagnosed with attention deficit disorder before his 2016 accident. Mr. Strawe's preaccident and postaccident record of antisocial behavior and criminal history—including a postaccident arrest on April 1, 2016, for battery and a September 5, 2018, arrest for selling oxycodone pills and driving with a suspended license—is also noteworthy. Mr. Strawe has had periods of work absence while incarcerated. His records also include evidence of illicit substance abuse. Along with personality factors previously noted (please refer to the Results of Testing section of this report), such factors likely would have had implications for Mr. Strawe's career development in the absence of his March 21, 2016, work-related accident.

III. After his March 21, 2016, work-related accident, Mr. Strawe underwent operations on his right knee (April 26, 2016), left shoulder (July 7, September 6, and November 23, 2016), and right ulnar nerve (July 20, 2017). Mr. Strawe testified in April 2021 that his back pain began in 2018, and a January 2020 record documents complaints of lower back pain after Mr. Strawe was helping a family member move and he overexerted himself lifting a piece of furniture. Dr. Roche, the surgeon who operated on Mr. Strawe's right knee and performed two of his left shoulder operations, released him to return to light-duty work without restrictions on September 19, 2016. Dr. Golding, the surgeon who performed Mr. Strawe's third left shoulder operation (November 23, 2016) and right ulnar nerve operation (July 20, 2017), determined he reached maximum medical improvement with no assignable impairment on September 20, 2017. The surgeon revised his assessment on May 21, 2018: he assigned a five percent upper extremity/three percent total body permanent impairment rating assignable to his patient's left shoulder. "The patient continues to be employable without restrictions," Dr. Golding stated in his last treatment record. Records indicate Dr. Roche had not treated Mr. Strawe after January 2017. Interestingly, however, on April 7, 2021, Dr. Roche performed an "independent medical examination" of Mr. Strawe. Dr. Roche prognosticated several surgeries and other interventions, now as an expert witness, for his former patient. The most recent record I reviewed is a report of an independent medical examination Dr. Melchoi performed on May 20, 2021. In his report, Dr. Melchoi provided his assessment and disagreement with many rehabilitation interventions Dr. Roche proposed. I consulted with Dr. Melchoi on June 10, 2021, to further discuss Mr. Strawe's future treatment needs secondary to his March 21, 2016, work-related accident. Mr. Strawe told me his primary problems relate to his left shoulder, lower back, and right knee. His left shoulder is his most painful body part; however, he conveyed his lower back pain can rival what he feels in his left shoulder. Presuming Dr. Golding's September 20, 2017, and May 21, 2018, assessments are correct, within a reasonable degree of vocational rehabilitation probability, Mr. Strawe would have been able to resume his former stevedore job during that timeframe. By extension, this would have negated any claim of loss of earning capacity. Mr. Strawe testified in 2020 that he does not have work restrictions from his physicians. I asked him about physician restrictions during my June 7, 2021, clinical interview. He referenced Dr. Golding and said, "He just told me to lift what I can." No specific physician-imposed restrictions were presented. Clearly, Mr. Strawe has been capable of ongoing employment, and my prognosis for his career development is good.

IV. Mr. Strawe possesses several assets facilitative to his career development. He is a cognitively intact, younger individual nearing his 31st birthday. He demonstrated average intelligence (Full Scale IQ = 103) on testing administered during my exam. His performance was commensurate with my estimate of his preaccident level of intellect. Mr. Strawe demonstrated strengths on measures of mental organization and planning and attention to detail. From a functional perspective, Mr. Strawe estimated he can safely lift and carry 20 to 40 pounds. His fine motor functioning is intact. He denied having problems with cervical spine movements. He told me he can perform pushing/pulling movements with his left arm "if I keep a short range." He operates a motor vehicle daily. The records I reviewed included surveillance of Mr. Strawe on three consecutive days in May 2021—most recently, approximately three weeks before my June 2021 clinical interview. Mr. Strawe used no adaptive aids and performed several activities—including pumping gas into his Jeep, driving his Jeep and various golf carts, and climbing onto a trailer on which he affixed straps to fasten golf carts—uninhibitedly and without any overt manifestations of pain. My observations also included Mr. Strawe initiating, without any apparent problems, the full range of neck movements, bending his waist, bimanual tasks, and various movements below the waist. His gait was normal. He denied having problems with fatigue. Mr. Strawe assessed he does not need mental health treatment. On a personal level, I found him pleasant and likable. He has education, training, work experience, and transferrable skills as previously delineated. Additionally, Mr. Strawe has demonstrated the capacity to perform several jobs after his postaccident reentry to the workplace, along with the capacity to launch a successful business.

V. Of course, Mr. Strawe's postaccident record of criminal behavior is disadvantageous to his career development. He did not respond to my question about whether he had been selling oxycodone and/or Adderall, which is quite relevant to his claim for future rehabilitation needs specified in a life care plan his lawyer commissioned. Mr. Strawe apparently failed to complete his pretrial intervention program after his arrest for possession of drug paraphernalia and cocaine in February 2016, and he is currently participating in a pretrial intervention program for his arrest and admission that he was guilty of possession of oxycodone and unlawful use of a two-way communication device. Mr. Strawe's criminal record is relevant in his claim for damages related to loss of earning capacity and to the need for future treatment.

VI. As noted earlier, my prognosis for Mr. Strawe's career development is good. At a minimum, from an exertional perspective, he has been capable of pursuing sedentary, light, and light/medium exertion work, and, if Dr. Golding's assessment is accurate, he has the capacity to resume employment comparable to his former stevedore job. Mr. Strawe had the option of reapplying for his former employment with Longshoreman but chose not to pursue it. Of note, his two work-related accidents during his tenure in which he was found to be negligent might have been an impediment to his reemployment with Longshoreman. If he were to so choose, Mr. Strawe could pursue retraining and enhance his skillset, increasing his earning capacity. It is impressive that he founded a business in February 2020, has more work made available to him than he can independently perform, hired an employee, and is able to generate a profit from his employee's labor. I am not aware of a reason Mr. Strawe would be unable to expand his business in line with the objectives he presented to me. Of course, he could also search for a job and reenter the workplace as an employee—an option he advised me does not interest him because he plans to maintain and expand his business, Pyramid Portfolio. If he reentered the workplace as an employee, however, within a reasonable degree of vocational rehabilitation probability, Mr. Strawe would be able to secure employment offering compensation and employee benefits comparable to those he earned while an employee of Longshoreman. Examples of occupations for which Mr. Strawe would be competitive include crane operator, no-touch truck driver, property manager, and warehouse manager. If he continues to choose to pursue self-employment, in addition to expanding his business via hiring additional employees and securing new accounts, he could pursue part-time employment during months he noted to be slower in demand for compliance officer services; this presumes that he would have time to pursue part-time employment. I appreciate that Mr. Strawe has had periods, postaccident, when he was unable to work and earn wages; however, a claim of loss of earning capacity associated with his March 21, 2016, work-related accident is unmerited.

VII. Again, I had the benefit of a consultation with Dr. Melchoi, an orthopedic surgeon, on June 10, 2021. With his assistance, I am preparing a life care plan intended to address future care needs Mr. Strawe acquired secondary to his March 21, 2016, work-related accident. Records from Pain Relief Express and Mr. Strawe's criminal records are important to consider when assessing his future care needs. These records have implications related to symptom magnification, manipulation, secondary gain, antisocial behavior, and noncompliance, among other things. Mr. Strawe refused to answer questions I posed to help elucidate these matters.

Deposition Testimony

Beyond discovering evidence an expert could present to a trier of fact, depositions provide opposing lawyers opportunities to test and hone their cases. They allow lawyers to, among other things, evaluate the likely impact experts will make on triers of fact and test theories that could cause expert opinions to falter.

Before the event, lawyers deposing experts prepare through several means including reviewing expert reports from the pending case and from prior cases; obtaining through subpoena expert case files, which subsequently undergo extensive review; consulting with their retained, similarly qualified experts to review opinions and provide deposition questions intended to challenge the opposing expert's opinions; gathering intelligence through the litigation community about the expert, including fodder for impeachment; and conducting relevant case-specific research that could debunk an expert's credibility and/or opinions rendered.

The preparation experienced experts undergo before their depositions begins well before the event: they anticipate the adversarial processes to which they and their opinions will be subjected, and they employ sound methodologies as espoused throughout *The Valuation of Monetary Damages in Injury Cases* and other such works to avert and minimize challenges to the integrity of their opinions. Predeposition attorney/expert conferences can help to ensure an expert has relevant updated records and information that might have evolved since an expert's last review; these conferences also enable the parties to express their views on a case and address differences with opposing viewpoints.

Immediately before their depositions, experts review reports they authored and related key documents. Their preparation also includes complying with subpoena duces tecum requirements, which specify documents a witness must bring to a deposition or provide before it.

Generally, experts perform best when giving deposition and/or other testimony by complying with three cardinal guidelines:

- Listen carefully to questions posed and answer them fully and succinctly. Avoid expounding on an answer beyond the limits of a question asked unless supplemental information is necessary to provide context and/or support.
- Avoid being lured into subject matter beyond one's expertise.
- Remain an objective witness, providing evidence derived from the science of one's profession.

At the conclusion of a deposition, experts express their right to read or waive reading of a court reporter's transcript memorializing the event, which includes verbatim expert testimony. Accepting the right to read is recommended. In addition to allowing an expert to correct errors a court reporter might have made, this review provides an opportunity to create an errata sheet clarifying testimony and adding supplemental, relevant information an expert might have inadvertently omitted.

For instructional purposes, following are excerpts from a deposition during which testimony could have been more effectively presented. The case involved a plaintiff who experienced a cerebrovascular accident and pursued a claim of medical malpractice, prompting the need for his counsel to retain a life care planner. Facts in the evidence included a remote history of the plaintiff's cocaine use, and defense counsel advanced their theory that this caused the plaintiff's cerebrovascular accident, attempting to exonerate their client's alleged malpractice as the cause of life care plan damages.

Plaintiff's life care planner, a nonmedical doctor who held a doctorate in rehabilitation counseling and certifications as a rehabilitation counselor and life care planner, underwent aggressive interrogation during his deposition that blurred the lines between his scope of expertise and questions better posed to a medical doctor. While reviewing the following testimony, readers are encouraged to focus on how it diverges from the three testimony guiding principles summarized earlier. An analysis of defense counsel's questioning and the deposition testimony follows the transcript excerpt.

1	**Q**	You had a many-hour conversation with Mr. Drake, right?
2	**A**	I did.
3	**Q**	And did you ask him about drug use?
4	**A**	I did not.
5	**Q**	Drug use is an important factor for you as a life care planner?
6	**A**	Yes.
7	**Q**	Cocaine use is an important factor for you as a life care planner, is it not, also because it is associated with intracerebral bleeds, isn't that true?
8	**A**	I would defer to a medical doctor for that.
9	**Q**	Well, I realize that. But as a life care planner, don't you understand that there are certain ramifications of cocaine use, and intracranial bleeding is one of them?
10	**A**	According to the literature I have seen—

11 Q It's literature that you—

12 A But I would not diagnose that.

13 Q I understand that.

14 A OK.

15 Q Literature is important, though, for you from the standpoint of rehabilitation, because cocaine use has a number of features with it that can result in massive life care plan implications, correct?

16 A Correct.

17 Q And you never asked that question, right?

18 A I did not.

19 Q Even though there were depositions on the subject in this case, right?

20 A It was—the only record that I had of cocaine use was remote, from 2010.

21 Q So you did see that, though, and you didn't ask him questions about cocaine use?

22 A I did not.

23 Q Didn't it occur to you—did you understand, at least, that cocaine use is associated with intracerebral hemorrhages?

24 A I did not see a pattern of abuse. I saw, you know, just one incident.

25 Q I didn't ask you that, though. Did you know that cocaine use was associated with brain bleeds?

26 A Yes.

27 Q You saw that he had a brain bleed, right?

28 A Yes.

29 Q That's why he had a stroke in 2018, right?

30 A That is correct.

31 Q And you never put together that the brain bleed might have some association with cocaine use for ten years, right?

32 A I did not have any record that he was using cocaine for ten years. I have one incident of the 2010 preinjury record where he tested positive. I did not see— in any of his examinations for his truck driver renewal license, no drug test came back positive.

33 Q OK. All right. Now, as far as drug use, cocaine use is associated not only with medical conditions. Let me just ask you if you're familiar, as a life care planner, with what kind of ramifications it has. It can cause strokes, right?

34 A There is reassurance that states that, yes.

Opposing counsel doggedly pursued several lines of related questioning during the deposition, including an unproven undertone of sustained plaintiff cocaine use, accusation that the deponent was remiss in not fully evaluating evidence of the plaintiff's drug use habits, and innuendo that cocaine use was a probable cause of the plaintiff's cerebrovascular accident—all central defense theories. The expert witness likely could have preempted and avoided much of this inquiry, along with not providing evidence to further fuel the defense theories, through more thoughtful and careful responses.

For instance, a better, truthful answer to the question posed on line 5—*Drug use is an important factor for you as a life care planner?*—instead of *Yes* would have been *Possibly. Your question is quite broad, and in this case there was insufficient evidence for me to conclude any impact on the life care plan I prepared.*

The life care planning expert provides an appropriate response on line 8 when indicating he defers to a medical doctor for an opinion on the association between intracerebral bleeds and cocaine use. This response sets a needed boundary in which the expert demarcates his area of expertise. Thereafter, however, the expert retreats and succumbs to answering questions he is at best marginally qualified to answer when the defense lawyer continues to badger him, posing medically based questions to which a medical doctor is clearly better qualified to respond.

Rather than maintaining a posture that the types of questions posed are beyond his expertise and better posed to a medical doctor—responses that could have ended the ongoing line of inquiry—the life care planning expert made admissions beyond those he was qualified to make. These include knowledge of a body of literature that could undermine the life care plan he prepared (lines 15 and 16), of cocaine being associated with brain bleeds (lines 25 through 28), and of brain bleeds potentially causing strokes (lines 33 and 34). A better answer to these types of questions would have been a terse *I defer to a qualified medical expert on that matter, as it is beyond my expertise and scope of what I was retained to address.*

Trial Testimony

Trial testimony offers the sole occasion afforded to experts for an in-person audience (a term loosely used during the COVID-19 pandemic era, as experts more frequently present their testimony remotely or via video recordings) with the trier of fact they envision throughout their assessments. Most cases settle well before reaching a courtroom. Nonetheless, from the onset, skilled experts frame their work and the evolution of their opinions mindful of how the many interested parties will evaluate, judge, and assimilate their efforts en route to their terminal presentation to triers of fact.

Many events and dynamics interplay before an expert's opinions can advance to presentation at trial. Parties adverse to experts will attempt to eradicate, erode, or otherwise encroach on the expert's methods and ability to develop opinions. They attempt to accomplish this latter aim, for example, through objecting to the types of questions an expert can pose, the duration of an exam, types of tests that can be administered, and examination logistics. Before trial, they persist in efforts to filter potential evidence not favorable to their case via new objections—such as asserting portions of opinions should be stricken or limited—on which the court will again rule.

Chapter 11 elaborated on opposing counsel's bases for objections when attempting to strike or limit evidence admitted at trial. Indeed, an opinion must survive much scrutiny and resistance before an expert can present it to those empaneled to reconcile disputed issues. The process associated with this scrutiny sometimes transmutes the opinion; nonetheless, experts are obligated to comply with expressing their opinions in accord with court rulings.

Triers of fact evaluate experts and their messages on many unconscious, idiosyncratic levels, based on their frames of reference and subjective reality. Their educational backgrounds, work histories, socioeconomic status, and myriad personal experiences, for example, will influence how they perceive and process evidence presented. Experts do not have an opportunity to tailor their message to each trier of fact; however, they can ensure their message is organized and coherent, communicating their qualifications to render an opinion, describing methods employed, and summarizing findings to help triers of fact evaluate expert opinions in their frames of reference.

Appendix O features sample questions prepared in advance of an expert's testimony. The questioning begins with a review of the expert's education, training, and experience, thus establishing the expert's qualifications to provide the upcoming testimony and offer opinion evidence for the trier of fact's consideration. Questions follow about methods used to perform the evaluation, leading to the expert's development of opinions. This line of questioning provides the foundation for the expert's presentation of substantive opinions—in this case, opinions pertaining to both vocational rehabilitation and life care plan matters. Questions for redirect examination are also included. Attorneys adapt their redirect examination questioning in accord with their analysis of opposing counsel's attacks on their expert and the need to rehabilitate damage opposing counsel might have inflicted.

More discussion on the three parts of an expert's trial testimony follows. Mangraviti, Babitsky, and Donovan (2016) provided guidance on the finer points of presenting testimony beyond the scientific bases and structural elements enumerated herein.

Direct Examination

Direct examination provides lawyers opportunities to present their experts' opinions to the audience of triers of fact and opposing counsel, eliciting expert evidence they weave into their arguments. Lawyers, of course, know in advance their experts' opinions; the parties customarily consult before trial to discuss the best way to present testimony in the context of other relevant evidence—both supportive of and contrary to an expert's opinions.

As indicated in Appendix O, direct examination typically proceeds through three sequential parts: qualifying questions, methodology, and substantive questions; these questions were used with the sample expert report presented earlier in this chapter. This logical order first informs those who evaluate expert evidence what qualifies an expert to provide opinion testimony before explaining how opinions were developed and, finally, the substance of those opinions.

Effective direct examination features key activities and processes undertaken during an analysis, including those described in Part II and Part III of *The Valuation of Monetary Damages in Injury Cases*. This dialogue provides the necessary foundation to communicate that opinions presented were carefully derived through the application of relevant standards of practice and the science of the expert's profession. The importance of building this foundation cannot be overstated, as opposing counsel will scrutinize opportunities to attack the bases of an expert's opinions during cross-examination.

Direct examination culminates in the proffering of an expert's opinions. Plainspoken, understandable communication facilitates this presentation.

The tenor of testimony apt to resonate with laypeople has three hallmark qualities: objectivity, credibility, and sincerity. Experts communicate these qualities beyond their words: their demeanor and presentation transmit nonverbal elements that encase their testimony, affirming the message put forth deserves careful weighing and consideration.

Additionally, effective experts avoid dry, esoteric, and overly technical explanations. They present their testimony in relatable terms, connecting science with matters at hand.

Demonstrative aids—such as poster boards featuring portions of a life care plan—can facilitate an expert's communication of complex, important points.

Cross-Examination

Cross-examination provides defense lawyers opportunities to challenge the integrity of an opposing expert's opinions, as well as to elicit and appropriate any testimony that supports their case. Their attacks focus on any scintilla of perceived weakness, including those evaluated while contemplating fodder for Daubert challenges (please refer to Chapter 11). Alleged biases, inconsistencies, methodological flaws, ethics infractions, noncompliance with standards of practice, lack of knowledge of key information, reliance on erroneous or unreliable information, monetary gain . . . creative, resourceful lawyers' attempts to impeach and discredit opposing experts and their opinions know no bounds.

Experts, of course, anticipate questions opposing counsel will likely pose to discredit them and their opinions. Invariably, unanticipated questions surface. The best answers are earnest, grounded in facts and science. Regardless of the propriety of opposing counsel's tactics, effective experts maintain their composure and professionalism. They remain resolute and avoid sarcasm and condescending posturing, making reasonable concessions and standing their ground when bullied.

Further, seasoned experts listen carefully to questions and answer only the question asked. They do not respond as advocates beholden to their retention sources and do not go beyond answering a question posed unless necessary to provide context and/or clarity.

A case in which a plaintiff lawyer retained a vocational expert and a life care planning expert, while a defense lawyer retained a single expert to perform both roles, serves to illustrate the finesse an expert employed while responding to a superficially benign cross-examination question. While interrogating the defense expert, plaintiff's counsel asked whether his retention was akin to "one-stop shopping," since the expert was performing dual roles. The defense expert responded: "No. I think a better way to conceptualize my work in this case is to recognize that I have specialized training and expertise that qualifies me to provide expert analysis and testimony in two subspecialty areas: vocational rehabilitation and life care planning."

Expanding on this example, embedded in opposing counsel's use of the word "shopping" is the notion the expert's opinions can be bought; obviously, this parlays into the lawyer's attempt to characterize the expert witness as an untrustworthy hired gun. When compounded as the term "one-stop shopping," opposing counsel cheapens and denigrates the value the expert offers to those entrusted with weighing his testimony. The expert's response provided necessary context, dismantled opposing counsel's attempt to undermine him, and reinforced his value as an expert witness. In effect, the expert turned the tables on the lawyer—an outcome that facilitates experts' efforts to preserve the integrity of their opinions.

Davies (1993) discussed cross-examination from a lawyer's perspective. Among those who authored books addressing cross-examination from an expert's perspective are Babitsky and Mangraviti (1999, 2003), Brodsky (2004), and Deutsch (1990).

Redirect Examination

Redirect examination provides retaining lawyers an opportunity to clarify their expert's testimony following opposing counsel's attack and to undo/mitigate any harm cross-examination may have caused. Sage experts use it to restore aspects of their testimony that opposing counsel might have distorted and/or taken out of context and to provide needed supplemental testimony to reinforce key points made during direct examination.

To remain viable in influencing decision-makers, experts' direct examination testimony must survive any damage opposing counsel inflicted during cross-examination. Redirect examination, conducted under the supportive auspices of the retaining lawyer, provides the final occasion when experts can defend their opinions and assert their validity.

Experts do not have an opportunity to confer with their retaining lawyer between cross-examination and redirect examination. Retaining lawyers carefully tend to their expert's testimony they believe opposing counsel might have tarnished during cross-examination and decide on testimony needing redress. Accordingly, they typically conduct redirect examination via a combination of open-ended questions and very specific questions. Open-ended questions allow an expert latitude in providing a technical explanation supporting opinions challenged, and very specific questions elicit terse responses that integrate facts in evidence and other information the retaining lawyer desires to impart in support of overarching case objectives.

Unless redirect examination testimony convinces those weighing it that cross-examination did not effectively damage an expert's testimony, they likely will dismiss points made during direct examination. Further, unremedied damage cross-examination inflicted on an expert's testimony can harm other aspects of a party's case. While redirect examination is typically much shorter than direct and cross-examination, the importance of its outcome cannot be overstated.

Trial Exhibits

Before a trial, experts identify exhibits they propose to use in conjunction with their testimony. Of course, like all evidence potentially presented to a trier of fact, proposed exhibits must submit to opposing counsel's scrutiny and challenges akin to those discussed earlier.

When contemplating trial exhibits, experts should reflect on technical aspects of their testimony that may be better understood when supplemented by a visual presentation. Exhibits that summarize testimony can also reinforce a message communicated orally, serving to make it more memorable and impactful.

Quite often, life care planners use as exhibits poster boards presenting information contained in their life care plans. They then refer to the boards while testifying. In the same vein, boards that summarize life care plan cost information serve as exhibits that promise to remain in the trier of fact's memory beyond the expert's exit from the witness chair. Shahnasarian (2016) discussed experts' use of exhibits to supplement their testimony.

Billing Records

Opposing lawyers invariably inquire about expert fee schedules, billing practices, and amounts paid in pending and other cases. They often pursue this line of inquiry in excruciating detail, attempting to elicit information that helps extrapolate compensation an expert generated in both a pending case and historically—especially as it relates to retentions/compensation derived through work with the current retention source.

It is not uncommon for inquiries about fees to consume more than 30 minutes of questioning during depositions—especially with experienced witnesses who bill at high rates. Through requests for records and subpoenas preceding expert testimony, opposing counsel can secure information on expert fees in advance of an expert's testimony; accordingly, experts should anticipate very specific questions about their billings, including:

- Retainer agreements including amounts billed for varying services, how fees are billed against retainers, and dates retainers are received with respect to a retaining source's disclosure of the expert as a witness

- Fee schedules (along with specific questions including whether the expert bills for travel time, for example, to a courthouse) and any variances in them depending on factors that include retention sources and volume of work
- Date-specific billings of services and specific services provided; opposing counsel will seek to discover/expose, among other things, any potentially plausible excessive/duplicative billings and findings they could cast to suggest an expert has been extravagant, such as costs billed for first-class air travel or a luxury hotel in conjunction with conducting an examination
- Total amounts paid, outstanding fee balances, and anticipated additional expenses
- Historical billings with a specific retention source
- Total amounts of earnings as an expert witness

In sum, experts should anticipate opposing counsel's interrogation will include extraordinarily detailed inspection and evaluation of their billing records, motivated to advance theories—regardless of whether facts support them—that an expert witness has ill-gotten motives in providing opinion testimony and represents the antithesis of an objective expert witness. This inquiry, like many other impeachment initiatives lawyers propound, aims to impress on triers of fact experts' high pay, implying this predisposes them to give biased opinions to please their retaining sources. Variations on this theme depend on factors that include opposing counsel's aggressive nature and availability of evidence to support their assertions, spawning thinly veiled portrayals of opposing experts as untrustworthy mercenaries who deserve being discounted and/or dismissed, which is a common refrain in lawyers' characterizations of opposing experts.

Since most experts' bills amount to far greater amounts than what most triers of fact earn, opposing lawyers seek to shock triers of facts' consciences by focusing on expert fees, subliminally implying a clandestine quid pro quo agreement between experts and their retaining sources. Namely, testimony favorable to the retaining source is contingent on payment. Straightforward handling of fee questions can help dispel such illegitimate subterfuge.

Experts should place their fees in proper perspective. For example, consider being confronted with a question laced with half-truths such as "So, to summarize what you did, you were paid $X,XXX to come to the conclusion that my client's crash caused her no loss of earning capacity, correct?" A proper retort along the following lines is in order: "No. I was compensated for all the work I did necessary to conduct my analysis in this case. That included reviewing volumes of records, conducting a lengthy clinical interview, administering a battery of tests, consulting with two physician specialists, and conducting necessary labor market research. I then wrote two detailed reports that describe my work and present my opinions, and I submitted to a two-hour deposition you requested. For all of my work I was paid $X,XXX. You are correct in stating that, after performing my analysis, I concluded your client's accident did not affect her earning capacity."

Additionally, in most cases, it is best to deal with fees openly during direct examination at trial. This helps to communicate expert witnesses, like all professionals, charge for their services and their fee schedules are proportionate to the expertise they offer and commensurate with prevailing billing practices in their specialty.

Further, preempting questions pertaining to expert fees by addressing them during direct examination can desensitize triers of fact on the matter when opposing counsel persists in this questioning during cross-examination, belaboring and attempting to sensationalize amounts billed. After a retaining lawyer has explicitly dealt with fee questions in short order during direct examination, opposing counsel risks triers of fact perceiving additional lengthy, detailed inquiry on this matter as a redundant harangue, offering little value to the jurisprudence process and threatening to diminish the attacking lawyer's stature.

Experts should alert the trier of fact about any irregularities that contributed to higher-than-normal billings, such as an examinee arriving very late or no-showing for one or more appointments, extraordinary time associated with travel to examination locales, and/or complex, time-consuming research undertaken to perform an analysis. In the end, experts who factually, matter-of-factly, and nondefensively deal with fee questions fare best.

Evidence Extraneous to a Case at Hand

An expert's entire history—both related and unrelated to litigation—is subject to being discovered, examined, and aggressively challenged by opposing counsel. Most often, opposing lawyers troll reports and testimony an expert provided in prior cases because they are readily obtainable, in search of evidence that suggests the expert provided opinions inconsistent with those rendered in a pending case with similar facts. They use any apparent discrepancies they detect to confront and discredit the expert.

Likewise, lawyers can easily locate professional publications an expert has authored. Their aims in reviewing these documents are similar: to secure evidence supporting a theory that an expert published findings and statements inconsistent with testimony currently given—despite similar underlying factual bases.

Even an expert's affiliation with professional associations can become a point of attack. A well-credentialed, published, and respected leader in industry associations was accused during a deposition of holding a "vanity membership" in an organization that required only a fee and self-report of credentials meeting entry requirements.

Evidence and information opposing lawyers introduce extraneous to issues directly related to a pending case invariably intend to defame an expert. The less-than-subtle attacks, laced with smears as discussed throughout this chapter, aim to cast the expert in a range of unflattering lights: liar and/or bought-and-paid-for hired gun at one limit of the range and, at the less toxic limit of the range, sloppy and/or incompetent professional.

If an expert does not recall specific details of a prior case that opposing counsel alleges had a fact pattern similar to a pending case and implies the expert is now giving inconsistent testimony, the expert should clearly state the lack of memory. Further, if the questioning persists at any level, the expert should request to review documents supporting a lawyer's allegations. Quite often, such attacks derive from opposing counsel misrepresentations and half-truths and can be countered by showing that fact patterns in a prior case are distinguishable from those at hand. Experts should not capitulate to sleight-of-hand, unproven accusations perpetuated by those motivated to destroy their credibility.

Like all work experts perform, they fare best when dealing factually, objectively, and nondefensively with the myriad challenges they encounter. When necessary and appropriate, they provide proper context to explain and place in correct perspective distorted opposing counsel representations. Again, when indicated, experts also make appropriate concessions.

Internal Consistency of Evidence Presented

Lawyers constructing and evaluating damages claims consider how individual claim elements logically fit when integrated and juxtaposed. While they consider evidence favorable and adverse to their case, the overall picture they frame invites, among other questions, the following: *When considering claimed damages in view of admissible evidence, will the claim make sense to those entrusted with evaluating it?*

Inconsistencies in facts, opinions, testimony, and arguments advanced among expert witnesses providing evidence on the same side of an argument can seriously derail a lawyer's efforts to prove damages. Competent opposing lawyers cull through details of all expert evidence, including how experts' evidence and testimonies interrelate, and seek mismatches in their opponents' attempts to advance a seamless damages presentation. Internally inconsistent expert evidence a party attempts to present usually becomes magnified and trumpeted as reasons why triers of fact should dismiss arguments relying on inconsistent expert testimony.

The question just posed also has significant implications for damages experts: their assessments evaluate, among other things, whether damages they determined correlate with other damages assessments their retention source commissioned. An example of inconsistent assessments arose in a case in which plaintiff's counsel retained one expert to perform a vocational rehabilitation analysis and one expert to prepare a life care plan. The case is described next.

Briefly, a carpenter in his mid-30s sustained bilateral lower extremity injuries requiring two operations on each limb, and an orthopedic surgeon determined he likely would require three future surgeries. The plaintiff made an unsuccessful postinjury attempt to return to his carpenter job; however, experts retained by counsel on both sides agreed the plaintiff remained capable of performing sedentary and light exertion work.

During an exam plaintiff counsel's vocational expert conducted, the plaintiff expressed an interest in retraining and reentering the workplace as a welder. The expert provided other alternatives including ones more traditionally associated with sedentary/light work. The plaintiff rejected these suggestions and enrolled in a welding training program. In an update report, the vocational expert wrote:

> I appreciate Mr. Smith is interested in welding, and I respect his selection of an occupation he believes will best suit his vocational profile. My concerns about his career development as a welder pertain to his accessibility to work opportunities, the compatibility between job requirements and his residual capacities, and his work life longevity. Frankly, I recommend Mr. Smith consider less physically demanding employment along the lines I described in my June 18, 2021, report. The additional information I have had an opportunity to consider has not changed the opinions I previously rendered.

In the meantime, the plaintiff's life care planner prepared a plan that included the three prognosticated surgeries, related treatment, and a home health aide to provide caregiver services two hours per day for the remainder of the plaintiff's life. The independently conducted vocational damages and life care plan damages assessments, enjoined by the overarching umbrella claim of damages sought, are at odds. Specifically, it is counterintuitive and inconsistent that a person who voluntarily believes himself capable of competitive employment as a welder requires a home health aide two hours per day.

Rather than independently defending the damages claims—namely, addressing the vocational damages claim apart from the life care plan damages claim—defense counsel capitalized on the internal inconsistencies of the two damages opinions, juxtaposing and conflating them while posing questions such as:

> Why would someone who claims to have the types of limitations Mr. Smith claims to have voluntarily retrain for a profession he would be unable to pursue? Maybe he's not as disabled as he alleges? Why does someone who voluntarily pursues a physically demanding profession such as welding need a home health aide two hours a day?

The metaphor of a three-legged stool seems apropos. In this case the stool, aiming to support the weight of an overall damages claim, rests on legs that include one representing future medical care, a second representing earning capacity damages, and a third representing pain and suffering. If one leg buckles, the damages claim collapses. This case demonstrates how two disjointed components of a claim seeking to support an overall demand for damages can threaten the effort.

A Final Word on Presenting Evidence

Even highly experienced experts encounter a plethora of challenges from opposing counsel during their journeys to gather and evaluate evidence necessary to formulate opinions. The challenges continue to mount through the time triers of fact can hear and consider the filtered, oft-maligned opinions that survive the human-made, adversarial, judicial tests to which experts submit while performing their work. Arguably, experienced experts encounter more roadblocks to performing their work than nascent experts, since the potential damage they can inflict threatens greater consequences to their opponents' cases.

Such is the justice system by which experts, lawyers, and all its other stakeholders abide. Holy Scripture imparts the ultimate guidance on providing testimony in Colossians 4:6: "Let your conversation be always full of grace, seasoned with salt, so that you may know how to answer everyone" (Holy Bible, 1989).

APPENDIX A

Sample Boecher Interrogatory Questions

IN THE CIRCUIT COURT OF THE
EIGHTH JUDICIAL CIRCUIT
IN AND FOR ALACHUA COUNTY,
FLORIDA CIVIL DIVISION

JOSEPH JOHNSON, CASE NO.: 2018 CA 2651
Plaintiff,
v.
PROPERTY AND CASUALTY INSURANCE COMPANY,
Defendant.

_____/

DEFENDANT'S RESPONSE TO PLAINTIFF'S FIRST SET
OF BOECHER INTERROGATORIES

COMES NOW, Defendant, PROPERTY AND CASUALTY INSURANCE COMPANY, by and through its undersigned counsel and pursuant to Florida Rule of Civil Procedure 1.340 and responds to Plaintiff's First Set of Boecher Interrogatories and states the following in support thereof.

CERTIFICATE OF SERVICE

I HEREBY CERTIFY that on this ___ September, 2020, a true and correct copy of the foregoing was filed with the Clerk of Alachua County by using the Florida Courts e-Filing Portal, which will send an automatic e-mail message to the following parties registered with the e-Filing Portal system: [contact information for] Attorney for Plaintiff, Joseph Johnson, and [contact information for] Attorney for Defendant, PROPERTY and Casualty Insurance Company.

Counsel for Defendant PROPERTY AND
CASUALTY INSURANCE COMPANY
Address
Telephone
Facsimile
Primary e-mail:
Secondary e-mail:
By: attorney name

_____

ATTORNEY NAME
Florida Bar No.: 012345

1960.0986-00/20803377

SPECIFIC RESPONSES AND/OR OBJECTIONS

1. Please state your name, address, and, if you are answering for someone else, your official position.
RESPONSE:

2. State the name, title, employer, employment address, employment description, and relationship to Defendant of any individual assisting in the answering of these interrogatories and the information reviewed to arrive at earlier answers.
RESPONSE:

3. Please identify each person whom the Defendant expect(s) to call as an expert witness at trial and relative to each, please state the following:
   a. the expert's full name, professional address, and specialty field or expertise;
   b. a description of the information furnished to each expert to date for his or her consideration and review;
   c. the subject matter upon which each expert is expected to testify;
   d. a summary of facts and opinions to which each expert is expected to testify;
   e. the basis for each opinion;
   f. a description of any exhibits to be used as a summary of or support for the expert's opinion;
   g. the qualifications of the expert, including a list of all publications authored by the witness within the preceding ten (10) years (please provide a current curriculum vitae);
   h. a listing of any medical/professional literature that the witness has read in connection with this case;
   i. a listing of books in the witness's possession or control that relate to the subject matter of the witness's testimony; and
   j. a listing of the professional journals to which the witness has subscribed during the past four (4) years.
RESPONSE:

4. As to each such expert referred to earlier, please state the following:
   a. the compensation for such service; and
   b. the expert's general litigation experience. (Include the percentage of work performed for plaintiffs and defendants; an approximation of the portion of the expert's involvement as an expert witness, based on the percentage of hours or percentage of earned income derived from serving as an expert witness.) See FRCP 1.280(b).
RESPONSE:

5. As to such expert referred to earlier, please state the amount of fees paid to the expert witness by this Defendant's or their insurance company or any agent, servant, or employee of this Defendant's insurance company for each of the preceding three years. See *Allstate v. Boecher*, 733 So. 2d 993 (Fla. 1999).
RESPONSE:

6. As to each such expert referred to earlier, please state the amount of fees paid to the expert witness by this Defendant's law firm or any agent, servant, or employee of this Defendant's law firm for each of the preceding three years. See *Allstate v. Boecher*, 733 So. 2d 993 (Fla. 1999).
RESPONSE:

7. As to each such expert referred to earlier, please identify the cases in which the expert has rendered opinions (either formally or informally) for the Defendant or insurance company nationally in the preceding three years, being sure to include the following:
   a. all cases in which each expert has rendered an opinion;
   b. the names of Plaintiff's counsel;
   c. the name of defense counsel;
   d. the court before which each case was pending, if filed;
   e. the style of the case, if filed;
   f. the date of the deposition testimony of the expert;
   g. the date of the trial testimony of the expert;
   h. whether the expert has a copy of the transcript of the deposition and/or the trial testimony; and
   i. a summary of the expert's opinion.

See *Allstate Insurance Co. v. Hodges*, 855 So. 2d 636 (Fla. Ct. App. 2nd Dist. 2003); *Vazquez v. Martinez*, 175 So. 3d 372 (Fla. Ct. App. 5th Dist. 2015); *Orkin Exterminating Co. v. Knollwood Properties, LTD*, 710 So. 2d 697 (Fla. Ct. App. 5th Dist. 1998); F.S. 390.608(2); and FLA. R. CIV. P. 1.280.

RESPONSE:

8. As to each such expert referred to earlier, please identify the cases in which the expert has rendered opinions (either formally or informally) for the Defendant's law firm nationally in the preceding three years, being sure to include the following:
   a. all cases in which each expert has rendered an opinion;
   b. the names of Plaintiff's counsel;
   c. the name of defense counsel;
   d. the court before which each case was pending, if filed;
   e. the style of the case, if filed;
   f. the date of the deposition testimony of the expert;
   g. the date of the trial testimony of the expert;
   h. whether the expert has a copy of the transcript of the deposition and/or the trial testimony; and
   i. a summary of the expert's opinion.

See *Allstate Insurance Co. v. Hodges*, 855 So. 2d 636 (Fla. Ct. App. 2nd Dist. 2003); *Vazquez v. Martinez*, 175 So. 3d 372 (Fla. Ct. App. 5th Dist. 2015); *Orkin Exterminating Co. v. Knollwood Properties, LTD*, 710 So. 2d 697 (Fla. Ct. App. 5th Dist. 1998); F.S. 390.608(2); and FLA. R. CIV. P. 1.280.

RESPONSE:

9. As to each such expert referred to earlier, please state whether the expert advertises in any type of periodical, journal, or otherwise concerning his or her profession and, if so, please state the following:
   a. the name of such periodical, journal, or other publication;
   b. the dates the advertisement(s) appeared; and
   c. the nature of the advertisement(s).

If you are willing to do so without the necessity of a Request to Produce, please attach copies of any and all such advertisement(s).

RESPONSE:

10. Identify specifically (by plaintiff's name, case number, court, and defense attorney's name and address) the most recent case where the information described in 3a earlier was requested from you or anyone acting on your behalf (including your insurance company) regarding the identified expert(s).
RESPONSE:

11. Please state when each expert was retained in this case by Defendant; each expert's hourly rate; any additional charges for each expert; and the amount of money each expert has been paid to date on this case.
RESPONSE:

12. Please state the number of times and identify the case style in which each of Defendant's experts have testified in trial in the last five years as a treating physician and/ or on behalf of the Plaintiff.
RESPONSE:

13. Please identify (by the number of cases, the case names, the case number, and the dates) any automobile accident case where a lawsuit was filed since the year 2014 where each of Defendant's experts opined that the Plaintiff from that case sustained a permanent injury as a result of the automobile accident being sued for. If there are none, then state none.
RESPONSE:

VERIFICATION

Under penalties of perjury, I declare that I have read the foregoing response to Plaintiff's First Set of Interrogatories and that the facts stated in it are true, to the best of my knowledge and belief.

> PROPERTY AND CASUALTY INSURANCE
> COMPANY
> BY:
> NAME

STATE OF FLORIDA
COUNTY OF _____

The foregoing instrument was acknowledged before me by means of physical presence or online notarization, this _____ day of _____ «current_date_yyyy» who is personally known to me or who has produced _____ as identification.

(SEAL)

> Notary Public—State of Florida
> My Commission Expires:

APPENDIX B

Sample Engagement Letter

May 12, 2021
Sammie Dillon, Esq.
Hacks, Choppe & Dillon
9th Floor
555 N.E. 5th Street
Miami, FL 33134
Re: Eugenia Levy

Dear Ms. Dillon:

Thank you for your interest in my rehabilitation consultation services. The areas I am most frequently asked to address relate to vocational rehabilitation and future medical needs (e.g., developing a life care plan or treatment plan). My curriculum vitae is attached.

Vocational Rehabilitation Evaluations

My typical procedures in conducting a vocational rehabilitation evaluation include first reviewing pertinent records, detailed later, and then conducting a comprehensive examination. Examinations typically have two parts: a clinical interview, which is billed at my hourly rate, and the administration of various tests, which is billed at my hourly testing rate. The entire examination generally takes approximately six to eight hours to complete. Of course, examinees are extended opportunities to take breaks as needed, including a lunch break.

I conduct my examinations in English. If English is not the examinee's first language, please notify me in advance and arrange for an interpreter. Examinations that involve an interpreter typically take longer, and I will need to plan accordingly. I also attempt to accommodate examinees as requested (e.g., seating preferences, special equipment needs, meal service). Again, please notify me in advance regarding any special needs an examinee may require.

While I prefer to conduct examinations in my office, I can, if necessary, conduct them at alternate locations. Please provide as much advance notice as possible for out-of-town examinations. Members of my staff provide assistance as needed, including assistance with test administration.

Typically, I prefer to review the following records before an examination:

- Complaint
- Questions and responses to interrogatories
- Deposition of plaintiff
- Depositions of physicians
- Depositions of employers
- Medical records (including reports of diagnostic evaluations, hospital admission and discharge reports, operative reports, assessments, and available preinjury medical records)
- Psychological records
- Employment records
- School records
- Tax returns and any other earnings records
- Medical bills
- Criminal records
- Military service records
- Surveillance records
- Social Security Administration records

Please send records **at least 7 to 10 days** before the scheduled examination date. **We prefer paper copies of records** rather than flash drives or discs. Please **do not send two-sided copies,** as this only serves to slow the sorting process. Please also send **full page version deposition transcripts only, not condensed.**

Of course, I am also interested in new records that may have been generated or discovered after my examination. Please keep me abreast of any information concerning my areas of inquiry.

My clinical interview generally requires three to four hours to complete. During this time, examinees will be asked detailed questions about presenting problems, treatment, limitations and capabilities, medical history, activities of daily living, mental health status, educational background, work history, and vocational rehabilitation. **WE WILL NOT ACCOMODATE A VIDEOGRAPHER AND/OR COURT REPORTER IF WE ARE NOT NOTIFIED 48 HOURS IN ADVANCE.**

Vocational Testing

The vocational tests I prescribe, and members of my staff usually administer, typically require between three to four hours for an examinee to complete. While I generally vary the battery of tests prescribed depending on the examinee's background, the tests I administer assess mental functioning (including intelligence testing and aptitude testing), occupational interests, and personality. The following tests are among those I frequently prescribe:

- Wahler Physical Symptoms Inventory
- Beck Depression Inventory
- Wide Range Achievement Test—Revision 3
- Shipley Institute of Living Scale
- Multidimensional Aptitude Battery
- Minnesota Multiphasic Personality Inventory—II
- Self-Directed Search—Form R or Form E
- Purdue Pegboard
- Strong Interest Inventory

- Campbell Interest and Skills Inventory
- Wechsler Memory Scale
- Wechsler Adult Intelligence Scale—3
- Grooved Pegboard

Life Care Planning

If significant future care is anticipated for an examinee, I will, on request, after conducting a rehabilitation evaluation, prepare a life care plan that identifies future care needs and associated costs. My practice in developing a life care plan is to consult with other practitioners who have treated or evaluated the examinee to obtain comprehensive, multidisciplinary recommendations for future care. Of course, I add my recommendations when appropriate. Then I determine future care costs by contacting and eliciting pertinent information from service providers and researching medical billing codes, vendors, and other generally accepted sources. Finally, I assemble a life care plan and invite those who have made recommendations to review and comment on it. Suggested revisions are subsequently incorporated, and, if necessary, I will author additional drafts.

Following the examination, I provide a written report of my rehabilitation evaluation that includes opinions on vocationally relevant and general rehabilitation matters. I usually complete this report within 30 business days after my examination; an expedited report will be provided upon request.

Retention

Along with a signed retention agreement, I require a nonrefundable retainer in the amount listed later to consummate a retention. I do not consider myself engaged until my office has received a signed retainer with the appropriate retention fee, which is applied to services and expenses as accrued. **Please make the check payable to Career Consultants of America.**

Trial Testimony and Court Appearances

If a trial date is scheduled in Hillsborough County or an adjacent county and I am notified that my testimony is anticipated, I require a trial deposit in the amount listed later. The trial deposit is applied toward preparation for trial, trial appearance and testimony time, travel, and other costs incurred. I do not require a deposit for court appearances. I will reserve four hours, charged at the hourly rate listed later, to ensure availability on the appointed scheduled trial or hearing date. If I need to block a full day, I bill at my daily rates listed later to ensure availability upon notification of anticipated testimony at other locales. I enforce the following cancellation policy: **No cancellation fee if scheduled trial or hearing is cancelled 48 hours or more in advance, but the full time reserved for scheduled trial or hearing is charged if cancelled less than 48 hours in advance.**

Invoicing

I bill semimonthly. Payment is due upon receipt of an invoice and shall be directed to Career Consultants of America at its office in Tampa. **Please make the check payable to Career Consultants of America.** Expenses incurred with services, such as travel expenses, are billed at cost. My office charges 15 cents per page for any pages requested to be copied from email, and we charge our cost for any out-of-office copying. Written authorization must be received before out-of-office copying.

If payment is not received within 30 days of receipt of invoice, interest shall accrue at the rate of one and one-half percent per month until paid. If it becomes necessary to retain the services of an attorney to collect any balance due, you agree to pay all attorney fees associated with the collection of the account. You also agree to waive trial by jury. Legal proceedings resulting from nonpayment of fees related to my services shall be conducted in Hillsborough County, Florida.

Fee Schedule Effective July 1, 2019	Michael Shahnasarian, PhD
Retainer *Retainer is to be sent with the signed retention agreement*	$3,500
Hourly Rates *Standard 30-day report turnaround*	$595
Expedited Hourly Rates *Less than a 30-day report turnaround*	$795
In-Office Assessment Cancellation Fee *No cancellation fee if 48 hours or more in advance; one-half if cancelled 24 to 48 hours in advance; full fee if notified less than 24 hours in advance. Our office is closed Saturday and Sunday; therefore, the 24–48-hour notice does not include Saturdays, Sundays, and holidays.*	$4,000
Hourly Testing Rate *Includes testing instruments, test administration, scoring, and test interpretation*	$350
Out-of-Office Assessment and Daily Rate *Includes testing instruments, test administration and scoring, test interpretation, consultations, trial testimony, and other related services. Fees are capped regardless of the length of the business day. Full daily rate is charged if assessment is cancelled less than 48 hours in advance. Our office is closed Saturday and Sunday; therefore, the 48-hour notice does not include Saturdays, Sundays, and holidays.*	$7,500 per day

Weekend Examination Rate	$8,500 per day

Life Care Plans	
Standard	$ 7,000
Catastrophic	$10,000
International	$12,000

Expedited Rates for Life Care Plan	Additional $1,000
Less than a 30-day report turnaround	

Deposition Fee	$695 per hour
We reserve two hours and bill a minimum of this amount in advance of the deposition, unless a request for more or less time is received. No cancellation fee if 48 hours or more in advance; one-half if cancelled 24 to 48 hours in advance; full fee if notified less than 24 hours in advance. Our office is closed Saturday and Sunday; therefore, the 24–48-hour notice does not include Saturdays, Sundays, and holidays.	

Trial Deposit	$1,000
Applied to services and costs	

Rates remain in effect for six months from the date a retainer is received.

Since a full day is commonly required to conduct a rehabilitation examination, compliance with scheduled appointments is important in the management of my practice. Consequently, I enforce the following cancellation policy for scheduled examinations: In-office—No cancellation fee if the appointment is cancelled 48 hours or more in advance; one-half of the examination fee is billed for appointments cancelled 24 hours to 48 hours in advance; and the full fee is billed for no-show appointments and appointments cancelled less than 24 hours in advance. Out of office—No cancellation fee if appointment is cancelled 48 hours or more in advance and full daily rate fee if appointment is cancelled less than 48 hours in advance. Our office is closed Saturday and Sunday; therefore, the 48-hour notice does not include Saturdays, Sundays, and holidays.

Zoom Videoconferencing

As an accommodation due to the COVID-19 pandemic and social distancing recommendations, I am offering to conduct my examinations via Zoom videoconferencing—both the clinical interview and the testing portions. I request that third parties attending my examination sit behind the examinee and refrain from participating in any way.

Videographers

If a videographer plans to be present at my examination, please notify my office at least 48 hours in advance so that I can prepare for the necessary logistics. **WE WILL NOT ACCOMODATE A VIDEOGRAPHER AND/OR COURT REPORTER IF WE ARE NOT NOTIFIED 48 HOURS IN ADVANCE.** Only certified videographers will be permitted in my offices, and I require disclosure of the videographer's name 48 hours in advance of the examination. He/she should arrive between 15 and 30 minutes before the appointed examination time to set up equipment and to prevent any delay in the examination. No interference by the videographer during the examination will be tolerated, and the videographer may not remain in the examination room during the examination. I require that cameras be unattended once setup is completed. Further, the videographer should not interact with the examinee, my staff members, or other patients in my office. If a tape requires changing, a member of my staff should be notified, as the videographer is prohibited from entering the interview room independently or unescorted. At least ten minutes advance notice should be provided for changing a videotape.

Career Consultants of America, Inc., maintains a position statement on video recording of examinations. Please notify us at least 48 hours in advance of a scheduled examination if a videographer is anticipated to be present at an examination, and I will provide a copy of my position statement. I expect videographers to be made aware of and to fully comply with my video-recording requirements.

Animals

Animals are NOT allowed in my office building. This includes but is not limited to service dogs and emotional support animals/pets. If an evaluee desires to bring an animal to my exam, I must be notified in advance, and the exam must be set up offsite, such as at a hotel conference room that accommodates animals.

Mobile Telephone Usage

Examinees should limit the use of mobile telephones to breaks. Mobile telephones must be set to vibrate mode or turned off completely while examinees are in my office. An examinee who uses a mobile telephone or other communication device during an examination to obtain input or information specific to the examination risks invalidating the examination; this will be noted in the file.

Location

Career Consultants of America, Inc., is located in a busy, suburban area of Tampa that is approximately 15 minutes northeast of Tampa International Airport. Three restaurants are less than one-half block from my office, and many others are within a short drive.

I do not permit smoking or soliciting in my office. Since examinations commonly last up to a full day, please do not bring children to my office if they are not involved in the examination. Guests in my office are asked to remain in designated areas and respect the privacy of others they may encounter.

Please sign the attached form and return it to my office with the appropriate retainer fee. Of course, let me know if you have any further questions. I look forward to working with you.

Sincerely,

Michael Shahnasarian, PhD
Certified Life Care Planner #258
Certified Rehabilitation Counselor #3701
Certified Vocational Evaluator #58360
Certified International Psychometric Evaluator #985
Licensed Psychologist PY5644
Fellow, American Psychological Association
Fellow, International Academy of Life Care Planners
Fellow, National Career Development Association

Enclosures
Dictated by Dr. Shahnasarian and signed in his absence to avoid delay.

APPENDIX C

Sample Retention Agreement

TAX ID No. 592699058
May 12, 2021
Sammie Dillon, Esq.
Hacks, Choppe & Dillon
9th Floor
555 N.E. 5th Street
Miami, FL 33134
Fax: (305) 555-xxxx
Re: Eugenia Levy

Terms: Due upon Receipt
To retain Dr. Shahnasarian, the nonrefundable fee indicated below is required. Dr. Shahnasarian is not officially retained until my office has received a signed retention agreement and retainer fee. This fee will be applied to services as they are provided. Promulgation of Dr. Shahnasarian as an expert before official retention is misrepresentation. **Please send retention payment no later than five days after receipt of signed retention agreement and make the check payable to Career Consultants of America. Placing Dr. Shahnasarian on your witness list will also be considered a contract of retention, and the nonrefundable retention fee will be expected.**

Retainer Fee	$3,500.00
Balance Due	$3,500.00

Career Consultants of America INC.

Retention Agreement

I would like to retain Dr. Shahnasarian's services in the case of Eugenia Levy.

I have read Dr. Shahnasarian's letter dated May 12, 2021, and I understand that signing this agreement shall acknowledge the fees associated with retaining Dr. Shahnasarian, including a $3,500.00 nonrefundable retainer fee, in connection with this matter and that I and my client shall be jointly and severally responsible for the payment of all fees as explained in the letter.

Signature _____ Date _____

Print complete name and title

Firm

Mailing address

Telephone no.

Email

APPENDIX D

Sample Letter Explaining Copying Costs and Associated Logistics

June 24, 2021
Cheryl A. Frank, Esq.
Dumas and Frank, P.A.
555 NE Maple Street
Locanto, FL 35001
Re: Linda Sky Higginbotham, MD

Dear Ms. Frank:

This letter is regarding the taking of my deposition in the above-styled matter, scheduled for September 29, 2021, 4:00 p.m., via Zoom. I await the link.

My policy in scheduling a deposition is to block off two hours of time. If you anticipate that less or more time will be required, please notify my office in advance, and I will attempt to accommodate you. I require a prepayment in the amount of $1,390.00, 48 business-day hours before the onset of the deposition. I will not make myself available for the deposition unless I receive this prepayment by September 27, 2021. If the deposition exceeds the allotted time, I will bill you for this additional time at an hourly rate of $695.00. In the event the deposition is rescheduled to another location, you will incur an additional fee for travel time at the $695.00 billing rate. Costs associated with any copies that you may request during or after the deposition will also be billed to you. Pursuant to Florida Administrative Rule FS-64B8-10.003, costs of reproducing medical records shall not be more than $1.00 per page.

Shipping is accomplished via FedEx (or Choice, if local) for the amount we are charged. The cost for our personnel to handle copying is billed at $50.00 per hour. *Note:* We require a purchase order or authorized signature before beginning the copying process.

Concerning my cancellation policy, I will provide you with a full refund if the deposition is cancelled 48 business-day hours in advance. **If the deposition is cancelled between 24 business-day hours and 48 business-day hours in advance, I will refund one-half of your prepayment. No refund will be provided for cancellations less than 24 business-day hours before the scheduled deposition.**

Please contact me if you have any questions.

Sincerely,

Michael Shahnasarian, PhD
President

Dictated by Dr. Shahnasarian and signed in his absence to avoid delay.

APPENDIX E

Sample Affidavit Stating the Need for a Vocational Rehabilitation Examination

IN THE CIRCUIT OF THE ELEVENTH JUDICIAL COURT
IN AND FOR RADIANT COUNTY, FLORIDA

James F. Falfano

CASE NO.: XXXXXX
DIVISION: A

vs.

Midtown Grocers, LLC

_____/

AFFIDAVIT OF MICHAEL SHAHNASARIAN, PhD,
IN SUPPORT OF METHODOLOGY NORA TAO APPLIED
IN HER VOCATIONAL EVALUATION OF JAMES F. FALFANO

1. I have been a practicing vocational rehabilitation expert in the Tampa Bay area since 1986. In terms of my professional background, I earned a doctorate in counseling psychology at Florida State University in 1985 and have amassed 3,000 hours of residency work and continuing professional education concentrating in career development, vocational psychology, and vocational rehabilitation. I am a certified rehabilitation counselor, certified vocational evaluator, nationally certified career counselor (Board Emeritus), and licensed psychologist. A copy of my curriculum vitae appears in Exhibit A.

2. During the past approximately 25 years, my work as a vocational rehabilitation expert has included testifying in approximately 50 depositions and ten to 15 trials per year. Exhibit B identifies testimony I have provided as a vocational expert during the past three years.

3. I have known Nora Tao professionally during the past approximately 20 years. I have never had a personal or business relationship with her, and I have no plans to this end.

4. At Ms. Tao's request, I reviewed a report of a vocational evaluation she performed on James F. Falfano. My review and analysis of Ms. Tao's work led me to several conclusions, including:

   A. Ms. Tao appropriately applied the vocational assessment model and methodology detailed in my peer-reviewed textbook, *Assessment of Earning Capacity (4th Edition)*. The book, and earlier versions of it, have been favorably peer-reviewed since 2001 in industry publications that include *The Rehabilitation Professional, Estimating Earning Capacity, Journal of Forensic Economics, The Rehabilitation Counseling Bulletin,* and *Foundations of Forensic Vocational Rehabilitation*. Further, the methods outlined in *Assessment of Earning Capacity* have ubiquitously been determined to be in harmony with standards of practice in the vocational rehabilitation profession.

   B. Ms. Tao obtained sufficient facts on Mr. Falfano's background including education, work history, past earnings, and physical condition. Relevant governmental and local statistical data on wages for the geographical areas in question were also obtained. Additionally, Ms. Tao appropriately researched and identified open positions for Mr. Falfano.

   C. Ms. Tao's procedures and methods complied with standards of practice in the vocational rehabilitation profession, enabling her to apply the science of the profession to arrive at reasonably probable expert opinions.

STATE OF FLORIDA
COUNTY OF HILLSBOROUGH

Sworn to or affirmed and signed before me on _____ by Michael Shahnasarian, PhD

_____
NOTARY PUBLIC OR DEPUTY CLERK

_____
(Print, type, or stamp commissioned name of notary or clerk)

___ Personally known
___ Produced identification
___ Type of identification produced _____

APPENDIX F

Sample Guidelines on Video Recording a Vocational Rehabilitation Exam

Position Statement on Recording Rehabilitation Evaluations
Career Consultants of America, Inc.

Overview

Career Consultants of America, Inc., has been performing rehabilitation examinations for cases in litigation for approximately 35 years, and we respect the right of evaluees to have the exam recorded. Additionally, we do not object to others besides the evaluee attending the examination, provided they do not interfere with the exam process and conduct themselves professionally. This includes not participating in the exam, remaining out of eyesight of the evaluee while the examination is in progress, and minimizing equipment-related interruptions. Further, we request that any third party present abide by the 2007 Florida 3rd District Court ruling that states, "A third party's presence, particularly an attorney's presence, during a medical exam is premised upon a requirement that the third party will not interfere with the doctor's examination" (*Bacallao v. Dauphin*, 963 So. 2d 962).

The exams we conduct do not involve a physical exam. Information is gathered through a clinical interview and various forms and tests evaluees complete. Evaluees may take breaks as needed, and our staff will make every attempt to accommodate evaluees' requests.

If a videographer will be present, we require at least 48 hours' advance notice. No additional fee will be charged for video recording. Use of video recordings must be limited to the instant litigation.

We will make every attempt to accommodate those who record an exam. This includes cooperating with videographers to make tape changes and to configure the exam room as requested to enhance recording quality. Especially close coordination is necessary during portions of the examination that involve the administration of timed tests; those recording the exam are not permitted to interrupt the process to change tapes or for any other reason. We request that only certified videographers perform the video recording.

If an exam is video recorded, the videographer does not have the right to include the evaluator or our staff in the video-recording picture without obtaining prior consent. Audio recording via the video recording is permissible, and we will cooperate with wearing microphones and/or using other audio-recording equipment; however, the video recording is to be of the evaluee only, similar to the type of recording made when a deposition is video recorded. Our rationale for this policy includes the following:

1. The evaluator and assisting staff have a right to privacy. We will fully cooperate with recording efforts that provide an avenue to verify that information reported comports with actual information and events that occurred—namely, by allowing all audio recording and video recording of the evaluee.
2. The psychological literature is rife with empirical studies and analyses describing how any outside observation affects an event (e.g., Hawthorne Effect, Yerkees-Dodson Law). A camera aimed at or recording a nonconsenting professional attempting to perform his or her job, in particular, adds unnecessary stress, compromises the individual's ability to perform her or his job, and is a violation of privacy.

In-Person Examinations

In-person exams occur in our office or at other locations such as a hotel conference room, court reporter's office, evaluee's home, or hospital/rehabilitation facility. Again, we do not object to others attending, provided they do not interfere with the exam process and conduct themselves professionally. This includes not interfering with the operations of our practice outside the examination room, respecting the privacy of patients and other individuals in our office, remaining in designated areas within our office when not in the exam room, and interacting professionally and courteously with our staff.

Our office space is limited, and our staff will need to ensure an appropriate exam room and additional space is available to accommodate any extra individuals in attendance. Additionally, we request that the videographer arrive at the examination site before the exam to set up equipment, so as not to delay the exam schedule.

We prefer that the camera used to video record exams be unattended. Further, during portions of the examination when an evaluator or assisting staff member is not present with the evaluee (e.g., during standardized testing), we require that outside parties, likewise, remain out of the exam room. Of course, the unattended camera can continue running. Additionally, we request the camera remain stationary, such as on a tripod, in the exam room, without panning or other movement.

The videographer's equipment should be consolidated in and confined to the exam room and not placed in any of our office's public areas. We serve patients who have disabilities, many of whom have mobility problems and use adaptive equipment, and we must also ensure their safety. Further, the videographer should remain in designated areas while in our office: the reception area, recording area, and hallways necessary to access the exam room.

Videoconference Examinations

Videoconference exams are conducted via Zoom or another platform viable for remote interviewing and testing. We request that the evaluee use either a desktop or laptop computer and avoid using a mobile phone or tablet computer. Please ensure the evaluee participates in the videoconference in a place with sufficient bandwidth to optimize transmission and to avoid screen freezes and audio problems.

Further, if our office is not hosting the remote videoconference, the evaluee must provide a way for the test administrator to display testing materials, such as the "screen share" option in Zoom or the equivalent in other videoconferencing apps/programs. To ensure standards of testing protocols, we emphasize the need for evaluees to minimize all extraneous distractions such as household/phone interruptions, third-party interference, dogs barking, etc.

Career Consultants of America, founded in 1986, is a respected practice that takes pride in its tradition of professionalism and courteous service to evaluees, patients, and others. We request that outside/remote guests and exam attendees comply with the guidelines this position statement sets forth to ensure the recording of an exam will respect the rights of all involved and maintain the integrity of our examinations.

Revised February 2021. Career Consultants of America, Inc.

APPENDIX G

Sample Client Intake Form

Client Intake Form

Please complete this form in detail. If needed, ask for assistance. Not all questions will apply; write *N/A* (not applicable) if questions do not apply. Use the back of pages, if necessary.

BACKGROUND INFORMATION (please print)

First:	Middle:	Last:
Address:		
City:	State:	Zip:

Date of Birth: _____ Age: _____

Home Phone: _____ Mobile Phone: _____

E-mail Address: _____

How did you get to the exam? _____

_____

_____

Do you have a valid driver's license? ___yes ___no _____

_____

Do you have doctor-advised driving restrictions? ___yes ___no _____

_____

_____

_____

_____

Do you have problems with driving? ___yes ___no _____

_____

_____

_____

_____

_____

Employment day of accident/incident _____

_____

_____

_____

_____

_____

Date of Accident/Incident _____

Please generally describe accident/incident. _____

_____

Did you strike your head?   ☐ Yes ☐ No ☐ Don't Know

Did you lose consciousness? ☐ Yes   ☐ No   ☐ Don't Know   If so, for how long?

_____

_____

Currently, the examinee reported experiencing the following problems they attribute to the incident:

1 _____

2 _____

3 _____

4 _____

5 _____

6 _____

7 _____

8 _____

9 _____

10 _____

11 _____

12 _____

13 _____

14 _____

15 _____

16 _____

17 _____

18 _____

19 _____

20 _____

What problems listed above, if any, did you have **before** the accident/incident? _____

_____

_____

_____

_____

_____

_____

_____

_____

_____

_____

_____

_____

_____

Check problems with mental functioning you have had **since** the accident/incident.

- ☐ No Problems
- ☐ Memory Problems
- ☐ Concentration Problems
- ☐ Mental Alertness Problems
- ☐ Speech Problems
- ☐ Attention Span Problems
- ☐ Other

Please provide examples of any problems you checked, and describe what you believe is causing these problems:_____

Race: _____ Are you: ☐ Right-handed ☐ Left-handed ☐ Both

Birthplace:_____

_____

_____

_____

_____

Citizenship:_____

First Language (if not English): _____

Height: _____ **Current** Weight: _____ Weight **Before** Injury/Incident: _____

Has your weight been stable? If not, please explain_____

_____

_____

_____

Describe your efforts to control your weight: _____

Marital Status _____

_____

_____

Date Married _____ Number of times married? _____

Spouse/Partner's Name (first and last) _____

Spouse/Partner's Date of Birth _____

Spouse/Partner's Job Title and Place of Employment _____

_____

Names, ages and gender of your children: _____

Are your spouse/partner and/or children healthy and without disabling problems? If not, describe disabling problems and/or special needs:_____

_____

_____

If you lived somewhere other than your current home at the time of the accident or incident, explain your reasons for relocation: _____

_____

_____

_____

_____

_____

_____

Describe your home (*Example: 2,000 sq. ft. 2-story house, 800 sq. ft. apartment, 2-bedroom mobile home, etc.*): _____

_____

_____

_____

_____

What is the size of property your home is located on?_____

How long have you lived at your present home? _____

_____

_____

Do you: ☐ rent your home or ☐ own your home?

Do you plan to leave your home? Explain if necessary:_____

_____

Describe any changes you have made to your home due to disabilities (*Example: installed ramp, installed handrails, etc.*): _____

_____

_____

_____

_____

_____

_____

Is access within your home limited? If so, how? _____

_____

_____

_____

Do you have any pets or farm animals? If so, please describe:_____

How many people live with you and how are they related? (*Example: John Smith, Uncle, 72 years old*)_____

_____

_____

At the time of your injury/incident, what was your job title? _____

Employer _____ Rate of pay _____

Present employment status: ☐ Employed ☐ Unemployed ☐ Disability

Present job title:_____

Present employer: _____

Present rate of pay:_____

PHYSICAL CONDITION AND MEDICAL INFORMATION

List each surgery you had **before** the accident/incident. Continue on back.

Type of Surgery	Year or Age	Surgeon

Of the problems you acquired as a result of the accident/incident, what is your primary problem(s)? Please explain._____

_____

_____

_____

_____

_____

_____

_____

_____

_____

If you are having problems with pain, please identify the affected body part(s) and rate your pain intensity using a 0-to-10 scale (zero indicates no pain and 10 represents the worst pain possible):

Body Part in Pain	Pain Intensity on 0-10 scale	Activities/conditions that worsen pain

List the doctors treating you for problems associated with the accident/incident in question:

Doctor's Name	Specialty	Last Appointment

List the doctor, examination date, and reason for your last doctor's visit.

_____

List scheduled appointments with medical professionals and note the reason.

_____
_____
_____
_____
_____
_____

List each surgery you had **after** the accident/incident. Continue on back if needed.

Type of Surgery	Year or Age	Surgeon

Are you scheduled for surgery?   If so, list the surgeries and dates, and also list recommended/ anticipated surgeries.

Type of Surgery	*Date of Surgery*	*Surgeon*

Check each type of treatment you have had **since** the incident/injury:

- ☐ Physical Therapy
- ☐ Occupational Therapy
- ☐ Speech Therapy
- ☐ Massage Therapy
- ☐ Aquatic Therapy
- ☐ Psychotherapy/Counseling
- ☐ Group Therapy
- ☐ Biofeedback
- ☐ Other: _____

- ☐ Cognitive Rehabilitation
- ☐ Acupuncture
- ☐ Chiropractic Treatment
- ☐ Prescribed Home Exercise
- ☐ Pain Management
- ☐ Specify any injections you have had:

_____

_____

_____

_____

_____

_____

List **current** treatment/therapy. _____

_____

_____

_____

_____

_____

List all adaptive aids you use (*Example: cane, TENS unit, lumbar support pillow, traction device, cervical collar, etc.*). _____

_____

_____

_____

_____

_____

_____

List your medications. Continue on back of this page if necessary, or provide a medication list, if available.

Medication	Purpose	Dosage/Frequency

Which medications listed above were you taking **before** the accident/incident?

_____

Describe side effects caused by medication:_____

_____

_____

Have you taken medication within the last 24 hours? If so, describe. _____

_____

_____

PHYSICAL CAPACITIES

How much weight can you safely lift and carry? _____

_____

_____

Has any physician advised a lifting restriction? If so, explain. _____

_____

What problems, if any, do you have when lifting?_____

_____

Check all problems below that you have. Describe your problems in the space provided.

- ☐ Turning head to right _____
- ☐ Turning head to left _____
- ☐ Bending head forward_____
- ☐ Leaning head back _____

- ☐ Use of right hand or arm _____
- ☐ Use of left hand or arm _____

- ☐ Use of right foot or leg_____
- ☐ Use of left foot or leg _____

OTHER PROBLEMS: _____

_____

_____

_____

_____

_____

_____

_____

_____

Physical, Everyday Activities

Walking _____

Standing _____

_____

_____

_____

Sitting _____

_____

_____

_____

Bending at waist _____

_____

Squatting _____

Kneeling/getting on hands/knees _____

Climbing stairs _____

_____

Pushing/pulling _____

Reaching with right hand _____

Reaching with left hand _____

Handling _____

Gripping right hand _____

Gripping left hand _____

Right-arm extension overhead _____

Left-arm extension overhead _____

Right-arm extension horizontal _____

Left-arm extension horizontal _____

Driving _____

In general, how many minutes/hours are you able to do the following without resting or overexerting yourself?

Walk_____

Stand_____

Sit_____

Drive _____

What type of transmission does the vehicle you drive have? ☐automatic   ☐manual
Have changes been made to it? _____

_____

How often do you drive? _____
Do you have a parking placard for persons with disabilities? _____
Describe any problems you have with driving:_____

_____

Do you have trouble with the following? If so, explain.
Balance***   N   Y   _____

_____

_____

_____

Hearing   N   Y   _____

_____

Vision   N   Y   _____
Smell   N   Y   _____
Taste   N   Y   _____
Breathing   N   Y   _____
Bowel/bladder   N   Y   _____

_____

_____

_____

Dental Health   N   Y   _____
Fatigue   N   Y   _____

_____

_____

***Have you fallen since the accident/incident? Describe any falls.

_____

_____

_____

_____

_____

_____

*** Have you had medical care or additional problems because of falls? Please explain.

_____

_____

Check all conditions that worsen your problems, and explain your difficulty.

<u>Explanation</u>

☐   Outdoors   _____

☐   Cold Temperatures   _____

☐   Hot Temperatures   _____

☐   Dampness/High Humidity   _____

☐   Changes in Barometric Pressure _____

☐   Noise   _____

☐   Vibration   _____

☐   Fumes, dusts, gases   _____

List all restrictions your physicians have advised.

Physician	Restrictions

ACTIVITIES OF DAILY LIVING

Preincident/preaccident difficulty sleeping? _____

_____

Do you have problems sleeping? _____ If so, what is the cause? _____

_____

_____

_____

_____

_____

Did you have difficulty sleeping before your accident/incident? If so, explain. _____

_____

How many hours do you now sleep per night? _____

What time do you usually go to sleep? _____

_____

_____

_____

What time do you usually wake up? _____

Do you nap? If so, explain. _____

_____

List all sleep aid medications you take. _____

_____

Do you have problems with nightmares? If so, how frequently? Describe any repeated themes.

_____

_____

_____

_____

Do you have problems with grooming or self-care? If so, describe.

_____

_____

_____

_____

_____

Are Caregiver Services provided?

_____
_____
_____
_____
_____
_____
_____
_____
_____
_____
_____
_____
_____
_____
_____
_____
_____
_____
_____
_____
_____
_____
_____
_____
_____

Are there household chores you did **before** the injury/incident that you cannot do now? If so, list them here. _____

Do you employ any of the following services because of the accident/incident: housekeeping, yard maintenance, pool, or personal care? If so, please explain why and provide monthly costs.
_____
_____
_____

Please describe your leisure activities before the accident/incident. If applicable, explain any change **since** the accident/incident in question.
_____
_____
_____
_____
_____
_____
_____
_____
_____

Please describe in detail how you spend a typical day. _____
_____
_____
_____

MENTAL HEALTH

Please indicate if you have experienced any of the following, and provide an explanation for items you checked yes:

Yes   No   **Explanation**

☐   ☐   Mental health treatment before
            the subject incident

            _____

            _____

            _____

            _____

            _____

            _____

            _____

            _____

☐   ☐   Family history of mental illness

            _____

☐   ☐   Prescriptions of antidepressants
            or other psychotropic drugs
            before the subject incident

            _____

☐   ☐   Head trauma or loss of
            consciousness before the subject
            incident

            _____

☐   ☐   Do you believe you currently
            need mental health treatment?

            _____

            _____

            _____

            _____

            _____

            _____

Have you ever had any mental health treatment **before** the incident in question? If so, please describe.

_____

_____

Please describe all mental health treatment you had **after** the incident in question.

_____

_____

Use the following scale (1 - 4) to indicate the extent that the mental health problems listed concern you:

    (1) Not at all   (2) Somewhat   (3) Moderately   (4) Very much

__ Anger   __ Financial Problems

__ Anxiety/Stress Management   __ Legal Problems

__ Change in Eating Pattern   __ Loneliness

__ Child Management Problems   __ Use of Alcohol or Drugs

__ Conflict with Family Members   __ Sexual Problems

__ Concern about Physical Health   __ Thoughts of Suicide

__ Feeling Depressed   __ Feeling Guilty

__ Marital or Significant Other Relationship

_____

_____

_____

_____

_____

_____

_____

_____

_____

_____

EDUCATION AND SPECIAL TRAINING

	Name	Major/Degree	Dates Attended	Graduation Date
High School				
Vocational Training				
College				
College				
Graduate School				
Employer-Sponsored Training				
Employer-Sponsored Training				
Employer-Sponsored Training				
Continuing Education				
Other Training				

How did you perform in school?_____

_____

_____

_____

If you were tested in the following, note your score.

SAT _____   ACT _____   Other _____

☐ I do not recall scores from prior standardized testing.

Did you ever repeat a grade in K-12? If so, what grades and why? _____

_____

_____

While in school, what kind of classes were you in:

☐ Regular classes   ☐ Honors classes

☐ Accelerated classes   ☐ Remedial classes

☐ Special education   ☐ Emotional disabilities

☐ Other special programming: _____

Please explain: _____

_____

List any special skills you have (*Example: computer, foreign languages, musical, athletic, artistic, etc.*)._____

_____

List all the work-related credentials you hold or have held (*Example: licenses, certifications, registrations, etc.*). _____

_____

_____

_____

_____

_____

Describe on-the-job training you have had. _____

_____

Do you have access to a computer?   ☐ Yes ☐ No   Describe your computer skills *(Example: software you are able to use, programming skills, etc.)*:_____

_____

_____

_____

_____

_____

_____

_____

List all skills that you have developed through training and work experience. Please be specific.

_____

_____

_____

_____

_____

_____

_____

_____

_____

_____

_____

_____

_____

_____

Have you considered retraining?   ☐ Yes ☐ No   If so, describe. _____

_____

_____

_____

WORK EXPERIENCE

List each job you have held. Start with your most recent job and continue in reverse order. **It is important to fully complete this information.**

FULL JOB TITLE	EMPLOYER	DATES	WAGES	REASON FOR LEAVING

CAREER DEVELOPMENT

Which job do you consider your most skilled or challenging? _____

_____

Have you always filed income tax returns?_____

_____

_____

_____

Were you ever terminated from a job?   ☐ Yes ☐ No   If so, from what job(s) and why? _____

_____

_____

Have you ever made a claim for workers' compensation benefits?   ☐ Yes ☐ No. If so, explain.

_____

_____

How many hours per week did you work at the time of the injury/incident?_____

Describe employment benefits associated with the job you held at the time of the injury/incident.

_____

Describe the job responsibilities you had at the time of the injury/incident. _____

_____

What was the heaviest amount of weight you lifted/carried in your job? _____

List your job's physical requirements (*Example: extended sitting or standing, climbing ladders, exposure to extreme temperatures, etc.*). _____

Did you take time off work **after** the injury/incident? If so, how long? _____

Describe any military experience you have had. Include branch of service, dates, discharge rank, military occupation, and type of discharge. _____

List volunteer work experience you have had during the past 5 years. _____

_____

List other organizations in which you participate (*Example: church, social clubs, community organizations, etc.*). _____

What were your employment earnings during the year **before** the injury/incident? _____

What were your highest earnings during your work career? List the amount and year. _____

Estimate your average monthly expenses. _____

Describe your financial situation. _____

List all sources and amounts of your present income. Continue on back if needed.

Source	*Amount per Month*

Have you applied to the Social Security Administration for disability benefits? _____

_____

_____

If so, what was the disposition on your application? _____

I certify that I have completed the information requested accurately and to the best of my ability.

_____   _____

Signature   Date

APPENDIX H.1

Cost Analysis

Endora Bailey

Date of Birth:	October 26, 1942; 75 years (per Dr. Wilson's report dated 11/05/17)
Life Expectancy:	Age 83; 8 years (for comparison purposes; Dr. Wilson's report dated 11/05/17)
Date of Injury:	July 29, 2016
Residence:	Port St. John, Florida

Note: This document is a cost comparison as requested by defense counsel, comparing Dr. Wilson's costs to Dr. Shahnasarian's costs only. It should not be assumed that Dr. Shahnasarian agrees with Dr. Wilson's recommendations and/or protocols.

The *National Fee Analyzer* is published by FAIR Health, a nonprofit agency developed to ensure transparency in medical costs. The *National Fee Analyzer* provides physician practices with three percentiles (50th, 75th, and 90th) of charge data; only the 50th and 75th percentiles are incorporated into this life care plan. This resource provides physician practices with national charge data for fee scheduled evaluation and competitive analysis for contracting purposes. Compiled from a database of 650 million charge records arranged by CPT Codes, the *National Fee Analyzer* has no insurance company paid amounts incorporated into its product.

The American Hospital Directory is an online resource that compiles annual average cost data from hospitals nationwide.

Anesthesia costs are derived from the American Society of Anesthesiologists (ASA) *2019 Relative Value Guide* and *2019 Cross-walk; A Guide for Surgery/Anesthesia CPT Codes.*

PHYSICIAN AND PROFESSIONAL CARE

Item	Duration	Frequency	Dr. Wilson's Estimated Cost	Dr. Shahnasarian's Estimated Cost
Physiatrist	Year 1–Life	1 Visit per Year	$160.25 per Visit	$200–$250 per Visit

Per Brittany Labutka, medical receptionist at Florida Medicine and Rehabilitation, office of Dr. Antonio Scheffel, 321-555-xxxx (Cocoa Beach, FL): Physiatrist follow-up, $200 per visit using CPT Code 99214.

Per 2019 National Fee Analyzer, physiatrist follow-up, CPT Code 99214 (office visit for the evaluation and management of an established patient, which requires at least two of these three components: a detailed history; a detailed examination; and medical decision-making of moderate complexity. Counseling and/or coordination of care with other physicians, other qualified health care professionals, or agencies are provided consistent with the nature of the problem(s) and the patient's and/or family's needs. Usually the presenting problem(s) are of moderate to high severity. Typically, 25 minutes are spent face to face with the patient), $200 to $250 per visit.

Item	Duration	Frequency	Dr. Wilson's Estimated Cost	Dr. Shahnasarian's Estimated Cost
Physiatrist EMG/ NCV Testing Both Extremities	Year 1–Life	2 Times Total	$1,613 Each Time	$1,152–$1,582 Each Time

Per Brittany Labutka, medical assistant at Florida Medicine and Rehabilitation, office of Dr. Antonio Scheffel, 321-555-xxxx (Cocoa Beach, FL): EMG/NCV testing for two extremities, $1,100 total using CPT Codes 95886 and 95909.

Per 2019 National Fee Analyzer, electromyogram (EMG), CPT Code 95886 (needle electromyography; each extremity with related paraspinal areas, when performed, done with nerve conduction, amplitude, and latency/velocity study; complete, five or more muscles studied, innervated by three or more nerves or four or more spinal levels), $222 to $300; and CPT Code 95909 (nerve conduction studies; five to six studies), $354 to $491, totaling $576 to $791 x 2 = $1,152 to $1,582 each time.

PHYSICIAN AND PROFESSIONAL CARE

Item	Duration	Frequency	Dr. Wilson's Estimated Cost	Dr. Shahnasarian's Estimated Cost
Orthopedist or Podiatrist	Year 1–Life	1 Visit per Year	$169.88 for Orthopedist $119.88 for Podiatrist	$84–$167 per Visit $104–$167 per Orthopedist Visit $84–$109 per Podiatrist Visit

Per Pam McHughs, patient care coordinator at Florida Orthopaedics, office of Dr. Robert West, 321-555-xxxx (Merritt Island, FL): Orthopedic follow-up visit, $104 using CPT Code 99213.

Per 2019 National Fee Analyzer, orthopedist follow-up, CPT Code 99213 (office or other outpatient visit for the evaluation and management of an established patient, which requires at least two of these three components: an expanded problem-focused history; an expanded problem-focused examination; and medical decision-making of low complexity. Counseling and/or coordination of care with other physicians, other qualified health care professionals, or agencies are provided consistent with the nature of the problem(s) and the patient's and/or family's needs. Usually the presenting problem(s) are of low to moderate severity. Typically, 15 minutes are spent face to face with the patient and/or family), $131 to $167 per visit.

Per Debora Smith, office manager at the office of Dr. Charles Jones, 321-555-xxxx (Cocoa Beach, FL): Podiatrist follow-up, $105 using CPT Code 99212.

Per 2019 National Fee Analyzer, podiatrist follow-up visit, CPT Code 99212 (office or other outpatient visit for evaluation and management of an established patient, which requires at least two of these three components: a problem-focused history; a problem-focused examination; and straightforward medical decision-making. Counseling and/or coordination of care with other physicians, other qualified health care professionals, or agencies are provided consistent with the nature of the problem(s) and the patient's and/or family's needs. Usually the presenting problem(s) are self-limited or minor. Typically, ten minutes are spent face to face with the patient and/or family), $84 to $109 per visit.

Item	Duration	Frequency	Dr. Wilson's Estimated Cost	Dr. Shahnasarian's Estimated Cost
Ankle Intra-Articular Steroid Injections	Year 1–Life	One Time	$324.03 per Injection	$228–$340 per Injection

Per Vanessa Smith, office manager at Xyz Orthopedics and Rehabilitation, office of Dr. Drahmane Jones, 321-555-xxxx (Rockledge, FL): Ankle steroid injections, $228 per injection using CPT Code 20606.

Per 2019 National Fee Analyzer, steroid injections ankle, CPT Code 20606 (arthrocentesis, aspiration, and/or injection, intermediate joint or bursa; with ultrasound guidance, with permanent recording and report), $248 to $340 per injection.

Item	Duration	Frequency	Dr. Wilson's Estimated Cost	Dr. Shahnasarian's Estimated Cost
Ankle Arthroscopy	To Be Determined	One Time	$16,464.77 Total	$14,690–$15,691 Total

Ankle arthroscopy ranges from $14,690 to $15,691. This is an outpatient procedure performed under general anesthesia.

Physician fee: $2,044 to $3,045

CPT Code 29898 (arthroscopy, ankle (tibiotalar and fibulotalar joints), surgical; debridement, extensive), $2,044 to $3,045 according to the 2019 *National Fee Analyzer*.

Facility fee: $11,182

$11,182 per outpatient procedure at Health First Cape Canaveral Hospital (Cocoa Beach, FL) according to the American Hospital Directory, https://www.ahd.com/.

Anesthesia: $1,464

$1,464 for CPT Code 29898 with procedure time of 45 minutes according to the American Society of Anesthesiologists (ASA) *2019 Relative Value Guide* and *2019 Crosswalk; A Guide for Surgery/Anesthesia CPT Codes*.

PHYSICIAN AND PROFESSIONAL CARE

Item	Duration	Frequency	Dr. Wilson's Estimated Cost	Dr. Shahnasarian's Estimated Cost
Ankle Arthroplasty	To Be Determined	One Time	$70,025.57 Total	$50,092–$75,030 Total

The cost of a total ankle replacement ranges from $50,092 to $75,030. This procedure requires a two-to-three-day inpatient hospital stay and is performed under general anesthesia.

Physician fee: $3,400 to $5,572

CPT Code 27702 (arthroplasty, ankle; with implant (total ankle)), $3,400 to $5,572 according to the 2019 *National Fee Analyzer.*

Facility fee: $41,532 to $62,298

$41,532 for a two-day inpatient stay and $62,298 for a three-day inpatient stay at Health First Cape Canaveral Hospital (Cocoa Beach, FL) according to the 2019 American Hospital Directory, https://www.ahd.com/.

Anesthesia fee: $3,660

$3,660 for CPT Code 27702 with procedure time of two hours according to the American Society of Anesthesiologists (ASA) *2019 Relative Value Guide* and *2019 Crosswalk; A Guide for Surgery/Anesthesia CPT Codes.*

Knee hardware: $3,500

Per Doug Smith, Tampa sales representative for Spinner, 727-555-xxxx (Tampa, FL), $3,500 for the knee hardware.

Internist Follow-Up	Year 1–Life	1 Visit per Year	$151.25 per Visit	$131–$167 per Evaluation

Per Janet Smith, patient care coordinator at HRQ Medical Group, office of Dr. Dale Jones, 321-555-xxxx (Cocoa Beach, FL): Internist follow-up, $150 per visit using CPT Code 99213.

Per 2019 *National Fee Analyzer,* internist follow-up, CPT Code 99213 (office or other outpatient visit for the evaluation and management of an established patient, which requires at least two of these three components: an expanded problem-focused history; an expanded problem-focused examination; and medical decision-making of low complexity. Counseling and/or coordination of care with other physicians, other qualified health care professionals, or agencies are provided consistent with the nature of the problem(s) and the patient's and/or family's needs. Usually the presenting problem(s) are of low to moderate severity. Typically, 15 minutes are spent face to face with the patient and/or family), $131 to $167 per visit.

Pain Management Follow-Up	Year 1–Life	1 Visit per Month	$192.75 per Visit	$131–$167 Each Time

Per Vanessa Smith, office manager at Xyz Orthopedics and Rehabilitation, office of Dr. Drahmane Jones, 321-555-xxxx (Rockledge, FL): Pain management follow-up, $150 using CPT Code 99213.

Per 2019 *National Fee Analyzer,* pain management follow-up, CPT Code 99213 (office or other outpatient visit for the evaluation and management of an established patient, which requires at least two of these three components: an expanded problem-focused history; an expanded problem-focused examination; and medical decision-making of low complexity. Counseling and/or coordination of care with other physicians, other qualified health care professionals, or agencies are provided consistent with the nature of the problem(s) and the patient's and/or family's needs. Usually the presenting problem(s) are of low to moderate severity. Typically, 15 minutes are spent face to face with the patient and/or family), $131 to $167 per visit.

PHYSICIAN AND PROFESSIONAL CARE

Item	Duration	Frequency	Dr. Wilson's Estimated Cost	Dr. Shahnasarian's Estimated Cost
Lumbar Epidural Steroid Injection	Year 1–Life	2 Times Total	$3,904.24 per Injection	$820–$1,212 per Injection

Per Vanessa Smith, office manager at Xyz Orthopedics and Rehabilitation, office of Dr. Drahmane Jones, 321-555-xxxx (Rockledge, FL): Lumbar epidural steroid injection, $1,099 using CPT Code 64483. This does not include cost of the steroid.

Per 2019 *National Fee Analyzer*, lumbar epidural injections, CPT Code 64483 (injection(s), anesthetic agent, and/or steroid, transforaminal epidrual, with imaging guidance; lumbar or sacral, single level), $820 to $1,212.

Item	Duration	Frequency		
Lumbar Facet Blocks	Year 1–Life	2 Times Total	$1,200.75 per Injection	$992–$1,585 per Injection

Per Vanessa Smith, office manager at Xyz Orthopedics and Rehabilitation, office of Dr. Drahmane Jones, 321-555-xxxx (Rockledge, FL): Lumbar facet blocks, $1,100 per injection using CPT Codes 64493 and 64494. This does not include the cost of the medication.

Per 2019 *National Fee Analyzer*, CPT Code 64493 (injection(s), diagnostic or therapeutic agent, paravertebral facet joint with image guidance; single level), $642 to $1,000; and CPT Code 64494 (second level), $350 to $585, totaling $992 to $1,585.

Item	Duration	Frequency		
Lumbar Medial Branch-Facet Rhizotomies	Year 1–Life	3 Times Total	$9,395.11 Each Time	$13,395–$14,739 Each Time

Radiofrequency ablation lumbar ranges from $13,395 to $14,739. This is an outpatient procedure performed with a local anesthetic.

Physician fee: $1,713 to $2,557

CPT Code 64635 (destruction by neurolytic agent, paravertebral facet joint nerve, with imaging guidance; lumbar), $1,181 to $1,768; and CPT Code 64636 (each additional facet joint), $532 to $789 according to 2019 National Fee Analyzer.

Facility fee: $11,182

$11,182 per outpatient procedure at Health First Cape Canaveral Hospital (Cocoa Beach, FL) according to the American Hospital Directory, https://www.ahd.com/.

Anesthesia and miscellaneous: $500 to $1,000

This includes syringes, gauze, local anesthesia, etc.

Item	Duration	Frequency		
Toxicology/Urine Screens	Year 1–Life	3–12 Times per Year	$425.86 Each Time	$45–$75.50

Per 2019 *National Fee Analyzer*, toxicology/urine screen, CPT Code 80305 (drug test(s), presumptive, any number of drug classes, any number of devices or procedures, capable of being read by direct optical observation only, includes sample validation when performed, per date of service), $45 to $75 each time.

Per Florida price line for Quest Labs, 800-786-6890, toxicology urine screen, test code 91359, $75.50 each time.

No CPT Codes were provided; unable to determine exact cost.

PHYSICIAN AND PROFESSIONAL CARE

Item	Duration	Frequency	Dr. Wilson's Estimated Cost	Dr. Shahnasarian's Estimated Cost
Spinal Cord Stimulator Trial	Year 1–Life	One Time	$34,508 Total	$19,287–$20,878

The cost for spinal cord stimulator trial ranges from $19,287 to $20,878. The implantation of a spinal cord stimulator is performed in two steps: trial implantation and permanent implantation. If the trial is successful, the patient returns to have the permanent spinal cord stimulator implanted. This is an outpatient procedure.

Specifications are as follows:

Physician's fee: $2,909 to $4,500

CPT Code 63650 (percutaneous implantation of neurostimulator electrode), $2,909 to $4,500 according to the 2019 *National Fee Analyzer.*

Facility fee: $11,182

$11,182 per outpatient procedure at Health First Cape Canaveral Hospital (Cocoa Beach, FL) according to the American Hospital Directory, https://www.ahd.com/.

Anesthesia charges: $2,196

$2,196 for anesthesia for CPT Code 63650 and procedure time of one hour per American Society of Anesthesiologists (ASA) *2019 Relative Value Guide* and *2019 Crosswalk; A Guide for Surgery/Anesthesia CPT Codes.*

Trial unit: $3,000

Per David Smith, sales representative at RE Neuromodulation, 813-555-xxxx, the trial spinal cord stimulator unit is approximately $3,000. This is the cost to the facility.

Spinal Cord Stimulator Implantation	Year 1–Life	One Time	$101,402.89 Total	$47,020–$48,761 Total

The cost for implantation of permanent spinal cord stimulator ranges from $47,020 to $48,761. The implantation of a spinal cord stimulator is performed in two steps: trial implantation and permanent implantation. If the trial implant is successful, the patient is scheduled for permanent implantation. This is an outpatient procedure.

Specifications are as follows:

Physician's fee: $2,910 to $4,651

CPT Code 63655 (laminectomy for implantation of neurostimulator electrode), $2,910 to $4,651 according to the 2019 *National Fee Analyzer.*

Facility fee: $11,182

$11,182 per outpatient procedure at Health First Cape Canaveral Hospital (Cocoa Beach, FL) according to the American Hospital Directory, https://www.ahd.com/.

Anesthesia charges: $2,928

$2,928 for anesthesia for CPT Code 63655 and procedure time of one hour per American Society of Anesthesiologists (ASA) *2019 Relative Value Guide* and *2019 Crosswalk; A Guide for Surgery/Anesthesia CPT Codes.*

Spinal cord stimulator (permanent), $30,000

Per David Smith, sales representative at RE Neuromodulation, 813-555-xxxx, the permanent spinal cord stimulator unit is approximately $30,000. This is the cost to the facility.

PHYSICIAN AND PROFESSIONAL CARE

Item	Duration	Frequency	Dr. Wilson's Estimated Cost	Dr. Shahnasarian's Estimated Cost
Spinal Cord Stimulator Battery Replacement	Year 1–Life	Every 9 Years	$78,968.23 Total	$31,629–$32,634 Total

The cost of a spinal cord stimulator replacement ranges from $31,629 to $32,634. This is an outpatient procedure.

Specifications are as follows:

Physician's Fee: $1,495 to $2,500

CPT Code 63685 (replacement of spinal neurostimulator pulse generator or receiver), $1,495 to $2,500 according to the 2019 *National Fee Analyzer*.

Facility fee: $11,182

$11,182 per outpatient procedure at Health First Cape Canaveral Hospital (Cocoa Beach, FL) according to the American Hospital Directory, https://www.ahd.com/.

Anesthesia charges: $1,952

$1,952 for anesthesia for CPT Code 63685 and 45 minutes procedure time per American Society of Anesthesiologists (ASA) *2019 Relative Value Guide* and *2019 Crosswalk; A Guide for Surgery/Anesthesia CPT Codes*.

Battery replacement charge, $17,000

Per David Smith, sales representative at RE Neuromodulation, 813-555-xxxx, the battery replacement charge is approximately $17,000. This is the cost to the facility.

Spinal Cord Stimulator Analysis	Year 1–Life	3 Times per Year	$321 per Visit	$150–$209 per Visit

Per Vanessa Smith, office manager at Xyz Orthopedics and Rehabilitation, office of Dr. Drahmane Jones, 321-555-xxxx (Rockledge, FL): Spinal cord stimulator analysis, $150 per visit using CPT Code 95971.

Per 2019 *National Fee Analyzer*, spinal cord stimulator analysis, CPT Code 95971 (electronic analysis of implanted neurostimulator pulse generator/transmitter by physician or other qualified health care professional; with simple spinal cord or peripheral nerve neurostimulator pulse generator/transmitter programming by physician or other qualified health care professional), $153 to $209 per visit.

MEDICATIONS

Item	Duration	Frequency	Dr. Wilson's Estimated Cost	Dr. Shahnasarian's Estimated Cost
Acetaminophen 650 mg	Year 1–Life	6 Tablets per Day	$18.25 per Month	$11.16–$16.02 per Month

Per Walgreens Pharmacy, www.walgreens.com: Acetaminophen 650 mg, $8.99 per 100 ($0.089 per tablet); $16.02 per month.

Per CVS Pharmacy, www.cvs.com: Acetaminophen 650 mg, $6.24 per 100 tablets ($0.062 per tablet); $11.16 per month.

Item	Duration	Frequency	Dr. Wilson's Estimated Cost	Dr. Shahnasarian's Estimated Cost
Oxycodone 5 mg	Year 1–Life	3–4 Tablets per Day	$135.35 per Month	$52.39–$52.99 per 90 Tablets; $68.99–$71.99 per 120 Tablets

Per Lee Smith, pharmacy technician at Walgreens Pharmacy, 321-555-xxxx (Cocoa Beach, FL): Oxycodone 5 mg, $55.49 per 90 tablets; $71.99 per 120 tablets.

Per Brianna Reed, pharmacy technician at CVS Pharmacy, 321-555-xxxx (Cocoa Beach, FL): $52.39 per 90 tablets; $68.99 per 120 tablets.

Item	Duration	Frequency	Dr. Wilson's Estimated Cost	Dr. Shahnasarian's Estimated Cost
Lidocaine Patch 5%	Year 1–Life	1 Patch per Day	$363.18 per Month	$249.99–$359.70 per Month

Per Lee Smith, pharmacy technician at Walgreens Pharmacy, 321-555-xxxx (Cocoa Beach, FL): Lidocaine patch 5%, $249.99 per 30 patches.

Per Brianna Reed, pharmacy technician at CVS Pharmacy, 321-555-xxxx (Cocoa Beach, FL): Lidocaine patch 5%, $359.70 per 30 patches.

Item	Duration	Frequency	Dr. Wilson's Estimated Cost	Dr. Shahnasarian's Estimated Cost
Gabapentin (Neurontin) 300 mg	Year 1–Life	3 Tablets per Day	$261.89 per Month	$85.99–$86.99 per Month

Per Lee Smith, pharmacy technician at Walgreens Pharmacy, 321-555-xxxx (Cocoa Beach, FL): Gabapentin 300 mg, $86.99 per 90 tablets.

Per Brianna Reed, pharmacy technician at CVS Pharmacy, 321-555-xxxx (Cocoa Beach, FL): Gabapentin 300 mg, $85.99 per 90 tablets.

It is unclear whether Dr. Wilson's costs are label or generic for this medication. Therefore, above cost is generic. The label medication Neurontin is priced at $649.99 to $794.99 per 90 tablets.

Item	Duration	Frequency	Dr. Wilson's Estimated Cost	Dr. Shahnasarian's Estimated Cost
Clonazepam (Klonopin) 0.5–1 mg	Year 1–Life	3 Tablets per Day	$162 per Month $5.40 per Day	$44.89–$53.99 per Month

Per Lee Smith, pharmacy technician at Walgreens Pharmacy, 321-555-xxxx (Cocoa Beach, FL): Clonazepam 0.5 to 1.0 mg, $44.89 per 90 tablets.

Per Brianna Reed, pharmacy technician at CVS Pharmacy, 321-555-xxxx (Cocoa Beach, FL): Clonazepam 0.5 to 1.0 mg, $53.99 per 90 tablets.

MEDICATIONS

Item	Duration	Frequency	Dr. Wilson's Estimated Cost	Dr. Shahnasarian's Estimated Cost
Fluoxetine (Prozac) 40 mg	Year 1–Life	1 Tablet per Day	$188.10 per Month $6.27 per Day	$48.20–$52.99 per Month

Per Lee Smith, pharmacy technician at Walgreens Pharmacy, 321-555-xxxx (Cocoa Beach, FL): Fluoxetine 40 mg, $52.99 per 30 tablets.

Per Brianna Reed, pharmacy technician at CVS Pharmacy, 321-555-xxxx (Cocoa Beach, FL): Fluoxetine 40 mg, $48.20 per 30 tablets.

It is unclear whether Dr. Wilson's costs are generic or label for this medication. Therefore, above cost is generic. The label medication Prozac is $1,148.99 to $1,186.99 per 30 tablets.

Item	Duration	Frequency	Dr. Wilson's Estimated Cost	Dr. Shahnasarian's Estimated Cost
Famotidine (Pepcid) 20 mg	Year 1–Life	1 Tablet per Day	$9.73 per Month	$7.49–$8.99 per Month

Per Walgreens Pharmacy, www.walgreens.com: Famotidine 20 mg, $8.99 per 30 tablets.

Per CVS Pharmacy, www.cvs.com: Famotidine 20 mg, $7.49 per 30 tablets.

Item	Duration	Frequency	Dr. Wilson's Estimated Cost	Dr. Shahnasarian's Estimated Cost
Probiotics	Year 1–Life	1 Tablet per Day	$31.63 per Month	$25.89–$25.99 per Month

Per Walgreens Pharmacy, www.walgreens.com: Ultimate Flora Probiotic 10, $25.99 per 30 tablets.

Per CVS Pharmacy, www.cvs.com: Renew Life Probiotics, $25.89 per 30 tablets.

Item	Duration	Frequency	Dr. Wilson's Estimated Cost	Dr. Shahnasarian's Estimated Cost
Zolpidem Tartrate (Ambien) 10 mg	Year 1–Life	1 Tablet per Day	$286.53 per Month	$58.99–$61.99 per Month

Per Lee Smith, pharmacy technician at Walgreens Pharmacy, 321-555-xxxx (Cocoa Beach, FL): Zolpidem Tartrate 10 mg, $61.99 per 30 tablets.

Per Brianna Reed, pharmacy technician at CVS Pharmacy, 321-555-xxxx (Cocoa Beach, FL): Zolpidem Tartrate 10 mg, $58.99 per 30 tablets.

It is unclear whether Dr. Wilson's costs are label or generic for this medication. Therefore, the above cost is generic. The label medication Ambien is $625.99 to $635.99 per 30 tablets.

Item	Duration	Frequency	Dr. Wilson's Estimated Cost	Dr. Shahnasarian's Estimated Cost
Docusate (Colace) 100 mg	Year 1–Life	2 Tablets per Day	$15.82 per Month	$9.98–$11.58 per Month

Per Walgreens Pharmacy, www.walgreens.com: Docusate 100 mg, $4.99 per 30 tablets.

Per CVS Pharmacy, www.cvs.com: Docusate 100 mg, $5.79 per 30 tablets.

DIAGNOSTIC TESTING

Item	Duration	Frequency	Dr. Wilson's Estimated Cost	Dr. Shahnasarian's Estimated Cost
X-ray Hand/Wrist	Year 1–Life	4 Times Total	$127 Each Time	$108–$136 Each Time

Per 2019 *National Fee Analyzer*, X-ray hand/wrist, CPT Code 73100 (radiologic examination; wrist; two views), $84 to $106; with reading fee, $24 to $30; totaling $108 to $136 each time.

Item	Duration	Frequency	Dr. Wilson's Estimated Cost	Dr. Shahnasarian's Estimated Cost
MRI Hand/Wrist	Year 1–Life	4 Times Total	$2,149 Each Time	$1,590–$2,064 Each Time

Per 2019 *National Fee Analyzer*, MRI hand/wrist, CPT Code 73221 (magnetic resonance, imaging, any joint of upper extremity; without contrast material), $1,232 to $1,600; with reading fee, $358 to $464; totaling $1,590 to $2,064 each time.

Item	Duration	Frequency	Dr. Wilson's Estimated Cost	Dr. Shahnasarian's Estimated Cost
X-ray Cervical	Year 1–Life	2 Times Total	$120 Each Time	$128–$169 Each Time

Per 2019 *National Fee Analyzer*, X-ray cervical spine, CPT Code 72040 (radiologic examination, spine, cervical; two views), $98 to $129; with reading fee, $30 to $40; totaling $128 to $169 each time.

Item	Duration	Frequency	Dr. Wilson's Estimated Cost	Dr. Shahnasarian's Estimated Cost
MRI Cervical	Year 1–Life	2 Times Total	$2,229 Each Time	$1,729–$2,188 Each Time

Per 2019 *National Fee Analyzer*, MRI cervical spine, CPT Code 72141 (magnetic resonance, imaging, spinal canal and contents, cervical; without contrast material), $1,300 to $1,645; with reading fee, $429 to $543; totaling $1,729 to $2,188 each time.

Item	Duration	Frequency	Dr. Wilson's Estimated Cost	Dr. Shahnasarian's Estimated Cost
X-ray Lumbar	Year 1–Life	2 Times Total	$276 Each Time	$139–$177 Each Time

Per 2019 *National Fee Analyzer*, X-ray of lumbar spine, CPT Code 72100 (radiologic examination, spine, lumbosacral; two to three views), $105 to $134; with reading fee, $34 to $43; totaling $139 to $177 each time.

Item	Duration	Frequency	Dr. Wilson's Estimated Cost	Dr. Shahnasarian's Estimated Cost
MRI Lumbar	Year 1–Life	2 Times Total	$3,352 Each Time	$1,874–$2,239 Each Time

Per 2019 *National Fee Analyzer*, MRI lumbar spine, CPT Code 72148 (magnetic resonance, imaging, spinal canal and contents, lumbar; without contrast material), $1,331 to $1,671; with reading fee, $543 to $568; totaling $1,874 to $2,239 each time.

Item	Duration	Frequency	Dr. Wilson's Estimated Cost	Dr. Shahnasarian's Estimated Cost
X-ray Ankle	Year 1–Life	4 Times Total	$134 Each Time	$102–$128 Each Time

Per the 2019 *National Fee Analyzer*, X-ray ankle, CPT Code 73600 (radiologic examination, ankle, complete, two views), $80 to $100; with reading fee, $22 to $28; totaling $102 to $128 each time.

DIAGNOSTIC TESTING

Item	Duration	Frequency	Dr. Wilson's Estimated Cost	Dr. Shahnasarian's Estimated Cost
MRI Ankle	Year 1–Life	4 Times Total	$2,151 Each Time	$1,589–$1,929 Each Time

Per 2019 *National Fee Analyzer*, MRI ankle, CPT Code 73721 (magnetic resonance, imaging, any joint of lower extremity; without contrast material), $1,232 to $1,573; with reading fee, $357 to $456; totaling $1,589 to $1,929 each time.

Diagnostic costs—such as X-rays, MRIs, and CT scans—are obtained solely from the 2019 *National Fee Analyzer* because costs cited by diagnostic centers are based on insurance reimbursement, thereby undervaluing the true cost.

LABORATORY TESTING

Item	Duration	Frequency	Dr. Wilson's Estimated Cost	Dr. Shahnasarian's Estimated Cost
CBC	Year 1–Life	Annually	$42 Each Time	$50–$66.87 Each Time

Per 2019 *National Fee Analyzer*, complete blood count (CBC), CPT Code 85025 (automated CBC and automated differential WBC count), $35 to $42 each time; and venipuncture, CPT Code 36415 (collection of venous blood by venipuncture), $15 to $21; totaling $50 to $63 each time.

Per Florida price line for Quest Labs, 800-786-6890, CBC, test code 6399, $45.50; and venipuncture, test code 36415, $21.37; totaling $66.87 each time.

Liver Profile	Year 1–Life	Annually	$60 Each Time	$55.57–$71 Each Time

Per 2019 *National Fee Analyzer*, liver profile, CPT Code 80076 (hepatic function panel), $42 to $50; and venipuncture, CPT Code 36415 (collection of venous blood by venipuncture), $15 to $21; totaling $57 to $71 each time.

Per Florida price line for Quest Labs, 800-786-6890, liver profile, test code 10256, $34.20; and venipuncture, test code 36415, $21.37; totaling $55.57 each time.

Renal Profile	Year 1–Life	Annually	$59 Each Time	$63–$85 Each Time

Per 2019 *National Fee Analyzer*, renal profile, CPT Code 80069 (renal function panel), $48 to $64; and venipuncture, CPT Code 36415 (collection of venous blood by venipuncture), $15 to $21; totaling $63 to $85 each time.

Per Florida price line for Quest Labs, 800-786-6890, renal function panel, test code 10314, $55.66; and venipuncture, test code 36415, $21.37; totaling $77.03 each time.

Urine Toxicology Screen	Year 1–Life	Monthly	See Pain Management	See Pain Management

MEDICAL EQUIPMENT

Item	Duration	Frequency	Dr. Wilson's Estimated Cost	Dr. Shahnasarian's Estimated Cost
Power Scooter	Year 1–Life	Replace Every 5 Years	$1,229.83 Each Time	$799–$1,349 Each Time

Per SpinLife, www.spinlife.com: Spitfire Pro SE 4-Wheel Scooter, $799 each; GoGo Elite 4-Wheel Scooter, $1,019 each.

Per Hoveround, www.hoveround.com: Scout 4-Wheel Scooter, $899 each; Scout DST 4-Wheel Mobility Scooter, $1,349 each.

Item	Duration	Frequency	Dr. Wilson's Estimated Cost	Dr. Shahnasarian's Estimated Cost
Power Scooter Maintenance	Year 1–Life	Annually	$122.98 per Year	$90–$135 per Year

Per Jackie Smith, administrator at Wheelchair Scooter and Lift, 321-555-xxxx (Melbourne, FL): Power scooter maintenance, $90 per hour. Annual maintenance typically takes 1 to 1.5 hours. Except year of purchase.

Item	Duration	Frequency	Dr. Wilson's Estimated Cost	Dr. Shahnasarian's Estimated Cost
ROHO Cushion	Year 1–Life	Replace Every 2 Years	$458 Each Time	$220–$374 Each Time

Per Southwest Medical Supply, www.southwestmedical.com: Roho Cushion—Roho MiniMax, $280 each; Roho Harmony, $220 each; and Roho Enhancer Cushion, $374 each.

Per Allegro Medical Supply, www.allegromedical.com: Roho Cushions—Roho High Profile Cushion, $357 each; The Galaxy Roho Cushion, $339; and Roho Hybrid Elite, $369 each.

Item	Duration	Frequency	Dr. Wilson's Estimated Cost	Dr. Shahnasarian's Estimated Cost
ROHO Cushion Cover	Year 1–Life	Annually	$53.50 Each Time	$39–$43 Each Time

Per Southwest Medical Supply, www.southwestmedical.com: Roho cushion cover, $43 each.

Per Allegro Medical Supply, www.allegromedical.com: Roho cushion cover, $39 each.

Item	Duration	Frequency	Dr. Wilson's Estimated Cost	Dr. Shahnasarian's Estimated Cost
Wheelchair Backpack	Year 1–Life	Replace Every 2–3 Years	$46.12 Each Time	$33.65–$37.50 Each Time

Per Allegro Medical, www.allegromedical.com: Wheelchair side backpack, $37.50 each; Easy Access Wheelchair Back Pack, $33.65 each.

Item	Duration	Frequency	Dr. Wilson's Estimated Cost	Dr. Shahnasarian's Estimated Cost
Portable Ramps 3' and 5' (2)	Year 1–Life	Replace Every 10 Years	$361.78 Each Time	$267.99–$389.90 Each Time

Per USA Ramp Store, www.usarampstore.com: PVI Single Fold 3' Ramp $139.95 each; PVI Single Fold 5' Ramp, $249.95 each; totaling $389.90 each time.

Per Medmart, www.medmart.com: EZ Access Suitcase Portable Ramp 3', $175 each; EZ Access Suitcase Portable Ramp 5', $250.99 each; totaling $267.99 each time.

TRANSPORTATION

Item	Duration	Frequency	Dr. Wilson's Estimated Cost	Dr. Shahnasarian's Estimated Cost
Passenger Van with Adaptive Modifications	Year 1–Life	Replace Every 5 Years	$32,640 Each	$34,990–$34,995 Each

Per Mobility Works, www.mobilityworks.com: 2018 Dodge Grand Caravan SXT with Braunability adaptive equipment and rear entry and ramp, $34,995 each; 2018 Dodge Grand Caravan SXT with Braunability adaptive equipment and rear entry and ramp, $34,990 each.

Item	Duration	Frequency	Dr. Wilson's Estimated Cost	Dr. Shahnasarian's Estimated Cost
Adapted Modifications	Year 1–Life	Replace Every 7–10 Years	$22,000 Each Time	Adapted modifications are included in the cost of the passenger van.

HOME MODIFICATIONS AND ACCESSORIES

Item	Duration	Frequency	Dr. Wilson's Estimated Cost	Dr. Shahnasarian's Estimated Cost
Architectural Modifications	Year 1–2	One Time	$77,307 Total	$50,000 Total

At this time, Dr. Shahnasarian estimates $50,000 for architectural modifications.

NURSING CARE

Item	Duration	Frequency	Dr. Wilson's Estimated Cost	Dr. Shahnasarian's Estimated Cost
Home Health Aide/ CNA	Year 1–Life	10 Hours per Week	$21.13 per Hour	$18.95–$21 per Hour

Per Shara Smith, staffing coordinator at Florida Homecare, 321-555-xxxx (Melbourne, FL): Home health aide, $21 per hour.
Per Lisa Jones, director of nursing at Caregiver Services, 321-555-xxxx (Palm Bay, FL): Home health aide, $18.95 per hour.

Homemaker Care

Item	Duration	Frequency	Dr. Wilson's Estimated Cost	Dr. Shahnasarian's Estimated Cost
Heavy Housekeeping	Year 1–Life	2 Hours 2 Times per Month	$110 Each Time	$105–$135 Each Time

Per Maggie Smith, sales associate at Lotsa Cleaning, 321-555-xxxx (Melbourne, FL): Housekeeper, $105 each time.
Per Donna Jones, owner of Donna's Housekeeping, 321-555-xxxx (Melbourne, FL): Housekeeper, $135 each time.

Item	Duration	Frequency	Dr. Wilson's Estimated Cost	Dr. Shahnasarian's Estimated Cost
Lawn Service	Year 1–Life	Weekly	$39.76 per Week	$31.25–$33.73 per Week

Per Rick Martin, owner of RM Lawn Maintenance, 321-555-xxxx (Palm Bay, FL): Lawn maintenance services, $31.25 per week.
Per Paul Cook, owner of Complete Lawn Service, 321-555-xxxx (Palm Bay, FL): Lawn maintenance services, $33.73 per week.

Item	Duration	Frequency	Dr. Wilson's Estimated Cost	Dr. Shahnasarian's Estimated Cost
Home Maintenance	Year 1–Life	4–6 Hours per Month	$64.64 per Hour	$65 per Hour

Per Precision Handyman Services, 321-555-xxxx (Melbourne, FL): Home maintenance, $65 per hour.

Life Care Plan Valuation

Endora Bailey

CCA Work Product
12/18/19

Date of birth: October 26, 1942; 75 years
Life Expectancy: Age 83; 8 years
(for comparison purposes; Dr. Wilson's report dated 11/05/17)
(Additional 13.7 Years)

	UNIT COST			TOTAL COST	
	LOW	**HIGH**	**Frequency**	**LOW**	**HIGH**
Physician and Professional Care					
Physiatrist	$200.00	$250.00	Year 1–life/ 1 visit per year	$2,740.00	$3,425.00
EMG/NCV Testing	$1,152.00	$1,582.00	Year 1–life/ 2 times total	$2,304.00	$3,164.00
Orthopedist or Podiatrist	$84.00	$167.00	Year 1–life/ 1 visit per year	$1,150.80	$2,287.90
Ankle Intra-Articular Steroid Injection	$228.00	$340.00	Year 1–life/ 1 time	$228.00	$340.00
Ankle Arthroscopy	$14,690.00	$15,691.00	To Be Determined	$-	$-
Ankle Arthroplasty	$50,092.00	$75,030.00	To Be Determined	$-	$-
Internist Follow-Up	$131.00	$167.00	Year 1–life/ 1 visit per year	$1,794.70	$2,287.90
Pain Management Follow-Up	$131.00	$167.00	Year 1–life/ 1 visit per month	$21,536.40	$27,454.80
Lumbar Epidural Steroid	$820.00	$1,212.00	Year 1–life/ 2 times total	$1,640.00	$2,424.00
Lumbar Facet Blocks	$992.00	$1,585.00	Year 1–life/ 2 times total	$1,984.00	$3,170.00
Lumbar Medial Branch/Facet Rhiz.	$13,395.00	$14,739.00	Year 1–life/ 3 times total	$40,185.00	$44,217.00
Toxicology Urine Screen	$45.00	$75.50	Year 1–life/3–12 times per year	$1,849.50	$12,412.20

	UNIT COST			TOTAL COST	
	LOW	**HIGH**	**Frequency**	**LOW**	**HIGH**
Spinal Cord Stimulator Trial	$19,287.00	$20,878.00	Year 1–life/ one time	$19,287.00	$20,878.00
Spinal Cord Stimulator Implantation	$47,020.00	$48,761.00	Year 1–life/ one time	$47,020.00	$48,761.00
Spinal Cord Stimulator Battery Replace	$31,629.00	$32,634.00	Year 1–life/ every 9 years	$48,146.37	$49,676.20
Spinal Cord Stimulator Analysis	$150.00	$209.00	Year 1–life/ 3 times per year	$6,165.00	$8,589.90
				$196,030.77	**$229,087.90**

Medications					
Acetaminophen 650 mg	$11.16	$16.02	Year 1–life/ monthly	$1,834.70	$2,633.69
Oxycodone 5 mg	$52.39	$71.99	Year 1–life/ monthly	$8,612.92	$11,835.16
Lidocaine Patch 5%	$249.99	$359.70	Year 1–life/ monthly	$41,098.36	$59,134.68
Gabapentin 300 mg	$85.99	$86.99	Year 1–life/ monthly	$14,136.76	$14,301.16
Clonazepam 0.5–1.0 mg	$44.89	$53.99	Year 1–life/ monthly	$7,379.92	$8,875.96
Fluoxetine 40 mg	$48.20	$52.99	Year 1–life/ monthly	$7,924.08	$8,711.56
Famotidine 20 mg	$7.49	$8.99	Year 1–life/ monthly	$1,231.36	$1,477.96
Probiotics	$25.89	$25.99	Year 1–life/ monthly	$4,256.32	$4,272.76
Zolpidem Tartrate	$58.99	$61.99	Year 1–life/ monthly	$9,697.96	$10,191.16
Docusate 100 mg	$9.98	$11.58	Year 1–life/ monthly	$1,640.71	$1,903.75

	UNIT COST			TOTAL COST	
	LOW	HIGH	Frequency	LOW	HIGH
Diagnostic Tests					
X-ray Hand/Wrist	$108.00	$136.00	Year 1–life/ 4 times total	$432.00	$544.00
MRI Hand/Wrist	$1,590.00	$2,064.00	Year 1–life/ 4 times total	$6,360.00	$8,256.00
X-ray Cervical	$128.00	$169.00	Year 1–life/ 2 times total	$256.00	$338.00
MRI Cervical	$1,729.00	$2,188.00	Year 1–life/ 2 times total	$3,458.00	$4,376.00
X-ray Lumbar	$139.00	$177.00	Year 1–life/ 2 times total	$278.00	$354.00
MRI Lumbar	$1,874.00	$2,239.00	Year 1–life/ 2 times total	$3,748.00	$4,478.00
X-ray Ankle	$102.00	$128.00	Year 1–life/ 4 times total	$408.00	$512.00
MRI Ankle	$1,589.00	$1,929.00	Year 1–life/ 4 times total	$6,356.00	$7,716.00
				$21,296.00	**$26,574.00**
Laboratory Testing					
CBC	$50.00	$66.87	Year 1–life/ annually	$685.00	$916.12
Liver Profile	$55.57	$71.00	Year 1–life/ annually	$761.31	$972.70
Renal Profile	$63.00	$85.00	Year 1–life/ annually	$863.10	$1,164.50
Urine Toxicology Screen	$-	$-	See pain management	$-	$-
				$2,309.41	**$3,053.32**

	UNIT COST			TOTAL COST	
	LOW	HIGH	Frequency	LOW	HIGH
Medical Equipment					
Power Scooter	$799.00	$1,349.00	Year 1–life/ replace every 5 years	$2,189.26	$3,696.26
Power Scooter Maintenance	$90.00	$135.00	Year 1–life/ annually/except purchase year	$986.40	$1,479.60
ROHO Cushion	$220.00	$374.00	Year 1–life/every 2 years	$1,507.00	$2,561.90
ROHO Cushion Cover	$39.00	$43.00	Year 1–life/ annually	$534.30	$589.10
Wheelchair Backpack	$33.65	$37.50	Year 1–life/every 2–3 years	$153.67	$256.88
Portable Ramps (3′ and 5′)	$267.99	$389.90	Year 1–life/ replace every 10 years	$367.15	$534.16
				$5,737.78	**$9,117.90**
Transportation					
Passenger Van with Adaptive Modif	$34,990.00	$34,995.00	Year 1–life/every 5 years	$95,872.60	$95,886.30
Adaptive Modifications	$-	$-	See passenger van	$-	$-
				$95,872.60	**$95,886.30**
Architectural Modifications and Accessories					
	$50,000.00	$50,000.00	Year 1–life/one time	$50,000.00	$50,000.00
				$50,000.00	**$50,000.00**

	UNIT COST			TOTAL COST	
	LOW	**HIGH**	**Frequency**	**LOW**	**HIGH**
Home/Facility Care					
Home Health Aide/ Cert. Nursing Asst.	$18.95	$21.00	Year 1–Life/10 hours per week	$134,999.80	$149,604.00
				$134,999.80	$149,604.00
Homemaker Care					
Heavy Housekeeping	$105.00	$135.00	Year 1–life/2 times per month	$34,524.00	$44,388.00
Lawn Services	$31.25	$33.73	Year 1–life/ weekly	$22,262.50	$24,029.25
Home Maintenance	$65.00	$65.00	Year 1–life/4–6 hours per month	$42,744.00	$64,116.00
				$99,530.50	**$132,533.25**

	TOTAL COST	
	LOW	**HIGH**
Physician and Professional Care	$196,030.77	$229,087.90
Medications	$97,813.09	$123,337.84
Diagnostic Tests	$21,296.00	$26,574.00
Laboratory Testing	$2,309.41	$3,053.32
Medical Equipment	$5,737.78	$9,117.90
Transportation	$95,872.60	$95,886.30
Architectural Modifications & Access	$50,000.00	$50,000.00
Home/Facility Care	$134,999.80	$149,604.00
Homemaker Care	$99,530.50	$132,533.25
	$703,589.95	**$819,194.51**

APPENDIX I

Sample Life Care Plan

2nd Update
Life Care Plan
Prepared for
Edwina Jones
Michael Shahnasarian, PhD
May 29, 2020

Table of Contents

CONTRIBUTORS TO LIFE CARE PLAN

The following individuals provided recommendations for this life care plan:

Contributor	Specialty	Consultation Date	Telephone
Dr. Michael Shahnasarian	Rehabilitation Psychologist	11/06/19	(813) 555-xxxx
Dr. Ron Wilson	Pain Management Physician	05/27/20 12/20/19	(813) 555-xxxx
Dr. Gabriel Taylor	Neurologist	05/19/20 01/14/20 Confirmation Form 12/16/19 05/26/20	(863) 555-xxxx
Dr. Thuy Richards	Neurosurgeon	05/06/20 Report	(813) 555-xxxx

All opinions presented herein are within a reasonable degree of life care planning certainty.

Year 1 in the duration section of this life care plan begins on the date this life care plan is published.

The *National Fee Analyzer* is published by FAIR Health, a nonprofit agency developed to ensure transparency in medical costs. The *National Fee Analyzer* provides physician practices with three percentiles (50th, 75th, and 90th) of charge data; only the 50th and 75th percentiles are incorporated into this life care plan. This resource provides physician practices with national charge data for fee scheduled evaluation and competitive analysis for contracting purposes. Compiled from a database of 650 million charge records arranged by CPT Codes, the *National Fee Analyzer* has no insurance company paid amounts incorporated into its product.

Diagnostic costs such as X-rays, MRIs, and CT scans are obtained solely from the 2020 *National Fee Analyzer* because costs cited by diagnostic centers are based on insurance reimbursement, thereby undervaluing the true cost.

Medication costs in this life care plan are pharmacy cash prices.

BACKGROUND INFORMATION

NAME:	Edwina Jones
DATE OF BIRTH:	July 11, 1960
ONSET OF DISABLING PROBLEM:	January 30, 2018, fall incident
RACE:	Caucasian
DOMINANT HAND:	Right
HEIGHT:	Approximately 5 feet 8 inches
CURRENT WEIGHT:	187 pounds
PREINCIDENT WEIGHT:	Uncertain
MARITAL STATUS:	Married, Davey Jones, age 60
CHILDREN:	Five adults
RESIDENCE:	Lakeland, Florida
PRESENTING PROBLEMS:	Severely impaired mobility Ongoing left lower extremity pain, most intense in knee Ongoing left hip pain Intermittent lower back pain due to altered gait, tends to flare up when bearing weight Intermittent right ankle/heel pain due to altered gait, tends to flare up when bearing weight Depression due to unwelcome postincident lifestyle changes and functional decline

EVALUATIONS

Item	Duration	Frequency	Estimated Cost	Recommended By
PAIN MANAGEMENT EVALUATION	Year 1*	One Time	$325–$1,326 per Evaluation	Dr. Wilson

*Note: Per Dr. Wilson, additional recommendations will follow the implantation of a permanent spinal cord stimulator.

Per October 29, 2019, billing from Florida Spine, office of Dr. Wilson, 813-555-xxxx (Tampa, FL): Pain management evaluation, $1,326 per evaluation using CPT Code 99204.

Per 2020 *National Fee Analyzer*, pain management evaluation, CPT Code 99204 (office or other outpatient visit for the evaluation of a new patient requires these three key components: a comprehensive history; a comprehensive examination; and medical decision-making of moderate complexity. Counseling and/or coordination of care with other physicians, other qualified health care professionals, or agencies are provided consistent with the nature of the problem(s) and the patient's and/or family's needs. Usually the presenting problem(s) are of moderate to high severity. Typically, 45 minutes are spent face to face with the patient and/or family), $325 to $415 per evaluation.

Item	Duration	Frequency	Estimated Cost	Recommended By
PHYSIATRIST EVALUATION	Year 1*	One Time	$214–$275 per Evaluation	Dr. Shahnasarian

*Note: Per Dr. Shahnasarian, additional recommendations will follow.

Per Eve Arden, financial representative at Lakeland Medical Center, 863-555-xxxx (Lakeland, FL): Physiatrist evaluation, $225 per evaluation using CPT Code 99203.

Per 2020 *National Fee Analyzer*, physiatrist evaluation, CPT Code 99203 (office or other outpatient visit for the evaluation of a new patient requires these three key components: a detailed history; a detailed examination; and medical decision-making of low complexity. Counseling and/or coordination of care with other physicians, other qualified health care professionals, or agencies are provided consistent with the nature of the problem(s) and the patient's and/or family's needs. Usually the presenting problem(s) are of moderate complexity. Typically, 30 minutes are spent face to face with the patient and/or family), $214 to $275 per evaluation.

Item	Duration	Frequency	Estimated Cost	Recommended By
ORTHOPEDIC SURGEON EVALUATION	Year 1*	One Time	$205–$260 per Evaluation	Dr. Taylor

*Note: Per Dr. Taylor, additional recommendations will follow.

Per Eve Arden, financial representative at Lakeland Medical Center, office of Dr. Alex Hamilton, 863-555-xxxx (Lakeland, FL): Orthopedic surgeon evaluation, $225 per evaluation using CPT Code 99203.

Per 2020 *National Fee Analyzer*, orthopedic surgeon evaluation, CPT Code 99203 (office or other outpatient visit for the evaluation of a new patient requires these three key components: a detailed history; a detailed examination; and medical decision-making of low complexity. Counseling and/or coordination of care with other physicians, other qualified health care professionals, or agencies are provided consistent with the nature of the problem(s) and the patient's and/or family's needs. Usually the presenting problem(s) are of moderate complexity. Typically, 30 minutes are spent face to face with the patient and/or family), $214 to $275 per evaluation.

EVALUATIONS

Item	Duration	Frequency	Estimated Cost	Recommended By
PSYCHIATRIC EVALUATION	Year 1*	One Time	$300–$375 per Evaluation	Dr. Shahnasarian

*Note: Per Dr. Shahnasarian, additional recommendations will follow.

Per Emily Smith, office manager at the office of Dr. Bob Dillon, 863-555-xxxx (Lakeland, FL): Psychiatric evaluation, $300 per evaluation using CPT Code 90792.

Per 2020 *National Fee Analyzer*, psychiatric evaluation, CPT Code 90792 (psychiatric diagnostic evaluation with medical services), $300 to $375 per evaluation.

Item	Duration	Frequency	Estimated Cost	Recommended By
PHYSICAL THERAPY EVALUATION	Year 1*	One Time	$150–$200 per Evaluation	Dr. Taylor

*Note: Per Dr. Taylor, additional recommendations will follow.

Per Tony Smith, owner at ABC Rehab Specialists, 813-555-xxxx (Lakeland, FL): Physical therapy evaluation, $180 per evaluation using CPT Code 97162.

Per 2020 *National Fee Analyzer*, physical therapy evaluation, CPT 97162 (physical therapy evaluation: moderate complexity, requiring these components: history of present problem with –one to two personal factors and/or comorbidities that impact the plan of care; an examination of body systems using standardized tests and measures addressing a total of three or more elements from any of the following: body structures and functions, activity limitations, and/or participation restrictions; an evolving clinical presentation with changing characteristics; and clinical decision-making of moderate complexity using standardized patient assessment instrument and/or measurable assessment of functional outcome. Typically 30 minutes are spent face to face with the patient and/or family), $150–$200 per evaluation.

Item	Duration	Frequency	Estimated Cost	Recommended By
UPDATE LIFE CARE PLAN	Year 10	One Time	$7,000 Total	Dr. Shahnasarian

Per Dr. Shahnasarian, update life care plan, year 10, one time; $7,000 total.

THERAPEUTIC NEEDS

Item	Duration	Frequency	Estimated Cost	Recommended By
PAIN MANAGEMENT FOLLOW-UP	Year 1–Life	1 Visit Every 6–12 Months	$206–$585 per Visit	Dr. Wilson

Note: Per Dr. Wilson, additional pain management intervention recommendations to follow.

Per Tara Smith, billing manager at Florida Spine Institute, office of Dr. Wilson, 813-555-xxxx (Tampa, FL): Pain management follow-up, $585 using CPT Code 99214.

Per 2020 *National Fee Analyzer*, pain management follow-up, CPT Code 99214 (office visit for the evaluation and management of an established patient, which requires at least two of these three components: a detailed history; a detailed examination; and medical decision-making of moderate complexity. Counseling and/or coordination of care with other physicians, other qualified health care professionals, or agencies are provided consistent with the nature of the problem(s) and the patient's and/or family's needs. Usually the presenting problem(s) are of moderate to high severity. Typically, 25 minutes are spent face to face with the patient), $206 to $263 per visit.

Item	Duration	Frequency	Estimated Cost	Recommended By
NEUROLOGIST FOLLOW-UP	Year 1*	One Time	$332–$529 per Visit	Dr. Taylor

*Note: Per Dr. Taylor, following NCV/EMG study. Additional recommendation to follow.

Per billing dated February 26, 2018, from Wilber Clinic, office of Dr. Taylor, neurologist follow-up, $332 using CPT Code 99244.

Per 2020 *National Fee Analyzer*, neurologist follow-up, CPT Code 99244 (office consultation for a new or established patient, which requires these three key components: a comprehensive history; a comprehensive examination; and medical decision-making of moderate complexity. Counseling and/or coordination of care with other physicians, other qualified health care professionals, or agencies are provided consistent with the nature of the problem(s) and the patient's and/or family's needs. Usually the presenting problem(s) are of moderate to high severity. Typically 60 minutes are spent face to face with the patient and/or family), $408 to $529 per evaluation.

Item	Duration	Frequency	Estimated Cost	Recommended By
NEUROSURGEON FOLLOW-UP	Year 1*	3 Visits Total	$206–$862 per Visit	Dr. Richards

*Note: Per Dr. Richards, postoperative visits following permanent spinal cord stimulator implantation. Additional follow-up treatment to be determined.

Per Tara Smith, billing manager at Florida Spine Institute, office of Dr. Richards, 813-555-xxxx (Tampa, FL): Neurosurgeon follow-up, $862 using CPT Code 99214.

Per 2020 *National Fee Analyzer*, neurosurgeon follow-up, CPT Code 99214 (office visit for the evaluation and management of an established patient, which requires at least two of these three components: a detailed history; a detailed examination; and medical decision-making of moderate complexity. Counseling and/or coordination of care with other physicians, other qualified health care professionals, or agencies are provided consistent with the nature of the problem(s) and the patient's and/or family's needs. Usually the presenting problem(s) are of moderate to high severity. Typically, 25 minutes are spent face to face with the patient), $206 to $263 per visit.

THERAPEUTIC NEEDS

Item	Duration	Frequency	Estimated Cost	Recommended By
BIOFEEDBACK TRAINING	Year 1–2*	8–12 Sessions Total	$80–$195 per Session	Dr. Shahnasarian

*Note: Per Dr. Shahnasarian, reassess potential to benefit from additional treatment at the end of this time. The goal of biofeedback training is to teach the individual to take control of physiological functions such as heart rate, respiratory rate, and muscle tension. In a typical training session, a person is affixed to electrical sensors that provide information about those functions. Over time the person can learn to pace breathing or relax muscles to produce a desired change in physiology.

Per David Smith, patient care coordinator at Holistic Center of Lakeland, office of Dr. Catherine O'Hara, 863-555-xxxx (Lakeland, FL): Biofeedback training, $80 per session using CPT Code 90901.

Per 2020 *National Fee Analyzer*, biofeedback training, CPT Code 90901 (biofeedback training by any modality), $100–$195 per session.

Item	Duration	Frequency	Estimated Cost	Recommended By
EPIDURAL INJECTIONS	To Be	To Be	$4,872	Dr. Wilson
MEDIAL BRANCH BLOCKS	Determined	Determined	$6,044	

Note: Per Dr. Wilson, depending on residual lower back pain following implantation of permanent spinal cord stimulator.

Note: Per Dr. Wilson, Ms. Jones may continue to require interventional pain management modalities after her permanent spinal cord stimulator has been implanted. Dr. Wilson will finalize his assessment after the device is implanted and he can assess her needs.

Per Tara Smith, billing manager at Florida Spine Institute, office of Dr. Wilson, 813-555-xxxx (Tampa, FL): Epidural injections lumbar, $2,436 for one side, $4,872 for bilateral using CPT Codes 64483 and 64484; medial branch blocks, $3,022 for one side, $6,044 for bilateral using CPT Codes 64493, 64494, and 64495. Per Tara, epidural injections are performed first, followed by medial branch blocks.

Item	Duration	Frequency	Estimated Cost	Recommended By
PSYCHOLOGICAL COUNSELING	Year 1 Year 2 to 3–4*	1 Session per Week for 20–30 Weeks; Then 1 Session Every 2 Weeks 1 Session per Month	$120–$180 per Session	Dr. Shahnasarian

*Note: Per Dr. Shahnasarian, reassess need to continue with this intervention at the end of this period.

Per Rebecca Smith, office manager at Psychological Group, office of Dr. Richard Thorogood, 863-555-xxxx (Lakeland, FL): Psychological counseling, $120 per session using CPT Code 90837.

Per 2020 *National Fee Analyzer*, psychological counseling, CPT Code 90837 (psychotherapy, 60 minutes with patient), $150–$180 per session.

THERAPEUTIC NEEDS

Item	Duration	Frequency	Estimated Cost	Recommended By
FAMILY COUNSELING	Year 1–2*	5–10 Sessions Total	$140–$188 per Session	Dr. Shahnasarian

*Note: Per Dr. Shahnasarian, reassess need to continue with this intervention at the end of this period.

Per Arielle Smith, patient coordinator at the Counseling Group, office of Dr. Diane Ladd, 863-555-xxxx (Lakeland, FL): Family counseling, $140 per session using CPT Code 90847.

Per 2020 *National Fee Analyzer*, family counseling, CPT Code 90847 (family psychotherapy (conjoint psychotherapy) (with patient present), 50 minutes), $150–$188 per session.

Item	Duration	Frequency	Estimated Cost	Recommended By
PHYSICAL THERAPY	Year 1–Life	12 Sessions per Year	$100–$158 per 30-Minute Session	Dr. Wilson

Note: Per Dr. Wilson, palliative care prescription.

Per Tony Smith, owner at ABC Rehab Specialists, 813-555-xxxx (Lakeland, FL): Physical therapy, $100 per 30-minute session using CPT Code 97110.

Per 2020 *National Fee Analyzer*, physical therapy, CPT Code 97110 (therapeutic procedure, one or more areas, each 15 minutes; therapeutic exercises to develop strength and endurance, range of motion, and flexibility), $60 to $79; $120 to $158 per 30-minute session.

DIAGNOSTIC TESTS

Item	Duration	Frequency	Estimated Cost	Recommended By
NERVE CONDUCTION STUDY (NCS)/ ELECTROMYOGRAPHY (EMG)	Year 1–2*	One Time	$490–$800 Each Time	Dr. Wilson Dr. Taylor

Per Dr. Taylor's January 14, 2020, confirmation form, "Would suggest repeating NCS/EMG at Westgate Center to see if she still has denervation of the quadriceps or if it has resolved before making further arrangements."

*Note: Per Dr. Wilson, additional recommendations will follow.

*Note: Per Dr. Taylor, year 1, one time to determine recovery of femoral nerve to assess functional recovery potential. Additional recommendations will follow.

Per billing dated March 12, 2018, from Wilber Clinic, office of Dr. Taylor, nerve conduction study, $347 using CPT Code 95909; and needle EMG, $143 using CPT Code 95886; totaling $490.

Per 2020 *National Fee Analyzer*, electromyogram (EMG), CPT Code 95886 (needle electromyography; each extremity, with related paraspinal areas, when performed, done with nerve conduction, amplitude, and latency/velocity; complete, five or more muscles studied, innervated by three or more nerves or four or more spinal levels), $229 to $300; and nerve conduction study, CPT Code 95909 (nerve conduction study, five to six studies), $365 to $500; totaling $594 to $800 each time.

X-RAY LUMBAR SPINE	To Be Determined	To Be Determined	$105–$134 Each Time	Dr. Richards

Note: Per Dr. Richards, X-ray lumbar spine (SCS device), if pain relief following implantation of permanent spinal cord stimulator is insufficient.

Per 2020 *National Fee Analyzer*, X-ray of lumbar spine, CPT Code 72100 (radiologic examination, spine, lumbosacral; two to three views), $105 to $134 each time.

MRI LUMBAR SPINE	Year 1*	One Time	$1,332–$1,750 Each Time	Dr. Wilson Dr. Richards

*Note: Per Dr. Wilson, additional recommendations will follow.

Note: Per Dr. Richards, to be determined.

Per 2020 *National Fee Analyzer*, MRI lumbar spine, CPT Code 72148 (magnetic resonance, imaging, spinal canal and contents, lumbar; without contrast material), $1,332 to $1,750 each time.

CT SCAN LUMBAR SPINE (SCS DEVICE)	To Be Determined	To Be Determined	$716–$935 Each Time	Dr. Richards

Note: Per Dr. Richards, CT scan lumbar spine (SCS device), if pain relief following implantation of permanent spinal cord stimulator is insufficient.

Per 2020 *National Fee Analyzer*, CT lumbar spine, CPT Code 72131 (computed tomography, lumbar spine; without contrast material), $716 to $935 each time.

ORTHOTICS

Item	Duration	Frequency	Estimated Cost	Recommended By
SOFT KNEE BRACE LEFT	Year 1–Life	Replace Every 2–3 Years	$29.99–$44.99 Each	Dr. Shahnasarian

Per BraceMe, www.braceme.com: Non-Slip Knee Wrap, $34.99 each; Neoprene Knee Sleeve, $29.99 each; Breathable Open Patella Knee Sleeve, $34.99 each.

Per Supreme Braces, www.supremebraces.com: DonJoy Stabilizing Knee Sleeve, $44.99 each; DonJoy Deluxe Knit Knee Sleeve, $29.99 each.

Item	Duration	Frequency	Estimated Cost	Recommended By
LONG LOWER EXTREMITY BRACE LEFT (HARD)	Year 1–Life	Replace Every 2–3 Years	$136.97– $269.97 Each	Dr. Shahnasarian

Per Orthoway, www.orthoway.com: Long Lower Extremity Knee Brace, $136.97 to $269.97 each.

Per National Ortho, www.nationalortho.com: Long Lower Extremity Knee Brace, $139.99 to $219 each.

AIDS FOR INDEPENDENT LIVING

Item	Duration	Frequency	Estimated Cost	Recommended By
HURRYCANE	Year 1–Life	Replace Every 5–7 Years	$39.95 Each	Dr. Shahnasarian

Per Hurrycane, www.hurrycane.com: Hurrycane Freedom Folding Cane, $39.95 each; Hurrycane Go Non-Folding Cane, $39.95 each.

Item	Duration	Frequency	Estimated Cost	Recommended By
WHEELED WALKER	Year 1–Life	Replace Every 5–7 Years	$59.99–$199.99 Each	Dr. Shahnasarian

Per Walgreens Pharmacy, www.walgreens.com: Nova Traveler 3 Wheeled Walker, $99.95 each; Medline Empower Rolling Walker, $199.99 each.

Per CVS Pharmacy, www.cvs.com: Drive Medical Two Wheeled Walker, $59.99 each; Drive Medical Clever Lite LS Walker, $152.99 each.

Item	Duration	Frequency	Estimated Cost	Recommended By
MISCELLANEOUS ADAPTIVE AIDS/PATIENT EDUCATION	Year 1–Life	Annually	$300–$400 per Year	Dr. Shahnasarian

Per Dr. Shahnasarian, miscellaneous adaptive aids/patient education, $300 to $400 per year. Examples include hot/cold packs, grab rails, handheld shower nozzle, shower chair, emergency signaling devices, and personal care devices.

DRUG AND SUPPLY NEEDS

Item	Duration	Frequency	Estimated Cost	Recommended By
GABAPENTIN (NEURONTIN) 300 MG	Year 1–Life	3 Tablets per Day	$15.39–$85.99 per 90 Tablets	Dr. Wilson

Per pharmacies listed below, gabapentin is the generic medication for Neurontin. Per Walgreens, Neurontin 300 mg, $602.49; per CVS, $549.99 per 90 tablets.

Per GoodRX/Walgreens, Neurontin 300 mg, $572.39; per GoodRX/CVS, $559.99 per 90 tablets.

Per Janet Smith, pharmacy technician at Walgreens Pharmacy, 863-555-xxxx (Lakeland, FL): Gabapentin 300 mg, $81.99 per 90 tablets.

Per Barney Miller, pharmacy technician at CVS Pharmacy, 863-555-xxxx (Lakeland, FL): Gabapentin 300 mg, $85.99 per 90 tablets.

Per GoodRX/Walgreens: Gabapentin 300 mg, $25.82 per 90 tablets.

Per GoodRX/CVS: Gabapentin 300 mg, $15.39 per 90 tablets.

Item	Duration	Frequency	Estimated Cost	Recommended By
BACLOFEN (LIORESAL) 10 MG	Year 1–Life	3 Tablets per Day	$44.24–$69.99 per 90 Tablets	Dr. Wilson

Note: Per Dr. Wilson, for spasms.

Per pharmacies listed below, baclofen is the generic medication for Lioresal. Per Walgreens, Lioresal 10 mg, $69.89; per CVS, $72.99 per 90 tablets.

Per GoodRX/Walgreens and GoodRX/CVS, Lioresal is no longer available.

Per Janet Smith, pharmacy technician at Walgreens Pharmacy, 863-555-xxxx (Lakeland, FL): Baclofen 10 mg, $67.99 per 90 tablets.

Per Barney Miller, pharmacy technician at CVS Pharmacy, 863-555-xxxx (Lakeland, FL): Baclofen 10 mg, $69.99 per 90 tablets.

Per GoodRX/Walgreens: Baclofen 10 mg, $60.72 per 90 tablets.

Per GoodRX/CVS: Baclofen 10 mg, $44.24 per 90 tablets.

Item	Duration	Frequency	Estimated Cost	Recommended By
DICLOFENAC (VOLTAREN) 50 MG OR MELOXICAM (MOBIC) 7.5 MG	Year 1–2*	1 Tablet per Day as Needed	$18.31–$28.19 per 30 Tablets	Dr. Taylor

*Note: Per Dr. Taylor, reassess need to continue this medication at the end of this period.

Per pharmacies listed below, diclofenac and meloxicam are equivalent in relieving pain. Diclofenac is the generic medication for Voltaren. Voltaren is not available. Meloxicam is the generic medication for Mobic. Per Walgreens, Mobic 7.5 mg, $328.99; per CVS, $318.99 per 30 tablets.

Per GoodRX/Walgreens, Voltaren is not available; Mobic 7.5 mg, $296.48 per 30 tablets; per GoodRX/CVS, Voltaren is not available; Mobic 7.5 mg, $290.17 per 30 tablets.

Per Janet Smith, pharmacy technician at Walgreens Pharmacy, 863-555-xxxx (Lakeland, FL): Diclofenac 50 mg, $25.49 per 30 tablets; meloxicam 7.5 mg, $25.99 per 30 tablets.

Per Barney Miller, pharmacy technician at CVS Pharmacy, 863-555-xxxx (Lakeland, FL): Diclofenac 50 mg, $24.69 per 30 tablets; meloxicam, $28.19 per 30 tablets.

Per GoodRX/Walgreens: Diclofenac 50 mg, $21.49 per 30 tablets; meloxicam 7.5 mg, $24.97 per 30 tablets.

Per GoodRx/CVS: Diclofenac 50 mg, $19.82 per 30 tablets; meloxicam 7.5 mg, $18.31 per 30 tablets.

DRUG AND SUPPLY NEEDS

Item	Duration	Frequency	Estimated Cost	Recommended By
ICY HOT TOPICAL PAIN CREAM	Year 1–Life	Apply Daily as Needed*	$7.99–$9.29 per 3.5 Ounces per Month	*

*Per Dr. Shahnasarian's November 6, 2019, evaluation, Ms. Jones indicated she applies Icy Hot Topical Pain Cream daily as needed.

Per Walgreens, www.walgreens.com: Icy Hot Pain Relieving Balm, $7.99 per 3.5 ounces per month.

Per CVS, www.cvs.com: Icy Hot Pain Relieving Balm, $9.29 per 3.5 ounces per month.

HOME/FACILITY CARE

Item	Duration	Frequency	Estimated Cost	Recommended By
PERSONAL CARE ATTENDANT	Year 1–10 Year 11–Life	2–4 Hours per Day 4–6 Hours per Day	$18–$20 per Hour	Dr. Shahnasarian

Per Amber Smith, scheduling coordinator for Helping Hands Home Health Care, 863-555-xxxx (Lakeland, FL): Personal care attendant, $20 per hour.

Per Dane Miller, staff administrator at Care at Home, 863-555-xxxx (Winter Haven, FL): Personal care attendant, $18 per hour.

Item	Duration	Frequency	Estimated Cost	Recommended By
HOUSEKEEPER	Year 1 to Year 5–10 Year 6–11 to Life	1 Visit Every 2 Weeks 1 Visit per Week	$112–$150 per Visit $85–$100 per Visit	Dr. Shahnasarian

Per Keith Smith, manager at Clean Pro of Polk County, 863-555-xxxx (Lakeland, FL): Housekeeper, $85 for weekly visits; $112 for biweekly visit.

Per Stephanie Miller, manager at Side by Side, 863-555-xxxx (Lakeland, FL): Housekeeper, $100 for weekly visit; $150 for biweekly visit.

Item	Duration	Frequency	Estimated Cost	Recommended By
LAWN MAINTENANCE SERVICES	To Be Determined	To Be Determined	$70–$80 per Visit	Dr. Shahnasarian

Per Kyle Smith, owner of Kyle Smith's Lawn Service, 863-555-xxxx (Lakeland, FL): Lawn maintenance services, $80 per visit.

Per Charles Miller, owner of Mo My Lawn, 863-555-xxxx (Lakeland, FL): Lawn maintenance services, $70 per visit.

Item	Duration	Frequency	Estimated Cost	Recommended By
CASE MANAGER	Year 1*	20–25 Hours	$110 per Hour	Dr. Shahnasarian

*Note: Per Dr. Shahnasarian, reassess need to continue with this intervention at the end of this period.

Per Care Professionals, LLC, Diane Smith, MA, CMC, 813-555-xxxx (Tampa, FL): Case management visits including travel time, $110 per hour.

TRANSPORTATION NEEDS

Item	Duration	Frequency	Estimated Cost	Recommended By
AAA AUTO CLUB OR ONSTAR	Year 1–Life	Annually	$68–$349.90 per Year	Dr. Shahnasarian

Per AAA Auto South Club, www.aaa.com: There are three different auto club membership levels depending on the choice of coverage: AAA Classic, $68 per year; AAA Plus, $104 per year; and AAA Premier, $131 per year.

OnStar services are available on select new cars (GM, Cadillac, etc.). Either the system is factory installed or the car must meet the requirements to have the system installed. Initial costs for installing the system vary. Per OnStar Plans & Pricing at www.onstar.com, depending on the choice of coverage: OnStar Remote Access, $149.90 per year; Safety & Security, $249.90 per year; and Premium, $349.90 per year.

Item	Duration	Frequency	Estimated Cost	Recommended By
DISABLED PERSON PARKING PERMIT	Year 1–Life	Replace Every 4 Years	No Charge	Dr. Shahnasarian

Per the State of Florida, Department of Highway Safety and Motor Vehicle, https://www.flhsmv.gov/motor-vehicles-tags-titles/disabled-person-parking-permits/ : Chapter 320.0848, Florida Statutes, allows for the issuance of Disabled Parking Permits. There is no charge for a four-year disabled person parking permit. The fee for a temporary disabled person parking permit is $15, including tax collector fees. Form HSMV 83039 must be completed and signed by the certifying authority within the last 12 months that establishes eligibility for a disabled parking permit. Proof of the disability must be indicated on Form HSMV 83039, certifying authority's Statement of Certification section.

ARCHITECTURAL RENOVATIONS

Item	Duration	Frequency	Estimated Cost	Recommended By
HOME ENVIRONMENTAL ANALYSIS	Year 1*	One Time	$789 Total	Dr. Shahnasarian

*Note: Per Dr. Shahnasarian, additional recommendations will follow.

Per Joe Smith, project manager estimator at Nevada Construction, Inc., www.nevadaconstruction.com or 800-555-xxxx, the cost of a home assessment for accessibility and modifications is $789 for central Florida.

HOSPITALIZATIONS/SURGERIES

Item	Duration	Frequency	Estimated Cost	Recommended By
SPINAL CORD STIMULATOR IMPLANTATION	Year 1	One Time	$75,200 Total	Dr. Richards Dr. Wilson

Per Dr. Richards's May 6, 2020, report, "Patient had successful spinal cord stimulator trial with Dr. Wilson stating 50% pain relief in back and leg. Due to the patient's condition I am recommending spinal cord stimulator placement at T8."

Note: Per Dr. Richards, Ms. Jones underwent a successful spinal cord stimulator trial on April 29, 2020.

Note: Per Dr. Wilson, Dr. Richards will be implanting within three months of the trial.

Per Tara Smith, billing manager at Florida Spine Institute, office of Dr. Wilson, 813-555-xxxx (Tampa, FL), Dr. Wilson uses CPT Code 63655, and his physician fee is $7,147 (for two leads); CPT Code 63685, and his physician fee is $3,081; and CPT Code 95972, and his physician fee is $472. He also uses a physician assistant for this procedure, and the PA fee is $5,350. This is an outpatient procedure performed at Florida Surgcenter.

Physician fee: $10,700

Physician assistant fee: $5,350

Facility fee: $28,000

Per Laura Miller, surgical scheduler at Surgcenter, 727-555-xxxx (Dunedin, FL), facility fee for CPT Codes 63655, 63685, and 95972 is $28,000.

Anesthesia: $1,150

Per Laura Miller, surgical scheduler at Surgcenter, 727-555-xxxx (Dunedin, FL), anesthesia for CPT Codes 63655, 63685, and 95972 with a procedure time of two hours is $1,150.

Spinal cord stimulator (permanent), $30,000

Per David Ricardo, sales representative at Blount Neuromodulation, 813-555-xxxx, the permanent spinal cord stimulator unit is approximately $30,000. This is the cost to the facility.

Item	Duration	Frequency	Estimated Cost	Recommended By
SPINAL CORD STIMULATOR BATTERY REPLACEMENT	Year 7–10 to Life	Replace Every 7–10 Years	$47,279.50 Each Time	Dr. Richards Dr. Wilson

Per Dr. Richards's May 6, 2020, report, "Patient had successful spinal cord stimulator trial with Dr. Wilson stating 50% pain relief in back and leg. Due to the patient's condition I am recommending spinal cord stimulator placement at T8."

Note: Per Dr. Richards, Ms. Jones underwent a successful spinal cord stimulator trial on April 29, 2020.

Per Tara Smith, billing manager at Florida Spine Institute, office of Dr. Wilson, 813-555-xxxx (Tampa, FL), Dr. Wilson uses CPT Code 63685, and his physician fee is $3,081 (for two leads); and CPT Code 95972, and his physician fee is $472. He also uses a physician assistant for this procedure, and the PA fee is $1,776.50. This is an outpatient procedure performed at Florida Surgcenter.

Physician fee: $3,553

Physician assistant fee: $1,776.50

Facility fee: $24,000

Per Laura Miller, surgical scheduler at Surgcenter, 727-555-xxxx (Dunedin, FL), facility fee for CPT Codes 63685 and 95972 is $24,000.

Anesthesia: $950

Per Laura Miller, surgical scheduler at Surgcenter, 727-555-xxxx (Dunedin, FL), anesthesia for CPT Codes 63685 and 95972 with a procedure time of one hour and 30 minutes is $950.

Battery replacement charge: $17,000

Note: Per David Ricardo, sales representative at Blount Neuromodulation, 813-555-xxxx, the battery replacement charge is approximately $17,000. This is the cost to the facility.

POTENTIAL COMPLICATIONS

Per Dr. Shahnasarian:

At risk for fracture injuries secondary to falls.

Sample Authorization Form Extending Permission to Consult with Treating Healthcare Providers

Date
Name, Esq.
Company
Suite ___
Address
City
Email
RE: ___

Dear Mr./Ms. ___:

When retained by defense counsel, Dr. Shahnasarian has been questioned, both at deposition and at trial, whether he had asked permission from plaintiff's attorney to speak to plaintiff's treating physicians to obtain future care recommendations for the life care plan.

Accordingly, can you please ask _____'s attorney whether they will give Dr. Shahnasarian permission to speak to plaintiff's treating physicians, so we have documentation in the file? Please document the reply and send back to me to place in my file.

Sincerely,

_____

Contributor Verification Form (Two Pages)

Date

Doctor

Address

RE: _____

Dear:

Attached is a life care plan developed for _____.

Thank you for your assistance in identifying the future needs anticipated for _____. Please let us know, by faxing back the attached confirmation form, whether you have any changes or wish to add to any of your recommendations. A hard copy will follow in the mail.

Thank you again for your help regarding this matter.

Sincerely,

Michael Shahnasarian, PhD

President

MS/rb

Encl.

Dictated by Dr. Shahnasarian and signed in his absence to avoid delay.

Michael Shahnasarian, PhD

11019 North Dale Mabry Highway

Tampa, FL 33618

813-265-9262   813-265-4226 FAX

CONFIRMATION FORM

DATE:

_____

FROM: Doctor Name

_____

TO: Michael Shahnasarian, PhD

_____

FAX NO: (813) 265-4226

_____

RE: Life Care Plan _____

MESSAGE:

____ I have received the life care plan prepared by Michael Shahnasarian, PhD, reviewed my recommendations, and have no changes to offer.

____ I have received the life care plan prepared by Michael Shahnasarian, PhD, reviewed my recommendations, and suggest the following changes:

Signature   Date   _____   _____

Confidentiality Notice

The information contained in this facsimile message is legally privileged and confidential information intended only for use of the individual or entity named. If the reader of this message is not the intended recipient or an employee or agent of the addressee, please do not read, use, disclose, copy, or distribute this message. If you have received this facsimile in error, please notify us immediately by telephone to arrange for its return.

Notes Summarizing a Life Care Planner's Consultations and Visits to Rehabilitation Facilities

Report of January 21, 2020, Site Visits in Guatemala City

On January 21, 2020, I toured four healthcare facilities in Guatemala City: Hospital Universitario Esperanza, Clinicas Blue Medical, Clinica Nino Sano (affiliated with Hospital Roosevelt), and Hospital Herrera Llerandi. Maya Bolanos provided English/Spanish translation services, as needed. Most of the physicians with whom I met spoke English, as they had trained in the United States and/or the United Kingdom. A report of information I gathered during my consultations/site visits follows. Appendix A includes various photos I took during my site visits.

Hospital Universitario Esperanza

The Hospital Universitario Esperanza is a private hospital that also provides opportunities for medical students to complete their training. I initially met the medical director, Dr. Duarte, and then Dr. Steiger (chief of internal medicine) met with me to discuss Mr. Sanchez's special care needs. Specifically, I reviewed with Dr. Steiger my January 4, 2020, life care plan. He conveyed that Hospital Universitario Esperanza has physicians and allied healthcare providers who can fully implement the plan.

After my initial consultation with Dr. Steiger, he provided a tour of the hospital, including its diagnostic facilities, general hospital room section, and therapy facilities including physical therapy, operating room, and intensive care unit.

Hospital Universitario Esperanza has six ICU beds and 75 general hospital beds. There are seven pulmonary specialists and six or seven dermatologists on staff.

I met with the physical therapy staff and reviewed with them Mr. Sanchez's pulmonary and respiratory care needs. They assured me they had the expertise and resources necessary to implement the recommendations stated in the life care plan I prepared for Mr. Sanchez.

Again, at the conclusion of my tour of Hospital Universitario Esperanza, I reviewed Mr. Sanchez's entire life care plan with Dr. Steiger. He reiterated that the hospital has the expertise and resources necessary to implement the plan in its entirety including the mental health treatment recommendations. Dr. Steiger elaborated about the quality of instruction and training at the hospital. Further, he noted the hospital has residential facilities on its premises for family members to stay—one person per night, at no charge. I found the hospital quite clean, and it appeared well organized.

Clinicas Blue Medical

Clinicas Blue Medical is a private facility. Patients make appointments for services, which are all outpatient services. The facility takes both private pay and insurance reimbursement.

Dr. Martinez, the medical director of Clinicas Blue Medical, initially met with me and then provided a tour. He explained that there are three Blue Medical clinics in Guatemala City and one in Costa Rica.

Almost all services at Clinicas Blue Medical are outpatient, although the facility does take some short-term patients with non-life-threatening conditions. They do not provide respiratory therapy, but they do provide physical and occupational therapies. Mental health services are not available at Clinicas Blue Medical. Dr. Martinez advised me his facility refers patients to specialists, as needed. A pharmacy is on site.

While touring Clinicas Blue Medical, I spoke with a physical therapist on staff and explained Mr. Sanchez's manual limitations/capacities. She advised me she has worked with other burn patients, and she described physical therapy modalities she would likely advise.

I also spoke with a trauma physician and reviewed the projected contracture release procedures for Mr. Sanchez. He noted a plastic surgeon would have to perform them, and he recommended the Hospital Herrera Llerandi for this.

Dr. Martinez showed me exam, therapy, and diagnostic testing rooms. While I was touring the latter, a technician demonstrated on a computer how the facility takes and uses ultrasound and digital X-rays.

The Clinicas Blue Medical facility I toured is near Roosevelt Hospital. I found it quite clean and, like Hospital Universitario Esperanza, apparently well organized.

Clinica Nino Sano (affiliated with Hospital Roosevelt)

The Clinica Nino Sano is on the Hospital Roosevelt campus and is a public facility that is a freestanding burn unit. Services are provided free to patients, although patients are encouraged to make donations as they are able. The Clinica Nino Sano is funded by private sources—a domestic sugarcane company was noted as the primary source.

Dr. Lourdes Santizo, a cosmetic surgeon specializing in burn and reconstruction surgery, met with me and then provided a tour of Clinica Nino Sano. I presented Mr. Sanchez's life care plan to her, and she told me the operations included in the life care plan are ones she performs "all the time." Dr. Santizo advised me she has privileges at Hospital Universitario Esperanza and likely would perform the surgeries there. She went on to note she would probably supervise Mr. Sanchez's rehabilitation at Clinica Nino Sano.

Dr. Santizo informed me her burn unit has full therapy services available to burn patients. Additionally, she noted the facility has a psychologist on staff. The unit I toured provides outpatient rehabilitation treatment to burn patients, mostly pediatric burn patients. Dr. Santizo noted Clinica Nino Sano is the premier burn-treatment facility in Guatemala. While touring the facility, I was shown places in the unit where both pressure garments and splints are made on site for patients.

Again, after reviewing the Arizona-based life care plan I prepared for Mr. Sanchez, Dr. Santizo assured me that she is able to perform the requisite surgeries and that her burn unit could then provide the outpatient therapies. Any imaging, if needed, could be performed at nearby Roosevelt Hospital. Additionally, Roosevelt Hospital provides a full complement of medical and rehabilitation services.

At the conclusion of my tour, Dr. Santizo indicated she was interested in pictures of Mr. Sanchez. We discussed his heterotopic ossification, and she went on to note he would likely require pressure garments and topical ointments. We also discussed his mental health treatment needs.

The time required to schedule an appointment at Clinica Nino Sano is approximately one week. Two physical therapists are on staff.

Hospital Herrera Llerandi

Dr. Bautista (director of medical services) and Dr. Constanza (plastic and reconstructive surgeon) consulted with me about Mr. Sanchez's treatment needs. Like my other site visits, I began by reviewing with the physicians and healthcare professionals my January 4, 2020, life care plan. After discussing the plan, I was provided a site tour. During the tour, I interacted with other physicians and healthcare professionals and discussed Mr. Sanchez's injuries and treatment needs.

Hospital Herrera Llerandi is a private facility that is ISO certified. Dr. Constanza informed me that he will be in Scottsdale, Arizona, in late January, and he offered to examine Mr. Sanchez at no cost on January 29, 2020. Dr. Bautista also suggested a Skype interview of Mr. Sanchez that would enable physicians at Hospital Herrera Llerandi to visually assess his burns and available donor sites.

The Hospital Herrera Llerandi uses a peer-review system, Dr. Constanza explained. Most of its physicians are trained in the United States, although Dr. Constanza advised me he trained at the Nottingham City Hospital in the United Kingdom.

Dr. Bautista explained that Hospital Herrera Llerandi is in the process of becoming affiliated with Hospital Universitario Esperanza. Hospital Herrera Llerandi is a private facility with 11 ICU beds and 63 general beds. Additionally, it has an emergency room and several surgical suites. While touring the surgical suites, I was advised the hospital is preparing one for an upcoming renal transplant. A new MRI facility was under construction.

After reviewing the Arizona-based life care plan I prepared for Mr. Sanchez, Dr. Bautista and Dr. Constanza reported Hospital Herrera Llerandi could fully meet Mr. Sanchez's treatment needs. While reviewing my life care plan, they indicated they know several of the physicians listed on it, including Dr. Amenadar and Dr. Moralejo—both pulmonologists who have privileges at Hospital Herrera Llerandi. Dr. Constanza advised me he performs the two surgeries listed on the life care plan I prepared for Mr. Sanchez. While touring the hospital, I was introduced to another plastic surgeon on staff.

Hospital Herrera Llerandi also has outpatient therapy services. Additionally, Dr. Bautista and Dr. Constanza advised me physical therapy is provided bedside to patients after surgeries during the acute recovery phase.

I referenced Mr. Sanchez's home in Huehetenango, and Dr. Constanza advised me he has contacts at a hospital there. He indicated he would be willing to staff Mr. Sanchez's case with his colleague.

Dr. Bautista and Dr. Constanza discussed with me a case management system that Hospital Herrera Llerandi implements. A primary care physician is the center of this system, they noted.

In addition to reviewing Mr. Sanchez's life care plan with Dr. Bautista and Dr. Constanza, I reviewed with them my narrative reports dated July 27 and October 7, 2020. Dr. Constanza was particularly interested in the surgeries Mr. Sanchez has undergone, and he noted he has performed all of them. He spoke at length about a surgery Dr. Smith performed on November 19, 2010—a procedure that involved tangential excision of all full-thickness burn wounds and application of allograft—noting he trained under a physician in the United Kingdom who developed the technique. Then, in 1977, Dr. Constanza introduced the technique in Guatemala.

Hospital Herrera Llerandi was quite clean and, like the other facilities I visited, appeared well organized. Additionally, it appeared well staffed, and I was particularly impressed by the attentiveness and attention to detail the staff members demonstrated.

Sample Order Denying a Daubert Motion to Exclude or Otherwise Limit the Testimony of a Defense Expert in a Medical Malpractice Case

UNITED STATES DISTRICT COURT
MIDDLE DISTRICT OF TENNESSEE
NASHVILLE DIVISION

STEVEN HARMON,
Plaintiff,
v.   Case No.
ACE HEALTH SERVICES, INC.
Defendants.

_____/

ORDER

This cause comes before the Court upon Plaintiff's *Daubert* Motion to Exclude or Otherwise Limit the Testimony of Defense Expert, Dr. Michael Shahnasarian. Ace Correctional Health Services, Inc. (Defendants), filed a Response in Opposition thereto (Doc. 308). Upon consideration of the relevant filings, case law, and being otherwise fully advised, plaintiff's motion is denied.

I. Standard of Review

The decision to exclude an expert's testimony is reserved to the discretion of the district courts. *Hughes v. Kia Motors Corp.*, 766 F.3d 1317, 1331 (11th Cir. 2014). "Federal Rule of Evidence 702, as explained by the Supreme Court in *Daubert v. Merrell Dow Pharmaceuticals, Inc.*, 509 U.S. 579, 589, 113 S. Ct. 2786, 2794–95, 125 L. Ed. 2d 469 (1993), and its progeny, controls determinations regarding the admissibility of expert testimony." *City of Tuscaloosa v. Harcros Chems., Inc.*, 158 F.3d 548, 562 (11th Cir. 1998). Under Daubert and Rule 702, the Court serves as the gatekeeper to the admission of scientific, technical, or other specialized evidence. *Quiet Tech. DC-8, Inc. v. Hurel-Dubois UK Ltd.*, 326 F.3d 1333, 1340 (11th Cir. 2003); *McCorvey v. Baxter Healthcare Corp.*, 298 F.3d 1253, 1256 (11th Cir. 2002); *Rink v. Cheminova, Inc.*, 400 F.3d 1286, 1291 (11th Cir. 2005). The "gatekeeper role, however, is not intended to supplant the adversary system or the role of the jury." *Allison v. McGhan Med. Corp.*, 184 F.3d 1300, 1311 (11th Cir. 1999). "Vigorous cross-examination, presentation of contrary evidence, and careful instruction on the burden of proof are traditional and appropriate means of attacking" expert testimony. *Daubert*, 509 U.S. at 596.

With that in mind, Federal Rule of Evidence 702 requires district courts to ensure "that an expert's testimony both rests on a reliable foundation and is relevant to the task at hand." *Daubert*, 509 U.S. at 597. Rule 702 states that a witness, qualified as an expert by knowledge, skill, experience, training, or education, may testify in the form of an opinion or otherwise, if

> (a) the expert's scientific, technical, or other specialized knowledge will help the trier of fact to understand the evidence or to determine a fact in issue; (b) the testimony is based on sufficient facts or data; (c) the testimony is the product of reliable principles and methods; and (d) the expert has reliably applied the principles and methods to the facts of the case.

FED. R. EVID. 702. As such, in determining the admissibility of the proffered expert testimony under Rule 702, the party proffering the expert bears the burden of demonstrating that the expert is qualified to render a competent opinion on the matter to be addressed, that the methodology of such opinion is reliable as determined by a Daubert inquiry, and that the testimony would assist the trier of fact to understand the evidence or determine a fact in issue through the application of such expertise. *United States v. Frazier*, 387 F.3d 1244, 1260 (11th Cir. 2004) (citations omitted); *Adams v. Lab'y Corp. of Am.*, 760 F.3d 1322, 1328 (11th Cir. 2014) (citing *Kilpatrick v. Breg, Inc.*, 613 F.3d 1329, 1335 (11th Cir. 2010)). The Eleventh Circuit refers to these three considerations separately as "qualification, reliability, and helpfulness." *Frazier*, 387 F.3d at 1260. Additionally, *Kumho Tire Co., Ltd. v. Carmichael*, 526 U.S. 137 (1999), highlighted the fact that the *Daubert* factors do not constitute a definitive test and "may or may not be pertinent in assessing reliability, depending on the nature of the issue, the expert's particular expertise, and the subject of his testimony" as "[a] trial judge [has] considerable leeway in deciding in a particular case how to go about determining whether particular expert testimony is reliable." *Id.* at 150, 152. Finally, a party offering testimony from an expert must show by a preponderance of evidence that the testimony is admissible. *Allison*, 184 F.3d at 1306 (citations omitted).

II. Discussion[1]

Dr. Shahnasarian was disclosed by the defendant as their life care plan expert. Dr. Shahnasarian's life care plan for Mr. Harmon provides for his placement in a skilled nursing home facility. Dr. Shahnasarian testified that he adopted the life care plan of Plaintiff's expert, Dr. Kyle Lamb, in pertinent part. The main difference in the experts' life care plans is that Dr. Shahnasarian included a recommendation for a skilled nursing facility, along with a home-based placement option, while Dr. Lamb's life care plan includes a home-based placement option only.

Plaintiff asserts that Dr. Shahnasarian's testimony should be excluded because he is not a medical doctor and, therefore, not qualified to make recommendations for Mr. Harmon's placement in a skilled care facility. Plaintiff, however, fails to cite any legal authority for his proposition.[2] The defendant, on the other hand, cites numerous cases supporting Dr. Shahnasarian's methodology and the argument that he should be permitted to testify despite not being a medical doctor. See Doc. 308 at 6 (citing *Marcano Rivera v. Turabo Med. Ctr. P'ship*, 415 F.3d 162, 170–71 (1st Cir. 2005) (finding district court did not abuse its discretion in holding the fact that the life care planner did not have a physician review his projections regarding plaintiff's future medical needs went to "the weight, not to the expertise"); *Garcia v. Kelly-Springfield Tire Co.*, No. 8:99-cv-1611-T-17TGW, 2004 WL 5642430, at *1–2 (M.D. Fla. Mar. 2, 2004) (holding objections that the life care planner was not a physician and was not qualified to render an opinion as to plaintiff's future medical needs go to weight, not admissibility); *Blair v. Samardjich, M.D.*, No. CV202-114, 2003 WL 25764890, at *1 (S.D. Ga. Sept. 23, 2003) (holding that issues raised by defendant including that life care planner is not qualified to testify on the medical matter at issue are credibility issues, not admissibility); *Frometa v. Diaz-Diaz*, No. 07 Civ. 6372(HB), 2008 WL 4192501, at *2–3 (S.D.N.Y. Sept. 11, 2008) (holding that a life care planner's experience and review of medical records was sufficient to qualify under Daubert); *Rosiere v. Wood Towing, LLC*, No. 07-1265, 2009 WL 982659, at *1 (E.D. La. Apr. 8, 2009) (determining that a life care planner's opinions had a proper and reliable medical basis); *North v. Ford Motor Co.*, 505 F. Supp. 2d 1113, 1119–20 (D. Utah 2007) (holding life care planner had sound methodology and met *Daubert*, and she could rely on other experts' reports or information)). Importantly, Dr. Shahnasarian is not offering opinions as to what medical care Mr. Harmon requires; rather, he is opining as to the means for providing the medical care deemed necessary by Mr. Harmon's medical providers. As such, the Court finds this argument to be wholly without merit.

Moreover, upon review of his "Rehabilitation Analysis," "Life Care Plan," curriculum vitae, and testimony history, the Court finds Dr. Shahnasarian is qualified to testify as a life care expert in this matter and his methodology is sound and comports with *Daubert* requirements. Plaintiff's objections to Dr. Shahnasarian's life care plan go to the weight and credibility of Dr. Shahnasarian's testimony, not the admissibility.

Accordingly, it is hereby **ORDERED** that Plaintiff's *Daubert* Motion to Exclude or Otherwise Limit the Testimony of Defense Expert, Dr. Michael Shahnasarian, is **DENIED**.

ORDERED in Nashville, Tennessee, March 8, 2021.

JODY P. BELLE
UNITED STATES MAGISTRATE JUDGE

---

1. The Court notes that the rulings made herein are preliminary and subject to change at trial depending on how the evidence actually unfolds and whether the evidence turns out to be different than that represented in the motion. See *QBE Ins. Corp. v. Jorda Enters., Inc.*, 10-21107-CIV, 2012 WL 913248, at *2 (S.D. Fla. Mar. 16, 2012).

2. Ironically, Plaintiff cites to an article published by Dr. Paul Deutsch, a life care planner who, like Dr. Shahnasarian, is not a medical doctor.

APPENDIX N

Supplemental Report Regarding Vocational Opinions and Bases for Opinions

Suzanne O'Neal versus XYZ

Overview

At the request of Walter S. Cannon, I conducted a vocational rehabilitation analysis of Suzanne O'Neal, who is pursuing a claim for lost wages and other benefits associated with her former employment. Ms. O'Neal alleges sex/pregnancy discrimination and Family Medical Leave Act interference and retaliation related to the termination of her director of pharmacy operations position with XYZ in November 2000.

I authored a report on August 19, 2021, that outlined the methods I applied. My report also identifies documents I reviewed, relevant information I considered, and my analyses—including Ms. O'Neal's documented job search efforts and labor market research I conducted—and opinions relative to Ms. O'Neal's claimed lost wages attributable to her severance from XYZ. I also provided testimony in a deposition taken on October 31, 2021.

I submit this Supplemental Report in response to Plaintiff's Motion to Exclude Expert Testimony of Michael Shahnasarian to summarize my qualifications and elaborate on the bases of my previously stated opinions.

Summary of Qualifications

I have worked in the field of vocational assessment for more than 35 years, specializing in areas relating to career development, human resources consulting, and vocational rehabilitation. Attachment A to this Supplemental Report is a true copy of my CV, which accurately describes my education, licenses and certifications, professional experience, participation in professional and community organizations, media experience, publications, workshops and presentations, and membership in professional associations.

In addition to my education, certifications and licensures, and 30 years' experience, a few other highlights of my qualifications as a vocational expert are:

a. I have authored approximately 70 peer-reviewed articles in professional journals along with 12 books. The great majority of those publications concern vocational assessment and career development. My book *Assessment of Earning Capacity*, listed in my CV, is in its fourth edition and is widely used as a textbook. It includes a chapter on evaluating claims of loss of earning capacity in employment law. Attachment B to this report is a peer review of the third edition of this textbook from the publication *The Rehabilitation Professional.*

b. I served as the president of the National Career Development Association, a professional organization composed of approximately 10,000 career counselors practicing worldwide.

c. For approximately five years, I had a question/answer column on work-related issues that was published by *USA Today.* I also did two workplace studies for *USA Today.*

d. My professional recognition includes Outstanding Practitioner of the Year in Business and Industry by the Florida Career Development Association and Outstanding Practitioner of the Year by the National Career Development Association.

e. I developed the only standardized test used worldwide by vocational experts to assess claims of loss of earning capacity, the Earning Capacity Assessment Form-2 (ECAF-2). A true copy of that instrument, which uses the same methodology I applied in this case, is Attachment C to this report. A peer review of the instrument from the publication *The Rehabilitation Professional* is Attachment D to this report. Attachment E to this report is an article from another issue of the same publication that I coauthored about the ECAF-2's usage. The article notes that during its first 30 months, practitioners on five continents purchased 4,500 ECAF-2s, which demonstrates that a large number of practitioners worldwide are using the same type of methodology I applied in Ms. O'Neal's case.

I have testified as an expert witness in more than 500 cases in various state and federal courts. I have never been disqualified as an expert. Attachment F to this report is an accurate list of the cases in which I have testified either in deposition or at trial during the years 2018 to 2021. I testified as an expert in the field of vocational assessment in approximately 80 percent of those cases.

I have had extensive training in statistics at the graduate level for both my master's degree and my doctorate. I have also published books and numerous articles over the past 35 years that involved statistical analysis of work-related issues, including my textbook Assessment of Earning Capacity and all of the articles listed on pp. 8–10 of my CV concerning the use and methodology of the ECAF-2 instrument.

Bases of Opinions

1. **Ms. O'Neal's job search efforts were unimpressive and do not represent a reasonable effort to secure employment comparable to what she demonstrated a capacity to perform.**

    • According to records Ms. O'Neal submitted to document her job search efforts, approximately 91 percent of her job applications were submitted online. The time required to submit an online job application is de minimis. Other job search documentation Ms. O'Neal submitted indicates 9 percent of her job applications were initiated via telephone. Similar to making an online job application, the amount of time required to submit a telephone job application is also nominal. Ms. O'Neal's documented job search efforts fail to provide support for a concerted effort, inspired to resume employment comparable to her former employment. Again, the basis of this opinion also has significant implications for the opinion stated next. Had Ms. O'Neal maintained an aggressive, consistent job search, her job search time would have diminished, and she would have been in a more advantageous position to both compete for and negotiate compensation packages commensurate with her terminal position with XYZ.

- Career development professionals encourage those in the midst of a job search to treat their job search as a job, for example, committing 40 hours or more per week to job search activity. The documentation Ms. O'Neal submitted falls far short of this standard.

- Ms. O'Neal is an intelligent, educated, and professional business executive. She has held professional positions with national business organizations. Further, her job responsibilities as a senior executive with a national retail organization required her to recruit, select, and hire other professionals. Through her own experiences, she knew or should have known the rudiments of what is required to conduct a job search aimed at optimizing one's chances of securing employment in line with one's earning capacity. Assuming Ms. O'Neal applied her best efforts—based on her experiences as a hiring professional and her own experiences as a job candidate— her job search efforts would have been far greater than what she documented.

- Based on information Ms. O'Neal submitted to support her lost wages claim, she did not avail herself of the "hidden job market"—a term of art within the vocational profession that describes unadvertised jobs. Over 90 percent of her documented job search initiatives involved traditional means such as responding to advertised jobs and telephone job applications. Career counselors estimate that 80 percent of jobs in the labor market are not advertised, and this is especially true of professional positions of the types Ms. O'Neal held as director of pharmacy operations with XYZ. She failed to provide evidence of any networking, job development, unsolicited job availability inquiries, or other initiatives she made to obtain job leads. The basis of this opinion also has implications for the three opinions specified next.

- Documentation that Ms. O'Neal submitted to support her job search efforts and her deposition testimony indicate that she complied with the minimum standards necessary to qualify for unemployment compensation benefits—approximately five job applications per week. This is further support for the previously stated assertion that Ms. O'Neal's job search efforts were de minimis.

- Considering Ms. O'Neal's vocational profile, documented job search efforts, and labor market accessible to her, her job search efforts are unimpressive. The information she submitted falls far short of any suggestion that she initiated a sustained, aggressive job search campaign aimed to reenter the workplace expediently at a rate of pay representative of her earning capacity.

- I addressed in detail factors affecting earning capacity and considerations in front pay assessments of mitigation of vocational damages in a 2003 peer-reviewed article I authored, "Front Pay Damage Assessment: A Summary of Vocational and Psychological Considerations," a true copy of which is Attachment G to this report. Included in that article are guidelines for evaluating a claimant's vocational profile and methods to evaluate job search efforts. Those guidelines and methods form part of the basis of my opinion that Ms. O'Neal failed to conduct an aggressive job search aimed at expeditiously returning to the workplace and realizing her earning capacity.

- Attachment H to this supplemental report is an article from a recent issue of *The Rehabilitation Professional* by Stewart and Turner entitled "What Is a Reasonable Job Search? Developing a Theoretical Framework." Although this article does not form part of the basis of my opinions in this case, its methodology and conclusions support this opinion and my second opinion next. I serve on the editorial board of this publication, and I performed a blind peer review of the manuscript during the same time I was evaluating Ms. O'Neal's claim. This is the type of professional literature I routinely review and rely on in my day-to-day work as a practicing vocational expert.

2. **Assuming Ms. O'Neal initiated a good-faith, aggressive job search, she would have secured new employment making use of her education, training, work experience, and skills within nine to 12 months.**
    - Ms. O'Neal was 43 years old and in an age category the Social Security Administration recognizes as a younger individual at the time of her severance from XYZ. This is a facilitative factor in her job search.
    - Ms. O'Neal has not had physical or mental health problems posing constraints on her job search. Likewise, she requires no employer accommodations. These are facilitative factors in her job search.
    - Ms. O'Neal has been residing in a major metropolitan area—Nashville, Tennessee—with a large, accessible labor market. This is a facilitative factor in her job search.
    - Ms. O'Neal has an impressive educational background including a bachelor's degree in pharmacy from the University of Tennessee. This is a facilitative factor in her job search.
    - Ms. O'Neal holds pharmacy certification in two states, Tennessee and Georgia, along with licenses in these states as a registered pharmacist and/or doctor of pharmacy, PharmD. These work-related credentials are facilitative to her job search.
    - Ms. O'Neal has a work history that includes executive-level employment and progressive advancement with a large, well-known business organization—XYZ. This is a facilitative factor in her job search.
    - Ms. O'Neal has demonstrated the capacity to command an executive-level salary (approximately $190,000 annually) with a large, well-known business organization—XYZ. This is a facilitative factor in her job search.
    - Ms. O'Neal's employment with XYZ ended because of a reduction in the organization's workforce and change in business plan. Her severance was not related to job performance. This is a facilitative factor in Ms. O'Neal's job search.
    - Related to the previous fact, after her severance, XYZ offered Ms. O'Neal alternate employment. This is a facilitative factor in Ms. O'Neal's job search.
    - Through her education, training, and work experience, Ms. O'Neal acquired a diverse, sophisticated skill set, along with specialized knowledge specific to retail business management and pharmacy operations management. Indeed, her director of pharmacy operations position included responsibility for approximately 200 to 500 stores, depending on the time frame. Ms. O'Neal developed specialized transferable skills and business acumen that have value in the workplace. These factors are facilitative to Ms. O'Neal's job search.

- Ms. O'Neal has a history of conducting successful job search campaigns. She has had two tenures of employment with XYZ and previously held employment with two related organizations. This job search history is facilitative to Ms. O'Neal's job search.

- The methods Ms. O'Neal employed to conduct her job search were limited. She testified that she relied on recruiters and job websites—LinkedIn, CareerBuilder, and Monster.com. Had she supplemented and integrated these methods with other methods—such as consulting with professional career counselors; networking with peers and developing new professional contacts; attending and participating in meetings of business, industry, and professional organizations; and targeting desired employers and using her resources to obtain strategic introductions—she would have enhanced her capacity to generate job leads. Implementing these methods would have facilitated her efforts to mitigate any claimed vocational damages.

- Ms. O'Neal testified, "I've been looking for director, pharmacy operations, pharmacy operations managers. I haven't broadened my search to pharmacist." My analysis of her job search activity via documentation she submitted confirms that her job search efforts were solely focused on pharmacy-related management positions. She conducted a unidimensional job search. As noted earlier, Ms. O'Neal possesses many factors facilitative to her job search, including her executive-level business management experience and acumen. Had she broadened her job search efforts and applied her transferable skills to seek employment in other industries and other business management positions—for example, retail management, logistics management, and medical sales—her job search prospects would have been enhanced.

- Ms. O'Neal declined employment opportunities XYZ extended to her after her severance. The adage "A bird in the hand is worth two in the bush" is apropos in her case. Had she accepted employment XYZ offered and continued her job search, Ms. O'Neal would have been in an advantaged position while conducting her job search, which would have contributed to a diminution in her job search time.

- My 2003 peer-reviewed article, "Front Pay Damage Assessment: A Summary of Vocational and Psychological Considerations," which forms part of the basis of my opinion that a reasonable job search time for Ms. O'Neal was from nine to 12 months, includes a discussion on job search time after severance from a defendant employer. Specifically, I state at p. 183: "Regarding job search time after severance from a defendant employer, factors such as the plaintiff's locale and accessibility to jobs, level of specialization, former compensation, and vocational profile will affect success in securing new employment. We have found that many employment recruiters and career counselors forecast one month of job search time for every $10,000 of annual compensation sought, or a maximum interval of 6 to 10 months regardless of compensation level to obtain new employment representative of an individual's earning capacity." The United States Department of Labor has also published treatises specifying the same standard (one month of search time for every $10,000 of annual salary sought), as have executive placement firms such as Stewart, Cooper & Coon. My 2003 article also supports my third and fourth opinions next.

- It is rare, from my experience, that an individual with Ms. O'Neal's vocational profile—presuming they expended an earnest job search effort—would have had a job search in excess of 12 months.

3. **On her reentry into the workplace, Ms. O'Neal's compensation would have been approximately 10 percent lower than her terminal rate of pay at the time of her severance from XYZ.**

    - During her deposition, Ms. O'Neal was asked her opinion of her earning capacity. She assessed that, on her reentry to the workplace, she would earn from $175,000 to $200,000 per year in a director's position or as a consultant. As a basis for her opinion, Ms. O'Neal referenced her job search and interviews she had had. Her estimate of her compensation on her reentry into the workplace is considerably above my estimate.

    - As noted earlier, XYZ offered Ms. O'Neal employment after her severance. The compensation associated with this employment was approximately 27 percent less than what she earned as director of pharmacy operations. Had she accepted the XYZ job offer(s) and employed more aggressive job search efforts along the lines outlined previously, Ms. O'Neal would have been able to offset the 17 percent differential between my anticipated rate of pay on her workplace reentry and the rate of pay XYZ offered within the interval I specified (one to two years, per the opinion delineated next), presuming she conducted an aggressive job search and had been a job incumbent in a professional position.

    - Labor market research I conducted in summer 2021 identified several job openings in Ms. O'Neal's locale that she would have been competitive to pursue. These positions included pharmacist manager, director of quality control with a biotech/pharma company, second-line pharma sales director, various pharmacist positions, and various pharmaceutical and medical sales representative positions. Ms. O'Neal's transferable skills qualify her to pursue operations management positions in related and other industries. I also conducted research identifying such opportunities and presented examples of them during my deposition.

4. **Within one to two years after reentering the workplace, Ms. O'Neal would have been capable of earning wages commensurate with those she would have generated if her employment with XYZ had continued.**

    - An oft-cited axiom in the behavioral sciences, based on multidiscipline longitudinal research, is that past behavior is a good predictor of future behavior. This axiom and research that supports it also apply to vocational behavior, and my professional experience and research (as detailed in my CV) comport with it. There is no vocationally relevant data, presuming Ms. O'Neal committed her best efforts, that suggests she could not replicate her prior record of career achievement and earnings.

    - The labor market research I conducted supports the premise that Ms. O'Neal, had she expended appropriate effort, would have been and remains capable of, conservatively, being competitive for positions offering compensation in the wage range I cited, allowing her to advance to her former rate within a period of one to two years.

    - As noted previously, Ms. O'Neal engaged in a constricted job search, and she failed to broaden her efforts beyond pharmaceutical-related positions. Many of the points made earlier apply to the basis for this opinion.

    - I have education, training, and approximately 35 years of experience as a vocational expert, evaluating individuals' earning capacity. This experience has included interviewing and recommending job candidates at the request both of employers and of individuals in search of job opportunities. My experiences have involved individuals with vocational profiles similar to Ms. O'Neal's.

- Ms. O'Neal is an attractive job candidate, based on my assessment of her vocational profile. The demand for healthcare occupations, according to the U.S. Department of Labor, is anticipated to increase much faster than other occupations, apart from occupations related to information technology. Ms. O'Neal—with a blend of pharmaceutical and retail business operations management skills—possesses knowledge and skills likely to be in continued demand in the workplace. Additionally, she possesses numerous skills directly transferable to other disciplines and industries.

- While considering work opportunities available to Ms. O'Neal, my labor market research focused not only on areas related to her experience in retail pharmacy management, but also on ancillary opportunities making use of her transferable skills. An appropriate job search strategy Ms. O'Neal failed to initiate is pursuing opportunities outside retail pharmacy management for which she was competitive. My research identified many such opportunities. Ms. O'Neal, had she chosen, could have segued her career development to alternate areas, positioning herself to assume variegated career development opportunities offering compensation commensurate with her historical rates.

- The labor market research I conducted provides support for this opinion, as do the guidelines and methods discussed in my article "Front Pay Damage Assessment: A Summary of Vocational and Psychological Considerations."

- In my day-to-day work as a vocational evaluator and career counselor during the past 35 years, I have been regularly reviewing labor market data. Additionally, I regularly communicate with employers, human resource professionals, and other vocational experts throughout the United States. I integrated in my analyses and opinions my familiarity with labor market data and facts specific to her case when rendering opinions about Ms. O'Neal's compensation on her reentry to the workplace (i.e., approximately 90 percent of her level of compensation when her employment with XYZ ended) and the amount of time required for her to realize her level of compensation had her employment with XYZ continued (i.e., one to two years). For example, although not part of the basis of my opinions, statistics published by Stewart, Cooper & Coon, a national executive placement firm, indicate individuals with earnings records of approximately $150,000 annually had job search times of approximately seven months in 2019 and 2020, and those individuals reentered the workplace at approximately 97 percent of their former rates. A true copy of that publication is Attachment I to this report.

All of my opinions are based on my assessment of Ms. O'Neal's vocational profile, her deposition testimony and discovery responses, labor market research I conducted, and my education, training, and experience as a vocational expert for the past 35 years. In conducting a vocational analysis such as my analysis in this case, vocational counselors generally use the same methodology I used in this case. That methodology applies whether or not the subject of the analysis is disabled. If the subject is disabled, there are simply additional considerations not present when the subject is not disabled. The opinions and bases for the opinions herein are both stated within a reasonable degree of vocational rehabilitation probability and predicated on generally accepted methodologies within vocational rehabilitation.

APPENDIX O

Sample Expert Witness Trial Questions

Proposed Direct Examination Questions
for Dr. Michael Shahnasarian

Johnny Joseph Strawe, Jr.

Qualifying Questions

1. Dr. Shahnasarian, tell the jury about your areas of specialization.
   - Vocational Rehabilitation.
   - Life Care Planning.
   - Career Counseling.
   - Human Resources Consultation.
2. Describe for us, please, the professional practice of vocational rehabilitation.
   - Assisting individuals with various types of disabilities on career-related problems to realize their highest potential level of vocational functioning.
3. Describe for us, please, the professional practice of life care planning.
   - Life care planning pertains to identifying reasonably anticipated future rehabilitation interventions an individual will require, along with associated costs.
4. Please provide us with your educational background.
   - Bachelor's degree in Psychology from Indiana University.
   - Master's degree in Psychology, with a specialty in Clinical Psychology, from Texas A&M University.
   - Doctorate (PhD) in Counseling Psychology, with a specialty in Rehabilitation Psychology, from Florida State University.
   - Postdoctoral residency completed at Florida State University and the University of Wisconsin.

5. What licensures or specialty certifications do you hold?
   - Licensure as a Psychologist.
   - Licensure as a Mental Health Counselor.
   - Board Certification as a Rehabilitation Counselor.
   - Board Certification as a Life Care Planner.
   - International Psychometric Evaluation Certification.
   - Board Certification as a Vocational Evaluator.
   - Board Certification as a Career Counselor.

6. Your curriculum vitae also indicates that several professional associations recognize you as a Fellow. What does that mean? Tell the jury about your Fellow appointments.
   - Fellow, American Psychological Association.
   - Fellow, International Association of Life Care Planners.
   - Fellow, National Career Development Association.

   For the sake of reference, Dr. Shahnasarian, do you know the percentage of psychologists in the American Psychological Association who have been named a Fellow? How many practitioners have been designated a Fellow by the International Association of Life Care Planners?

7. Please tell us about your practice.
   - I founded Career Consultants of America, Inc., in 1986 and continue to serve as president.
   - The practice employs approximately nine professionals in a 3,200-square-foot building in Tampa and has been the training site of graduate interns from several universities.
   - Career Consultants of America, Inc., has provided services to more than 200 different business organizations and several thousand individuals throughout Florida, the United States, and North America.

8. Do business organizations or public organizations utilize your services as a consultant? Give us some examples.
   - Selection work for companies such as Gerdau/AmeriSteel Corporation, Cemex Corporation, and Florida Tile Corporation.
   - Outplacement work after downsizing for organizations such as Moffitt Cancer Center.
   - Consultation on issues specific to the Americans with Disabilities Act for organizations such as Honeywell and FiServ.
   - Surveys for organizations such as Snelling International (placement firm).
   - Training on career development issues throughout North America.

9. Your curriculum vitae indicates that you have hospital privileges—is that correct, Dr. Shahnasarian? Tell us about your hospital-based rehabilitation practice.

10. Have you had university-level teaching experience?
    - Assistant Professor in the Department of Neurology at the University of South Florida Medical School (consulted on life care planning).
    - Doctoral and master's level supervisor of students in my practice.
    - Adjunct Psychologist at the University of South Florida.
    - Prior teaching experience at the graduate level at Florida State University.

11. Dr. Shahnasarian, are you an author of any professional publications?
    - Published approximately 70 articles in refereed journals (many articles on the topic of computer-assisted career guidance initially, and during the past 20 to 25 years, I have concentrated on topics related to assessing earning capacity).
    - Published 12 books and am completing my 13th book with the American Bar Association.
    - One book, *Decision Time: A Guide for Career Enhancement*, was translated into Italian.
    - Another book, published in January 2006, includes a foreword written by General Norman Schwarzkopf.
12. Tell the jury topics you have addressed in your publications.
    - Articles relate to career development and vocational rehabilitation.
    - Published books on use of a popular vocational test, career decision-making, and assessment of earning capacity in forensic matters.
    - One publication, the Earning Capacity Assessment Form-2, is an assessment measure other vocational evaluators throughout North America use. Thousands of copies of it have sold since initial publication in 2010.
13. Have you served on any editorial boards related to publications in your profession?
    - Served two terms on the *Journal of Career Development* board and one term on the Journal of Counseling and Development board.
    - Guest editor and invited author on numerous occasions.
    - Currently a member of the following editorial boards: *The Rehabilitation Professional* and the *Journal of Life Care Planning*.
14. Dr. Shahnasarian, during your career, have you received any special recognition or awards from your professional peers? Your curriculum vitae lists numerous awards; for the sake of brevity, please list what you consider your most important and most recent awards.
    - Awarded Outstanding Practitioner of the Year by the National Career Development Association and the American Rehabilitation Counselors Association.
    - Presented a research award for my work developing a standardized test by the National Rehabilitation Association.
    - Presented with a 2020 Medal of Honor by the Ellis Island Medal of Honor Society.
    - Presented a 2020 Distinguished Service Award by the National Rehabilitation Counseling Association.
15. Your curriculum vitae identifies several professional leadership positions you have held. For the sake of brevity, please tell the jury about your experience as Chairman of the Board of the Multiple Sclerosis Society and President of the National Career Development Association. This is all in addition to your private practice work—correct?
    - Served as Chairman of the Board of the Gulf Coast Chapter of the National Multiple Sclerosis Society (1993–1995), a 5,000-member organization.
    - Served as President of the National Career Development Association (1997–1998). This organization was founded in 1913 and includes 10,000 members.

16. Dr. Shahnasarian, your curriculum vitae indicates that you have also served as a vocational expert with the Social Security Administration—correct? Please tell the jury what that involves. In addition to your work at disability hearings, have you performed any other vocational rehabilitation services for the Social Security Administration?
    - On the request of administrative law judges, have testified in approximately 400 disability hearings since 1987.
    - Career Consultants of America was previously one of four pilot test sites in the United States for a return-to-work program sponsored by the Social Security Administration.

17. Dr. Shahnasarian, prior to today, have you ever testified as an expert witness? On what subjects have you been found qualified to testify? Please give us some idea of your testimonial experiences.

18. Dr. Shahnasarian, have you served in an official capacity to the state of Florida on rehabilitation-related issues?
    - Appointed by Governor Chiles to the Florida Rehabilitation Council in 1998.
    - Reappointed by Governor Bush and served in this capacity through June 2002.

19. Your curriculum vitae indicates that you served as a columnist for *USA Today*—correct? Tell the jury what this involved. Have you had any other experience as a consultant to the media?
    - Became a columnist for the *USA Today* website in September 1998 and continued through 2003.
    - Responded to disability-related questions submitted by readers and offered tips on job finding.
    - Have been interviewed for articles in numerous publications including *Business Week*, the *Wall Street Journal*, and *Forbes*.

20. Dr. Shahnasarian, have you on prior occasions been invited to speak at national conferences related to serving as an expert witness? In this capacity, were you a member of a panel composed of other leaders including federal court judges? What specific topics did you address?
    - Served as a panelist along with federal court judges, circuit court judges, and others.
    - Addressed topics that include withstanding cross-examination in which opposing attorneys employ techniques such as bullying, taking information out of context, manipulation, distorting testimony, and other related tactics.

Methodology

1. When were you retained in Mr. Strawe's case, Dr. Shahnasarian? What were you asked to do?

2. What is a vocational rehabilitation evaluation? Are there generally accepted standards of practice to perform a vocational rehabilitation evaluation? Did you apply these standards in your analysis of Mr. Strawe's claim of loss of earning capacity he associates with his March 21, 2016, work-related accident?

3. Dr. Shahnasarian, I will ask you some similar questions related to the life care plan work you did in Mr. Strawe's case. What is a life care plan? Are there standards of practice in the profession that pertain to preparing a life care plan? Did you apply these standards in your work in Mr. Strawe's case?

4. Briefly, give the jury an overview of the methods you applied to perform your analyses.

5. What types of records did you review? How do these records relate to your assessment?

6. Did you have an opportunity to conduct a face-to-face examination of Mr. Strawe? Tell us about your exam protocol including your clinical interview and prescription of standardized tests.

7. Generally, what type of information did you obtain during your clinical interview of Mr. Strawe? I will ask you about his standardized test results later.

8. Did you perform any independent research to assist in your analysis? What did you do in this regard?

9. Did you have an opportunity to consult with any healthcare professionals during your assessment? Dr. Melchoi is an orthopedic surgeon who examined Mr. Strawe—correct? How did your consultation with him relate to your work?

10. How did you integrate all the information you obtained? Did you prepare any reports that describe what you did, report test results, summarize Mr. Strawe's medical records, and present your opinions? Tell us about these documents.

11. You charge a fee for your services—correct, Dr. Shahnasarian? In Mr. Strawe's case, you told us you reviewed a volume of records, interviewed Mr. Strawe for approximately four hours, prescribed a battery of tests that required almost three more hours to complete, performed labor market research, consulted with Dr. Melchoi, and wrote two reports—correct? What were your fees for all of the work you performed in Mr. Strawe's case?

Substantive Questions—Vocational Rehabilitation

1. During your clinical interview of Mr. Strawe earlier this month, Dr. Shahnasarian, what did he tell you were the primary problems he was experiencing because of his March 21, 2016, work-related accident? Of these problems, what did he tell you was his major problem or problems? During your review of Mr. Strawe's medical records, do you recall seeing when his lower back pain complaints first began? Was there any indication that an event apart from his 2016 work-related accident might have been associated with his lower back pain complaints, which do not appear in his records until approximately two years after his 2016 accident?

2. Please provide for us your understanding of Mr. Strawe's education and work history. When did his employment with Longshoreman Peninsular begin? What is your understanding of the job responsibilities Mr. Strawe performed as a stevedore? What was Mr. Strawe's rate of pay at the time of his accident? Did you review any records of his historical earnings? What did he earn during the last two years before his 2016 accident? Did Mr. Strawe explain to you the reason for the drop in his earnings between 2014 and 2015, the two years before his 2016 accident?

3. Dr. Shahnasarian, do you know whether Mr. Strawe ever returned to Longshoreman? What employment did he subsequently hold?

4. At the time of your June 7, 2021, clinical interview, what was Mr. Strawe's employment status? Do you know when he founded his business, Pyramid Portfolio? What type of work was he performing when you examined him? What did he earn? What is your understanding of the career plans he conveyed to you? What type of physical demands are required of a compliance officer? Did Mr. Strawe tell you whether he has any problems performing his current job?

5. The jury has already heard considerable testimony about Mr. Strawe's injuries and postaccident medical treatment, Dr. Shahnasarian. Briefly, provide for us your understanding of the surgeries Mr. Strawe has undergone and the type of treatment in which he participated. Did your review of Mr. Strawe's medical records include assessments of his restrictions and capacity to return to work? Are you aware that Dr. Golding is the surgeon who performed Mr. Strawe's last left shoulder operation (November 23, 2016) and his right ulnar nerve procedure (July 20, 2017), the last operation Mr. Strawe has undergone? Are you familiar with Dr. Golding's office notes dated September 20, 2017, and May 21, 2018? What do these notes indicate in terms of Mr. Strawe's restrictions and work capacity?

6. Dr. Shahnasarian, do you recognize the term "functional capacity" as a term of art in the rehabilitation profession? Tell us what that term means. Beyond reviewing Mr. Strawe's medical records, did you consult with Dr. Melchoi about Mr. Strawe's functional capacities? Dr. Melchoi is an orthopedic surgeon who examined Mr. Strawe—correct? Did Dr. Melchoi, during your consultation, place any restrictions on Mr. Strawe? When you examined Mr. Strawe, did you inquire about his subjective restrictions? Briefly, tell us about this. Did you review any surveillance of Mr. Strawe? Do you know when the surveillance was taken? What, if anything, did you find remarkable in terms of Mr. Strawe's functional capacities when you viewed his surveillance?

7. You told us that the records you reviewed included Mr. Strawe's criminal records—correct? Are these records relevant in your analysis of Mr. Strawe's claim of loss of earning capacity? Why? Is your review of Mr. Strawe's criminal records relevant in your assessment of his claim of future care needs? Why?

8. Dr. Shahnasarian, tell us what you found to be significant, from your expert perspective, about Mr. Strawe's criminal records. Did you ask him if he was selling Adderall and/or oxycodone when you interviewed him? What did he tell you? Did his lawyer facilitate your ability to obtain this information from Mr. Strawe?

9. Among the records you reviewed, Dr. Shahnasarian, were any from Pain Relief Express? What is your understanding about the relationship of this pain management practice with Mr. Strawe? Were any of the records from Pain Relief Express particularly remarkable to you? As a rehabilitation professional, do you find it unusual for a person who complains of intense pain not to be taking prescribed medication to relieve the pain? How is that relevant to a life care planner's work?

10. During your examination of Mr. Strawe, did you attempt to assess the types of skills he acquired through his education, training, and work experience? Tell us about this.

11. I would like to ask some questions now about Mr. Strawe's test results. Did you administer any tests to assess Mr. Strawe's intellect? How did he perform? Were there any noteworthy findings on his personality test results?

12. Dr. Shahnasarian, I would like to refer you to page 49 of your 53-page report dated June 14, 2021. Does this page begin with a summary and presentation of your opinions, based on your analysis of Mr. Strawe's claim that his 2016 accident caused him a loss of earning capacity? Please present us an overview of the opinions you formulated in this regard.

Substantive Questions—Life Care Plan

1. Dr. Shahnasarian, at the start of my direct examination of you, you told us about your education and training—correct? I believe one of the specialty credentials you identified was board certification as a life care planner—correct? Do you hold any other distinction as a life care planner? How many professionals have been elected to Fellow status by the International Association of Life Care Planners?

2. You told us earlier that your work in Mr. Strawe's case included preparing a life care plan—correct? Briefly, what method did you apply to prepare a life care plan in Mr. Strawe's case? Does this method conform with standard of practice mandates?

3. What information is included in the life care plan you prepared for Mr. Strawe? How did you obtain the cost information?

4. Dr. Shahnasarian, while discussing the life care plan you prepared, would it assist you to have the benefit of referring to some demonstrative aids?
   Note—Dr. Shahnasarian would like to have boards of the life care plan he prepared, beginning on page 3, to present to the jury. At this point in his direct examination, request that he come out of the witness box and present the boards to the jury. Acknowledge there is much technical information on the boards and instruct him to present the information in a summary fashion. After his presentation, instruct him to return to the witness box.

5. You mentioned you prepared this life care plan in conjunction with Dr. Melchoi—correct? Did Dr. Melchoi have an opportunity, after you prepared the life care plan, to independently review it and make any amendments he deemed necessary? To the best of your knowledge, does Dr. Melchoi have a disagreement with your life care plan?

6. Have all the opinions you presented been within a reasonable degree of rehabilitation probability, Dr. Shahnasarian?

Redirect Examination Questions

1. In Mr. Strawe's case, Dr. Shahnasarian, I retained you and I represent the defense, correct? Does your expert witness work involve retentions solely by defense lawyers? As an expert witness, what percent of the time are you retained by plaintiff lawyers as compared to defense lawyers?

2. Does it matter to you, Dr. Shahnasarian, whether a plaintiff lawyer or defense lawyer retains your services? Why not? I would like you to assume that, in Mr. Strawe's case, Mr. Syfrett rather than I retained you. Would the methods you applied be any different? Would the opinions to which you testified be any different? Would the fees you billed be any different?

Bibliography

Acosta v. Richter, 671 So. 2d 149, 152 (1996).

Aguila-Rojas v. City Management Group Corp., 606 So. 2d 765, 766 (Fla. 3d Dist. Ct. App. 1992).

Allison v. McGhan Medical Corp., 184 F.3d 1300, 1311 (11th Cir. 1999).

American Hospital Directory. (n.d.). https://www.ahd.com/

American Society of Anesthesiologists. (2020). *2021 Relative value guide: A guide for anesthesia values*. Author.

Annette, M. C., Dubas, J. S., & Gerris, J. (2010). Value transmissions between parents and children: Gender and developmental phase as the transmission belts. *Journal of Adolescence, 33,* 21–31.

Austin, T., Barzegarian, B., Ciddio, M., Cottle, R., Diaz, F., Fera, K., & Winn-Boaitey, K. (2009). White paper: IARP/DFEC work group. *The Rehabilitation Professional, 17,* 147–156.

Babitsky, S., & Mangraviti, J. J. (1999). *How to excel during depositions: Techniques for experts that work*. SEAK, Inc.

Babitsky, S., & Mangraviti, J. J. (2003). *Cross-examination: The comprehensive guide for experts*. SEAK, Inc.

Babitsky, S., Mangraviti, J. J., & Melhorn, J. M. (2004). *Writing and defending your IME report: The comprehensive guide*. SEAK, Inc.

Barros-Bailey, M., & Robinson, R. (2012). Thirty years of rehabilitation forensics: Inclusion of occupational and labor market information competencies in earning capacity models. *The Rehabilitation Professional, 20*(3), 157–166.

Battle, J. (2002). *Culture free self-esteem inventory—3*. Pro-ed.

Berens, D. E. (2019). A journey through the history of life care planning research: *The Journal of Life Care Planning* and the foundation for life care planning research. *Journal of Life Care Planning, 17*(3), 61–69.

Bloom, B. (1956). *Taxonomy of educational objectives: The classification of educational goals*. McKay.

Boecher v. Allstate Insurance Co., 733 So. 2d 993 (Fla. 1999).

Brodsky, S. L. (2004). *Coping with cross-examination and other pathways to effective testimony*. American Psychological Association.

Committee on the Judiciary, U. S. House of Representatives. (2009). *Federal rules of evidence*. Author.

Committee on the Judiciary, U. S. House of Representatives. (2010a). *Federal rules of civil procedure*. Author.

Committee on the Judiciary, U. S. House of Representatives. (2010b). *Federal rules of evidence*. Author.

Crowley, J., & Huber, S. (Eds.). (2021). *The life care management handbook*. Academy Elite.

Daubert v. Merrell Dow Pharmaceuticals, Inc., 509 U.S. 579 (1993).

Davies, L. E. (1993). *Anatomy of cross-examination*. Prentice Hall Law and Business.

Davis v. Pfund, 479 So. 2d 230, 231 (Fla. 3d Dist. Ct. App. 1985).

Deutsch, P. M. (1990). *A guide to rehabilitation testimony: The expert's role as an educator*. Paul M. Deutsch Press, Inc.

Dunn, P. L., & Field, T. F. (2014). Understanding rules of evidence and their application to experts. In R. H. Robinson (Ed.), *Foundations of forensic vocational rehabilitation* (pp. 290–310). Springer Publishing Company, LLC.

Fair Health/FH Online. (n.d.). https://fhlogin.fairhealth.org/

Fans, C., Benson, M. J., & Kaestle, C. E. (2013). Parent resources during adolescence: Effects on education and careers in young adulthood. *Journal of Youth Studies*, 16, 151–171.

Field, T. F. (2008). Estimating earning capacity: Venues, factors, and methods. *Estimating Earning Capacity* 1(1), 3–40.

Field, T. F. (2012a). Estimating earning capacity: A historical review. *The Rehabilitation Professional 20*, 51–62.

Field, T. F. (2012b). Review of the ECAF-2. *The Rehabilitation Professional 20*(2), 147–148.

Field, T. F., & Dunn, P. L. (2014). Transferability of skills: Historical foundations and development. In R. H. Robinson (Ed.), *Foundations of forensic vocational rehabilitation* (pp. 133–144). Springer Publishing Company, LLC.

Fla. Stat. § 456.057(8).

Frye v. United States, 293 F. 1013 (D.C. Ct. App. 1923).

General Electric Co. v. Joiner, 522 U.S. 136 (1997).

H. K. Corp. v. Estate of Miller, 405 So. 2d 218, 219 (Fla. 3d Dist. Ct. App. 1981).

Holland, J. L., & Messer, M. A. (2017). *Self-directed search*. Psychological Assessment Resources, Inc.

Holy Bible. (1989). Armenian Church Edition, Harper Collins Publishers.

International Association of Rehabilitation Professionals. (2015). *Standards of practice for life care planners* (3rd ed.). Author. https://cdn.ymaws.com/rehabpro.org/resource/resmgr/files/RehabPro/Standards_of_Practice_for_Li.pdf

Keller Industries v. Volk, 657 So. 2d 1200, 1202–03 (Fla. 4th Dist. Ct. App. 1995).

Kumho Tire Co. v. Carmichael, 526 U.S. 137 (1999).

Law.com Legal Dictionary. (n.d.). Pain and suffering. https://dictionary.law.com/Default.aspx?selected=1433

LoBue v. Travelers Insurance Co., 388 So. 2d 1349 (Fla. 4th Dist. Ct. App. 1980).

Lombard v. Executive Elevator Service, Inc., 545 So. 2d 453, 455 (Fla. 3d Dist. Ct. App. 1989).

Mangraviti, J. J., Babitsky, S., & Donovan, N. N. (2016). *How to be an effective expert witness at deposition and trial*. SEAK, Inc.

Neulicht, A. T. (2011). Book review: *Assessment of Earning Capacity*, 3rd ed. *The Rehabilitation Professional, 19*(1), 39–40.

Neulicht, A. T., & Berens, D. E. (2005). PEEDS-RAPEL: A case conceptualization model for evaluating pediatric cases. *Journal of Life Care Planning, 4,* 27–36.

Neulicht, A. T., & Berens, D. E. (2015). PEEDS-RAPEL: A case conceptualization model for evaluating pediatric cases with acquired brain injury. *NeuroRehabilitation, 36,* 275–291.

Organization for Economic Cooperation and Development. (2018). Hours worked. https://data.oecd.org/emp/hours-worked.htm

Orpe v. Carnival Corp., 909 So. 2d 929, 932 (Fla. 3d Dist. Ct. App. 2005).

Orth, U. (in press). The family environment in early childhood has a long-term effect on self-esteem: A longitudinal study from birth to age 27 years. *Journal of Personality and Social Psychology.*

Pascal v. Dozier, 771 So. 2d 552, 554 (Fla. 3d Dist. Ct. App. 2000).

Rahman, M. (2020). Surviving a Daubert challenge: 6 tips for success." *Expert institute.* https://www.expertinstitute.com/resources/insights/surviving-daubert-challenge-6-tips-success/

Robinson, R. H. (2014). Forensic rehabilitation and vocational earning capacity models. In R. H. Robinson (Ed.), *Foundations of forensic vocational rehabilitation* (pp. 33–61). Springer Publishing Company.

Robinson, R., & Pomeranz, J. (2011). The vocational rehabilitation assessment model (VRAM): Introduction of an empirically derived model of vocational and rehabilitation assessment." *The Rehabilitation Professional, 19*(4), 91–104.

Robinson, R., Young, M. E., & Pomeranz, J. (2009). Content analysis of factors identified in vocational evaluation analysis reports. *The Rehabilitation Professional, 17,* 163–174.

Robinson v. Hunter, 506 So. 2d 1106, 1107 (Fla. 4th Dist. Ct. App. 1987).

Rojas v. Rodriguez, 185 So. 3d 710, 711 (Fla. 3d Dist. Ct. App. 2016).

Santos Wrestling Enterprise, Inc., v. Perez, 367 So. 2d 685, 686 (Fla. 3d Dist. Ct. App. 1979).

Shahnasarian, M. (2001). *Assessment of earning capacity.* Lawyers & Judges Publishing Co.

Shahnasarian, M. (2004a). *Assessment of earning capacity* (2nd ed.). Lawyers & Judges Publishing Co.

Shahnasarian, M. (2004b). *The earning capacity assessment form.* Elliott & Fitzpatrick.

Shahnasarian, M. (2004c). The earning capacity assessment form: An introduction and study of its efficacy. *The Rehabilitation Professional, 12,* 41–53.

Shahnasarian, M. (2008). The earning capacity assessment form: A study of its reliability. *The Rehabilitation Professional, 16,* 71–82.

Shahnasarian, M. (2009a). Perceptions of plaintiff or defense retention source as a confounding variable in the assessment of earning capacity: A reliability study of the earning capacity assessment form. *Estimating Earning Capacity, 2,* 85–98.

Shahnasarian, M. (2009b). Video recordings in forensic examinations. *The Rehabilitation Professional, 17,* 175–183.

Shahnasarian, M. (2010a). Earning capacity assessment: Operationalizing a theory. *Forensic Rehabilitation & Economics, 3*(2), 111–124.

Shahnasarian, M. (2010b). *Professional manual for the earning capacity assessment form-2.* Psychological Assessment Resources, Inc.

Shahnasarian, M. (2010c). *The earning capacity assessment form-2.* Psychological Assessment Resources, Inc.

Shahnasarian, M. (2010, October). *Al dia siguiente* [Programs presentation]. Por la Via Por la Vida Annual Meetings, Medellin and Bogota, Colombia.

Shahnasarian, M. (2011). *Assessment of earning capacity* (3rd ed.). Lawyers & Judges Publishing Co.

Shahnasarian, M. (2012). *A claimant's guide to understanding and presenting injury damages: A damages expert's perspective.* American Bar Association.

Shahnasarian, M. (2015). *Assessment of earning capacity* (4th ed.). Lawyers & Judges Publishing Co., Inc.

Shahnasarian, M. (2017). Eliciting rehabilitation recommendations during forensic life care plan consultations. *Journal of Life Care Planning, 15,* 13–19.

Shahnasarian, M. (2020). Implications of the coronavirus pandemic for vocational expert assessments: A preliminary analysis. *The Rehabilitation Professional, 28,* 135–140.

Shahnasarian, M., & Hill, A. M. (2014). The earning capacity assessment form-2: A status report. *The Rehabilitation Professional, 22*(3), 195–202.

Shahnasarian, M., & Hilby, D. A. (2020, August). *Optimizing contributor input in life care plan development* [Program presentation]. Annual Conference of the American Board of Vocational Experts, Tampa, FL.

Shahnasarian, M., & Hilby, D. A. (2020). Use of the earning capacity assessment form-2 (ECAF-2) in young adult cases: An overview and case study. *The Rehabilitation Professional, 28,* 15–26.

Shahnasarian, M., Kaiser-Ulrey, C., & Lassiter, D. (2006). The MMPI-2 and other personality measures in vocational assessment. *The Rehabilitation Professional, 14*(2), 39–46.

Shahnasarian, M., & Lassiter, D. H. (2002). Attorney perceptions of vocational evaluation methodologies. *The Rehabilitation Professional, 10,* 38–43.

Shahnasarian, M., & Leitten, C. L. (2008a). A longitudinal study of claimants' return to work and related factors. *Estimating Earning Capacity, 1,* 124–130.

Shahnasarian, M., & Leitten, C. L. (2008b). The earning capacity assessment form: A study of its reliability. *The Rehabilitation Professional, 16,* 71–82.

Shahnasarian, M., & Leitten, C. L. (2008c). The earning capacity assessment form: An exploratory study to assess the feasibility of establishing cut-off scores to determine impairment to earning capacity ratings. *The Rehabilitation Professional, 17*(2), 85–96.

Shahnasarian, M., Leitten, C. L., & Tremp, R. (2010). The earning capacity assessment form-2: An exploratory study of its interrater reliability. *The Rehabilitation Professional, 18*(4), 221–218.

Sizemore, A. M., & Walker, J. M. (2020). Adverse childhood experiences: Antecedents to occupational disability and lost time. *The Rehabilitation Professional, 28,* 127–134.

Social Security Administration. (n.d.). Life expectancy calculator. https://www.ssa.gov/OACT/population/longevity.html

U. S. Department of Labor. (1991). *The dictionary of occupational titles* (4th rev. ed.). Author.

Van de Bittner, E. E., Wallace, A., Cottle, R. B., & Simon, S. (2012). Comparison of a consensus methodology for evaluating employability and earning capacity by the CA-IARP DFEC work activity group with published, peer-reviewed methodologies. *The Rehabilitation Professional, 20*(2), 75–86.

Weed, R. O. (2000). Assessing the worth of a child in personal injury litigation cases. *The Rehabilitation Professional*, *1*, 29–43.

Weed, R. O., & Berens, D. (Eds.) (2019). *Life care planning and case management handbook* (4th ed.). Routledge Press.

Weed, R. O., & Field, T. F. (2012). *Rehabilitation consultant's handbook* (4th ed.). Elliott and Fitzpatrick.

Wilkerson, G. S., & Robertson, G. J. (2006). *Wide range achievement test—4*. Psychological Assessment Resources, Inc.

Woodard, L. (2021). IARP life care planning—IALCP section status report: A year-in-review. *The Rehabilitation Professional & Journal of Life Care Planning: A Year in Review*, *1*, 23–24.

Index

Page numbers followed by f indicate figure; page numbers followed by t indicate table.